For Harvey, Zachary, Daniel and Amanda

More milestones, more memories, and more moments I would like to freeze in time.

There is no place I would rather be; there are no others I would rather be with.

Families are the compass that guide us.
They are the inspiration to reach great heights,
and our comfort when we occasionally falter.

– Brad Henry

Senioropolis Inc. has endeavoured to ensure the completeness and accuracy of the information contained in this *Guide*. However, neither it nor the author assumes liability whatsoever for any errors or omissions, nor guarantees the accuracy of the information herein. All information pertaining to homes and advertisers has been provided by the homes and advertisers themselves in the summer of 2013. As the information is collected several months before we go to press, prices, contact information and other details may change. ***We encourage and advise you to research your care options carefully and verify all of the information directly with the retirement residences and long-term care homes, especially data related to cost factors and service provision.***

The author and publisher are not engaged in rendering legal, or other professional advice. If legal advice or other expert assistance is required, the services of a competent professional should be sought. The analysis contained herein represents the opinion of the author and is based on independent research. It should in no way be construed as being official or unofficial policy of any government or other body. The author/publisher does not have any financial or personal interest in any of the homes/residences, services or resources contained herein.

First Edition, 1998
Second Edition, 1999
Third Edition, 2000
Fourth Edition, 2001
Fifth Edition, 2002
Sixteenth Edition, 2013
Sixth Edition, 2003
Seventh Edition, 2004
Eighth Edition, 2005
Ninth Edition, 2006
Tenth Edition, 2007
Seventeenth, 2014
Eleventh Edition, 2008
Twelfth Edition, 2009
Thirteenth Edition, 2010
Fourteenth Edition, 2011
Fifteenth Edition, 2012

Comprehensive Guide to Retirement Living®
Comprehensive Guide to Retirement Living and Long-Term Care®

ISBN 978-0-9811432-5-5

Cover & divider photos were provided courtesy of Canterbury Place Retirement Residence, Four Elms Retirement Residence, Richmond Hill Retirement Residence, Stouffville Creek Retirement Residence and The Roxborough - all are part of the Diversicare Canada Management Services Inc. family of residences.

DID YOU KNOW TIPS:

Throughout the *Guide* we have highlighted important bits of information that might be of interest to our readers. Below is a list of the topics and the page numbers where you can find them.

REGIONAL GROUPINGS

For those wishing to expand their search to nearby cities, below are regional groupings and the cities within them across Ontario. In an effort to simplify things, we have used the 14 regions that the Ministry of Health and Long-Term Care uses to divide health care services in Ontario. Homes in each region tend to be in reasonable proximity to one another and might provide an added option if you are unable to locate a suitable residence in your chosen area. This list only includes regions and cities covered in this edition of the *Guide*.

ERIE ST. CLAIR REGION:
Chatham, Dresden, Leamington, Sarnia, Tilbury, Windsor
SOUTH WEST REGION:
Goderich, London, St. Thomas, Stratford
WATERLOO WELLINGTON REGION:
Cambridge, Elora, Guelph, Kitchener, Mount Forest, Waterloo
HAMILTON, NIAGARA, HALDIMAND BRANT REGION:
Ancaster, Brantford, Burlington, Dundas, Fort Erie, Grimsby, Hagersville, Hamilton, Niagara Falls, St. Catharines, Stoney Creek
CENTRAL WEST REGION:
Brampton
MISSISSAUGA HALTON REGION:
Georgetown, Milton, Mississauga, Oakville, South Etobicoke
TORONTO CENTRAL REGION:
Toronto
CENTRAL REGION:
Alliston, Aurora, Keswick, Maple, Markham, Newmarket, Richmond Hill, Stouffville, Thornhill, Toronto, Vaughan, Woodbridge
CENTRAL EAST REGION:
Brooklin, Campbellford, Cobourg, Courtice, Lindsay, Oshawa, Peterborough, Pickering, Port Hope, Port Perry, Scarborough, Uxbridge, Whitby
SOUTH EAST REGION:
Belleville, Kingston, Perth, Trenton
CHAMPLAIN REGION:
Alexandria, Arnprior, Carleton Place, Kanata, Nepean, Ottawa, Pembroke
NORTH SIMCOE MUSKOKA REGION:
Barrie, Collingwood, Midland, Stayner
NORTH EAST REGION:
Sudbury
NORTH WEST REGION:
Thunder Bay

LIST OF ADVERTISERS

Did we miss you this Edition?

For information on how to get your residence or business included in our 2015 Guide call us at **(416) 457-6554** or email **info@senioropolis.com.**

My perception of time seems to change with each passing year. Too much time, has become not enough time. As a child, a year felt like an eternity. Now, most days I wish I could push a 'go slower' button on my clock. I am convinced that time goes into 'fast forward' after you pass a certain age and/or after your kids pass the toddler stage. This book came into being the year I had my first baby and is often referred to as my '4th child'. In many ways, the early years for both my first born and this book were a bit of a blur filled with more work than is imaginable, growing pains and an incredibly large learning curve. Days seemed to last forever and nights were neverending. Yet today, that first year seems like yesterday despite the 17 years that have passed. Thankfully, my son, his two younger siblings, and this book, have all grown and thrived. I can say with certainty that every day there are still new experiences, joys and struggles but in the end, it is all incredibly worthwhile and tremendously satisfying.

In what seems like the 'blink of an eye' we have created 17 editions – each one has been bigger, better and more filled with information than the one before. Our website grows almost daily as we continue to add articles, resources and homes to meet the needs of Canada's growing population of seniors. We are always looking for new and innovative ideas and ways to present them and, to this end, we have expanded access to our information even further by creating a "GPS App" for Android and Apple Smartphones. I was an owner of one of the very first cell phones – we were so amazed that a phone could work outside without a phone cord despite its immense weight and size, that in our wildest dreams we never guessed what we would be able to do some 20 + years later with one of these now very small and compact mini-computers we call phones. For those of you with a smartphone, downloading our App will allow your phone to tell you how to get to a home you are interested in finding in a couple of simple steps!

The growth and scope of what we are able to provide in book, CD and web formats and the number of people that continue to use it one year after the next continues to amaze me. The feedback we get from seniors and families inspires us to move forward and continue growing our database of information. Hearing how useful our book or website has been in helping people find a new home or support them in their own homes is beyond satisfying and truly makes the work that we do something to be proud of. The fact that our website attracts people across Canada in huge numbers will astound me forever, especially when our monthly web stats seem to reflect that a significant number of people find us simply through the magic of search engines. And, despite knowing that most of our population including 'senior seniors' own a computer, I am always surprised when I hear how long people hold onto our books and continue to use them – several years is not uncommon and occasionally we hear as many as 10!

Though to some it might seem like we collect the same information year after year, the reality is that is simply not the case. Every year our book is different – in all sections. We spend many months updating our data and seeking out new contacts. For those of you who have multiple editions, you will see that each year many new homes join us, sadly a few leave – but often only temporarily as they quickly realize our resource is one so many use. In each new edition we incorporate new resources and updated information. Our goal with this *Guide* and the website is, and will continue to be, ever-evolving as we endeavour to stay up-to-date with the changes to care and housing for seniors occurring annually in Ontario and indeed, across Canada.

As I reflect back on the 17 year journey that has all come together to get us to this point in time, it is clear that none of it — book, website, CD or Apps — would exist were it not for our devoted supporters — our readers, our advertisers, various residences spanning the province (and now across Canada for our online network), professionals who use our *Guide* and refer people to it, and some very special people I need to thank, that help recreate this book every year from beginning to end.

The creation and continuity of this *Guide* would not have been possible without the assistance of the following important people: **Kate Hemi** for her lifelong support, encouragement, guidance, business expertise and teaching by example; **BTT Communications** for the endless hours of hard work and assistance in making this 17th edition something we could all be proud of; **Ruby Ezekiel** for her help with distribution; **Donna Beker**, our account executive, who spent many hours on the phone and computer helping us forge new contacts and create this edition; **Martha Rebelo**, our newest team member who joined us in the Fall of 2013 & played an important role in assisting us with the production phase of this

edition and **Bart Garner** of NTech, our amazing web designer, for his expertise, work and creativity on **www.senioropolis.com**.

Those of us involved in the production of this book would like to extend a special thank you to those who recognize its value and trust us enough to participate in its content: the residences that choose to be in our publication and the advertisers who purchase space throughout it. We welcome our many new supporters and again thank our regulars (some who have been with us for the full 17 years!) who faithfully respond to our quest for information and support year after year.

We would also like to thank **Diversicare Canada Management Services Co., Inc., Karen Kotanko** & **the Marketing Staff at Stouffville Creek, Four Elms, Canterbury Place, Richmond Hill & The Roxborough Retirement Residences** for providing us with the photographs we used on our front cover and dividers this year. In our desire to have images of real people who actually live in the residences you read about in our pages throughout the *Guide*, we are most grateful that they, as with other homes and companies in previous editions, have been so generous as to share the images of their residents with us. We also wish to thank **Mary Ellen Tomlinson** of Senior Care Options Inc., **Monica Black** of Simple Easy Transitions, **Edie Michel** of Leed Solutions, **Hilary Dunn** of Schlegel-UW Research Institute for Aging, **Alert/Best Nursing & Home Care** and **Amanda Stevenson**, RM of Coldwell (Lundar) for their contribution of articles in our SERVICES AND RESOURCES FOR SENIORS SECTION (PART 2). As well, for reviewing, updating and assisting with information on their organizations, we thank **Brenda McIntryre**, Communications Advisor, RHRA, **Debbie Humphreys,** Director of Communications & Public Affairs, OANHSS, **Joanna Rizi,** Senior Communications Advisor, OLTCA, **Christine Thomas,** Zock & Associates and **Central Community Care Access Centre staff.**

And finally, to those of you who have contributed and continue to do so without even knowing it:

To my many clients past, present, and future:

You have helped give me an understanding of the significance and meaning of my work, of dedication and devotion to aging relatives and of the importance of continuing this project.

Esther Goldstein

"What place would you choose for your parent?"

During the many years that I worked as a hospital social worker with seniors who required relocation, this was the most common question the families of my elderly clients would ask me. It was – and still is – a most difficult one to answer. My experience has taught me that it is not wise to recommend a retirement residence or long-term care home, especially for someone I barely know. I believe that even those of us who know something about these settings should not decide which one is the best place for someone else to call 'home'. From the outset, searching for retirement accommodation involves 3 important factors that must be taken into consideration – ***choice, cost and care***.

There are numerous residences/homes in Ontario, in many different price ranges, offering an array of care levels. The challenge is to find one that 'fits' on all 3 dimensions so you or your loved one can be comfortable both physically and financially knowing that your/their needs will be met now and hopefully in the future. Residences differ greatly on so many levels – including environment, amenities, services and care – and every person's needs and desires are unique. What one person might think is the perfect home, another might not. It is imperative that the family/caregiver, and if physically possible, the person themselves, assess their needs & financial limitations, shop around, and compare what is available.

Choosing a retirement residence or long-term care home for yourself or someone else is not an easy task. It is most often a very emotional decision that can be made more overwhelming if rigid time constraints – both personal and those set by a hospital or caregiver – are involved. Additionally, within the category of retirement living settings, there is tremendous choice (they number in the hundreds province-wide) and most published information about many places is limited at best.

The goal and purpose of this *Guide* is to give you the necessary tools to begin your search for the best place for yourself or a loved one. I hope it will help make what is often a difficult decision a little bit easier by giving you as much information as possible as you try and navigate the options before you. I do not rate the residences detailed in this book. The information contained in the following pages is intentionally objective. However, I believe that the subjective perspective is of equal, if not greater, importance when searching for a retirement or long-term care setting.

It is of utmost importance that you be an ***informed consumer***. No decision should be made without a visit to a residence, or preferably, a few residences. When looking for a retirement community meet with staff, sample a meal, speak with residents and their families, get references, spend time at the places that interest you and ask a lot of questions (see RETIREMENT RESIDENCE VISITING TIPS in Part 1). Research is equally important when looking for a long-term care home however the options are less, priorities are different and for many, time is of the essence (see information on LONG-TERM CARE in Parts 1 & 4).

A question I am often asked is why I don't have every residence in the province in the *Guide*. The answer is really quite simple: Although I would be very pleased if I did have comprehensive information on every setting, it is simply not possible. I cannot force retirement residences or long-term care homes to have a presence in this publication or on our website. Some choose other means of promoting themselves and others do not have a need to be in publications at all or only do so through local sources. In smaller communities where there are few options, word of mouth is often the way potential residents find a place that meets their needs. In compiling this book, we gave each residence in our search an opportunity to complete an online questionnaire. Information about the homes that chose to be in this publication (and on **www.senioropolis.com**) is contained in this *Guide*. I do not censor or change any of the information they provide. Essentially, the information in this *Guide* is a 'snapshot' of the data these homes submitted to us in the summer of 2013. As a result, some pricing information may not be accurate. (Some retirement residences were able to include 2014 pricing, others were not.) I encourage you to verify all information, especially the data related to cost factors, with the residences directly.

All residences/communities and long-term care homes in this book with internet access are invited to update their information as often as they wish on our website. Please visit our site regularly to check for updated information and added features. I do not endorse any residence or home, and I take no responsibility for the information provided. It is my assumption that in choosing to be in the *Guide* and on **www.senioropolis.com**, each retirement residence and long-term care home responded accurately.

How to Obtain More Copies of this *Guide*

Please send a cheque for **$28.94** ($18.95 plus $1.99 taxes, and $8.00 Shipping & Handling)

Payable to:

Senioropolis Inc.
8000 Bathurst Street, Unit 1,
P.O. Box # 30033 RPO New Westminster
Vaughan, Ontario L4J 0C6

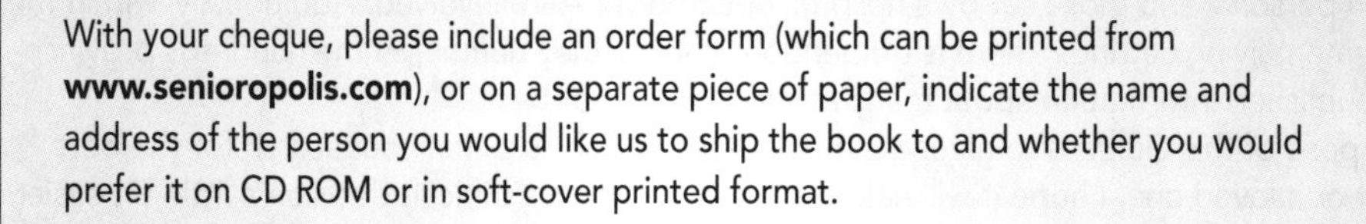

With your cheque, please include an order form (which can be printed from **www.senioropolis.com**), or on a separate piece of paper, indicate the name and address of the person you would like us to ship the book to and whether you would prefer it on CD ROM or in soft-cover printed format.

Allow two to four weeks for delivery.

If you prefer to pay by credit card, please visit our website, **www.senioropolis.com**, select the *Online Store* link and order through our shopping cart. Payment can be made through PayPal and orders will be filled as soon as they are received.

For large orders or further information, please contact us at:
PHONE: **(416) 457-6554**
FAX: **(905) 482-9142**
Email: **info@senioropolis.com**

Visit our dynamic, detailed website, **www.senioropolis.com**, for the most up-to-date information on retirement residences, long-term care homes and an array of resources for seniors

Where do I Begin?

Photos provided by Four Elms Retirement Residence and Richmond Hill Retirement Residence

WHAT IS A RETIREMENT RESIDENCE AND WHO NEEDS ONE?

Retirement residences and communities (also called retirement homes) are ideal for older persons in relatively good health who may have minimal or moderate care needs and cannot (or do not want to) be in their own homes. They provide a safe, supervised environment that allows for the opportunity to socialize with people their own age, enjoy organized activities and have their meals prepared and housekeeping done by someone else, while obtaining some care if needed. Such residences allow seniors to maintain privacy, dignity and independence. Residents of retirement homes have the freedom to choose how much to do for themselves, how much to have done for them and how and with whom to spend their time.

Residents can usually bring some of their own furniture. A few homes even allow small pets (as long as the resident can look after them). A number of people living in retirement residences still drive their own cars. Most are free to leave during the daytime without supervision. Retirement living residences vary greatly in location, size, accommodation, cost factors, services, amenities and staffing. In general, costs are market-driven and dependent on location. Residences in rural areas may be less expensive than comparable ones in large urban centres. They are all privately owned and operated. There are approximately 700 in Ontario and many new ones are currently under construction.

In June 2010 the provincial government passed the Retirement Homes Act which now governs residences across Ontario. Retirement residences in this province now have mandatory standards for resident care and safety. As well, all homes must continue to abide by the regulations set out in the Residential Tenancies Act[1], the Health Protection and Promotion Act (which sets standards that impact a variety of businesses, including retirement residences, related to water quality, sanitation and safe food preparation) and the Ontario Building and Fire Codes. Retirement residences in Ontario may be for profit or not-for-profit. Not-for-profit residences often have available subsidies or, in some cases, rent geared to income. They may be owned by a religious, charitable or community organization. Usually the management is responsible to a central board of directors. In private, for-profit residences, fees are based on factors determined by the residence. There are no government subsidies available for retirement home residents; however some costs related to care might be tax deductible. As of the 2002 tax year, Canada Customs and Revenue Agency allows retirement home residents who pre-qualify for the Disability Tax Credit (T2201) to make an additional claim (to a maximum amount) for the care services they receive as a medical expense (for more information, visit **www.cra-arc.gc.ca/nwsrm/fctshts/2003/m04/snrs-eng.html**).

Unlike in long-term care homes, there are no standard application forms for all residences and no central processing agency. Application to enter a retirement residence is made directly to the residence itself. Prospective residents may be required to undergo a physical examination by their physician (or have a medical form completed) prior to moving in to ensure that the residence can meet their physical and medical needs. Some residences may have waiting lists.

Residents usually enter a retirement residence while they are still healthy, active, cognitively alert and fairly independent. They are able to look after some or most of their personal care and can usually get to the dining room unassisted. Most retirement residences have health care aides and/or nursing staff available in the event of a medical emergency. Many can provide supervision with medication administration and bathing, if required, although some may charge an extra fee for these services. Meals (usually in a central dining room), housekeeping (and often some laundry services) and recreational programs are generally included in the monthly cost. Accommodation differs from one residence to another and ranges from ward to semi-private to variations of private rooms, suites and/or apartments. Some have suites with some form of a kitchenette to allow for light meal preparation; however there are often restrictions around using many kinds of electrical appliances in your suite. Depending on the residence, available personal care services may range from minimal assistance to a comprehensive continuum of care. A home that offers varying levels of care may enable residents to continue to be managed in their chosen

[1] Retirement residences are included in the definition of Care Homes in the Act.

residence in the event that their health deteriorates and their need for care increases (some residences term this "Aging in Place"[2]).

Community Care Access Centres may coordinate some personal support and/or professional services (e.g. physiotherapy, nursing, etc.) for residents of retirement residences. Provision of service is based on individual assessment of needs (by a CCAC Care Coordinator) and the services available in the residence. Professional services are usually time-limited and for the purpose of assessment and training.

Some homes offer Assisted Living (AL) programs or units (sometimes also called Special Care, Enhanced Care, Supportive Care or Personal Care) that provide more nursing and personal care than is usually available in the rest of the residence. In most homes that offer this option, there is an extra cost for receiving this kind of care or residing in this type of a unit, and sometimes a waiting list for the unit. Depending on the residence, one may need to be a current resident to access this kind of care. (It may not be possible to be admitted to the home from the community if substantial care or an AL unit is required.) In many retirement settings, extra personal care can be purchased on an hourly basis, either through the residence or from an external agency. In some homes, residents may hire private companions or "shared care" (two residents hire one person who attends to both of them, enabling them to share services, reducing the cost of extra care) if the amount of care included in a resident's monthly fee (or the amount of care the residence is able to provide) is not enough.

A few residences have secure units or floors for residents with dementia who are at risk for wandering. Depending on circumstances, someone exhibiting these behaviours may be better suited to a long-term care home. Factors such as cost and care needs should be considered carefully when making a placement decision for someone with dementia.

Many retirement residences provide short-term respite care for people who are recovering from an illness or to provide relief for a caregiver, vacation care while caregivers are on holiday and trial stays for a few days or weeks, to allow people to try out the residence before making a final decision.

Did you know?

The Retirement Homes Act, 2010 defines a retirement home for the purpose of licensing and regulation by the **Retirement Homes Regulatory Authority (RHRA)**, in the following way:

"A retirement home is a building, group of buildings, or a part of a building (with one or more rental units):

1. occupied primarily by persons who are 65 years of age or older;
2. occupied or intended to be occupied by at least six persons who are not related to the operator of the home; and
3. where the operator of the home makes at least two care services available (directly or indirectly) to residents.

A retirement home does not include buildings or parts of buildings that receive funding or are governed by certain other laws, for example the *Homes for Special Care Act and the Long-Term Care Homes Act, 2007.*"

Quoted directly from: Plain-Language Guide: An overview of the new *Retirement Homes Act, 2010* by the RHRA (Retirement Homes Regulatory Authority), Page 5. The entire document can be found at **www.rhra.ca/assets/en/pdf/RHRA-Plain-Language-Guide-Apr2012.pdf**

[2] In residences that offer the "Aging in Place" feature, costs may increase with care needs. Depending on the residence and the amount and type of care required, increasing care may involve moving within the residence to an AL or Supportive Care Unit.

WHAT'S THE DIFFERENCE?

People attempting to determine the type of care they need for themselves or a loved one are often unaware of, or confused by, the difference in terminology with respect to levels of care. The chart below is meant to assist in quickly clarifying the difference, but for greater detail please see the sections related to each topic. ***Please keep in mind that no decision for placement of any kind can or should be made without the consent and knowledge of the person involved, if they are competent.***

LEVEL OF CARE	KEY FEATURES
Independent Seniors' Apartments **page 24**	• Private rental apartment; may have Rent Geared to Income. • May have some Supportive Housing services, meals for purchase, social programs, visiting MD.
Supportive Housing **page 27 - 28**	• Independent apartments with a care component. • 24/7 availability of support workers – can assist with meal preparation and homemaking. • Subsidies are available in some buildings.
Retirement Residences *(sometimes called Assisted Living, Care Homes, Retirement Homes, Retirement Communities)* **page 314**	• Privately owned and operated (some are owned by not-for-profit organizations). • Accommodation is mostly private – rooms, suites or apartments, some homes have semi-private units, very few have ward-style units. • Services provided usually include: social/recreational activities, housekeeping, most/some/all meals, minimal assistance with personal care (may be a fee involved), 24-hour staff – additional care may have to be purchased. • Licenced and regulated by the Retirement Homes Regulatory Authority • Must abide by the *Retirement Homes Act, 2010*; the *Residential Tenancies Act, Health Protection and Promotion Act*, fire and building codes. • Apply directly to the home. • Cost is determined by individual homes based on various factors. • No government subsidies are available.
Long-Term Care Homes *(formerly called Nursing Homes)* **pages 25 - 26, 375 - 391**	• Ownership/operation may be private, not-for profit, municipal or charitable. • Provide 24-hour assistance with personal care, eating, bathing, medications, medical/nursing needs. • Amenities, recreational activities vary; housekeeping, laundry services and meals are included. • Cost of care/support is covered by the Ministry of Health and Long-Term Care. Residents pay room & board portion (called the "co-payment"). • Standardized rates across the province set by the Ministry of Health and Long-Term Care; subsidies available for those unable to pay ward rate. • May be waiting lists. • Apply through local CCAC – maximum of five choices, first one to come available must be accepted. • Residents must be medically stable but usually require care of some kind; may be cognitively impaired. • All homes are licenced, regulated and funded by the provincial government under the *Long-Term Care Homes Act, 2007*.
Complex Continuing Care *(formerly called Chronic Care)*	• Hospital-like facilities. • Patient must have very heavy care needs that cannot be managed in a long-term care home, be medically unstable or have complex issues that require frequent nursing/medical attention. • Usually admitted directly from an acute care hospital.

WHAT IS THE RHRA?

The Retirement Homes Regulatory Authority (RHRA) is a not-for-profit organization that oversees retirement homes and enforces the *Retirement Homes Act, 2010 (Act)*. Its mandate is to improve the lives of residents in Ontario retirement homes. RHRA staff process retirement home licence applications, respond to calls about harm to retirement home residents and inspect retirement homes to make sure they meet the standards in the Act. The RHRA is accountable to the government of Ontario through a written agreement called a "Memorandum of Understanding", which is available on the RHRA website (**www.rhra.ca**).

In Ontario, all retirement homes must have a licence from the RHRA to operate. Retirement homes that have applied for a licence, or that have received a licence, are listed in the Public Register, which can be viewed at **www.rhra.ca.** The Public Register also lists the services a home offers and includes copies of any inspection reports or conditions on a licence for each home. Retirement homes must post their licence in view of residents.

The RHRA is also responsible for responding to calls about harm or risk of harm to retirement home residents resulting from certain events. These events include abuse, neglect, improper care or treatment, unlawful conduct and misuse of a resident's money. Persons that suspect harm must report it to the RHRA at **1-(855) ASK-RHRA (275-7472)**[3].

WHAT IS ORCA?

The Ontario Retirement Communities Association (ORCA) is a non-profit association that represents operators of retirement residences in Ontario. For over 35 years, ORCA has set the standard for care and operation in retirement homes through its longstanding accreditation program and its leadership in retirement living education. ORCA represents more than 80 per cent of the retirement home sector in Ontario. ORCA's membership also includes many commercial members who provide products and services to retirement communities[4].

WHAT IS OANHSS?

The Ontario Association of Non-Profit Homes & Services for Seniors (OANHSS) is a provincial membership-based association that has represented, promoted and supported not-for-profit providers of care, services and housing for seniors for over 90 years. Member organizations operate over 27,000 long-term care beds and over 8,000 seniors' housing units. OANHSS works with member organizations, allied associations, consumer groups and governments to ensure high-quality care and services for seniors in Ontario. For more information on OANHSS, call **(905) 851-8821** or visit **www.oanhss.org**.[5]

WHAT IS THE ONTARIO LONG TERM CARE ASSOCIATION?

The Ontario Long Term Care Association (OLTCA) is Canada's largest long-term care association and represents a full spectrum of charitable, not-for-profit, private and municipal long-term care operators. The Association's 439 member homes are funded and regulated by the Ontario Ministry of Health and Long-Term Care. OLTCA members provide health care and a home to almost 70,000 seniors annually. This represents approximately 70% of the total long term care homes and 66% of the long term care residents in the province.

OLTCA works to promote safe, quality long-term care to Ontario's seniors. We strive to lead the sector in innovation and quality care and services and build excellence in long-term care through leadership, analysis, advocacy and member services. To learn more please visit **www.oltca.com**.[6]

RETIREMENT RESIDENCE VISITING TIPS

Choosing a retirement residence[7] for yourself or a loved one is an important decision that should not be made hastily. If you are assisting someone in this process, before beginning your search you should

---

[3] Information provided by Brenda McIntyre, Communications Advisor, RHRA (July 2013).
[4] Information obtained from **www.orcaretirement.com** (July 2013).
[5] Information provided by Debbie Humphreys, Director of Communications & Public Affairs, OANHSS (July 2013).
[6] Information provided by Joanna Rizi, Senior Communications Advisor, Ontario Long Term Care Association (August 2013).

know and understand their needs, both in terms of services required and the type of setting they would feel most at home in. In addition, since affordability is a key area of concern for many, you should determine available financial resources and a monthly budget prior to viewing residences. Keep in mind that beyond the posted room rate, there may be extra costs involved over time (care, cable, telephone, etc.) that should be factored into your calculations. If you have the luxury of time, take that time to research your options carefully. Spend some time thinking about (and making note of) things of importance to the person moving – activities they like, external resources that should be nearby, important safety & care features you would like, on-site amenities that are preferred/desired etc. Conduct a preliminary search of residences and choose a few places that you think will meet your needs and are within your – or your loved one's — budget. It is of utmost importance that the person making the move visits these homes before making a final decision. You may want to visit more than once, perhaps at different times of day. It is advisable to go for lunch or dinner and try the food. You may even wish to ask if you could spend a few hours or a day there to participate in some of the recreational programs and observe the interaction between staff and residents and the day-to-day activity. Beyond the walls and the amenities and décor you can see, every home has a unique environment, and it is only by spending an extended period of time there that you can get a sense of whether or not you would feel comfortable.

When you go on visits or tours, you may want to go a bit early so you can survey the neighbourhood and look around the grounds and lobby area. It is advisable to call ahead to make an appointment, rather than just showing up. This ensures that the Marketing Manager or Administrator is available and can give you the necessary time to tour and ask questions. Whether you go in person or call to make an appointment, be sure to ask for an information package that you can look over before your scheduled visit. You should visit at least three residences. Make sure you take along a list of questions to each one.

When constructing your list, be sure to note which things are mandatory (needs) and which things you would like, but may be willing to compromise (desires). Go into each home with an open mind. Take notes during your visits and if the homes will allow it, take a few photos to remind you of significant aspects of each residence when you review your notes and impressions later on. If you are looking for a home for yourself, you may want to take along a trusted friend or relative so that you can get a second opinion and have someone to discuss your options with.

Many people, in the early stages of a visit to a residence, get a 'gut feeling' as to whether or not it is the right place for them or their loved one. However, it is still important to research each residence carefully. While décor and physical environment are important, there are many other factors to investigate and consider before making a final decision. In addition to the objective questions we ask (the answers to which are in the Part 3 of this *Guide*), there are many things to look for and ask about when touring a retirement residence. It is best to start by using your physical senses[8] which will allow you to determine one of the most important things about any residence: quality of care. The greatest predictor of quality is the staff in any setting. A caring staff and a clean and welcoming environment are key factors in determining your comfort with the residence and can be ascertained easily, if you observe closely and listen carefully during your visit. Take the time to watch the interactions of staff with residents, talk with residents, try the food and observe the environment of each place you visit.

On the next few pages you will find a sample questionnaire which you can copy and use on your visits (or use as a guide to create your own questionnaire). Take a fresh questionnaire (and your list of needs vs.

[7] Tips and questions in this section are specifically for those looking for a retirement residence. While some might be modified for those requiring long-term care, often one does not have the luxury of time to visit and tour places nor the options available that abound in the retirement sector. As well, priorities are different for those seeking long-term care so the questions you will have and the amenities the homes offer, will be different. If you are using this *Guide* for long-term care, please see the beginning of Part 4 where we have included a modified questionnaire specifically for those visiting LTC homes, We do recommend that regardless of what type of residence you are investigating you research your options, visit more than one, speak to residents and/or their families, staff and administration and get references if at all possible.

[8] If you visit residences that are not in **Part 3** of this *Guide*, please see our questionnaire format and use it as a guide to determine additional important questions about the residence, staffing, accommodation and amenities that may not be in our ***Visiting Tips*** question list (see **UNDERSTANDING RETIREMENT RESIDENCE & LONG-TERM CARE HOME LISTINGS** in the beginning of **Part 3**).

desires) to each residence you visit and some extra note paper where you can jot down general impressions and extra information.

Residence Name:________________________ **Date of Visit:**______________

Residence Address:____

Residence Phone Number:____

Tour Guide/Contact Person:____

SMELL	COMMENTS
1. Is there a foul odour in any part of the building?	
2. Does it smell clean? (Notice the common areas, hallways, kitchen, dining area, different floors of the building and suites.)	
3. Is the building (and suites) well ventilated so smells do not linger?	

TOUCH	COMMENTS
4. What is the air quality like? Does it seem stale or fresh inside?	
5. Is the temperature in the building and suites comfortable?	
6. Are there individual temperature control units (for heat and/or cold) in each suite?	
7. Is there air-conditioning in suites and common areas? Do they have central air or window units?	
8. If suites have window air-conditioning units, do they supply and install them? What is the cost?	

SIGHT	COMMENTS
9. Does the residence have an "institutional look" to it?	
10. Is there an alarm system on the doors?	
11. Are all doors locked 24-hours a day or only at night?	
12. Is the building adjacent to a busy traffic intersection/area? If so, are there safety measures in place for seniors in the area, such as a well-defined crosswalk or extended green light?	
13. Is there a 24-hour concierge/attendant at the main desk?	
14. Does the building look clean and well-maintained? (Check inside and outside; high-traffic areas as well as those that are not used as frequently.)	
15. Is the landscaping attractive?	
16. Is there a patio area/shady spots/garden with seating?	
17. Is there adequate guest parking? Is there a cost?	
18. Is there resident parking? Is it indoor or outdoor? Is there a cost?	
19. Do residents seem to be well cared for/dressed/clean?	
20. Do residents appear happy?	
21. Are there residents that appear to be in your age range?	
22. What is the atmosphere like? Is there a lot of activity around? Are there many residents in the common areas?	
23. Does the environment seem like a "community"?	

24. Are there pictures on the walls, living plants, comfortable sitting areas, private spaces for quiet visits with friends and family?	
25. Is the décor visually pleasing? Are the public areas/lounges pleasant and inviting?	
26. Are there commonalities that you or your loved one share with other residents (i.e. languages, activities, culture, etc.)?	
27. Note the location of fire exits and the fire alarm and/or sprinkler system. Are they easily accessible, well-marked and easy to open?	
28. Are there handrails in the hallways?	
29. What is the lighting like in the residence? Is it bright and well-distributed or dark in hallways and public areas?	
30. Ask if you can see the kitchen. Does it appear clean?	
31. Is there a central dining area for all residents?	
32. Is there access to amenities within the residence or close by in the community? (e.g. shops, restaurants, coffee shops, theatres, banks etc.)	
33. Do the recreation facilities and/or programs meet your/your relative's needs?	
34. Are friends or relatives able to come with residents on outings?	

Ask for copies of newsletters and recreation schedules that you can take home and review.

SUITES	COMMENTS
35. Do you like the size and layout of the suites in your price range?	
36. Do suites have a kitchenette? Do they have a bar fridge or microwave oven? If not, can you bring your own bar fridge/microwave oven?	
37. Are the suites clean, bright and comfortable?	
38. Are bathrooms clean and in good condition?	
39. Which assistive devices are present in bathrooms and which can be installed, if necessary?	
40. Do bathrooms have enough space for a wheelchair or walker to move in and out, if necessary?	
41. Are bathrooms private? Are they two-piece (toilet/sink), three-piece (toilet/sink/shower) or four-piece (toilet/sink/tub/shower)?	
42. Do suites have sprinklers, smoke detectors, heat detectors, CO detectors and easy access electrical outlets?	
43. Do all or some of the windows in individual suites open?	
44. Is there a lot of natural light in the units and common areas?	
45. Are there cable TV, internet and phone outlets in all suites? What is the cost to residents for cable, internet and individual phone numbers in suites?	
46. Is there adequate storage/closet space for resident belongings in the suites and/or somewhere else in the building?	
47. What kinds of light fixtures are included in the suite?	
48. Are rooms carpeted, hardwood or tiled? What is the condition of the flooring?	
49. Do you notice any overt safety hazards or concerns?	
50. Are the suite doors fire-safe? Do they have a deadbolt lock and a peephole?	
51. Are suite doors clearly labeled with numbers or resident names?	

52. Are hallways, doorways and suites wide enough for walkers and wheelchairs to be used and maneuvered?	
53. In general, is this the type of place you or your relative would feel comfortable in? Will it meet your needs?	

Ask if they have floor plans (with square footage details) of the suite(s) you are interested in. Take them home with you so you can determine where your furnishings might fit.

TASTE	COMMENTS
54. Does the food taste good?	
55. Are the portions adequate?	
56. Are the meals nutritious?	
57. Are all/some meals prepared on-site from scratch?	
58. Is there a dietitian on staff?	
59. Are fresh fruits and vegetables served year-round?	
60. Is the presentation of meals appealing?	
61. Is there a varied menu?	
62. How many choices are available at every meal?	
63. What if residents don't like the selections available on the menu?	
64. Can special diets be accommodated? Specify if you have a special need.	
65. Is alcohol allowed/served in the dining room or is there a licensed bar area?	
66. Are meal times reasonable?	
67. Is sufficient time allowed for meals?	
68. Is there reserved or assigned seating for residents?	
69. Is there full table service at every meal?	
70. Are 3 meals/day and snacks included in fee? If not, what meals are included and can others be purchased?	
71. Do menus rotate/change? How often?	
72. How are guests accommodated at meal times? Is there an extra cost?	
73. Is there a private dining area for residents to use with their families? How is this arranged and how many people can fit comfortably in that space?	
74. Are there multiple dining locations/options for residents?	
75. Is there a 'hobby kitchen' for resident workshops and events?	
76. What kinds of refreshments are offered between meals and at what time of day? Is there an open pantry?	
77. Is room service available? Is there an extra cost? Are there any restrictions?	
78. If you are away for a meal, will they provide one to take with you?	

Ask for copies of old menus to take home with you to review.

SOUND: ***Speak with residents and their family members***
(Remember – they know best what the residence and staff are like and whether it is a place that is safe and enjoyable to live in)

	COMMENTS
79. How long they have been there and why did they move in?	
80. Do they feel as if it is their "home"?	
81. Do they like the residence, and if not, why not?	
82. What is most important to them?	
83. Are their needs being met?	
84. What are the activities like, and do they enjoy participating?	
85. What do they like most about this home?	
86. What do they like least about this home?	
87. Are they satisfied and would they recommend it?	

If you were unable to speak with residents or their families during your visit, ask for references that you may call on your own once you leave the residence.

Observe the attitude of the staff & their interaction with residents	COMMENTS
88. Are staff members friendly, polite and available?	
89. Are staff members wearing name tags and dressed professionally?	
90. Do they know the residents by name and greet them respectfully?	
91. Is confidentiality/privacy of residents respected?	
92. Does the staff check with residents before showing you their rooms?	
93. Do they talk about residents indiscriminately?	
94. If you dropped in without an appointment or to make an appointment, were you welcomed and treated respectfully?	

Ask to see a copy of the Tenancy Agreement, Mission Statement as well as their Care Home Information Package. Take it home and review it carefully before signing it.

Speak with the Administrator and other staff members

RESIDENCE GENERAL INFORMATION	COMMENTS
95. Is there a waiting list to get into the residence? If yes, how long is it?	
96. Who owns/manages the residence? How long have they owned/managed it? How many other residences do they own/manage? What is their reputation?	
97. How does the emergency call bell system work? Is there always someone who can answer your call on-site?	
98. Are there call bells in all rooms and bathrooms or do residents wear their call bells?	
99. Where (in the building or external to it) is the station where call bells are answered?	
100. What is the policy on having pets or visiting pets?	
101. What is the policy on having microwaves, kettles, toasters, hot plates, electric blankets or heating pads in individual suites?	
102. Are food and alcohol allowed in individual suites?	
103. Can you eat/prepare your own meals in your suite?	
104. Is there a procedure if a resident misses a meal? (i.e. are all residents monitored to ensure that they attend all meals daily?)	

105. What is the residence's policy around decorating, painting and wallpapering individual units? Are there any restrictions?	
106. Is there a charge for the residence to paint individual suites prior to residents moving in?	
107. Can the home provide furniture? If so, what pieces? Is there a charge?	
108. What possessions of your own can you bring?	
109. Is there a place where valuables can be stored safely outside of individual suites? (or does each suite have a safe?)	
110. Are residents free to come and go? Is there a sign out/in process?	
111. Does the residence have a policy or any restrictions about overnight guests or daytime visitors?	
112. Are guest suites available? What is the cost?	
113. Are there visiting hours?	
114. Are there transportation vehicles/services on site and for what purpose can they be used? (Will they take you to appointments or is it just for group outings?) Is there a cost involved?	
115. Is there close access to public transit?	
116a. Is the residence a member of any organizations? If yes, is their membership prominently displayed in the lobby and is it up-to-date?	
116b. If there was an accreditation process involved, what rating were they given?	
117a. All retirement homes in Ontario must be licenced, or have applied for a licence, to operate. Is the licence status of the home listed as "licenced" in the RHRA's Public Register (available at **www.rhra.ca**)?	
117b. Are there conditions on the retirement home's licence (check the Public Register at **www.rhra.ca/en/register/** where reports on individual homes are posted)?	
118. Ontario law states retirement home residents are entitled to specific rights. Does the home have the Residents' Bill of Rights posted in view of residents?	
119. Is there a poster in view of residents that provides information about how to report resident harm or risk of harm to the Retirement Homes Regulatory Authority?	
120. Which community supports/services/resources/amenities are available in the residence and in the neighbourhood (e.g., shops, library, parks)?	
121. How close are important resources such as hospital, dentist office, places of worship, bank, seniors' centre etc.?	
122. Do residents have input into activities or events?	
123. Are there scheduled activities in the evenings and on weekends?	
124. What kind of activities are there in the residence? (Social, exercise, entertainment, trips etc.)	
125. Are the activities of interest to you (the resident)?	
126. Is there special exercise equipment, areas and/amenity areas? (i.e. work-out room, swimming pool, game equipment, spa services etc.)	

127. Are religious/cultural holidays celebrated at the residence? Which ones?	
128. Can this home meet your spiritual needs?	
129. How is the home governed?	
130. How are disputes within the home or complaints from residents dealt with?	
131. Is there a Resident Council &/or a Family Council? If yes, what is the process to join it and what kinds of decisions are they able to make?	
132. Will they allow you to wander around the residence on your own and talk to residents? (if not, will they give you references of families to call?)	
133. Have they done a Resident Satisfaction Survey and can you see the results?	
134. Is there a written Tenancy Agreement that residents must sign before moving in? (By law, there should be one.) Will they give you a copy of it to take home and review?	
135. Is there an option of a trial stay?	
136. For how long can you stay before having to make a decision to relocate?	
137. What is the cost of a trial stay?	
MEDICAL REQUIREMENTS	
138. Do you require a medical assessment (by your own or the residence MD) before admission?	
139. If you require oxygen therapy – or think that you might in the near future – will they accept residents with oxygen and in what form (liquid, compressors etc.)? Will they assist with its use (i.e. filling portable tanks, etc.)?	
140. Are there restrictions around certain medical conditions that cannot be managed in this home (catheters, ostomies etc.)?	
141. Can the home manage residents who are incontinent?	
142. Do the staff in the home assist with toileting? Is there an extra charge for this or is it part of a care package?	
143. If a person requires assistance getting in or out of bed or transferring to a wheelchair, is this available? Is there a special lift device in the residence for residents requiring this?	
144. Does the home have an Assisted Living Area?	
145. Does the home have a secure Dementia Area?	
146. What are the criteria for admission to the Assisted Living/ Dementia Area and is there an extra cost involved?	
147. Exactly what and how much extra care do they provide on the Assisted Living/Dementia Area?	
148. What kind of security is available to prevent residents with dementia from wandering off the unit and out of the residence?	
149. If you require special equipment, programs or staff training for your specific needs – does this residence have what you need to meet those needs?	

150. Is there a policy on assistive devices such as wheelchairs and scooters? (Some homes may not allow scooters or may not be wheelchair accessible.)	
151. What happens if a resident becomes hospitalized?	
152. What happens if your health declines (physically and/or mentally) while you are a resident? Do they help you find an alternative living arrangement and allow you to stay while you look for a new home?	
COST FACTORS	
153. What is included in your monthly cost? (Ask about meals, housekeeping, laundry, activities, personal care and utilities.)	
154. Are there laundry machines so that residents can do their own laundry? Is there a cost?	
155. Are there optional care and meal packages?	
156. What is included in the basic monthly rent package?	
157. How is rent paid (cheques, pre-authorized payments etc.), and how often?	
158. Can your care needs be met at an affordable price?	
159. What is the cost of extra care if you should require it at a later date?	
160. Is there a limit to how much extra care the residence can/will provide?	
161. Can you hire your own caregivers privately from an agency of your choice? (By law, the answer to this should always be "yes".)	
162. Does CCAC service residents in this residence? If so, what support/ services do they provide and is there a time limit for service?	
163. Are there hidden/extra/unpublished costs? What are they?	
164. When was the last extra care fee increase and how much was it?	
165. When were the last two rental increases and how much were they?	
166. How often is rent increased in this residence and by how much (i.e. is there a set percentage)? (By law, rent can be increased annually – 90 days' notice of a rental increase is required – and the maximum allowable rent increase for 2014 without making an application to Landlord and Tenant Board is **0.8 %**.)	
167. Is there a rate reduction offered if you are away from the residence for a week or more (i.e. if you are in hospital or on a vacation)?	
168. How much notice do you have to give the residence if you decide to leave? Is there a financial penalty if you do not give the necessary notice?	
169. If you prepare one or more of your own meals per day and eat in your room, is there a rate reduction offered? Or are there optional meal packages?	
STAFFING	
170. What is the ratio of staff to residents? Does the ratio differ between the day-time and night-time and weekends?	
171. What training does the staff have?	
172. If language is an issue, are there staff that speak your (or your loved one's) language? If not, how do they communicate with residents who speak unfamiliar languages?	
173. Are staff members required to have police checks or vulnerable person screening done prior to being hired?	

174. How do the different staff shifts communicate vital resident information to each other?	
175. What kind of consultation occurs when there are health care concerns?	
176. Is management staff on site seven days/week? Which hours do they work?	
177. Is there nursing staff (RN or RPN) on-site or available 24-hours/day?	
178. Are there regular fire drills, fire inspections and staff training sessions for emergency situations?	
179. What kind of safety procedures are in place? (i.e. with respect to emergency situations, fire, exit doors etc.)	
180. How are daily activities and events communicated to residents?	

Once you have seen all of the places you are interested in, you may want to review your original wish list and modify it based on your visits, your current needs and desires and any issues — financial or other — that may have arisen during your search. With new thoughts or questions in mind, you may want to go back for another visit or two to the places you are most interested in, before making a final decision.

Some people will book a short trial stay before committing to a residence. If you do this, it may be wise to stay over a weekend because you may find the residence has a different atmosphere (with respect to staffing, environment and activities) that you may or may not like on those days. Be sure to pay special attention to how you feel while you are there: How do staff members respond to you and your requests? How do they interact with other residents? What are the other residents like? (Are they welcoming? Are you introduced to people? Do you have things in common with them?) Which activities and programs are available? What are the meals like (portion size, taste, variety etc.)? If a trial stay is not possible, you may want to find out if you can arrange to spend some daytime hours at the residence where you can participate in activities, try the food and meet other residents.

Before making a decision, discuss your impressions with a close friend or family member. Additionally, you may want to have a trusted friend, family member or lawyer review the Tenancy Agreement before you sign it. This would also be an ideal time to ensure that your Powers of Attorney and Will are completed and up-to-date.

IF THIS IS RIGHT, WHY DO I FEEL SO BAD?

Caring for our elderly has changed over the years. In many families, children live great distances from their parents and women work full-time, so a multi-generational family living under one roof is neither feasible nor realistic. Caregiving is something we do from a distance or something we squeeze in among our other daily responsibilities. For many of us, the only safe and realistic alternative is to relocate yourself or a family member to a residence. The decision to move yourself or a loved one into a care home can be a difficult, highly emotional, life-altering process, which may create tremendous stress for all involved — on your relationships with each other, and in your daily lives. Along with the overwhelming responsibility of finding the right place is the realization that your relative is (or you are) aging and becoming less independent. There are a number of normal feelings that both the caregiver and the senior may experience at this time.

Elderly people who now require care that they hoped they would never need may be angry with physicians who cannot make them 'normal' again. They may be angry with family for not taking them into their homes and looking after them, as they may have done for their parents. They may feel guilty that they are imposing on their busy families or pride may interfere as they try to resist the idea of extra care or relocation by denying that they are unable to manage.

Change for anyone is scary. It is perfectly normal to be afraid of changing your home (especially for someone who has been in the same home for what is often a lifetime), daily routine and social interactions

and relationships. This change may also involve a sense of loss (of control over one's life and decision making, independence, privacy, lifestyle, etc.). As people begin to feel dependent, they may become depressed or feel helpless. Financial issues often cloud decision-making. People are afraid they will spend their life savings and not have any money left for themselves or to leave to their families. A person in this situation may remain uncertain about what to do and may have difficulty expressing these fears and concerns to others.

Likewise, children or caregivers may also have difficulty discussing their feelings about their loved ones' increasing need for care. Some children may have trouble accepting or seeing their once-invincible parent and protector become dependent. Often the role reversal between parent and child is hard to accept and cope with. Caregivers may be afraid to discuss their concerns because of how they think the person will react or because discussing it suddenly makes it 'real'. They may have misconceptions about what a residence is like or how the person will cope physically and mentally. One may feel guilty because he/she cannot provide the care that is needed for the person to remain at home or with family. Many have grown up with their parents caring for their grandparents and there is an expectation (or promise, made years earlier) that they would follow in their parents' footsteps. They may be angry at other siblings or relatives for not helping or providing care or with medical personnel for not making the situation better.

Families may not notice deterioration occurring because of denial or infrequent contact. Realization may come suddenly, along with self-blame, sadness, depression, overwhelming anxiety, and feelings of failure, loss and confusion about what to do. If the decision involves letting go of the family home filled with memories of one's own childhood, this process may prove especially stressful for everyone involved. If your loved one does not have adequate funds, this transition may create financial difficulties for you as well.

CARING FOR THE CAREGIVER

For those of our readers who have added caregiver to their list of roles – whether through choice or necessity, I thought it important to include some information specifically for you in an effort to both acknowledge how very difficult this role is and to offer some thoughts that might help you cope better. Without doubt, it is most important that those providing care and support for a loved one "care" for themselves as much as their loved ones – seek out support, assistance and help that can allow you to carve out time to meet some of your own needs.

First and foremost caregivers must communicate – with medical personnel, family, friends and their support network. Avoiding or negating problems does not help anyone. Letting your employer know your situation — especially if crisis hits — is important as well. There may be available support groups, Employee Assistance Programs or paid family leave options available to you.

A key component to your role of caregiver is education. Educate yourself and help to educate other people assisting you with care. Knowledge is empowering and can help you provide the proper support to your loved one. You need to seek out information about their medical condition and the options & resources available to both/all of you. This will enable you to plan ahead as much as possible (although often this too is difficult as things may change frequently so, flexibility is necessary also).

Sharing responsibilities with others is one of the most significant aspects of this role that benefits both you and your loved one. Know when you need help and don't be afraid to ask or seek it out (accepting your limits and knowing the kind of care and help you are comfortable with is an important piece of this). Use community resources and delegate tasks to willing family members and friends. While learning to do this might be difficult, it's important to recognize that good care and help can also be provided by people outside the immediate family.

An important task in caring for yourself is stress management. By acknowledging your feelings and recognizing the signs of stress and its impact on you, you will be better able to cope with your situation and seek help before 'burnout' occurs. Understanding that you might not be able to change the situation, but you can control your reaction to it, will most definitely impact your ability to cope.

It's important to ensure a balance in your life. Prioritize tasks. Ensure that your goals are realistic. Accept that there will be good days and bad days. Do things for yourself: eat properly, exercise, sleep

and take breaks when you need them. Don't allow pressure from others or feelings of guilt to force you into doing something that you are not comfortable with or to take on more than you can cope with. If you are 'sandwiched' between an older generation and a younger still dependent one, do keep in mind the importance of not sacrificing one for the other or your own mental health. Often it is helpful to join a support group of people struggling with similar issues or to seek out professional help if caregiving is impacting your functioning and health. Keep in mind that in order 'give care' to another person, you need to be in good physical and mental health yourself. It is only through self-care that you can remain well and able to fulfill the incredibly difficult role of being a *care giver* to someone else.

EMERGENCY FILE & INFORMATION

A good idea for everyone, because unexpected illness or injury can happen to anyone regardless of age or circumstance, is the creation of an *Emergency File*. This becomes even more important when you have loved ones who are older. There may be a time (or several times) when you will have to locate information that might impact that person's care or needs quickly. Having all documents in one place will make this a far easier task than having to sort through what may be, years of papers.

This file should be update every so often (perhaps even annually) to ensure everything in it is accurate. If you are putting actual documents in this file, it would be best to keep photocopies only in the file and store originals in a safe place. If you are creating such a file for yourself, inform your close relatives where it is located in the event of an emergency. An accordion file works well for someone with many different kinds of papers but for others, simply a notebook with important data may be sufficient.

Suggested items to include in your file are:

1. *Basic personal information/documents* – birthdate, social insurance number, passport number/birth certificate (or copy of those documents), veteran status/number or military documents, immigration documents & marriage certificate.
2. *Financial documents* - credit card numbers (or photocopies of cards), banking information/bank statements (if you are a caregiver you may want to ask the bank about the process of getting signing authority on your loved one's bank accounts), insurance papers, any mortgage or loan papers (financial obligations), account numbers for all monthly bills (including utilities, insurance premiums etc.), last tax return or notice of assessment, safety deposit box information (you may want to ask about becoming an alternate contact/signature for the box), information on pensions and regular deposits, investment information/location/contact person, any additional assets & internet passwords if online banking is done.
3. *Legal documents* – powers of attorney, Will, living will/advanced directive & any prepaid funeral or burial documents.
4. *Medical information* – health card number, any documents related to health issues/list of health issues or disabilities, list of current medication and dosages, list of allergies, phone numbers of all doctors/specialists with the reason for visits (if you are a caregiver and take your loved one to all appointments, you might want to keep a journal of all appointments, what was discussed and any follow up decided upon), list of hospitalizations & any health insurance information.
5. *Miscellaneous* – phone numbers of family members and friends, neighbours, caregivers/involved seniors agencies, clergy, lawyer, accountant, financial advisors & insurance agent. Computer passwords. List of organizations that the person is a member of.

HOW TO MAKE THE TRANSITION EASIER

It is important to remember that change is difficult, especially when it involves coming to terms with a loss of independence and possibly relocating one's life and possessions. The transition and acceptance of what it entails, can be made easier with ***good communication, planning and patience***. It is best if communication begins early on – before a decision is forced by circumstance or illness. I have heard repeatedly from both children and seniors how the 'other one' does not want to discuss future care

issues. Children say that their parent won't accept that they may need care, while seniors say that their children cannot face seeing them age and become dependent. Often, at least one — if not both — of them is afraid to broach the subject, even though similar fears and concerns occupy their thoughts.

There is no 'easy way' or 'perfect time' to discuss the issue. The reality is that it ranks among one of the most difficult topics anyone will ever have to raise with someone they care about. But not talking about it does not make the problem go away. Discussing it (if all involved are open to it) can create a sense of relief for both parties. Often we make assumptions based on our own fears instead of actual knowledge. The only way to attempt to make things better is to begin discussions with your loved one. Timing is an important factor. Talking about it early on, before they need care or assistance, will allow you to get a sense of what your loved one wants without them questioning your motivation. (If it is raised when the person is already in failing health, they may perceive it as an attempt to institutionalize them rather than as concern for their future safety and health.) As well, discussing thoughts, ideas and options over time when the person is not under pressure, makes it far easier to accept & come to terms with a loss of independence and relocation then if it is raised when there is a crisis situation.

Talking about someone they know who did not have the foresight to plan ahead may be a safe starting point to begin a conversation. If your loved one refuses to discuss it, the task is more difficult and the issue may need to be approached from a different perspective or with the help of other trusted friends, relatives or medical personnel, especially if health and safety issues become evident. Keep in mind when exploring issues and concerns that ***a competent person has the right to live at risk if they so desire***, and as hard it is to witness, it is still his/her right. <u>No decision for placement of any kind can or should be made without the consent and knowledge of the person involved, if he/she is competent.</u>

Unfortunately, there are situations where people insist on living at risk and, because they are capable of making their own decisions, nothing can be done to change the situation. In these very difficult cases, things may have to worsen before intervention can occur and the situation can get better. Sometimes a crisis, scare or health issue needs to happen before someone will be open to considering options.

When raising the topic of future planning, it is important to listen and be supportive. This can be a very frightening experience, and both the caregiver and senior may experience a range of emotions throughout the process. Be patient and caring with your loved one as all of you try to process the conversation and implications of the available options on all family members as well as the person you are concerned about. The location of the meeting should be one that is comfortable for all parties and has limited or no distractions. It might be helpful for someone to create an agenda for the meeting (e.g. concerns, potential needs, options, tasks etc.) to act as a guide and keep everyone on topic. Ensure that there is an opportunity for all present to discuss any concerns, fears and feelings related to obtaining extra care and the possibility of moving. Stress the fact that when discussion begins early, there is much more choice available and a far better chance that the person will be able to remain independent in their own home for longer with the proper supports in place. Plan ahead and prepare yourself for the discussion. If possible, know the available options, resources and costs before you raise your concerns. Present options thoughtfully and focus on what you see as the greatest need at the present time.

During the discussion, stay focused on the senior – not on what the family needs and wants. Agree to leave all old "baggage" at the door. Keep in mind the importance of what you are doing and the need not to become side-tracked by childhood issues and resentments. Try not to argue, criticize or condescend; and stick to the facts. State observations and concerns – don't demand actions or try to force what you want on them (use wording like "I am", not "you must" e.g. "Mom, I am concerned about you...."). Allow your loved one to be part of the process and the solution. Give them an opportunity to speak and give their opinion. It is important to point out that if their wishes are not known in the event of a rapid health decline, the options may be much more limited and the person making the decision may make one that the senior is not happy with. Needless to say, it is also much more difficult to make such a decision on someone else's behalf if you are not confident that you know what their wishes are.

Be open and honest with each other and problem-solve together. Focus on the positives and do what you can to encourage independence where possible (and safe). Teamwork is often a helpful way to

relieve some of the stress for all parties. Involve trusted family members (who are all in agreement) in the process to assist with both emotional support and practical tasks. Clearly denote the tasks and expectations on all parties keeping in mind that if possible, no one person should be expected to take on all of the responsibility for care. Expect to have multiple meetings to deal with concerns and look at solutions. You might need to 'pick your battles' or compromise at some point especially if there are some things that your loved one stands firm on. Know when it's important to back down on something even if only temporarily.

For most, there is truly no place like home, so if at all possible, you should first look at options to help the person remain at home, albeit with help or support (and possibly some home modifications) for as long as possible (and as long as any safety concerns can be properly addressed). Ensure you visit often to monitor the situation. This will allow you to determine when added supports or intervention becomes necessary. Sometimes, if in-home options have been explored first, it makes it easier for the senior to accept the possibility of moving into a care setting (or their child's home, if that is a realistic consideration).

Start by researching the available services for seniors in their area. The local CCAC may be able to help you with this. If relocation is the ultimate decision, it may involve selling the family home and many of the possessions in it. This can prove to be a very emotional process for everyone involved. It is important to stress that moving will not erase the memories that are connected to the house or its contents.

If, after careful consideration, you decide that the best option is for your loved one to move into your home, do keep in mind that this will likely change the family dynamics and relationships of those within the home and potentially even of other family members who do not live with you. Issues around physical space, tasks, care needs, lifestyle changes, work schedules, personal time, home safety/modifications, finances and a host of other things need to be addressed before finalizing this as a viable solution.

If the decision is to relocate to a care home allow the search for – and move to – a new home to be a co-operative process. Involve the person who will be experiencing the change in the decision-making as much as possible. This will assist them in feeling that they still have control over their life and future. Address any financial concerns early on. Know your/their budget so you will know what is affordable before you start looking. Determine where the best location for a new home would be so that relatives & friends can visit often and without difficulty, and if able, your loved one can feel comfortable going out in the neighbourhood. If you are looking for a retirement community, get to know the *Retirement Homes Act* and Ontario's *Residential Tenancies Act* guidelines to know whether homes are abiding by these two important pieces of legislation when you interview them. Make a wish list of wants and needs with your relative, recognizing that some things may have to be compromised. Take special note of what they are unwilling to compromise on. This allows you to be aware of what is most important to them. Work with them to compose a list of questions to ask while touring places (see **RETIREMENT RESIDENCE VISITING TIPS**). Take them to visit residences. Make a list of pros and cons of each place. If possible, encourage a trial stay in the prospective residence before finalizing plans for moving. Talk to people you (or they) know who have been through this process already, either for themselves or for a loved one. They may be able to make some valuable suggestions on how to find the perfect home and how to help you or your loved one adjust to the new surroundings.

Family support throughout the process is of paramount importance. To help decrease anxiety, offer to help them make a list of everything that needs to be done before moving day[9]. It might be a good idea to help your relative decide which things they can take with them and how to dispose of what can't be accommodated in their new home. Keep in mind the overwhelming experience that sorting a lifetime of possessions entails. Help your loved one to maintain and relocate their memories. Where possible try to find ways to preserve some favourite items perhaps by giving them to a family member so they can be 'visited' or by taking photographs of items that hold special meaning. Focus on keeping furniture that

[9] For additional helpful tips on relocation/downsizing please see the article near the back of **Part 2** (**SERVICES AND RESOURCES FOR SENIORS**) entitled **'Planning a Move'** by Monica Black **(page 52).**

will easily fit in a small space, but will help them to feel like their new place is their home. Do spend time sharing memories and discussing feelings around the move.

Help pack[10], arrange for storage and movers, assist with change of address notifications, be present on the day of the move and, if possible, help them decorate the room and settle in. Ensure that the suite is cleaned and in good working order, if possible, before the furniture is in. You may want to spend your first few visits exploring and becoming familiar with the new neighbourhood together. Ask the home Administrator if they can match you/your loved one with a current resident with similar interests who can help with learning the routine and adjusting to the new surroundings. Many people are concerned that once they are in a retirement residence or long-term care home, their family will not visit them. Sometimes the only way to reassure them that this will not happen is by continuing to visit and taking them out as much as possible. Schedule outings, plan private time and activities you can enjoy together, continue to celebrate special events and update them on family happenings. You are still their caregiver, but the way in which you provide care has changed. Knowing they are safe and well cared for will afford you more time to socialize and spend quality time together. Your visits can be spent enjoying each other's company, rather than focusing on personal care and household tasks which may have consumed your time when your loved one lived independently.

Despite this positive change to your relationship, keep in mind that there will be an adjustment period. It is important to be supportive and continue communicating regularly and frequently, both with your loved one and residence personnel. Get to know the staff and help them get to know your loved one. If there are concerns, be sure to discuss them promptly with the appropriate staff.

Allow your loved one to talk about his/her feelings with you; don't avoid uncomfortable discussions. Listen and don't fear talking about the past but, if negative or depressed feelings persist for a prolonged period of time after the move — in either you or your loved one — you may want to consider seeking out support or counselling from a trained professional. If you require assistance in locating a counsellor, you can contact your local Family Service Association, community information agency or your family doctor.

RETIREMENT HOMES ACT, 2010

Retirement homes are now regulated and must follow legislation called the *Retirement Homes Act, 2010 (Act)*. The Act provides protections for retirement home residents so they can live with dignity and make choices about their care. The Act is enforced by the Retirement Homes Regulatory Authority (RHRA).

Under the Act, the RHRA is responsible for:

- Informing the public and educating the retirement home sector and residents about the Act, regulations and role of the RHRA
- Licensing retirement homes and maintaining a Public Register (available at **www.rhra.ca**)
- Inspecting retirement homes using a risk-based approach, overseeing compliance and enforcing the Act for the protection of residents

Among other consumer protection measures, the Act sets out a Residents' Bill of Rights. Operators of retirement homes must respect and promote these rights. They must also post these rights in the home and ensure staff members receive training about them.

The Residents' Bill of Rights includes:

1. The right to:
   - know what care services are provided and how much they cost
   - be informed before fees for a care service(s) are increased
   - receive notice before a care service(s) is discontinued
2. The right to apply for publicly funded care services and assessments

[10] If packing and disposing of items appears to be too overwhelming a task, there are some wonderful companies now that can assist from start to finish. See **Part 2** of this *Guide* (**SERVICES AND RESOURCES FOR SENIORS**) for information on **Downsizing and Relocation Specialists.**

3. The right to be informed about and apply for care services and assessments from an external care provider (i.e. not by the home)
4. The right to have choice of care services provided by qualified and trained staff
5. The right to:
   - participate fully in making care decisions
   - participate fully in the plan of care (e.g. development, revision and review)
   - give or refuse informed consent to any treatment, care or service where consent is required by law
6. The right not to be restrained except in keeping with the common law (i.e. permitted if risk of serious bodily harm to self or others)
7. The right to privacy during treatment and care
8. The right to live in a safe and clean environment with dignity and respect
9. The right to have lifestyle choices respected
10. The right to raise concerns or recommend changes in policies and services without fear of coercion, discrimination or reprisal

The Act does not regulate what retirement homes charge residents for or how much they charge, but residents do have the right to:

- know what care services are provided in the home and how much they cost; and
- be informed in advance of any increases in charges for care services provided in the home.

Retirement homes are also required to provide residents with an information package which must include a list of care services provided in the home and their price.

You can read the *Retirement Homes Act, 2010* at **www.e-laws.gov.on.ca**. Visit **www.rhra.ca**, or call **(855) ASK-RHRA (275-7472)**, for more information about the RHRA[11] .

THE RESIDENTIAL TENANCIES ACT (RTA) IN ONTARIO

Retirement Residences fall under the definition of "care homes" in the *Residential Tenancies Act, 2006*. Most of the same rules that apply to rental units also apply to care homes, but there are some additional rules that are specific to this type of housing[12]. A care home is defined as "a residential building where people live so that they can receive 'care services'". Care services include things like nursing care, medication supervision, assistance with Activities of Daily Living and rehabilitation services. Excluded from the Act are long-term care homes, hospitals, short-term respite and rehabilitation facilities.

Prior to the signing of a Tenancy Agreement, all care homes must give the tenant a *Care Home Information Package* which must contain disclosure required by the Act, including information relating to: types of accommodation; care service and meal packages available; staffing levels and qualifications; information about the emergency response system; a list and fee schedule of services and meals available; and any internal procedures for dealing with complaints, including rights of appeal.

A written Tenancy Agreement between landlord and tenant must list the details of the care services and meals to be provided, as well as pricing. It must also state that "the tenant has the right to consult" with a third party and can cancel the agreement in writing within five days of signing it.

Other highlights of the Act specifically for care homes include:

- The landlord must give at least 90 days' written notice of rent increases.
- Rent can only be increased once in a 12-month period.
- Rent and care services are two different things: Care services can be increased at any time, by any amount; but the landlord must give at least 90 days' notice of a rate increase for care services or meals.
- If the agreement requires the landlord to do so, he may enter the unit at regular intervals to check the condition of the tenant. The tenant may revoke this permission by written notice to the landlord.

[11] Information provided by Brenda McIntyre, Communications Advisor, RHRA (July 2013).

[12] Information for this section obtained from **www.ltb.gov.on.ca/en/Key_Information/162303.html** (July 2013).

- A tenant can hire whomever he/she wants to provide extra care services in addition to what has been agreed to in the Tenancy Agreement.
- If an agreement relating to a care home is not in writing or does not detail what has been agreed to with respect to care services and meals, the tenant can apply to the Board for an abatement of rent.
- A tenant may terminate the tenancy anytime by giving minimum of 30 days' written notice of termination to the landlord. However, the landlord must give 60 days' notice of its intention to terminate.
- A tenant of a care home who terminates a tenancy is permitted to require the landlord to stop the provision of care services and meals before the date the tenancy terminates with a minimum of 10 days' notice.
- The landlord may terminate the tenancy if the unit was occupied solely for the purpose of receiving rehabilitative or therapeutic services agreed upon for a fixed length of time.
- A landlord, who gives notice of termination because of the intended demolition or conversion of the unit or for repairs must "make reasonable efforts to find alternative accommodation" for the tenant.
- The landlord may apply to transfer the tenant if he "no longer requires the level of care the landlord provides...or requires a level of care that the landlord...is not able to provide". However, "appropriate alternate accommodation" must be available.

Important regulations that apply to all residential rental units include:

- The resolution of disputes is handled by the Landlord and Tenant Board.
- Rent increases are per Rent Control Guidelines – for 2014 the maximum a landlord can increase rent is 0.8%, unless he applies to the Board for a rental increase above the Guideline amount. The increase may be sought to cover increased taxes, charges or utility bills, major renovations or repairs, or the addition of security services to a maximum of 3% above the Guideline amount for a maximum of three years.
- A landlord cannot charge more than one month's rent (or if rent is paid weekly, not more than one week's rent) in advance as a security deposit and must credit the interest (based on the Consumer Price Index for Ontario) to the security deposit or pay it to the tenant.
- Landlords and tenants may also agree to add parking fees and other services such as cable, lockers, etc., without applying to the Board.
- The tenant may apply for a rent reduction if the landlord: does not make agreed-to repairs or improvements contained in the lease; does not provide a previously agreed upon service; experiences a decrease in taxes and charges; or reduces or removes a service or residence.
- A landlord cannot interfere with the reasonable supply of vital services such as heat, natural gas or water.

A prospective tenant should carefully review the Tenancy Agreement, especially with respect to requirements for pre-admission and medical reports, signing out procedures, rules for motorized equipment, smoking, overnight guests and electrical appliances. It is important to keep in mind that a landlord cannot create arbitrary rules that conflict with tenancy rights under the *Residential Tenancies Act*.[13]

WHAT IF A RETIREMENT COMMUNITY IS NOT THE RIGHT OPTION?

The aging process for some is gradual and for others seemingly sudden. Caregivers need to watch, look and listen for signs that things are changing and needs are increasing. *If you notice that someone you care about is experiencing the following:* increasing frailty, increasing/new health concerns/issues (or has recently been diagnosed with a chronic illness, psychiatric illness or dementia), difficulties with

---

[13] The information in this section is by no means complete and is only intended to highlight some important aspects of the RTA. It is not intended to be used in lieu of legal or professional advice. For further information on the legislation contact the Landlord and Tenant Board at **(888) 332-3234** or **www.ltb.gov.on.ca**, the Ministry of Municipal Affairs and Housing at **www.mah.gov.on.ca** or a lawyer. A copy of the *Residential Tenancies Act, 2006* can be ordered from Publications Ontario at **(800) 668-9938, www.publications.serviceontario.ca** or can be accessed online at **www.e-laws.gov.on.ca/index.html.**

shopping and/or preparing nutritious meals, weight loss/not eating properly, changes in habits/ behaviours/personality/communication patterns, unexplained signs of physical injury (bruising, bumps, broken bones), difficulty performing activities they did easily in the past (either cognitively, such as financial management, opening and processing mail or physically, such as walking, taking medications, etc.), difficulty looking after personal care needs (grooming, hygiene, toileting etc.) and/or cognitive issues (significant forgetfulness, confusion, changes in mood), loneliness or fear of being alone, it is advisable to start discussing options (see **HOW TO MAKE THE TRANSITION EASIER**). As a first step, you may want to speak with the family doctor and perhaps arrange for a geriatric assessment if he/she feels it is warranted.

It is always best to consider in-home options before addressing relocation issues, provided that the environment can be made safe and your loved one is willing to accept in-home assistance. For some, downsizing from a two-storey house to a single-level apartment-style dwelling and/or obtaining adequate support (personal support, homemaking, meals on wheels, assistance with shopping or transportation, day programs, emergency response system, etc.) through your local community/seniors' agency[14] or Community Care Access Centre may be sufficient.

Home Modifications - You may want to have the home environment assessed by a professional to determine if there are safety issues or a need for specialized equipment to assist in functioning. If you discover a need for home modification to help the senior stay independent at home, you may want to contact Canadian Mortgage and Housing Corporation (CMHC) about available programs, funding for assistive devices for the home for low income seniors (Home Adaptations for Seniors' Independence (HASI) program – (**www.cmhc-schl.gc.ca/en/co/prfinas/prfinas_004.cfm**), eligibility and/or publications related to improving home safety for seniors. The toll-free number for CMHC is **(800) 668-2642**. Their website is **www.cmhc-schl.gc.ca**.

Independent Seniors Buildings - Another option may be to relocate to an independent seniors' apartment building, where rent may be geared to income for qualified tenants. These buildings provide an opportunity to establish social relationships with other healthy seniors, and some complexes have regularly scheduled social events and activities. Some buildings may have features or special units for seniors with physical disabilities. In some of these buildings, a doctor visits tenants on-site at regularly scheduled days and times. Residents are assumed to be independent and able to manage their own care, although some buildings may have optional meal plans available. Some seniors' buildings (and some new condominium complexes for seniors) are affiliated with retirement homes where optional meal packages can be purchased. These 'joined' residences usually allow for easy transfer to the retirement residence if such a move is required in the future. Assistance with personal care or housekeeping would likely have to be purchased privately through a local seniors' agency or arranged through CCAC, unless supportive housing services (see **SUPPORTIVE HOUSING**) are available.

We have been unable to locate a comprehensive list of available seniors' buildings in the province. If there is one you know of that you are interested in, you should contact them directly about the application process and eligibility. There are some 'Seniors Affordable Housing' structures that are managed by local municipalities but are the responsibility of the Ministry of Municipal Affairs and Housing. For information on those structures visit **www.mah.gov.on.ca**. You may also wish to check the websites for The Ontario Association of Non-Profit Homes and Services for Seniors (**www.oanhss.org**), The Ontario Non-Profit Housing Association (**www.onpha.on.ca**) or Housing Connections (**www.housingconnections.ca**) to find out about additional options for independent seniors' (subsidized) housing.

Co-operative Housing - Also known as 'co-op housing' is a kind of non-profit housing in which the residents or 'members' are actively and equally involved in the running of the community in which they live. The members do not usually hold any ownership in the property (it's usually owned by a co-operative

[14] Fee for service would be determined by the provider. CCAC may be able to arrange or provide a referral to a local agency that has various services for seniors. Some private insurance companies may cover some services. Eligible veterans may be able to obtain assistance/funds for service from the Department of Veteran Affairs.

corporation) but they do pay monthly rent that may be income-based and possibly less than market rates depending on their situation and the rules of the co-operative. This option would be one geared to the independent person as opposed to someone with care needs. A search of the internet does reveal a few co-op listings specifically geared to seniors though there is also the Co-operative Housing Federation of Canada that can be contacted for further information at **(800) 268-2537** or **www.chfcanada.coop**.

Reverse Mortgage - If you are over 55 and own and live in your own home, an additional option may be available to you. If you require care, wish to stay in your home, but need an extra source of income to pay for your care needs, you may want to look into a reverse mortgage. With this option, homeowners may borrow up to 50% of the appraised value of their homes at current interest rates. The amount you are able to borrow is based on several factors, including age, gender, health, marital status, current interest rates and the location and appraised value of your home. The money can be used for anything. There are no required monthly payments, as long as you still live in your home. The full amount does not have to be repaid until the house is sold or the owners die, in which case the estate repays the mortgage and the accrued interest. *This option is not ideal for everyone, so if it is of interest to you, you should thoroughly investigate both the pros and cons very carefully before making a commitment.* Pay special attention to the impact of accrued interest on your equity over an extended time. Investigate the fees involved (including legal costs), the percentage financing you will receive and the mortgage rate being offered. Find out about early repayment and any financial penalties that may be involved. Ask for copies of all documentation prior to making a decision and have a trusted friend or lawyer review them with you. You may also want to speak to your bank manager or financial advisor about other ways you may be able to free up some equity from your home. Consider all potential options in light of your personal situation before making a final decision.

LONG-TERM CARE (LTC)

If none of the above options are feasible and if retirement home level does not appear to provide adequate care, you may require a long-term care home. Long-term care homes (formerly called Nursing Homes) are licenced, regulated and funded by the Ministry of Health and Long-Term Care (MOHLTC). Eligibility for placement in long-term care is determined by your local CCAC. Long-term care homes provide 24-hour/day supervision and/or assistance with personal care, eating, bathing, medications, and medical/nursing needs for medically stable individuals. Standard room furnishings are provided, as are linens, meals, laundry services, hygiene and medical supplies. Availability of private, semi-private or basic accommodation varies from home to home and depends on when the home was built and renovated.

Long-term care homes have a dining room, lounge/common areas and activities/programs for the residents. There is a doctor available for the residents with regular on-site office hours. The government pays the "care portion" of the cost directly to the home. The "co-payment" amount is standardized across the province and set by the government (MOHLTC)[15]. The resident is responsible for the co-payment which covers room and board costs. There may be an extra charge for some services (such as cable TV, telephone, hairdressing), depending on the residence.

A co-payment reduction may be available for individuals who have chosen ward/basic accommodation. If you wish to apply for a rate reduction, the CCAC will provide you with the Rate Reduction package most suitable to your circumstances. The package contains detailed instructions on the required list of documents and completion of the application, as well as phone numbers for assistance.

If both spouses are receiving OAS, an application for Involuntary Separation can be made through the Income Securities Program of Human Resources Development Canada, which would effectively give each

[15] The maximum long-term care home co-payment (the amount the resident pays) rates (set by the Ministry of Health and Long-Term Care for the province of Ontario) effective July 1, 2013 are: Basic $1,707.59/month; Semi-Private range (depends on when resident was admitted and when home was renovated or built) $1950.93 to $2,011.76/month; Private range $2,255.09 to $2,361.55/month. Short Stay Rate is $36.34/day. Rates do change periodically and should be verified with your local CCAC.

of them the benefit of receiving pensions – including Old Age Security (OAS), Guaranteed Income Supplement (GIS) & Guaranteed Annual Income System (GAINS) as if they were single individuals.

All nursing home applications are submitted to and through local Community Care Access Centres. There is no application fee. You must be over 18, have a valid Ontario Health Card and have care needs (eligibility criteria is set by the Ministry) that can be met in a long-term care home in order to be eligible for placement in one[16]. Most long-term care homes have waiting lists and you may have to wait for an available bed in your chosen residence(s), depending on bed availability, length of waiting list, level of care required and other factors.

A person can apply to up to five long-term care homes at any given time. If you turn down a bed offer from one of your chosen all of your applications will be withdrawn and your application for placement will be closed for 3 months. Should your circumstances or situation within that 3 month period, you will need to contact your CCAC Care Coordinator for reassessment.

For those who do not require permanent accommodation in a long-term care home, short stay respite and convalescent care is available. Application for any of these programs is managed by CCAC. Short stay respite is designed to provide relief for your caregiver. The maximum length of stay is 60 days at a time, up to a total of 90 days in a calendar year. Short stay convalescent care provides supportive and restorative services for people who are recovering from an illness or injury in hospital or in the community. The maximum length of stay is up to a total of 90 days in a calendar year.

The Ministry of Health and Long-Term Care conducts inspections of long-term care homes and creates reports that are posted on site of the home. For detailed information (and any noted concerns by inspectors) visit the webpage entitled Public Reporting on Long-Term Care Homes at: **www.health.gov.on.ca/en/public/programs/ltc/26_reporting.aspx**. To report any concerns about specific long-term care homes, you can call the *Long-Term Care ACTION Line* at **(866) 434-0144**. For additional information on long-term care homes and listings on several in Ontario, please see **Part 4** of this *Guide* beginning on **page 373.**

COMMUNITY CARE ACCESS CENTRES (CCACs)

Community Care Access Centres (CCACs) are local health care organizations funded and legislated by the Ministry of Health and Long-Term Care through Ontario's 14 Local Health Integration Networks (LHINs). CCACs' staff create individual care plans to help patients:

- Maintain independence in their own home
- Avoid hospital admission
- Connect with health and community organizations that provide services beyond what is offered by the CCAC
- Find the right housing or long-term care home options when living independently is no longer possible.

CCACs provide assessment, referral, case management, information and access to a full range of in-home services for children, palliative care patients, psychiatric, physically and mentally challenged individuals, those who are transitioning from hospital to home, and patients who require in-home services to remain in their home longer. CCAC services are provided at no cost to the patient.

Health care services provided by the CCAC may include: in-home or community clinic nursing, personal support, physiotherapy, occupational therapy, speech-language therapy, social work, nutritional counselling and medication management. Anyone can make a referral/request for service by calling their local CCAC. If you are an inpatient in a hospital, CCAC staff will transition you safely home or to services within the community. As a first step, individuals are assessed by a Care Coordinator who works with

[16] If you are looking at placement for a couple who may require different levels of care, it may be best to look at residences which will accommodate both or are connected to alternate homes offering different levels of care. Even if both people are currently at the same level, you may want to explore residences that would continue to manage both of them, if one's health declines before the others'.

patients, caregivers and your health care team to develop care plans to support your unique and changing needs. CCAC uses a globally recognized, research-based assessment tool to help deliver the best possible care plan. If living independently is no longer the best option, Care Coordinators work with eligible patients and their families to find the long-term care home that best fits each person's needs. Application for admission into a provincially-regulated long-term care home can only be made through the CCAC, who assess eligibility, have comprehensive listings of available homes for long and short stays, and will help with the application forms.

Whether it's a CCAC service, or a service that is available in the community, CCACs work with patients to find the care and services they need. CCAC in-home and community clinic services are available through your Ontario Health Card. Some community services are available, at a fee.

Additionally, certain medical supplies may, in some cases, be partially or fully covered by the program. We have included contact information for all CCACs in Ontario on **page 54** of this *Guide*. To obtain additional information, call the Ministry of Health INFOline at **(800) 268-1154** or **(866) 532-3161**, visit the government website at **www.health.gov.on.ca** or the website for Ontario CCAC's **www.ccac-ont.ca**.[17]

LOCAL HEALTH INTEGRATION NETWORKS (LHINS)

Local Health Integration Networks were created in 2006 by the government of Ontario. The 14 LHINs in Ontario are not-for-profit corporations that plan, integrate and fund health care services, and in doing so, work with community members and those that provide health care services in their defined areas. Each is governed by its own board of directors, appointed by the province. Health care has been decentralized away from the province, and the LHINs receive funding directly from the Ministry of Health and Long-Term Care (close to 2/3 of the Ministry's budget has been transferred to the LHINs). The services the LHINs oversee include: hospitals, community health centres, long-term care homes, CCACs, community support services and mental health and addiction services. The creation of LHINs is based on the premise that each community's needs are different and priorities for funding and healthcare services are best understood and should be determined by those who live, provide and use services within a given geographical area, rather than generically across the province by one central administrative body[18]. To find out further information about LHINs, visit **www.lhins.on.ca**.

SUPPORTIVE HOUSING

Some seniors' rental apartment buildings offer something called 'supportive housing services'. This means that, if required, minimal to moderate care through personal support (which may include daily visits/check-ins, bathing and dressing, assistance with shopping, meals and transportation) and/or homemaking services is available to residents. There is usually a contract that details the care arrangement between the service provider and the resident (the owner of the unit is usually not the same as the service provider). Apartments with this option may make it possible for a senior to remain at home independently longer than they would in an apartment without supportive housing services available. In some instances, this type of service is offered in a setting adjacent or connected to another type of home (i.e. a long-term care home), which allows residents to utilize some of the services or amenities in the adjoining home.

Personal support and homemaking services coordinated through the CCAC are usually not available to residents of these buildings if those services are available within the building. The ownership, operation, funding base and administration of monies for such structures varies and may come from municipal governments, the LHINS, the Ministry of Housing or a not-for-profit organization such as a church/faith based organization, seniors' organization or cultural group. As a result, accommodation, care

[17] Information provided by Central CCAC staff (July 2013).
[18] Information obtained from: **www.torontocentrallhin.on.ca** (link to Ontario LHINs) (July 2013).

requirements, service providers, on-site services such as personal care and homemaking, subsidies and cost factors may differ from one residence to another. Rental costs are based on market rates, however some may have subsidies available for eligible applicants. There is usually a waiting list for entry into these buildings. The Residential Tenancies Act governs the housing portion of the accommodation. If there is a specific building you are interested in finding out about you are best off contacting them directly to inquire about the application process, waiting list for service and amount of care available.

The LHINS provide funding for several assisted living or supportive housing programs "including Assisted Living Services for High Risk Seniors, and Assisted Living Services in Supportive Housing..."[19]. If service is provided in a Supportive Housing building (either in a special building designed for this purpose or a regular building which has a group of individual apartments that have been adapted for those with special needs) staff is usually available 24/7 either at set times or as needed. An innovative form of service is provided to those who are deemed high risk in a given community (either due to physical or cognitive impairment) but with support at home can avoid long-term care placement. "This program provides a combination of personal support and homemaking services, security checks or reassurance services, and care coordination. Services are available around the clock, on a scheduled and as-needed basis. Services are provided to clusters of clients in their homes with a geographic service area designated by the Local Health Integration Network as a "hub", or to a cluster of clients in apartment buildings. Clustering of clients provides an efficient and effective means to provide long-term care that helps to keep people independent and prevent/delay institutionalization. Staff providing services operate from a location in the centre of the "hub" which allows them to get to the client quickly in an emergency"[20].

There is not one list of supportive housing units/complexes in the province so, if you are looking for one, you may wish to contact your local CCAC, LHIN, community support agency or local housing authority to ask if they have information about supportive housing complexes or providers in your area. The Ontario Ministry of Municipal Affairs and Housing website (**www.mah.gov.on.ca**) has information on specific Affordable Housing projects. The Ontario Non-Profit Housing Association website (**www.onpha.on.ca**) contains contact information on region-specific groups (access centres) that can provide information or applications for non-profit housing complexes/services in Ontario. (Click on the "Looking for Housing?" link on their home page.) The OANHSS website (**www.oanhss.org**) contains listings of members of their organization by area, which includes those that offer "Seniors' Housing". A quick search of the internet will uncover several additional websites detailing specific information about social/non-profit housing and supportive housing for seniors throughout of the province.

LIFE LEASE/LIFE EQUITY HOUSING

Life Lease or Life Equity structures are another option for independent retirement living. This type of residence involves ownership but not in the traditional 'condominium-style' that most are familiar with. Usually, you would purchase a leasehold interest (the terms of which vary depending on the development) in a property when you are capable of independent living. The structure (bricks and mortar) can be a townhouse or, similar to a condominium in unit size, features and monthly maintenance fees. The purchase price and maintenance costs are presumably more affordable than traditional housing given the not-for-profit sponsors. The corporation (usually a non-profit or charitable organization) holds title to the property. It sets the eligibility guidelines for who may purchase a leasehold interest (which is the right to reside in the unit you choose and share use of the common amenities with other residents) in that structure. There is a monthly maintenance fee and the corporation maintains and manages the building.

One potential benefit of purchasing a Life Lease is that you may be able to remain at home even if

---

[19] Information obtained from **www.health.gov.on.ca/en/public/programs/ltc/13_housing.aspx** (July 2013).
[20] Information obtained from **www.health.gov.on.ca/en/public/programs/ltc/13_housing.aspx** (July 2013).

your care needs increase (potentially it allows for "Aging in Place"). This is because many of the structures being built are connected to or affiliated with other seniors' resources; part of this housing option is often the availability of on-site support services (which usually need to be purchased on a fee per service basis), through an affiliated seniors' agency, that can be utilized as needed. Depending on the residence, ***this may include***: housekeeping (assistance with laundry, meals, cleaning), personal care (bathing and dressing), emergency call systems, dining/meal services, transportation, nearby or on-site amenities and activities/recreational and social services. The units may have special safety features and fixtures designed for the seniors' needs (e.g. grab bars in the bathroom). The amenities available, purchase price, maintenance fees and costs to purchase services will vary depending on the structure, sponsor, location etc.

Unlike with standard condominiums, the government does not regulate Life Lease buildings. As such, it is important when looking into this option that you do some research and ask many questions to ensure that your needs can be met both financially and physically, now and in the future, should your health decline. As well, be sure to ask about their policies around terminating a leasehold interest and how much equity would be returned or paid to you upon a decision to vacate. (In most complexes, when the owner of a leasehold interest (or his estate) wishes to terminate the agreement, he or she receives funds based on the market-value of the leasehold interest of the unit. There are some residences, however, that are based on a different model, and the entitlement to increased equity at the sale or transfer of the leasehold interest is linked to the amount of the initial payment).

It may also be wise to review all documents with a lawyer to ensure that you have a clear understanding of all of the terms of the agreement prior to signing anything. If you are purchasing a Life Lease in a residence prior to construction being completed, you might want to research the organization that is sponsoring the structure and will hold title to it so that you can learn about their reputation and previous dealings.

There does not appear to be one comprehensive list of available Life Lease communities in the province; there are approximately 140 life lease communities already and several in the construction phase across Ontario. A quick internet search will provide you with the websites of several projects and articles related to this housing option. Since many structures are affiliated with not-for-profit organizations, you may wish to contact OANHSS at **(905) 851-8821** for information on buildings that are members of their association. Their website, **www.oanhss.org**, has links to websites of companies that assist with the planning of Life Lease structures in Ontario.

In 2007, the Ministry of Municipal Affairs and Housing held consultations with stakeholders to determine any necessary involvement. (You can view a discussion paper containing background information and issues prepared by the Ontario government for the consultations in 2007 called "Best Practices and Consumer Protection for Life Lease Housing in Ontario" at **www.mah.gov.on.ca/AssetFactory.aspx?did=4067**.) At the time of publication (Fall 2013), there is still not any legislation however a "Life Lease Resource Guide" is in production (through the Ministry) and will be released shortly. For additional information, consumers interested in knowing more about this option can contact the Ministry's General Inquiry number and ask for the Housing Policy Department at **(416) 585-7544**[21].

LUXURY SENIOR CONDOMINIUM COMPLEXES

Another relatively new housing opportunity for seniors which is growing in popularity in recent years is a twist on a concept that has been around for some time. Developers are building independent condominium units (as townhomes or in apartment buildings) — for purchase or rent — that are specifically geared toward seniors. Many will have special features such as grab bars, lower light switches and easy-to-turn door handles. Most will have a choice of service packages/amenities included for a set monthly fee. Suites all have full kitchens, but many will also have meal packages available. Some are affiliated with retirement residences or can provide extra care, if necessary, for a fee. While these complexes are geared to the independent senior, they also have the potential for 'Aging in Place'. A number of these developments are detailed in this edition of the *Guide*.

Did you know?

The Ontario Ministry of Citizenship and Immigration has established a Senior Achievement Award to honour those who have made an "outstanding contribution to their community after age 65". There are a range of qualifying fields including the arts, education, community service, fitness, humanitarian activities and others. Twenty recipients are chosen annually by a selection committee appointed by the Minister Responsible for Seniors. To find out more about this award or to nominate someone visit **www.citizenship.gov.on.ca/english/citizenship/honours/saa.shtml**.

Quoted from: **www.citizenship.gov.on.ca/english/citizenship/honours/saa.shtml** October 2013.

[21] With thanks to Christine Thomas, Zock & Associates for reviewing our information in this section (August 2013).

Services and Resources for Seniors

Photos provided by The Roxborough

DOWNSIZING & RELOCATION

MEDICAL SUPPLIES AND EQUIPMENT

ACCESSIBLE BATHTUB SERVICES

Is Bathtub Accessibility Presenting a Problem?
Convert an existing bathtub into a safe and accessible step-in shower.
Bathway's unique "Tub Cutting" service is a quick and economical alternative to messy, disruptive and costly bathroom remodeling.
www.bathway.ca
GTA 416-222-5333
Toll Free 1-888-778-3746
info@bathway.ca
Bathway
The tub cutting people
Tub to shower. Just over an hour.

IMPERIAL
Bathrooms
5% Senior Discounts
Bathtub Accessibility Problems?
We Have the Answer!
No need for costly tear-outs. We have the no-mess solution to bathtub accessibility. Imperial Bathrooms unique and affordable bathtub cutout service can convert your existing steel, cast iron, or fiberglass tub into an accessible step-in shower in just a few hours.
GTA (416) 312-5199
www.imperialbath.net

ACCOUNTING, ESTATE PLANNING & TAX SERVICES

Miles & Co.
Chartered Accountants
519-253-6077
www.serioustax.com
Estate Planning and Tax Services for Seniors

ADAPTIVE & SPECIAL NEEDS CLOTHING

Adaptive Clothing for Seniors
LEED SOLUTIONS
FASHION & FUNCTION FOR SENIOR LIFESTYLES
Canada's Favourite Adaptive Clothing Store for
• Wheelchair Users •
• Seniors with reduced mobility •
• Caregivers assisting with dressing •
Online catalogue available
www.leedsolutions.ca
416-483-7494 or 1-800-218-7774 • info@leedsolutions.ca
DOWNSIZING & RELOCATION
CORNER COMFORTS
Touching Lives, Encouraging Hearts
organizing, downsizing, decluttering
packing and unpacking
moving, estate sales, cleaning, staging
so much more....
416.319.7722
cornercomforts.ca

DENTAL SERVICES

Smiles to You
MOBILE DENTAL HYGIENE SERVICES
Fully mobile office
Professional and affordable
Free Assessments for new patients
Serving Toronto, Durham, and surrounding areas
(905) 925-6575
www.smilestoyou.net

ELDER CARE TRANSITIONS

A Caring Approach to a New Life

Complete *Care for Seniors* in Transition

Moving
- Organizing the move
- Packing & unpacking
- Intelligent downsizing
- Free in-home consultation

Care Services
- Personalized care management
- Coordination of health care appointments
- Many other support services

Finding the Right Retirement Residence
- Explaining the options
- Discuss different types of accommodations
- Arrange tours at suitable residences
- Attend the tours
- No charge for residence search services

www.ectransitions.com

Email: **talia@ectransitions.com** • Telephone: **647.268.3295**

Move Seniors Lovingly
Downsize • Move • Design • Set-up
Honouring Our Fathers and Our Mothers
416.408.0424
www.moveseniorslovingly.com
Serving God through Seniors Relocation

MOVINGSENIORS
with a smile INC.
416-697-8106
Downsizing and Move Management Services for Older Adults in the GTA
movingseniorswithasmile.ca
SHADOW SERVICES INC.
Your behind the scenes support team for:
• Home Organization
• De-cluttering
• Staging
• Personal Shopping
Please contact us for your free consultation!
Cheryl Hannaford
416.402.2100
Arlene Waldman
647.222.5368
www.shadowservicesinc.com
We make sure your move is
"Simple & Easy"!
Relocating. Decluttering.
Downsizing. Moving .Staging.
S E T
SIMPLE EASY TRANSITION INC.
Call us at 416-908-1181
www.simpleeasytransition.com
topcat
RELOCATION TRANSITION SOLUTIONS
416.534.3078
www.topcatrts.com
karen@topcatrts.com
MAKING ALL THE RIGHT MOVES WITH YOU
Move Organizing
Senior Transitions
Downsizing & Decluttering
Retirement Home Options
Estate Clearances
Home Staging
Room Makeovers
Trusted Transitions
Tending to the details of life-changes
We help...
Seniors and Estate Executors who are overwhelmed by the prospect of handling the physical transition out of the family home. With expertise and caring professionalism we save families time, money and countless headaches.
Serving locations across Ontario
info@trustedtransitions.com
www.trustedtransitions.com | 416-503-0006
ELDERCARE CONSULTANT
ElderCareCanada
Canadian eldercare solutions
Practical advice for you & your aging parents:
• Eldercare mediation
• Retirement living options
• Same-day moving
• Home contents clearing
• Care management
• Eldercare expert opinions
416-487-6248
www.eldercarecanada.ca
Elder Care. Don't go through it alone.
Our Empowered Aging Program™
helps adult children manage elder care effectively, and with dignity.
Imagine the relief of knowing you have the knowledge, tools and support to meet the physical and emotional needs of your family, during this stressful time.
There are options.
Call today
Senior Care Options INC.
416-932-9941
www.seniorcareoptions.ca
EVENT PHOTOGRAPHY
JB
Jack Beker Photography
Since 1984
All Event Photography
On Site Printing
Novelties
Portraiture
Private/Corporate Parties
On Location or in Studio
Jack Beker
Studio: 905-771-8878
Cellular: 416-816-6293
photobyjack@rogers.com
www.photobyjack.photoreflect.com

FAMILY LAWYER

HEALTH & WELLNESS

HARVEY S. GOLDSTEIN
BARRISTER, SOLICITOR & MEDIATOR
Family Law (Divorces)
Wills
Powers of Attorney
Seminars on Estate Planning
PHONE: (905) 761-6263 | FAX: (905) 761-6264
EMAIL: harvey@thedivorcelawyer.ca
WEBSITE: www.thedivorcelawyer.ca
SILVER COMPASS
Digital Health Tech
Age Friendly Help
Financial Wellness
Age Friendly Network of Professionals offering assistance
Simple, Affordable technologies that help individuals stay safe, well and connected
Financial, Tax/Estate Organizing and Support
www.silvercompass.ca
905-510-1393 or 1-877-793-9633

HEARING SOLUTIONS

Bernafon Canada Ltd.

Hearing and understanding are basic human needs. Bernafon believes in a world in which people with restricted hearing can communicate again, thanks to advanced technology. Find out more about the Swiss hearing systems from Bernafon.

bernafon®

Your hearing · Our passion

For more information visit us at www.bernafon.ca or call 1-800-265-8250.

HOME HEALTH CARE SERVICES

- Available 24 Hours/7 Days a Week
- Dependable Service
- Continuity of Caregivers

Healthcare Solutions

- Providers of RN, RPN & PSWs
- Free In-Home Assessment
- Peace of Mind for the Families

Alba Home Healthcare Solutions provides a comprehensive range of services delivered by compassionate, dependable and well selected nurses and caregivers. Our staff is bonded and insured and available 24 hours, 7 days a week. Service will be provided wherever the help is needed; at home, in hospital or facility.

- Personal Care
- Private Duty
- Respite Care
- Palliative Care
- Live In/ Live Out
- Companionship & Escorting
- Medication Reminders
- Power of Attorney (POA)
- Light Housekeeping & Laundry
- Grocery Shopping & Meal Preparation
- Alzheimer/Dementia/Parkinson/MS/ALS

Call us today for a free consultation and for more information on our ***"FREE 3 Hour"*** introductory discount.

Contact us at 416-234-0900 or 289-304-8306

Alert / Best
Nursing & Home Care
Provider of Quality RNs, RPNs, PSWs and Homemakers for Facilities and Private Care
Private Duty Nursing / Attendant Care / Home Support / ABI & Traumatic Injury / Elder Care / Chronic Care / Palliative Care /...and much more
Call: 905-524-5990 or 1-866-959-9913
Visit us at: www.alertbestnursing.com
OUR GOAL IS TO PROMOTE QUALITY OF LIFE

INTEGRA*care*

Since 1990, we remain committed to helping people maintain dignity in their home or choice of residence by providing caregivers at all levels and a broad range of support services and products.

396 Moore Avenue, Toronto, Ontario, M4G 1C7
(416) 421-4243 or (800) 891-4197

www.integracare.on.ca

Seniors for Seniors
Call us for a free Consultation
416-481-2733
www.seniorsforseniors.com
• Drop-In, Live-In and Overnight Companion Caregivers
• Personal Care, Alzheimer's and Dementia Care
• Driver Companions
• Home Cleaners and Handypersons
Toronto • Peel • Halton • Hamilton • Kitchener • London • Durham • Collingwood • Barrie
JUNK REMOVAL
Helping You Put the Pieces in Place
Senior Lifestyle Solutions
Professional One-on-one Care
• Companions / Homemakers
• Personal Support Workers
• Live in / Live out
• Up to 24 Hour Care
• Short or Long-Term
• Our Employee or Yours
• Veterans Affairs Canada Health ID Cards Accepted
416.436.1267
Bonded & Insured
Serving Toronto & Suburbs
Since 1996
www.srlifestylehomecare.com
JUSTJUNK.com
• We remove everything!
• We do the loading
• Recycle & donate
Lowest Price Guaranteed!
Call Today! 1-888-586-5888
JUST JUNK .com

Have the retirement you deserve in Lundar
It's a great place to visit, an even better place to live
(Just one hour from Winnipeg)
HISTORY
GOLF
FUN
Lundar
take a closer look...
www.lundar.ca

MEDICAL SUPPLIES AND EQUIPMENT

agecomfort.com
life should be comfortable™
Over 6,000 Home Health Care Products
Request a FREE 164 page Catalogue!
Don't overpay at your local store or pharmacy!
FREE SHIPPING on all orders over $50
www.agecomfort.com • 1.800.520.3259

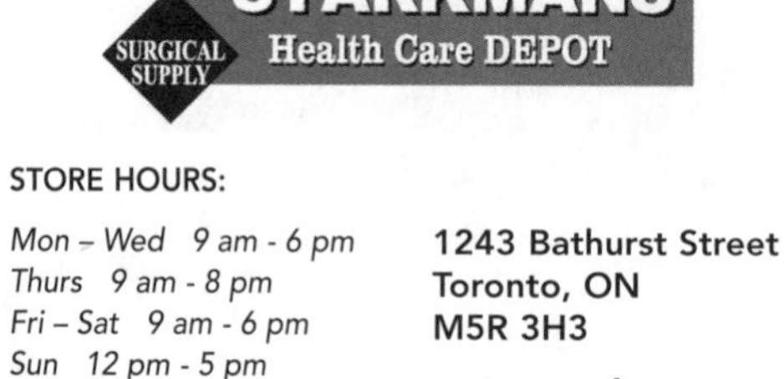

STORE HOURS:

Mon – Wed 9 am - 6 pm
Thurs 9 am - 8 pm
Fri – Sat 9 am - 6 pm
Sun 12 pm - 5 pm

1243 Bathurst Street
Toronto, ON
M5R 3H3

www.starkmans.com

Tel: 416-534-8411 • Toll Free: 1-800-387-0330

SHOPPERS HomeHealthCare®

Healthcare solutions for better living.

At **Shoppers Home Health Care** we are focused on providing Canadians with the most complete selection of specialty home health care products & services, tailored to meet your specific needs for health recovery and maintenance. **Shoppers Home Health Care** is Canada's largest retailer of home health care products and services. Visit us at: **www.shoppershomehealthcare.ca**

PUBLISHING

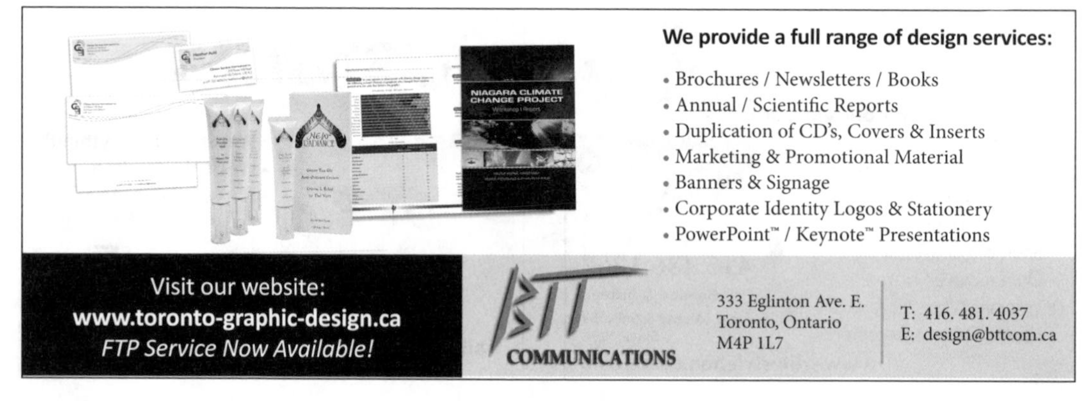

NIAGARA CLIMATE CHANGE PROJECT
We provide a full range of design services:
• Brochures / Newsletters / Books
• Annual / Scientific Reports
• Duplication of CD's, Covers & Inserts
• Marketing & Promotional Material
• Banners & Signage
• Corporate Identity Logos & Stationery
• PowerPoint™ / Keynote™ Presentations
Visit our website:
www.toronto-graphic-design.ca
FTP Service Now Available!
BTT COMMUNICATIONS
333 Eglinton Ave. E.
Toronto, Ontario
M4P 1L7
T: 416. 481. 4037
E: design@bttcom.ca

SENIORS' RESOURCE INFORMATION & ACTIVITIES

Help's Here!™

RESOURCES FOR SENIORS & CAREGIVERS

Help's Here!
RESOURCES FOR SENIORS & CAREGIVERS

HELP IS FINALLY AVAILABLE

Reach for The Help's Here Resource Guide! — a free directory of resources for seniors & caregivers with 12 distinct chapters of helpful information, telephone numbers, tips and articles.

* HOME CARE
* RESIDENTIAL
* ALZHEIMER/DEMENTIA
* COMMUNITY SUPPORT
* HEALTH & MEDICAL
* FINANCIAL
* LEGAL
* MOVING HOUSE
* TRANSPORTATION
* RECREATION
* SHOPS & SERVICES
* BEREAVEMENT

For locations to pick up your free copy visit www.HelpsHere.com or call 416-423-6547.

OLDER ADULT CENTRES' ASSOCIATION OF ONTARIO

Providing resources and support to volunteers and staff operating Older Adult Centres

OACAO

The Voice of Older Adult Centres
La voix des centres pour aînés

TO CONTACT YOUR LOCAL CENTRE
TOLL FREE 1.866.835.7693
www.oacao.org

DETAILED RESOURCE INFORMATION

ACCESSIBLE BATHTUB SERVICES

Bathway Inc. - For some individuals getting in and out of the bathtub can be difficult and even dangerous. Bathway offers a solution that will convert an existing bathtub into a safe and accessible step-in shower. Our unique "tub cutting" service is a quick, clean and economical alternative to traditional bathroom remodeling. Call **(416) 222-5333** or **(888) 778-3746** or visit us at **www.bathway.ca.**

Imperial Bathrooms - As we age, the high outer portion of the bathtub becomes increasingly hazardous for seniors and people with limited mobility. Imperial Bathrooms has 2 affordable solutions that will convert your existing bathtub into a step-in shower; we even have bathtub steps with a door option, so now there's no need to sacrifice your relaxing baths for safety. Our water-tight sealed door option has proven to be an affordable alternative versus a full bathtub remodel. Please call **(416) 312-5199** or visit us today at **www.imperialbath.net.**

ACCOUNTING, ESTATE PLANNING & TAX SERVICES

Miles & Co. Chartered Accountants - Effective estate planning in its simplest form involves the accumulation & distribution of personal assets in a tax-efficient manner. High net worth seniors need to ensure that financial needs of today are met, while having the peace of mind that loved ones will be provided for. Our team of professional advisors will work together to assist you in developing tax effective strategies specific to your needs. Seniors on a fixed income in Ontario may benefit from a variety of federal/provincial programs & tax credits. We can assist in receiving benefits such as the Ontario Seniors Homeowners Property Tax Grant, Ontario Trillium Benefit, Guaranteed Income Supplement & the Allowance Program to ensure that you receive all the tax benefits/grants that you are entitled to. Mention Senioropolis when you call for your consultation and receive 10% off. Call **(519) 253-6077** or visit **www.serioustax.ca.**

ADAPTIVE & SPECIAL NEEDS CLOTHING

Leed Solutions Adaptive Clothing and Accessories - When dressing a wheelchair dependent person becomes a challenge, adaptive clothing is a simple solution that helps to maintain dignity & self-esteem. Adaptive clothing allows a person to remain seated & passive during the process reducing anxiety & the risk of injury for the wheelchair dependent person & their caregivers. We specialize in fashionable, well-made adaptive clothing that makes the patient, family & caregiver confident that each day begins with dignity & the positive self-esteem that comes with being well dressed. Visit **www.leedsolutions.ca** or contact one of our personal shoppers for advice at **(416) 483-7494** or **(800) 218-7774.** See article on **page 48.**

DENTAL SERVICES

Smiles To You - Trudi Martin-Tate, Registered Dental Hygienist - Completely portable dental cleaning service, brought to you. Professional, thorough & gentle care. *Services:* Scaling (removes tartar & plaque), Polishing (removes surface stain), Desensitizing, Denture Cleaning, Fluoride Treatments, Sealants, Sports Guards & Whitening. Prices are about 30% lower than a traditional dental office. Most insurance plans accepted, cash, Visa & MasterCard. Estimates may be sent to insurance provider on your behalf. Flexible days & times. Servicing Oshawa, Whitby, Ajax, Pickering, Markham, Uxbridge, Sutton, Georgina, Port Perry, Sunderland, Bowmanville, Port Hope, Cobourg, Peterborough, Millbrook, Trenton, Belleville, Picton & other areas. SCHEDULE A FREE ASSESSMENT TODAY!!! Call us at **(905) 925-6575** or visit **www.smilestoyou.net**.

DOWNSIZING & RELOCATION

Corner Comfort Home Downsizing Services - Turning a corner in life? We are a complete service solution. Some of our services include decluttering, organizing, packing, unpacking, moving, estate sales, staging, disposal of unwanted items, professional services & most importantly helping you settle into your new home. Our service plans are flexible & customized to fit your needs. Our team is successful in helping seniors create an atmosphere that feels warm & relaxed in their transition so they can focus on a new beginning. We do it all with love, fun & compassion!! We look forward to meeting you. Please call Gillian Sweeney for a complimentary in-home assessment at **(416) 319-7722** or visit **www.cornercomforts.ca.**

Elder Care Transitions - We are Retirement Relocation Specialists. We assist in all aspects of a senior's move into a retirement home. ECT is a Toronto-based full service agency dedicated to making the move as comfortable as possible. We specialize In helping seniors & their families through all decisions surrounding a move. Some of our services include finding the perfect home, helping downsize, pack/unpack, coordinate the move, develop furniture layout plans, coordinate in-home care management, accompanying you on important appointments & more. Our unique services are customized to serve your specific needs which allows us to offer a very personalized service. Our goal is to help make your transition seamless. ECT offers care support services as well. Call us for a free in-home consultation at **(647) 268-3295** or visit **www.ectranstions.com.**

Move Seniors Lovingly - Serving God through seniors' relocation. Recommended by senior residences throughout the GTA & surrounding areas. Complete senior move management services includes: prepare home for the market, sale of estate & used furniture, downsizing, disposal, off-site storage, floor plan & design for new residence, pack, move, unpack & complete set-up including installation of art, mirrors, electronics. Certified, bonded & insured. Serving Toronto & surrounding areas, Southwestern Ontario/ Region of Niagara and all of Eastern Ontario & Newfoundland. Call us for a complimentary consultation at **(416) 408-0424** or **(888) 884-0804** or visit **www.moveseniorslovingly.com.**

Moving Seniors with a Smile Inc. - What to take? What to sell? What to give away? What to do with what's left over? We can help you decide – the final word is yours. Lots of personal items can accumulate & it can be daunting to face that kind of process on your own. . . You can set the pace & we will keep things running smoothly so that you stay on schedule. Moving Seniors with a Smile Inc. is bonded, insured and offers a full range of professional organizing, downsizing & move management services for older adults & families in the GTA. Focused on you & your individual needs, we do the worrying so you don't have to! Call us at **(416) 697-8106** or visit **www.movingseniorswithasmile.ca.**

Red Coats Moving Solutions Inc. - Downsizing? We are Red Coats, Ontario's most experienced and trusted move management team. Since 2004, we have helped over 1,000 families downsize and transition to their new homes. Red Coats offers you a complete range of personalized, peace-of-mind move management services. From downsizing, decluttering and staging your home for sale and home clear out, to moving and settling you comfortably in your new home. We even offer concierge services. We are bonded, insured and fully trained for your peace-of-mind. For a complimentary consultation call **(416) 920-1317** or visit **www.redcoatsmoving.com**.

Shadow Services Inc. - Are you downsizing and/or relocating? Do you need help to de-clutter, organize & stage your space? This can be a difficult & stressful time because of the emotional attachment you may have to many of your possessions. What do you take? What do you leave behind? Does lack of time or mobility issues make shopping difficult for you? Are the choices overwhelming when shopping for clothes, gifts or home décor? We will meet with you and/or your family to prioritize your requirements, listen to your likes, dislikes & your budget. Together we will decide how we can best help you get the job done with

empathy & skill. Bonded & insured. Call us at **(416) 402-2100** or **(647) 222-5368** for your free consultation or visit **www.shadowservicesinc.com**.

Simple Easy Transition Inc. – IMAGINE THIS SCENARIO: You have decided to sell your home. The realtor is knocking at your door and wants the house on the market yesterday. If you're feeling stuck, frustrated, and not sure what to do first when contemplating a move, think no further. That's where we come in. We take the pain of moving, downsizing and staging away to let you focus your time on the things you enjoy! Explore our services to see how we can help. Call us for a free consultation at **(416) 908-1181** or visit **www.simpleeasytransition.com.** See article on **page 52.**

Topcat Relocation Transition Solutions - will ease the stress and anxiety of later life transitions by arranging and coordinating a customized move management program for you. Our goal is to ensure that when you arrive at your new address, you will instantly feel comfortable and at home. Call us today for your FREE In-home assessment at **(416) 534-3078** or visit **www.topcatrts.com**.

Trusted Transitions - helps seniors and their families when they are overwhelmed by the process of physically transitioning out of the home they have lived in for many happy years. Our specific services include sorting, decluttering, packing, moving, unpacking, arranging for the sale or donation of unwanted household items and readying the home for sale. We are bonded and insured and have over 10 years' experience. We have branches in the GTA, Burlington, Hamilton, Collingwood and Peterborough. Call us at **(416) 503-0006** or visit **www.trustedtransitions.com.**

ELDERCARE CONSULTANT

ElderCareCanada - Since 1998, we have been the one-stop solution for adult children and their aging parents: expert eldercare options, information webinars, eldercare mediation, strategies for in-home care, retirement residence options, same-day moving, home contents clearing, care management. Practical, hands-on experience by a Certified Professional Consultant on Aging (CPCA), former banker, certified mediator and professor of Retirement Communities Management certification program. We've been there – we'll get you through it, too. Call us at **(416) 487-6248** or visit **www.eldercarecanada.ca.**

Senior Care Options Inc. - Services include The Empowered Aging Program™ which gives adults the knowledge, tools and support to manage the emotional and physical needs of elder care. Confidential family mediation sessions. Care Management and Guided Care Services. Elder Care Presentations and Seminars. Home Safety Audits. Relocation services. Call us at **(416) 932-9941** or visit **www.seniorcareoptions.ca.** See article on **page 49.**

EVENT PHOTOGRAPHY

Photo by Jack - We bring old photos to life! Restoring old memories is what we do. We create great family heirlooms. Large or small groups as well as individuals can be captured at family gatherings and all special occasions. We can create a special portrait, a collection of images on disc, and we can display them on our website for all to enjoy. Specializing in on-site photo giveaways, we can make any event a hit with instant commemorative images in a special frame. Share our passion for creating photo memories. Call us at **(905) 771-8878** or visit **www.photobyjack.photoreflect.com.**

FAMILY LAWYER

Harvey S. Goldstein, Barrister, Solicitor & Mediator - Family lawyer deals in all areas including Divorce, Separation, Custody, Support, Property Division and Wills and Power of Attorney. Call us at **(905) 761-6263** or visit **www.thedivorcelawyer.ca.** See larger ad for a full description of services on **page 361.**

HEALTH & WELLNESS

Silver Compass Inc. - strives to provide a holistic & common sense approach to helping by providing older individuals, their loved ones or caregivers a single point of contact for information & support to help with some of the challenges that can come with aging. Our trusted network of like-minded age-friendly professionals offer services in a variety of areas. We also supply a growing array of simple & affordable digital health technologies that are geared specifically towards helping individuals stay safe, well, connected & independent. These technology-enabled solutions offer great potential for helping older individuals as well as those who are challenged with a chronic illness or disability, avoid crisis & possible hospitalization. Call us at **(905) 510-1393** or visit **www.silvercompass.ca.**

HEARING SOLUTIONS

Bernafon Canada Ltd. - Hearing and understanding are basic human needs. Bernafon believes in a world in which people with restricted hearing can communicate again, thanks to advanced technology. Find out more about the Swiss hearing systems from Bernafon. For more information call us at **(800) 265-8250** or visit **www.bernafon.ca.**

HOME HEALTH CARE SERVICES

Alba Home Healthcare Solutions - is a well-established home healthcare agency. We offer a wide range of services for seniors and disabled individuals 24 hours/7 days a week. We provide RN, RPN and Personal Support Workers, personal care, companionship, respite care, housekeeping and escort services. Our goal is to provide quality care, allowing people to maintain their independence and dignity, and still be safe. We service Toronto (GTA) & York Region. Call Toronto at **(416) 234-0900** or York Region at **(289) 304-8306** or visit **www.albahomehealthcare.com.**

Alert/Best Nursing & Home Care - is a well-established nursing agency, whose principals have forty years combined experience in health care. Our goal is to provide support to clients and families to meet their health care needs. Our services include: attendant care/home support for brain injury and traumatic injury, elder care, convalescence, caregiver relief, chronic care, palliative care, facility staffing, referral to case management and occupational therapy. Our service area includes: Hamilton-Wentworth-Niagara, the GTA, Halton-Peel and Haldimand-Brant. Contact us at **(905) 524-5990** or **(866) 959-9913** or visit **www.alertbestnursing.com.** See article on **page 51.**

Bayshore Home Health and Bayshore Therapy & Rehab. - Canadian owned and operated, we are one of the country's largest provider of home and community health care services, with more than 50 offices, 20 community care clinics and over 10,000 employees. Offering a wide range of home and community health services, we strive to make a difference in our clients' lives – every visit, every time. Our nursing, personal care, home support and therapy and rehabilitation services are available privately as well as through government care programs, personal and group insurance plans and workplace safety insurance. For more information please call your local Bayshore Home Health office. Contact us at **(877) 289-3997** or visit **www.bayshore.ca.**

Integracare - is a Canadian company that provides a wide range of private nursing services and services needed by those requiring care in their place of residence. Contact us at **(416) 421-4243** or **(800) 891-4197** or visit **www.integracare.on.ca.**

Living Assistance Services - We are committed to bringing choice, comfort and dignity to seniors in their own homes or wherever else it may be required. Our Personal Support Workers are experienced and

reliable caregivers with meticulous references. From 3 to 24 hours, live-in or out, we provide personal care, meal preparation, housekeeping, laundry and joyful companionship. Contact us for a complimentary consultation. Our service area includes: Toronto/Etobicoke/Scarborough – **(416) 483-0070**; Mississauga – **(905) 286-0031**; Oakville/Burlington – **(905) 829-9214**; Willowdale/Thornhill/Richmond Hill/Markham/ Vaughan - **(416) 628-5072**; Durham Region/Northumberland County/Peterborough County – **(855) 548-2778**. For more information please visit **www.LAServices.ca.**

NHI Nursing & Homemakers Inc. - offers a wide range of personal and community healthcare services in the GTA. We focus on enhancing each client's quality of life by providing customized professional nursing care and personal assistance & support, as we strive to make our clients comfortable in their own home. We have been doing this for more than 27 years. NHI is committed to continuous quality improvement and we are accredited by Accreditation Canada and a Member of the Ontario Homecare Association, Toronto and GTA. Call us at **(416) 754-0700** or **(800) 567-6877** or visit **www.nhihealthcare.com.**

Saint Elizabeth - is a not-for-profit, charitable home care provider with over 100 years of experience helping Canadians stay at home. Our skilled team of home and personal support workers, nurses and therapists provide care to seniors, adults and children in their homes. Saint Elizabeth can provide you with companionship, personal care, light housekeeping, nursing care, foot care, end-of-life care, Alzheimer's care, in-home physiotherapy, and more. Our home care services are available in Ontario, Vancouver, and Victoria, British Columbia, both privately and through government providers. Saint Elizabeth is the only home care provider that has received Excellence Canada's Canada Order of Excellence Award. Saint Elizabeth is also fully accredited by Accreditation Canada. To discuss your home care options, call **(877) 625-5567** or visit **www.saintelizabeth.com.**

Senior Lifestyle Solutions Inc. - Join our list of selective clientele, who are looking for a highly personalized service. We are extremely selective in choosing the caregivers that represent us, whether in our client's home, in hospital, or in a Long-Term Care Facility. If you are looking for a professional service that provides respect, dignity, knowledge, reliability, and affordability, please call **(416) 436-1267** or visit **www.srlifestylehomecare.com.** Our passion is to provide the very best care available to you and your loved ones.

Seniors For Seniors™ - provides in-home care for seniors, by other seniors. 'Junior Seniors' (50 years of age +) provide home health aid (that doesn't require a medical professional) and other daily living services for 'Senior Seniors' (60 years of age +) who need assistance to remain at home, and independent. As the average age of our 'Junior Seniors' is 60 - 65 years, there is a minimal age difference between the 'Junior Seniors' and the 'Senior Seniors' whose average age is 85 - 90 years +, they therefore have many mutual life experiences to share. Since the inception of Seniors For Seniors™, we have successfully employed thousands of 'Junior Seniors' to provide this special and unique manner of in-home care for 'Senior Seniors'. Seniors For Seniors™ a Canadian company proudly serving seniors for 28 years. Call us at **(416) 481-2733** or visit **www.seniorsforseniors.ca**

JUNK REMOVAL

JUST JUNK® - is your local junk removal service. For all of your removal needs during a move or downsizing, let the professionals from JUST JUNK® help today! We remove everything: garbage, trash, rubbish, furniture, appliances and more! Call us today at **(888) 586-5888** to speak to a friendly member of the JUST JUNK® team, or book a removal online at **www.justjunk.com** and save!

LOT INCENTIVES

Lundar Lot Incentive Program - Is your retirement fund smaller than you'd like it to be? Would you like to get up to $5,000 for building your home in our beautiful community? Have the retirement you deserve by freeing up the equity in your current home - have more to spend on you! Lundar has much to offer - low taxes & lots of amenities. Golf Course, Sandy Beaches, Junior Olympic Pool, Hiking Trails, Bird-Watching, New Horizons Social Club, Handi-Van, Meals on Wheels, Old Time Dances, Senior Resource Council & Services, Resident Physician & Medical Clinic, Pharmacy, Ambulance Service, Victoria Lifeline, Public Library, Free Grocery Delivery in town. We are only 15 minutes from the Regional Hospital. Let us show you that Lundar is a great place to visit & an even better place to live. Call us at **(204) 762-5421** or visit **www.lundar.ca** for more information. We welcome you! See article on **page 53.**

MEDICAL SUPPLIES AND EQUIPMENT

AgeComfort.com - is Canada's leading online supplier for Home Health Care Products. We feature over 6,000 items in Daily Living Aids, Incontinence, Mobility, Physical Therapy, Low Vision, Orthopedics, Adaptive Clothing, Medical Supplies, Vitamins/Supplements & more. We offer FREE SHIPPING on all orders over $50 in Canada. We are CARP approved, Ontario Home Care Association Members and have an "A" rating with the BBB. Order online at **www.agecomfort.com** or call toll-free **(800) 520-3259**. SAVE 5% OFF any order. Enter coupon code "senior2014" at checkout (excludes incontinence items). Request a FREE 164 page catalogue on our website or give us a call!

Premier Mobility and Health Products - is a unique provider of mobility & accessibility products to clients with various disabilities. Our fully equipped mobile showrooms arrive at your doorstep! We provide service & product demonstrations that assist individuals at their point of need. In the comfort of your home enjoy the personal caring service provided by our knowledgeable consultants. We offer flexible appointments (day, evenings & weekends) to meet the needs of clients & family members. We are committed to senior safety by providing the best range of products to deliver barrier-free living. Ask about the many funding options you may qualify for. "Premier Mobility and Health Products, improving your quality of life" Call us at **(855) 777-9411** or visit **www.premiermobility.ca**.

Shoppers Home Health Care - has a wide variety of products. We have medical compression stockings, breast prosthesis and accessories, aids to daily living, CPAP machines (Continuous Positive Airway Pressure), bathroom products, blood pressure monitors, pillows, beds and more. We also offer rental products. Shoppers Home Health Care also provides mobility days and foot clinics. Shop for all your medical needs under one roof. Call us at Newmarket **(905) 953-9907** or Markham **(905) 887-9055** or visit our website **www.shoppershomehealthcare.ca**.

Starkmans Health Care Depot - FOR ALL YOUR HOME HEALTH CARE NEEDS....call **(416) 534-8411** or **(800) 387-0330** or visit **www.starkmans.com.**

PUBLISHING

BTT Communications – "Our commitment is the key to YOUR success"! We've been in business for over 30 years servicing graphic design and printing needs for many private corporations, non-profit organizations, educational institutions and government agencies. We strive to develop long term relationships with clients by cost-effective solutions to a variety of communication challenges. We have an FTP site for the convenience of our clients through which projects can be put for retrieval by us in an efficient manner. Call us at **(416) 481-4037** or visit **www.toronto-graphic-design.ca**.

REAL ESTATE

Maxine Povering BES, ABR, ASA, Broker, Harvey Kalles Real Estate Ltd., Brokerage -'Helping Toronto and GTA Seniors for over 35 years with Professional Sensitive and Caring Service.' Moving out of town? I can refer top realtors in Ontario and across Canada to look after your needs. Call Direct: **(647) 449-4663** or Office: **(416) 441-2888 ext. 308** or visit **www.MaxinePovering.com.**

Trudi Johnston, Sales Representative, M-ASA, Re/Max All Stars Realty Inc., Brokerage - When my parents sold their family home and had to move into a retirement residence, then one parent into a long-term care facility and one parent in with me, I realized how much I truly wanted to be part of helping this 50+ group find their way into their new homes wherever they are moving. This can be a stressful time for families and it doesn't need to be. Let me help and TELL ME YOUR STORY!!!! Call **(416) 265-2000** or **(416) 702-7319** or **(800) 265-2888** or visit **www.trudijohnston.com.**

Deirdre Slowey, Sales Representative, Royal LePage Real Estate Services Ltd., Brokerage - A people first approach ..... Serving West Toronto and Etobicoke, Deirdre has earned the SRES designation which recognizes her commitment to Seniors Real Estate. Whether you are 50+ and thinking of downsizing, or you are helping your parents move to a seniors facility, Deirdre will guide you and your family through the process of selling your home with patience and sensitivity. You can reach Deirdre by calling **(416) 762-8255** or visiting **www.dslowey.com.**

Magda Zecevic, Master-ASA Royal LePage Signature Realty - The Master-ASA Seniors Real Estate is the elite of Canadian Realtors that specialize in life transitions for seniors. The Master-ASA serve seniors & their families by transforming a typically stressful, hectic transition into a stress-free process. We have the information our clients are looking for through our network of professionals whether it is accessing government grants for disability retrofit, looking at smart-sizing options, creating a monthly income, knowledge of different housing options, market value assessment, wills & power of attorney, repair work or renovations etc. Our greatest asset is that we are the one person that a senior can come to who can fulfill all their needs & wishes. Call **(416) 443-0300** or **(416) 704-7011** or visit **www.magdalenazecevic.com.**

Barb Poretti, Sales Representative, Stonemill Realty Inc., Brokerage - Does your home suit your present or future needs? Are you ready to downsize, or are you helping your parents or a loved one move to a more manageable home environment or a seniors' facility? I will help you and your family through the process of selling your home with understanding, guidance and sensitivity. I'm committed to making this transitional time in your life as stress free and enjoyable as possible. Brokerage serving Oakville, Burlington and Halton areas. Please call Barb Poretti at **(905) 339-9830** or visit **www.barbporetti.com.**

SENIORS RESOURCE INFORMATION & ACTIVITIES

Helps Here! - Caring for an Elderly Parent? Can't find the time for everything you have to accomplish in a day? Help's Here! is a FREE BOOK full of essential senior resources. It is packed with interesting and unusual tips & useful articles. If you are caring for a loved one, this book will help! Help's Here! has 12 chapters encompassing all the needs of a seniors life, including Home Care, Hospices, Retirement Residences, Health & Medical Services, Legal & Financial Advice, Insurance Products, Shops & Services, Transportation, Moving House, Recreation, even Pets! Call us at **(416) 423-6547** or visit **www.HelpsHere.com.**

Older Adult Centres' Association of Ontario - The OACAO is a recognized leader in the development of quality services, resources and supports for our network of community-based older adult centres. For information call **(866) 835-7693** or visit **www.oacao.org.**

WHY SHOULD MY LOVED ONE BE DRESSED IN ADAPTIVE CLOTHING?

Contributed By: **Edie Michel,** Leed Solutions
Website: **www.leedsolutions.ca** • Phone: **(800) 218-7774**

Pain, agitation and injury are all potential consequences experienced by wheelchair dependent people while being dressed in regular clothing. The wheelchair dependent person is at an increased risk of injury when their weight is supported by caregivers. Commonly, dressing, an activity that provided pleasure and dignity becomes stressful when limbs become stiff, joints have pain, muscles weaken and cognitive ability lessens. With adaptive or special needs clothing, arms and legs can be simply placed through their respective openings and the clothing is secured at the back with fasteners minimizing pain, agitation and injury.

The psychology behind being well dressed is widely known. Each of us experiences confidence and energy when dressed well. Even when cognitive ability is reduced, the family and caregivers respond with pride and compassion in the good grooming of their loved ones and those they care for. Adaptive clothing provides a solution to regular and oversized clothing, hospital gowns and blankets when dressing becomes an unpleasant struggle.

Why Is Adaptive Clothing Important to the Caregiver?

The stress and agitation during the dressing process is shared with the caregiver of a wheelchair dependent person. Dressing an individual who cannot weight bear requires lifting, turning, rolling and repositioning. When there is cognitive impairment the physical and emotional strain is often greater as the patient becomes agitated and offers resistance. In a study conducted a number of years ago in BC, it revealed that 57% of staff injuries were due to patient handling including dressing. The use of adaptive clothing reduces both the number of staff required to dress a resident or loved one and the amount of time spent dressing, undressing and transferring to a commode.

What Adaptive Clothing Options are Available?

Adaptive, special needs or open-back clothing is modified in its design to allow easy access relative to regular structured clothing. Individuals suffering from arthritis, Parkinson or other conditions that limit dexterity or strength in the hands would benefit from side open designed pants. Open-back slacks, tops, shirts, undershirts, nightwear and dresses are appropriate for wheelchair dependent or bed dependent people. Regular clothing can be adapted or split up the back but often results in misplaced domes causing pressure sores and does not allow for adequate fabric to create dignity panels for the wearer. Adaptive clothing is readily available in Canada, manufactured to allow easy access with the safe placements of closures and the maintenance of dignity and self-esteem with generous dignity panels overlapping behind the user to ensure that skin or undergarments are not exposed. While larger clothes can be purchased and adapted by a tailor, a little known fact is that adaptive or special needs clothing is tax exempt when a prescription from the residents doctor is presented by fax, mail or email. For further reference see the Canada Revenue Agency Link **http:// www.cra-are.gc.ca/E/pub/gm/4-2/4-2-e.html** or speak with your tax advisor.

What Should I Consider Before Making a Purchase?

- Ensure that you choose a supplier that stands behind the quality of the garments and selects fabrics that are soft to the touch, uses generous dignity panels for slacks and ensures proper placing of fasteners to lessen the risk of skin breakdown. Adaptive clothing should be designed for institutional washing and drying and therefore has some polyester content in most everything.
- What is the lifestyle of the person you are purchasing adaptive clothing for? There is a wide variety of styles, function and fabric to choose from when making a purchase. Ask yourself if the main objective is comfort and softness and if it is, purchase knit outfits that provide a little stretch and are easy to wear. If it is important to you and your loved one to be fashionable dressed each day in a style they were accustomed to, there is a wide variety of fabrics and styles to choose from for both men and women.
- Generally speaking, adaptive clothing should be purchased in the same size that you would purchase regular clothing in. The adaptive style allows for ease of dressing and therefore there is no need to increase the size of the clothing.

BUTTON UP YOUR OVER COAT WHEN THE WIND IS FREE, TAKE GOOD CARE OF YOURSELF....*

Contributed By: **Mary Ellen Tomlinson,** Director, Senior Care Options Inc.
Website: **www.seniorcareoptions.ca** • Phone: **(416) 932-9941**

Healthy aging in Canada is neither the scary impossible outcome reported by some news media outlets nor, the carefree life reported in some glossy magazine pages. In fact, Stats Canada indicates that many older people are living not just longer but managing well on fixed incomes, even with some chronic diseases. This leads one to wonder firstly, why the reality for many is so different from reports through trusted news sources and secondly, how we can try to ensure that we too live longer and healthier?

Nutrition and exercise are well published strategies contributing to wellness in older people. However, one aspect missing in the reporting or conversation is the impact of a stress-free life. No one can lead a life totally devoid of stress, but some negative stress can be avoided which might contribute to a 'healthier' outcome. Mental or physical stress activates a hormone called adrenaline (epinephrine) - the "the fight or flight" hormone. Adrenaline is not the best hormone to have shooting into anyone's blood stream on a regular basis. Cutting down the reasons for experiencing negative stress can contribute positively to health and wellness.

Keeping a full and active social network is a wonderful de-stressing strategy. There are a number of things you can do to accomplish this:

1. If you don't like driving after dark, ask teenage grandchildren for rides to family dinners and events. They love the chance to drive and you will get a chance to chat with them and catch up on their lives.
2. If your family or friends have moved far away and you have a computer, sign up for Skype. It's an easy way to keep connected with those in your social network who are not close by or cannot visit in person with you often.
3. Be the first to phone your buddies to tell them about seasonal sighting - like the first Robin or Cardinal. It is something that is always good for a chuckle and a little friendly competition.
4. Sometimes when the weather is bad and it is hard to get out of the house, you want to share the events of the day with a friend or family member. If you know someone living alone, phone them up for a chat and a pre-dinner glass of sherry. That way they too can share their day's happenings and not feel like they are drinking alone. *Just remember that it's "a" glass of sherry.*
5. And last but not least "Button up your Overcoat when the Wind is Free, Take Good Care of Yourself...."(*Lyrics by D.G. DeSylva and Lew Brown and music by Ray Henderson)

Excerpted from a longer article entitled 'Strategies for Healthy Aging' © 2011

EXERCISE AND A GOOD NIGHT'S SLEEP FOR BETTER BRAIN HEALTH

This article was compiled by Hilary Dunn, MSc (Project Officer, Schlegel-UW Research Institute for Aging (RIA)) and Andrew Robertson, PhD (RIA Research Scientist and post-doctoral fellow at Sunnybrook Research Institute). For more information about the Schlegel-UW Research Institute for Aging, visit **www.the-ria.ca** *or email* **info@the-ria.ca**

Everyday activities, like exercise and sleep, can help to keep the brain healthy. For the past few years, Dr. Andrew Robertson has worked with a team of researchers, led by Dr. Richard Hughson (Schlegel Research Chair in Vascular Aging and Brain Health, a joint position between the Schlegel-UW Research Institute for Aging (RIA) and University of Waterloo) to examine how aspects of everyday living can affect how well the blood vessels in the brain work.

One aspect of this research examined the importance of everyday physical activity in maintaining adequate blood flow to the brain. As part of this work, seniors living in the community wore activity monitors for 3 days to determine their day-to-day activity levels. This allowed the researchers to examine not only scheduled exercise sessions, but also unplanned physical activity, such as taking the stairs instead of the elevator. Importantly, the results showed that increased activity levels, even when the activity was at a low to moderate intensity, such as walking briskly, was associated with higher brain blood flow – an observation that helps to confirm that regular physical activity is good for our mind, as well as our heart.

Another area of interest was how sleep quality can affect brain health. Disrupted sleep patterns are a major concern, with over half of older adults reporting difficulties falling asleep or frequently waking up throughout the night. Participants who reported sleeping at least 7 hours per day had better regulation of brain blood flow than individuals who reported 6 or less hours of sleep. Using a combination of simple, safe tools to measure brain blood flow and blood pressure, volunteers were tested on one day after dinner, and the following morning soon after they woke up. The volunteers wore an activity monitor to measure how much they moved around throughout the night. The results of this project showed that restless sleep seemed to be related to poorer regulation of brain blood flow the next morning. These observations suggest that our sleeping habits are important for brain health, and we should try to create an environment in the bedroom that promotes good sleep.

Robertson's graduate studies were supported by funding from the RIA, the Heart and Stroke Foundation of Canada, and the Canadian Institutes of Health Research.

HOME CARE: WHY WE NEED IT MORE THAN EVER!

Contributed By: **Alert / Best Nursing & Home Care**
Website: **www.alertbestnursing.com** • Phone: **(866) 959-9913**

So many youthful seniors are living in their homes longer – 80 or 90 years young is more common than ever. What can we do to help these seniors and ourselves live independent lives and keep them in their homes longer?

There are many factors impacting seniors 60 and up and the sandwich generation is being affected like never before; taking care of children and parents as well as yourself is a common problem. Having multiple generations living under one roof is something we see happening more often. Families need help, and home care is a great option to consider.

Imagine the following scenario: you have surgery, your spouse has appointments with his/her parents, your own aging parent needs help with medications, appointments, light duty around the house, your child needs help with their kids, what do you do? What if you have that trip of a lifetime planned and your parent or loved one is in a long-term care home or retirement residence and there is no one to watch over them while you're away? These questions can be answered easily by calling a home care professional to assist you and your family. We don't think twice about having someone come and clean for us; we don't think twice about having a professional care for us physically, why would we not consider someone to help with aging family members?

Home care is not just for seriously injured or elderly people that can't cope; it's for that active senior that has just had surgery, and needs some help until they feel better; it's for the active senior that has aging parents and wants to travel but feels guilty about leaving their parent.

Some of the questions you need to think about and ask before choosing a provider are:

- **Are the home care workers bonded?**
- **Will you be one in a long list of people waiting for home care?**
- **Will your questions be answered regarding the requirements needed to care for your loved one?**
- **Is the home care provider trained properly to administer medications?**
- **How will you know they are taking the BEST care of your loved one the way you would?**
- **How will you be alerted to important updates?**

It is important that if changes happen to either your loved one's condition or to the provider's situation, you are alerted right away so that the best approach to caring for them is administered. It's not wrong to want your family members to live independent lives in the comfort of their home; it's not wrong to want to travel and still have help with your aging parent or loved one. In today's fast paced world, turning to a reputable health care provider is the "BEST" way to make sure your family and yourself are being looked after, just the way you like.

PLANNING A MOVE

Contributed By: **Monica Black,** President, Simple Easy Transition
Website: **www.simpleeasytransition.com** • Phone: **(416) 908-1181**

Moving is one of the most difficult things one experiences in their lifetime. Seniors equate the stress of moving near the stress levels associated with the death of a spouse or divorce. During this time, one may experience a number of conflicting emotions simultaneously which paralyses you from getting the moving process started. These emotions are normal.

How do I reduce the stress and anxiety I am feeling?

Planning a move will help alleviate some of the stresses one is feeling and, in turn, decrease the anxiety so you can look forward to the change and the decision you have made.

Where do I begin?

Rome wasn't built in a day, and your years of accumulating possessions won't be organized in one day either. The only way to get to the finish line is to take the first step. So...let's get STARTED!

Plan

- Purchase a calendar and a notebook for organizing your move. Ensure that the notebook has pockets, dividers and a place for pens and highlighters.
- Make a master list of what needs to be done.
- Keep a log of all the suppliers you have contacted (movers, relocation specialists, real estate agents, lawyers, cleaners, etc.).
- Start a file for all moving papers and receipts.
- Set a moving budget.

Timelines

- Give yourself a minimum of eight weeks to get ready for the actual move.
- Start moving calendar lists (a list for every room in the house with notes on what each contains. Schedule other checklist tasks from the master list, especially ones with firm deadlines).

Movers/Senior Relocation Companies

Decide if you're going to move yourself or hire professionals. Contact a minimum of three moving companies/senior relocation companies and set-up interviews. Do your homework – remember, price is not always the best guide.

Ask for help

Ask a family member or friend to help you through the process. Have someone who is impartial and can help you make the tough decision on what you need to let go of.

Floor Plan

- Obtain a copy of the floor plan at the new residence. Ensure you have accurate measurements of the new residence (floor plans are not always to scale).
- Measure the furniture you will be taking to ensure it fits in your new residence.

Sorting

- Purchase three coloured stickers.
- Green - goes to the new residence.
- Red - goes to charity.
- Yellow – goes to family or friend.
- Do one room at a time, start in the room that is least used & start with the easy things.

Packing Supplies (tape, markers, packing paper, bubble wrap and boxes)

- Take an inventory of what needs to be packed this will assist you in deciding on the size and number of boxes you will need for packing.

- China – small boxes.
- Books – small boxes.
- Paintings – art boxes.
- Electronics – medium boxes.
- Clothes, Linens – large boxes.
- Canned Goods – small boxes.

Change of address

- Complete a change of address form at the post office.
- Keep a running list of who needs to be notified of your address change.

Moving is stressful in the best of circumstances. Ask for help whether you hire a Relocation Company or decide to do it yourself with the help of family and friends. Plan ahead by following the strategies above. Take a deep breath and know that you will get will get through this - it just takes time and planning.

MAKING YOUR RETIREMENT WORK FOR YOU

Contributed By: **Amanda Stevenson,** RM of Coldwell (Lundar)
Website: **www.lundar.ca** • Phone: **(204) 762-5421**

Over the last five years or so, many retirees and people nearing retirement have experienced a dramatic loss in value of their investments. Even when you own your own home or condominium it's hard to have a comfortable retirement without sufficient investment income for your day to day needs. Some seniors, in the unfortunate predicament of having substantial equity ($250,000 or more) in their current home, but little personal cash flow, have found a solution that works well for them.

To illustrate this point, consider this real-life example about a woman who saw the advantage of a great opportunity and acted on it. Mrs. D, a widow who had a condominium in Vancouver worth $400,000 and enjoys going south to a warm climate in the winter, saw the income realized from her investments shrinking. She recognized that if she didn't do something to increase her cash flow, she would soon be unable to travel and live the comfortable life she wanted. One day Mrs. D was browsing the internet and saw an ad from a small town in Manitoba that was offering incentives for people to build new homes in the area. Curious, she emailed and did some research to find out more about the community. She liked what she found – a nice friendly community with low taxes and all the amenities she wanted, including a local golf course and an international airport only an hour away.

Mrs. D took the plunge; she sold her condominium and built a comfortable home for about $150,000 in her new community. She made friends and settled in quickly; happy and secure now that she had another $200,000+ in money to invest.

This solution may not be for everyone but, some have found it works well for them. *How will you make your retirement income work for you?*

To learn about Lundar, Manitoba and see if it's right for you, please visit www.lundar.ca.

COMMUNITY CARE ACCESS CENTRES IN ONTARIO

- Erie-St. Clair Community Care Access Centre
  Head Office/Chatham-Kent Branch
  712 Richmond Street, Box 306,
  Chatham, ON N7M 5K4

(519) 436-2222 or (888) 447-4468 (Chatham-Kent)
(519) 337-1000 or (888) 447-4468 (Sarnia-Lambton) 0
(519) 258-8211 or (888) 447-4468 (Windsor-Essex)

- South West Community Care Access Centre
  Head Office/London Branch
  356 Oxford Street West,
  London, ON N6H 1T3

(519) 473-2222 or (800) 811-5146 (London)
(519) 371-2112 or (888) 371-2112 (Owen Sound)
(519) 631-9907 or (800) 563-3098 (St. Thomas)
(519) 527-0000 or (800) 267-0535 (Seaforth)
(519) 273-2222 or (800) 269-3683 (Stratford)
(519) 245-3233 or (800) 265-6235 (Strathroy)
(519) 881-1181 or (888) 371-2112 (Walkerton)
(519) 539-1284 or (800) 561-5490 (Woodstock)

- Waterloo Wellington Community Care Access Centre
  Head Office/Kitchener Branch
  141 Weber Street South Waterloo, ON N2J 2A9

(519) 748-2222 or (888) 883-3313 (Kitchener & Cambridge)
(519) 823-2550 or (800) 265-8338 (Guelph)

- The Hamilton Niagara Haldimand Brant CCAC
  Head Office/Brantford Branch
  195 Henry Street, Unit 4, Bldg 4, Brantford, ON N3S 5C9

(519) 759-7752 or (800) 810-0000 (Brantford/Brant)
(905) 523-8600 or (800) 810-0000 (Hamilton)
(905) 684-9441 or (800) 810-0000 (Niagara)
(519) 426-7400 or (800) 810-0000 (Haldimand-Norfolk)
(905) 639-5228 or (800) 810-0000 (Burlington)

- Central West Community Care Access Centre
  Head Office/Brampton Branch
  199 County Court Blvd.,
  Brampton, ON L6W 4P3

(905) 796-0040 or (888) 733-1177

- Mississauga Halton Community Care Access Centre
  Head Office/Etobicoke Branch
  401 The West Mall, Suite 1001,
  Etobicoke, ON M9C 5J5

(905) 855-9090 or (877) 336-9090

- Toronto Central Community Care Access Centre
  Head Office/Toronto Branch
  250 Dundas Street West, Suite 305,
  Toronto, ON M5T 2Z5

(416) 506-9888 or (866) 243-0061 (Toronto)

- Central Community Care Access Centre
  Head Office/Newmarket Branch
  1100 Gorham Street, Unit 1,
  Newmarket, ON L3Y 8Y8

(905) 895-1240 or (888) 470-2222 (Newmarket)
(905) 763-9928 or (888) 470-2222 (Richmond Hill)
(416) 222-2241 or (888) 470-2222 (Sheppard Ave/North York)

- Central East Community Care Access Centre
  Head Office/Whitby Branch
  920 Champlain Court,
  Whitby, ON L1N 6K9

(905) 430-3308 or (800) 263-3877 (Whitby)
(705) 653-1005 or (800) 368-8053 (Campbellford)
(705) 457-1600 or (800) 368-8027 (Haliburton)
(705) 324-9165 or (800) 347-0285 (Lindsay)
(905) 885-6600 or (800) 347-0299 (Port Hope)
(705) 743-2212 or (888) 235-7222 (Peterborough)
(416) 750-2444 or (866) 779-1931 (Scarborough)

- South East Community Care Access Centre
  Kingston Branch
  1471 John Counter Blvd, Suite 200,
  Kingston, ON K7M 8S8

(613) 544-7090 (Kingston)
(613) 332-2444 or (800) 717-2344 (Bancroft)
(613) 966-3530 or (800) 668 -0901 (Belleville)
(613) 283-8012 or (800) 267-6041 (Brockville & Smiths Falls)
(613) 336-8310 (Northbrook)
(613) 388-2488 (Selby)

- The Champlain Community Care Access Centre
  Head Office/Ottawa Branch
  4200 Labelle St., Suite 100, Ottawa, ON K1J 1J8

(613) 745-5525 or (800) 538-0520 (Ottawa & Orleans)
(613) 253-9000 or (800) 538-0520 (Carleton Place)
(613) 745-5525 or (800) 538-0520 (Carlingwood/Orleans)
(613) 764-0557 or (800) 267-0852 (Casselman)
(613) 936-1171 or (800) 267-0852 (Cornwall)
(613) 632-4861 or (800) 267-0852 (Hawkesbury)
(613) 732-7007 or (888) 421-2222 (Pembroke)
(613) 774-2800 or (800) 267-0852 (Winchester)

- North Simcoe Muskoka Community Care Access
  Centre (Barrie Branch)
  15 Sperling Drive, Suite 100,
  Barrie, ON L4M 6K9

(705) 721-8010 Ext. 6100 or (888) 721-2222

- North East Community Care Access Centre
  Head Office/Sudbury Branch
  Rainbow Centre, 40 Elm Street, Suite 41-C,
  Sudbury, ON P3C 1S8

(705) 522-3461 or (800) 461-2919 (Sudbury)
(705) 567-2222 or (888) 602-2222 (Kirkland Lake)
(705) 476-2222 or (888) 533-2222 (North Bay)
(705) 949-1650 or (800) 668-7705 (Sault Ste. Marie)
(705) 267-7766 or (888) 668-2222 (Timmins)
(705) 773-4602 or (800) 440-6762 (Parry Sound)

- North West Community Care Access Centre
  Head Office/Thunder Bay Branch
  961 Alloy Drive,
  Thunder Bay, ON P7B 5Z8

(807) 345-7339 or (800) 626-5406

For further information visit:

www.ccac-ont.ca
or **call 310-2222** from anywhere in Ontario

Comprehensive Guide to Retirement Living ®

Retirement Residences and Communities

Photos provided by Canterbury Place Retirement Residence

UNDERSTANDING RETIREMENT RESIDENCE & LONG-TERM CARE HOME LISTINGS

The Comprehensive Guide to Retirement Living and Long-Term Care® is set up in an easy-to-read format. The detailed questionnaire format is for the retirement residence section only. The long-term care home section is limited to contact information and limited information about the home only however city organization is the same for both sections. Headings are in bold print. Under each heading are responses provided by the residences to our online questionnaire. To simplify your search, we have listed the cities – and the homes within them – alphabetically. Additionally, Toronto has been subdivided into the former municipalities of Etobicoke, North York and Scarborough. All remaining areas and homes within them are listed under Toronto (Central). Due to the size of the Ottawa Region, we have also subdivided that section into Central and West and then alphabetically (in West) by former area designations/cities. All homes are listed alphabetically within each area.

QUESTIONNAIRE FORMAT AND CONTENT

Name of Residence:
Address:
Phone number: **Fax number:**
Toll-Free number: if available
Email:
Website:
Contact Person:
Capacity: Maximum number of residents (or number of units if resident capacity isn't indicated)
Subsidies: if available/source
Price: Range from minimum to maximum for retirement residences only (long-term care rates are standardized by the Ministry of Health and Long-Term Care). **Please note: Pricing may not be accurate as information was obtained in the summer of 2013, before some of the homes had finalized their 2014 rates. We encourage you to verify all prices with the homes directly.**

*(Long-Term Care Homes only have a descriptive introduction about the home and the **GENERAL HOME INFORMATION** section completed. This category for Retirement Residences is called **RESIDENCE INFORMATION**. Retirement Residences have all categories available to them to complete however, if some homes do not have information in certain areas, the heading is not displayed.)*

DESCRIPTIVE INTRODUCTION: Homes can include anything they wish as a summary about their home or, the special features they have.
RESIDENCE INFORMATION/GENERAL HOME INFORMATION: This section includes the number of years in operation, nearest intersection, when it was decorated, the existence of handrails in the hallways, the number of floors, the number of units, the number of elevators, wheelchair accessibility, the existence of a central public address (PA) system, the funding base (i.e. for-profit or not-for-profit), the owners and/or manager's name, the waiting period for admission, the average age of residents, the accommodation of cognitively-impaired and physically-challenged residents, the existence of a resident dress code, restrictions about smoking, alcohol use and visiting hours, procedures for residents to leave the premises, languages spoken, acceptance of Public Guardian and Trustee clients, when main doors are locked (night only or all the time), nearby amenities including local hospitals, predominant ethnic/cultural group if indicated, any organizations that the residence is a member of and retirement home licensing status with the RHRA.
STAFFING: This section includes staff/services available through the residence and/or CCAC. (Note: An individual must be deemed eligible for CCAC services by a CCAC Care Coordinator in order to receive services from them.) It also includes notation on who arranges external services if needed, staff training regarding visually, cognitively and hearing impaired people, type of staffing i.e., RNs (Registered Nurses), RPNs (Registered Practical Nurses), PSWs (Personal Support Workers), UCPs (Unregulated Care

Providers) and/or HCAs (Health Care Aides), availability of a visiting MD, possibility of retaining one's own MD/family physician, whether staff members are bonded, and if new staff members are subject to a police check or vulnerable person screening.
HEALTH SERVICES AVAILABLE: This includes availability of medication administration and/or supervision, whether or not staff can monitor vitals, acceptance of residents who require oxygen, catheters, feeding-tubes and ostomies (and if residence assists with care of these devices), if and how often assistance with bathing is provided (extra charge if indicated), if assistance with dressing is available, completion of care plans, availability and cost of an Assisted Living Area/Private Duty care/secure unit, accommodation of different levels of care, if there is a lab service – visiting or on-site – and the cost per visit, if residents can purchase outside resources and if they can use any agency for this, the availability of a clinic area for medical visits, and if assistance locating a higher level of care is provided, if required.
ACCOMMODATION: This section includes choice and number of suite types available, what is included in all suites (locks, storage, kitchenette, fridge, stove, window coverings, linens, patio/balcony, thermostats, light fixtures, fire alarms, smoke detector, sprinkler, air conditioning, *cable TV and telephone outlets, emergency call bell system, bathrooms), availability of furnished and unfurnished suites, any restrictions regarding electrical appliances, sharing suites and pets.
DINING SERVICES: This section details all meals included in the monthly fee and where they are served, sittings and choices per meal, availability of guest meals and cost, any special diets available, in-suite tray service if resident is ill, snacks/refreshments, party facilities, existence of an open pantry.
AMENITIES AND ACTIVITIES: This section includes parking, available on-site services (library, visiting library, banking service, lounges, TVs, pianos, barber/beauty shop, visiting hairdresser, guest suites, laundry machines for resident use, newspaper delivery, mail delivery, tuck/gift shop, chapel), recreation facilities and programs.
OTHER SERVICES: This section includes housekeeping, laundry, security, transportation, nightly security checks, telephone*, cable TV*, utilities and any other amenities/services. Note: It is possible that some or all of the services listed in this section are not included in the monthly fee and some might be priced separately or as part of "care packages". We encourage you to contact the home directly for clarification and specific pricing.
RENTAL/PRICING INFORMATION: This section includes the cost for couples sharing suites, how and how often rent is paid, if units can be purchased, standardized rent increases, amount of notice given for increases, whether help moving is available (cost), and the possibility of short-term respite (cost) and trial stays.

***Most homes will have outlets in each room or suite but, cable TV and telephone costs are usually not included in the monthly fee, unless specified in either ACCOMMODATION, OTHER SERVICES or both of these sections.**

We collected the information to create this edition of the Guide in the summer of 2013 through our online questionnaire. As such, pricing information may not be accurate for some residences. Readers are encouraged to contact the places they are interested in directly, to discuss up-to-date pricing.

GLOSSARY OF TERMS

ADL – Activities of Daily Living: Encompass the skills required for a person to live independently. They include: personal care activities such as feeding, dressing, bathing, daily hygiene tasks, toileting and other activities such as walking, thinking, speaking and hearing.

Assisted Living Services/Care: Also called ADL/AL care. Caregivers come to your suite to provide necessary care and assistance with Activities of Daily Living. Some residences may include some minimal care and assistance in their base fee, while others allow you to purchase assistance (or private duty care) on an hourly basis. Some residences have different Care Packages, offering varying degrees of in-suite assistance.

Assisted Living Area: Sometimes called Assisted Daily Living (ADL) Unit, Special Care Unit/ Floor, Enhanced Care Floor or Personal Care Unit. A separate unit, floor or area in a retirement residence devoted to the care of individuals who require assistance with their Activities of Daily Living beyond what is normally offered and available in the rest of the residence. In some homes where care for the cognitively impaired is offered in a special area/floor, they will have safety measures to prevent wandering off the unit, such as locked exits and coded elevators. If exits are locked, the unit is often referred to as a Secure Area/Floor. There is usually an extra charge to reside in this type of unit.

CHIP – Care Home Information Package: All retirement homes are required to provide new tenants with this document that outlines important information including cost factors. Information on the necessary content in this package is contained in the Residential Tendancies Act. See description on **page 22 - 23.**

DVA – Department of Veterans Affairs: Veterans Affairs Canada provides services, programs and funding to eligible veterans in need of assistance. For further information, you may visit **www.veterans.gc.ca**.

HCA – Health Care Aides: Perform tasks that are similar to those performed by PSWs. They usually have a Health Care Aide certificate, which is a level below the PSW certificate.

LTC – Long-Term Care: Denotes nursing-home level of care. See **pages 25 - 26 & 375.**

OANHSS – Ontario Association of Non-Profit Homes and Services for Seniors: See description on **Page 6.**

OLTCA – Ontario Long Term Care Association: See description on **Page 6.**

ORCA – Ontario Retirement Communities Association: See description on **Page 6.**

OT – Occupational Therapy/Therapist: A type of therapy that assists a person to become more independent with tasks involving personal care/ADLs as well as many other activities that help maintain or attain skills for living and functioning as independently as possible.

POA – Power of Attorney: A document authorizing someone else to act on your behalf. In Ontario there are two kinds of documents – *POA for Personal Care* allows someone else to make health related decisions for you when you are ill & a *Continuing POA for Property* which allows someone to make financial decisions for you.

PSW – Personal Support Workers: Are trained to provide assistance with basic homemaking tasks such as cleaning, meal preparation and shopping, as well as personal care tasks such as bathing, personal hygiene, mobility and other activities of daily living. The Regulated Health Professions Act governs their

scope of practice but they are not regulated or registered by any government or other body. Training is available through some community and private colleges and other organizations.

RHRA – Retirement Homes Regulatory Authority: Are responsible for licensing and regulating Retirement Residences in Ontario. They keep a database of all homes in Ontario, handle complaints and educate the public about the Retirement Homes Act, 2010. For additional information visit **www.rhra.ca.** See **page 6.**

RN – Registered Nurse: Requires a four-year Bachelor of Nursing/Bachelor of Science in Nursing degree for all graduates as of 2005 (prior to this RNs could also have a three year diploma from a college). RNs are regulated by the College of Nurses.

RPN – Registered Practical Nurse: As of 2005, all new RPNs must have a two-year college diploma in Practical Nursing. Education is less comprehensive than that of an RN and geared more toward medically-stable and less complex patients. RPNs are regulated by the College of Nurses.

RHA – Retirement Homes Act, 2010: is the legislation in Ontario that governs & regulates retirement homes. The RHRA is the organization that is mandated with ensuring all homes abide by the legislation. See **pages 20 - 21.**

RTA – Residential Tenancies Act: Is the provincial legislation that governs interactions between landlords and tenants. The RTA replaced the Tenant Protection Act (TPA) in 2007. See **page 22 - 23** for details.

UCP – Unregulated Care Provider: Are care providers similar to PSWs who are not registered or licensed by a regulatory body. In some retirement homes, they may provide personal care and/or assist with some tasks delegated by an RPN/RN i.e. medication administration.

Helpful Websites for Seniors in Ontario

- Government of Canada Programs and Services for Seniors: **www.seniors.gc.ca**
- Canada Revenue Agency (CRA): **www.cra-arc.gc.ca** - information for Canadian seniors on income programs, income tax, financial credits
- Public Health Agency of Canada - Aging and Seniors (Canada): **www.phac-aspc.gc.ca/seniors-aines/index-eng.php** - information on issues related to seniors and aging in Canada
- Veterans Affairs Canada: **www.veterans.gc.ca/eng/** - information on services and benefits for war veterans in Canada
- Canada Mortgage and Housing Corporation: **www.cmhc-schl.gc.ca** - information on funding for assistive devices for low income seniors
- The National Seniors Council: **www.seniorscouncil.gc.ca/en/home.shtml**
- Ontario Seniors' Secretariat: **www.seniors.gov.on.ca** - information on Ontario programs and services for seniors
- Retirement Home Regulatory Authority: **www.rhra.ca** – view the Public Register to check the license status of an Ontario retirement home, report resident harm or risk of harm

◆ ALEXANDRIA ◆

CHATEAU GLENGARRY

105 St. Paul Street, Alexandria, ON K0C 1A0
Tel: (613) 525-4440 • Fax: (613) 525-0898
Email: **chateauglengarry@bellnet.ca**
Website: **www.chateauglengarry.ca**
Contact: **Diane St-Denis**
Capacity: **95 residents**
Subsidies: **available through the City of Cornwall**
Price: **$1,675.00 - $2,035.00/month**

Chateau Glengarry ensures an unparalleled level of personalized service in a comfortable and friendly environment. Our staff members are on-site 24-hours/day to assist our residents with any needs. There's no better way to experience the warmth of Chateau Glengarry than to see for yourself!

RESIDENCE INFORMATION: 29 years in operation. *Near:* Main Street and St. Paul Street. Decorated in 2012. Handrails in hallways. 2 floors, 1 elevator. Wheelchair accessible. *Funding Base:* Corporate/for profit. Privately owned. *Managed by:* PGW Ltd. 60 units. *Average Waiting Period*: none. *Average Age*: 82. Can accommodate cognitively impaired people with restrictions (circumstances to be discussed with Administrator). Can accommodate physically challenged people (to be discussed with Administrator). Residents have a dress code (proper attire expected in dining room). Smoke-free residence. *Procedures to leave the premises on a temporary basis...*Overnight & Holidays: advise staff. *Languages:* English & French. Will accept Public Guardian and Trustee clients. Main doors of residence secured at all times. *Close to:* Public Transit, Shopping, Churches, Seniors' Centre, Library, Major Highway and Local Hospital (5 minutes from Glengarry Memorial Hospital). Member of Chamber of Commerce. Licensed under the Retirement Homes Act.
STAFFING: *Available Staff/Services*: Social Work (CCAC), Recreation Therapy, Occupational Therapy (CCAC), Physiotherapy and Hairdresser. Lab service on-site. Walk-in tub available. *External services arranged by:* residence and/or family/resident. Staff trained *re*: visually and hearing impaired. 24-hour staff. RPNs, HCAs and PSWs on staff. Visiting MD (weekly and on-call). Can retain own MD. Police Check or Vulnerable Person Screening is done for all new staff.
HEALTH SERVICES: Medication administration and/or supervision. Vitals monitored if required. Will accept (but not provide special assistance for) residents who require oxygen, catheters and ostomies. Assistance with dressing available. Assistance with bathing available twice a week. *Extra baths:* $10.00/half hour. Care plans done. Different levels of care available. Lab service (on-site, $5.00/visit). Residents can purchase outside resources and use agency of their choice. MD visits residents in their rooms/suites. Clinic area for medical visits. Will help locate higher level of care if needed (find appropriate care for each case).
ACCOMMODATION: *Choice of suites available*: large private (38), medium private (14), small private (15) & semi-private (11) units. *In all suites*: locks, storage, window coverings, light fixtures, linens, smoke detector and thermostats for heating. Furniture available. Bathrooms (6 rooms available with common bathroom) with grab bars, showers with non-slip surfaces and elevated toilet seats. In-suite cable TV provided by residence (residence charges extra $15.00/month). Can have own phone number if resident arranges with phone company. Furnished suites available on request. Restrictions on electrical appliances. Suites can be shared (to be discussed), roommate picked by resident. No pets allowed.
DINING SERVICE: All meals included in fee and served in dining room daily. *Sittings per meal:* Breakfast: 1, Lunch: 1, Dinner: 1. *Menu choices available:* Breakfast: 5, Lunch: 2, Dinner: 2. *Guest Meals*: Breakfast $5.00, Lunch $10.00, Dinner $6.00. *Special Diets*: Vegetarian, Low Salt, Diabetic and Others can be

discussed. Tray service to room if ill (no charge for a maximum time of 5 days). 2 snacks/day. Party facilities. Fresh home-cooked meals daily.

AMENITIES AND ACTIVITIES: Parking available (outdoor for visitors and residents). *6 lounges with:* TV (1). Guest suites available ($70.00/night). *Residence has a:* library, barber/beauty shop, visiting hairdresser and laundry room(s) (no cost). Resident can arrange newspaper delivery to dining room. Mail delivered to dining room. *Recreation Facilities*: exercise room, craft room, card room, outdoor gazebo and large sun deck. Posted schedule of activities. *Recreational Programs*: exercise, theatre, parties, entertainment, pet visiting and day trips.

OTHER SERVICES: *Housekeeping*: daily and weekly (included in fee). *Laundry*: linen & towel (included in fee), personal (included in fee - up to 2 loads/week). Transportation to medical appointments and for group social activities (resident pays for transportation and assistants). 24-hour security. Nightly security checks. Telephone (resident pays phone company). Cable TV ($15.00/month). Utilities (included in fee). Walk-in tub available for use.

RENTAL INFORMATION: Rates may vary. Small private - $1,675.00/month; medium private - $1,785.00/month; large private - $1,915.00/month. Extra cost for 2nd person sharing suite ($1,275.00/month). Rent paid monthly. *Payment Options*: cheques, post-dated cheques, direct deposit, pre-authorized payments and cash. Rent increases are a set percentage as per Provincial Tenancy Legislation, annual with 3 months' notice given. Will help resident move into residence. Short-term respite and trial stays available (both $70.00/day).

THE PALACE RESIDENCE

69 St. Paul Street East, Alexandria, ON K0C 1A0
Tel: (613) 525-1574 • Fax: (613) 525-0608
Email: **nbourbonnais@clmi.ca**
Website: **www.thepalace-lepalais.ca**
Contact: **Nicole Bourbonnais**
Capacity: **36 residents** • Subsidies: **yes, contact us for details**
Price: **$1,700.00 - $2,410.00/month (rates may vary)**

The Palace has proudly served Alexandria and the surrounding communities for over 40 years. This historic residence sits on beautifully-landscaped grounds that breathe an environment of peace and tranquility. Our bilingual, courteous staff members offer personalized services that focus on our resident's well-being so that they truly feel at home.

RESIDENCE INFORMATION: 41 years in operation. *Near:* Bishop Street and St. Paul Street. Decorated in 2002. Handrails in hallways. 4 floors, 1 elevator. Wheelchair accessible. Central PA system. *Funding Base:* Corporate/for profit. *Owned and managed by:* Community Lifecare Inc. 32 units. *Average Waiting Period*: none. *Average Age*: 80. Smoke-free environment. Alcohol allowed (monitored). *Procedures to leave the premises on a temporary basis...*inform staff. *Languages:* English & French. Will accept Public Guardian and Trustee clients. Main doors of residence secured at night only. *Close to:* Shopping, Churches, Seniors' Centre, Library, Major Highway and Local Hospital (Glengarry Memorial Hospital). *Predominant Cultural Group:* Bilingual. Member of Chamber of Commerce. Licensed under the Retirement Homes Act.

STAFFING: *Available Staff/Services*: Pharmacy, Social Work (CCAC), Recreation Therapy, Occupational Therapy (CCAC), Physiotherapy (CCAC), Dietitian, Podiatry, Speech Pathology (CCAC) and Audiology/Hearing Clinic. *External services arranged by:* residence and/or family/resident. 24-hour staff. RPNs, PSWs and UCPs on staff. Visiting MD (weekly). Can retain own MD. Staff members are bonded. Police Check or Vulnerable Person Screening is done for all new staff.

HEALTH SERVICES: Medication administration (some restrictions may apply) and/or supervision. Will accept (but not provide special assistance for) residents who require oxygen, catheters and ostomies. Assistance with dressing available. Assistance with bathing available (cost). Care plans done. Different levels of care available. Private Duty/Extra Care available ($35.00/month). Lab service (visiting, $25.00/visit). Residents can purchase outside resources and use agency of their choice. MD visits residents in their rooms/suites. Clinic area for medical visits. Will help locate higher level of care if needed (Wellness Coordinator on-site to assist resident/family locate appropriate care to meet needs).
ACCOMMODATION: *Choice of suites available*: 1-bedroom apartment or studio suite. *In all suites*: locks, kitchenette, bar fridge, microwave, storage, window coverings, light fixtures, fire alarm, smoke detector, sprinkler, call bell, air conditioning (window units – seasonal usage fee) and thermostats for heating. Fridge and microwave available in some studios. Private bathrooms with call bells, grab bars, tubs and showers with non-slip surfaces. Can have own phone number if resident arranges with phone company. Furnished & unfurnished suites available. *Restrictions on electrical appliances*: no cooking appliances. Suites can be shared (by couples or siblings if requested), roommate picked by resident. Pets allowed (upon approval of Management).
DINING SERVICE: All meals included in fee and served in dining room daily. *Sittings per meal:* Breakfast: 1, Lunch: 1, Dinner: 1. *Menu choices available:* Breakfast: 2, Lunch: 2, Dinner: 2. *Guest Meals*: Breakfast $7.00, Lunch $7.00, Dinner $7.00. *Special Diets*: Vegetarian, Low Salt, Diabetic and Gluten Free. Tray service to room if ill (no charge for a maximum time of 7 days). 2 snacks/day and unlimited snacks available at any time. Party facilities. Open pantry. Air-conditioning in dining room, lounge and hallway on each floor.
AMENITIES AND ACTIVITIES: Parking available (outdoor for visitors and residents). *2 lounges with:* TV (1) and computer & organ (1). Guest suites available. *Residence has a:* barber/beauty shop, laundry room(s) (no cost) and tuck/gift shop (open weekly). Resident can arrange newspaper delivery to individual suite (extra cost). Mail delivered to private mailbox (no key). *Recreation Facilities*: exercise room, craft room, card room, Grotto and Wii game. Posted schedule of activities. *Recreational Programs*: exercise, shopping, theatre, parties, entertainment, art classes, pet visiting, day trips and movies. Professional Senior fitness program/physiotherapy can be arranged extra cost.
OTHER SERVICES: *Housekeeping*: bi-weekly (extra cost for weekly). *Laundry*: linen, towel & personal ($35.00/month if required weekly; included in fee if every 2 weeks). Transportation for group social activities/outings. 24-hour security. Nightly security checks. Utilities (included in fee).
RENTAL INFORMATION: Rates may vary. Extra cost for 2nd person sharing suite ($720.00/month). Rent paid monthly. *Payment Options*: pre-authorized payments. Rent increases as per Provincial Tenancy Legislation, annual for resident with 3 months' notice given. Short-term respite and trial stays available (both $70.00/day).

♦ ALLISTON ♦

BAYBRIDGE - KINGSMERE RETIREMENT SUITES

287 King Street South, Alliston, ON L9R 0C4
Tel: (705) 434-4600 • Fax: (705) 434-4655
Email: **lmkingsbury@kingsmeresuites.ca**
Website: **www.kingsmeresuites.ca**
Contact: **Laurena-Mae Kingsbury**
Capacity: **190 residents** • Subsidies: **none**
Price: **$2,806.00 - $4,450.00/month**

If you are looking for a beautiful apartment-style suite, with a selection of first-rate services, all in a building that offers lively amenities such as a café, fitness room, movie theatre and outdoor LifeTrail™

wellness walking track around a private pond, look no further. Kingsmere Retirement Suites offers 100 studio, 1-bedroom & 2-bedroom suites, in a variety of sizes and styles, and each with its own balcony. Choose from 2 or 3 meals/day, participate in our varied leisure & fitness programs or catch a ride into picturesque downtown Alliston in our van. At Kingsmere, we have it all for those charting a course for a new, active lifestyle. Corner of King Street and Industrial Parkway in Alliston. A beautiful location close to shopping, churches and other amenities.

RESIDENCE INFORMATION: 6 years in operation. *On:* King Street and Industrial Parkway. Decorated in 2008. 6 floors, 2 elevators. Wheelchair accessible. *Funding Base:* Corporate/for profit. *Owned by:* Baybridge Senior Living. *Managed by:* BayBridge Senior Living. 98 units. *Average Waiting Period*: none. *Average Age*: 80. Can sometimes accommodate cognitively impaired & physically challenged people. Residents have a dress code (full dress). Smoke-free residence. Alcohol allowed. *Procedures to leave the premises on a temporary basis...*Short-term: simply use our Sign In/Out Book. Overnight: please mention it to the staff. Holidays: please inform the General Manager as a courtesy discount may apply. *Languages:* English. Main doors of residence secured at night only. *Close to:* Shopping, Churches, Seniors' Centre, Library, Major Highway and Local Hospital (Stevenson Memorial Hospital). Member of ORCA & Alliston and District Chamber of Commerce. Licensed under the Retirement Homes Act.
STAFFING: *Available Staff/Services*: Pharmacy, Social Work (CCAC), Recreation Therapy, Occupational Therapy (CCAC), Physiotherapy (CCAC), Dietitian (CCAC), Speech Pathology (CCAC), Assisted Living Services and À La Carte Services. *External services arranged by:* residence and/or family/resident. Staff trained *re*: visually and hearing impaired. 24-hour staff. RPNs and PSWs on staff. Can retain own MD. Police Check or Vulnerable Person Screening is done for all new staff.
HEALTH SERVICES: Medication administration (as required; resident is required to use our pharmacy - no additional charges apply) and/or supervision (as required). Vitals monitored if required. Will accept (but not provide special assistance for) residents who require catheters, ostomies and feeding tubes. Will accept and provide special assistance for residents who require oxygen. Assistance with dressing available ($15.00/hour). Assistance with bathing available as needed ($15.00/hour). Care plans done. Residents can purchase outside resources and use agency of their choice. Will help locate higher level of care if needed (can provide added care at an additional cost).
ACCOMMODATION: *Choice of suites available*: studio (10), 1-bedroom (80) & 2-bedroom (8) suites. *In all suites*: locks, kitchenette, bar fridge, patio/balcony, window coverings, light fixtures, fire alarm, smoke detector, sprinkler, call bell, air conditioning (central) and thermostats for heating & cooling. Private bathrooms with grab bars and showers with non-slip surfaces. In-suite cable/satellite TV if resident arranges with cable/satellite company. Can have own phone number if resident arranges with phone company. Unfurnished suites, furnished suites available for short stays. *Restrictions on electrical appliances*: all appliances must be CSA approved and inspected for good repair & must have an automatic shut-off. Suites can be shared (by couples only). Small pets are welcome (fish, birds, cats, small friendly dogs).
DINING SERVICE: All meals included in fee and served in dining room daily. *Sittings per meal:* Breakfast: 1, Lunch: 1, Dinner: 1. *Menu choices available:* Breakfast: 2, Lunch: 2, Dinner: 2. *Guest Meals*: Breakfast $5.00, Lunch $8.00, Dinner $10.00. *Special Diets*: Vegetarian, Low Salt and Diabetic. Tray service to room if ill (no charge as long as doctor orders). Unlimited snacks available at any time. Party facilities. Bistro café open 24/7.
AMENITIES AND ACTIVITIES: Parking available (outdoor for visitors and residents). *6 lounges with:* TV (1), piano (1), billiards, card tables (1) and movie theatre (1). Guest suites available ($75.00/night). *Residence has a:* library, barber/beauty shop, visiting hairdresser, laundry room(s) (no cost) and tuck/gift shop. Resident can arrange newspaper delivery to individual suite. Mail delivered to individual suite. *Recreation Facilities*: pool table, billiards, exercise room, craft room, card room, bistro, home theatre, private dining and outdoor walking trail with LifeTrail fitness stations. Posted schedule of activities.

Internal newsletter for residents. *Recreational Programs*: exercise, shopping, theatre, parties, entertainment, art classes, day trips, walking program and excursions.
OTHER SERVICES: *Housekeeping*: weekly. Transportation to medical appointments. 24-hour security. Nightly security checks. Telephone & Cable TV (extra cost). Utilities (included in fee).
RENTAL INFORMATION: Rates may vary. Studio - $2,806.00/month; 1-bedroom $3,285.00 to $3,725.00/month; 2-bedroom - $4,300.00 to $4,450.00/month. Extra cost for 2nd person sharing suite ($650.00/month). Rent paid monthly. *Payment Options*: direct deposit and pre-authorized payments. Rent increases as per Provincial Tenancy Legislation, annual for resident with 3 months' notice given. Short-term respite ($85.00/day) and trial stays available. Convalescent stay ($93.50/day).

GOOD SAMARITAN RETIREMENT LODGE

481 Victoria Street East, Alliston, ON L9R 1J8
Tel: (705) 435-5722 • Fax: (705) 435-0235
Email: **lyndaw@goodsamseniors.com**
Website: **www.goodsamseniors.com**
Contact: **Lynda Weaver**
Capacity: **46 residents** • Subsidies: **none**
Price: **$2,480.88 - $3,880.00/month**

Come home to a warm and friendly place. The Good Samaritan Retirement Lodge is an intimate and unpretentious treasure of a residence. Residents enjoy our one-storey design with such lovely features as a charming dining room, a great room, activity lounge, private dining area, resident kitchen, walking path and gazebo. So many delightful surprises in a cozy size of only 24 well-designed studio and 1-bedroom suites. And we have the added benefit of being attached to a licensed, accredited long-term care home. *Visit us soon - you'll see for yourself why new residents quickly become old friends at the Good Sam.*

RESIDENCE INFORMATION: 10 years in operation. *Near:* Highway 89 Victoria Street and Tottenham Road. Decorated in 2004. Handrails in hallways. 1 floor, no elevators. Wheelchair accessible. Central PA system. *Funding Base:* Corporate/for profit. Privately owned by Clurelea LTD. 24 units. *Average Waiting Period*: varies. *Average Age*: 84. Can sometimes accommodate cognitively impaired people (early stage cognitive issues). Can accommodate physically challenged people (wheelchairs welcome; scooters not allowed indoors). Residents have a dress code (casual clothing suggested). Smoke-free residence (non-smoking building). Alcohol allowed (in suites only). *Restrictions around Visitors/Visiting Hours:* visitors are encouraged to enter up to 9:00 p.m., though welcome beyond this in some circumstances. *Procedures to leave the premises on a temporary basis...*Short-term & Overnight: residents are asked to inform staff, sign out and get any medication from registered staff. Holidays: residents are asked for a few days' notice so sufficient medication can be arranged. *Languages:* English. Will accept Public Guardian and Trustee clients. Main doors of residence secured at all times. *Close to:* Shopping, Churches, Seniors' Centre, Library, Major Highway and Local Hospital (Stevenson Memorial Hospital). Member of ORCA. Attached long-term care home is a member of OLTCA. Licensed under the Retirement Homes Act.
STAFFING: *Available Staff/Services*: Pharmacy, Social Work (CCAC), Recreation Therapy, Occupational Therapy (CCAC), Visiting Dentist, Physiotherapy (CCAC), Denturist, Dietitian, Podiatry, Chaplaincy, Speech Pathology (CCAC), Chiropody, Audiology/Hearing Clinic and Guest Attendants. *External services arranged by:* residence. Staff trained *re*: visually, hearing and cognitively impaired. 24-hour nursing and other staff. RPNs and UCPs on staff. Visiting MD (as required by telephone & bi-weekly visits). Can retain own MD. Police Check or Vulnerable Person Screening is done for all new staff.
HEALTH SERVICES: Medication administration and/or supervision. Vitals monitored if required. Will accept and provide special assistance for residents who require oxygen and catheters. Assistance with

dressing available. Assistance with bathing available twice a week. Care plans done. Lab service (visiting, $25.00/visit). Residents can purchase outside resources and use agency of their choice. MD visits residents in their rooms/suites. Will help locate higher level of care if needed (CCAC).
ACCOMMODATION: *Choice of suites available*: bachelor (15), private suite (3),1-bedroom suite (5) & respite (1) suites. *In all suites*: locks, storage, window coverings, light fixtures, fire alarm, smoke detector, sprinkler, call bell, air conditioning (unit is in a sleeve in the wall (air conditioners for rent)) and thermostats for heating. Private bathrooms with call bells, grab bars, tubs and showers. In-suite cable TV if resident arranges with cable company. Can have own phone number provided by residence (residence charges extra $25.00/month). Unfurnished suites, furnished suites available for short stays. *Restrictions on electrical appliances*: no toasters. Suites can be shared (by couples only). No pets allowed.
DINING SERVICE: All meals included in fee and served in dining room daily. *Sittings per meal:* Breakfast: 1, Lunch: 1, Dinner: 1. *Menu choices available:* Breakfast: 2, Lunch: 2, Dinner: 2. *Guest Meals*: Breakfast $3.00, Lunch $5.00, Dinner $7.00. *Special Diets*: Low Salt, Diabetic and Reducing. Tray service to room if ill (no charge or restrictions). 3 snacks/day. Party facilities. Residents may have a bar fridge in room and there is a resident kitchen area for making tea, coffee storing food in the fridge with kitchen equipment to use. There is a private dining room for family.
AMENITIES AND ACTIVITIES: Parking available (outdoor for visitors and residents). *3 lounges with:* TVs (2) and piano (1). *Residence has a:* library, barber/beauty shop and laundry room(s) (no cost). Banking services on premises (Monday to Friday). Residence provides newspaper delivery to main desk. Mail delivered to resident. *Recreation Facilities*: pool table, craft room and card room. Posted schedule of activities. Internal newsletter for residents. *Recreational Programs*: exercise, shopping, theatre, parties, entertainment, art classes, pet visiting and day trips. Residents' suggestions assist in determining activities.
OTHER SERVICES: *Housekeeping*: 3x/week & daily touch ups (included in fee). *Laundry*: linen, towel & personal (included in fee). Staff members are available to assist clients. 24-hour security. Nightly security checks. Telephone ($25.00/month + long distance). Cable TV (Roger's fees). Utilities (included in fee).
RENTAL INFORMATION: Rates may vary. Bachelor - $2,480.88 to $2,798.63/month; private suite - $2,957.50 to $3,060.00/month; 1-bedroom suite - $3,880.00/month; respite ($68.59/day or $2,086.25/ month). Extra cost for 2nd person sharing suite ($450.00/month). Rent paid monthly. *Payment Options*: cheques. Rent increases as per Provincial Tenancy Legislation, (depends on the market whether an increase process) with 3 months' notice given. Will help resident move into residence. Short-term respite ($68.59/day) available.

RIVERWOOD SENIOR LIVING

9 Evans Road; Box 938, Alliston, ON L9R 1W1
Tel: (705) 435-3806 • Fax: (705) 435-1875
Email: **ruth@riverwoodseniorliving.ca**
Website: **www.riverwoodseniorliving.ca**
Contact: **Ruth Green**
Capacity: **100 residents** • Subsidies: **none**
Price: **$2,482.00 - $3,524.00/month**

Nestled amongst the trees on the banks of the River Boyne, Riverwood Senior Living provides all of the features and services that create a retirement lifestyle of independence, security, convenience and fun. Riverwood also offers respite, rehabilitation, convalescent as well as palliative services. It would be our pleasure to welcome you into our home for a tour and a complimentary meal.

RESIDENCE INFORMATION: 30 years in operation. *Near:* Church Street and Victoria Avenue. Decorated in 2012. Handrails in hallways. 3 floors, 1 elevator. Wheelchair accessible. Central PA system. *Funding*

Base: Corporate/for profit. 90 units. *Average Waiting Period*: varies. *Average Age*: 80. Can accommodate cognitively impaired & physically challenged people. Smoking allowed (outside in designated area). Alcohol allowed (medication checked). *Procedures to leave the premises on a temporary basis...*Nurse notified, medication given and sign out. *Languages:* English. Will accept Public Guardian and Trustee clients. Main doors of residence secured at all times. *Close to:* Shopping, Churches, Library, Major Highway and Local Hospital (Stevenson Memorial Hospital). Licensed under the Retirement Homes Act.

STAFFING: *Available Staff/Services*: Pharmacy, Social Work, Recreation Therapy, Occupational Therapy, Visiting Dentist, Physiotherapy, Denturist, Dietitian, Chaplaincy, Speech Pathology, Chiropody, Audiology/Hearing Clinic, Hairdresser, Mail Delivery and In-house Banking. *External services arranged by:* family/resident. Staff trained *re*: visually, hearing and cognitively impaired. 24-hour nursing and other staff. RNs, RPNs, HCAs, PSWs and UCPs on staff. Visiting MD (when required). Can retain own MD. Police Check or Vulnerable Person Screening is done for all new staff.

HEALTH SERVICES: Medication administration supervised. Vitals monitored if required. Will accept and provide special assistance for residents who require oxygen, catheters and ostomies. Assistance with dressing available. Weekly assistance with bathing available. Care plans done. Different levels of care available. Lab service (visiting, $30.00/visit). Residents can purchase outside resources and use agency of their choice. MD visits residents in their rooms/suites. Will help locate higher level of care if needed (Riverwood Senior Living also offers palliative services so this does not happen very often).

ACCOMMODATION: *Choice of suites available*: double private for a couple (10) & single private (90) units. *In all suites*: locks, storage, window coverings, light fixtures, linens, fire alarm, smoke detector, sprinkler, call bell, thermostats for heating and furniture. Private bathrooms with call bells. In-suite cable TV if resident arranges with cable company. Can have own phone number if resident arranges with phone company. *Restrictions on electrical appliances*: must be approved by General Manager first. No pets allowed.

DINING SERVICE: All meals included in fee and served in dining room daily. *Sittings per meal:* Breakfast: 1, Lunch: 1, Dinner: 1. *Menu choices available:* Breakfast: 5, Lunch: 2, Dinner: 2. *Guest Meals*: Breakfast $4.00, Lunch $5.00, Dinner $6.00. *Special Diets*: Vegetarian, Low Salt, Diabetic, Gluten Free and Lactose Free. Tray service to room if ill (no charge or restrictions). 3 snacks/day. Party facilities. There is a Tea & Craft Room that has tea, coffee, juices and snacks left out for residents and their family and friends.

AMENITIES AND ACTIVITIES: Parking available (outdoor for visitors and residents). *5 lounges with:* TVs (4) and piano (1). *Residence has a:* library, visiting library, chapel, barber/beauty shop, laundry room(s) (no cost) and tuck/gift shop (open 9:00 a.m. - 5:00 p.m.). Banking services on premises (daily). Resident can arrange newspaper delivery to individual suite. Mail delivered to private mailbox (no key). *Recreation Facilities*: shuffleboard, exercise room, craft room and card room. Posted schedule of activities. Internal newsletter for residents. *Recreational Programs*: exercise, shopping, theatre, parties, entertainment, art classes, pet visiting, day trips, lunch outings and pre-school visits.

OTHER SERVICES: *Housekeeping*: daily (included in fee). *Laundry*: linen, towel & personal (included in fee); dry cleaning (extra cost). Transportation for group social activities. 24-hour security. Nightly security checks. Telephone & Cable TV (extra cost). Utilities (included in fee).

RENTAL INFORMATION: Rates may vary. No cost for sharing suite. Rent paid monthly. *Payment Options*: pre-authorized payments. Rent increases as per Provincial Tenancy Legislation, annual for resident with 3 months' notice given. Short-term respite and trial stays available (both $85.00/day).

Did you know?

Ontario is home to 1.9 million seniors. Over the next 25 years, that number will more than double.

ANCASTER **CARRINGTON PLACE RETIREMENT RESIDENCE**
HIGHGATE RESIDENCE
THE MEADOWLANDS RETIREMENT RESIDENCE

Please see HAMILTON (ANCASTER) for information on these residences.

◆ ARNPRIOR ◆

BAYBRIDGE - ISLAND VIEW RETIREMENT SUITES

30 Jack Crescent, Arnprior, ON K7S 3Y7
Tel: (613) 622-0002 • Fax: (613) 622-0011
Email: **sgray@islandviewsuites.ca**
Website: **www.islandviewsuites.ca**
Contact: **Sharon Gray**
Capacity: **145 residents** • Subsidies: **none**
Price: **$2,300.00 - $4,033.00/month**

Discover the joy of small town living at Island View Retirement Suites in the historic town of Arnprior. Though we're just minutes from the city, there's no hint of the hustle and bustle in our spacious studio, 1-bedroom & 2-bedroom suites overlooking our beautifully landscaped lawns and the scenic Madawaska River. Experience all the pleasure life has to offer at Island View Retirement Suites, where luxurious amenities, invigorating leisure excursions and programs, and attentive staff support are just some of the ways we welcome you with open arms.

RESIDENCE INFORMATION: 11 years in operation. *Near:* Madawaska Boulevard and Jack Crescent. Decorated in 2007. 6 floors, 3 elevators. Wheelchair accessible. *Funding Base:* Corporate/for profit. *Owned and managed by:* BayBridge Senior Living. 106 units. *Average Waiting Period*: none. *Average Age*: 81. Can accommodate cognitively impaired people (mild dementia, no secured unit). Can accommodate physically challenged people (ambulatory issues). Smoking allowed (exterior area). Alcohol allowed (in suite or in common areas when served by a trained staff member). *Procedures to leave the premises on a temporary basis...*Short-term: simply use our Sign In/Out Book. Overnight: please mention it to the staff. Holidays: please inform the General Manager as a courtesy discount may apply. *Languages:* English. Will accept Public Guardian and Trustee clients. Main doors of residence secured at night only. *Close to:* Shopping, Churches, Seniors' Centre, Library, Major Highway and Local Hospital (The Arnprior and District Memorial Hospital). Member of ORCA & Arnprior Chamber of Commerce. Licensed under the Retirement Homes Act.
STAFFING: *Available Staff/Services*: Pharmacy, Social Work (CCAC), Recreation Therapy, Occupational Therapy (CCAC), Physiotherapy (CCAC), Dietitian (CCAC), Podiatry, Speech Pathology (CCAC), Hairstylist, Foot Care and Dental Hygienist. *External services arranged by:* residence and/or family/resident. Staff trained *re*: visually, hearing and cognitively impaired. 24-hour staff. RPNs, HCAs, PSWs and UCPs on staff. Can retain own MD. Police Check or Vulnerable Person Screening is done for all new staff. Staff members have TB testing.
HEALTH SERVICES: Medication administration and/or supervision (as required). Vitals monitored if required. Will accept and provide special assistance for residents who require oxygen, catheters and ostomies. Assistance with dressing available (cost). Weekly assistance with bathing available (cost). Care plans done. Different levels of care available. Private Duty/Extra Care available. Residents can purchase outside resources and use agency of their choice. Clinic area for medical visits. Will help locate higher level of care if needed (we provide Assisted Living levels of care at an extra charge; if care exceeds safety parameters for resident or staff, we assist with CCAC referrals).

ACCOMMODATION: *Choice of suites available*: studio, 1-bedroom (46) & 2-bedroom (19) units. *In all suites*: locks, full kitchenette, window coverings, light fixtures, fire alarm, smoke detector, sprinkler, emergency response system with wearable pendant/bracelet, air conditioning (central wall unit) and thermostats for heating & cooling. Private bathrooms with grab bars, tubs and showers with non-slip surfaces. In-suite cable/satellite TV if resident arranges with cable/satellite company (residence charges extra). Can have own phone number if resident arranges with phone company. Unfurnished suites, furnished suites available for short stays. *Restrictions on electrical appliances*: small kitchen appliances such as kettles must be CSA approved and have an automatic shut-off. Suites can be shared (no restrictions), roommate picked by resident. Small pets are welcome (fish, birds, cats, small friendly dogs).
DINING SERVICE: All meals included in fee and served in dining room daily. *Sittings per meal:* Breakfast: 2, Lunch: 2, Dinner: 2. *Menu choices available:* Breakfast: 2, Lunch: 2, Dinner: 2. *Guest Meals*: Available. *Special Diets*: Vegetarian, Low Salt, Diabetic, Celiac, Renal and any Therapeutic Diets required. Tray service to room if ill (no charge for a maximum time of 7 days). Unlimited snacks available at any time. Party facilities. Residents can have snacks and refreshments whenever they wish at our self-serve coffee/tea café and 24/7 refreshment area.
AMENITIES AND ACTIVITIES: Parking available (outdoor for visitors and residents). *5 lounges with:* TVs (2), piano (1), activity/resident kitchen (1) and home theatre (1). Guest suites available ($80.00/night). *Residence has a:* library, visiting library, barber/beauty shop, visiting hairdresser, laundry room(s) (no cost) and tuck/gift shop (open daily). Resident can arrange newspaper delivery to individual suite. Mail delivered to individual suite. *Recreation Facilities*: pool table, shuffleboard, craft room, card room, theatre room and café bistro. Posted schedule of activities. *Recreational Programs*: exercise, shopping, theatre, parties, entertainment, art classes, day trips, bridge, euchre, billiards and cooking.
OTHER SERVICES: *Housekeeping*: weekly (included in fee). *Laundry*: linen, towel, personal & dry cleaning (extra cost). Complimentary laundry soap. Transportation to medical appointments and for group social activities (no charge for transportation). 24-hour security. Nightly security checks. Telephone & Cable TV (available through local supplier). Utilities (included in fee).
RENTAL INFORMATION: Rates may vary. Extra cost for 2nd person sharing suite ($650.00/month). Rent paid monthly. *Payment Options*: pre-authorized payments. Rent increases as per Provincial Tenancy Legislation and % on services, annual for resident with 3 months' notice given. Short-term respite ($80.00/day) and trial stays ($100.00/week) available.

♦ AURORA ♦

HOLLANDVIEW TRAIL RETIREMENT COMMUNITY

200 John West Way, Aurora, ON L4G 0E4
Tel: (905) 841-1001 • Fax: (905) 841-1091
Email: **info@hollandviewtrail.com**
Website: **www.hollandviewtrail.com**
Contact: **Executive Director or Marketing Manager**
Capacity: **125 units** • Subsidies: **none**
Price: **$3,460.00/month and up**

Opened in April 2009, Hollandview Trail is Aurora's newest retirement community. Spacious suites feature walk-in closets, and kitchenettes with full-size fridges. Outstanding amenities include an indoor heated saltwater pool, Victory Garden and movie theatre. Conveniently located in the heart of Aurora, Hollandview Trail is a brief walk to the Aurora Senior Centre, and great shopping!

RESIDENCE INFORMATION: 5 years in operation. *Near:* Wellington Street and Bayview Street. Decorated in 2009. Handrails in some of the hallways. 5 floors, 3 elevators. Wheelchair accessible. Central PA system. *Funding Base:* Corporate/for profit. *Managed by:* Signature Retirement Living. *Average Waiting Period:* none. Can accommodate cognitively impaired people (mild/moderate cognitive impairment on Assisted Living Unit). Can accommodate physically challenged people. Smoke-free residence. Alcohol allowed. *Languages:* English. Will accept Public Guardian and Trustee clients. Main doors of residence secured at night only. *Close to:* Public Transit, Shopping, Churches, Seniors' Centre, Library, Major Highway and Local Hospital (Southlake Regional Health Centre). Member of ORCA. Licensed under the Retirement Homes Act.
STAFFING: *Available Staff/Services:* Pharmacy, Social Work (CCAC), Recreation Therapy, Occupational Therapy (CCAC), Visiting Dentist, Physiotherapy (CCAC), Denturist, Dietitian (CCAC), Companions, Podiatry (CCAC), Chaplaincy, Speech Pathology (CCAC), Chiropody and Audiology/Hearing Clinic. *External services arranged by:* residence and/or family/resident. Staff trained *re:* visually, hearing and cognitively impaired. 24-hour nursing and other staff. RNs, RPNs, HCAs, PSWs and UCPs on staff. Visiting MD (1 day/week). Can retain own MD. Police Check or Vulnerable Person Screening is done for all new staff.
HEALTH SERVICES: Medication administered if required. Vitals monitored if required. Will accept and provide special assistance for residents who require oxygen. Assistance with dressing available. Weekly assistance with bathing available. Care plans done. Different levels of care available. Private Duty/Extra Care available. Assisted Living Area. Lab service (visiting). Residents can purchase outside resources and use agency of their choice. MD visits residents in their rooms/suites. Clinic area for medical visits. Will help locate higher level of care if needed.
ACCOMMODATION: *Choice of suites available:* 2-bedroom, 1-bedroom + den, 1-bedroom & studio suites. *In all suites:* locks, kitchenette, full-size fridge, microwave, storage, window coverings, light fixtures, fire alarm, smoke detector, sprinkler, call bell, emergency response system with wearable pendant/bracelet, air conditioning (central) and thermostats for heating & cooling. Private bathrooms with call bells, grab bars, showers with non-slip surfaces and elevated toilet seats. In-suite cable TV provided by residence. Can have own phone number if resident arranges with phone company. Furnished & unfurnished suites available. *Restrictions on electrical appliances:* toaster ovens. Suites can be shared (maximum, 2 per room), roommate picked by resident. Pets allowed (size restrictions - with Management approval).
DINING SERVICE: All meals included in fee and served in dining room daily. *Menu choices available:* Breakfast: 5, Lunch: 5, Dinner: 5. *Guest Meals:* Available. *Special Diets:* Vegetarian, Low Salt and Diabetic. Tray service to room if ill (no charge for a maximum time of 5 days). Unlimited snacks available at any time. Party facilities. Open pantry. Bistro is open all day, including mealtimes.
AMENITIES AND ACTIVITIES: Parking available (outdoor for visitors and residents). *12 lounges with:* TVs (6) and piano (1). Guest suites available. *Residence has a:* library, visiting library, chapel, barber/beauty shop, visiting hairdresser and laundry room(s) (no cost). Resident can arrange newspaper delivery to individual suite. Mail delivered to private mailbox with key. *Recreation Facilities:* pool table, billiards, shuffleboard, exercise room, greenhouse, craft room, card room, movie theatre, saltwater pool, craft kitchen, pub, outdoor raised garden beds, massage room and spa. Posted schedule of activities. Internal newsletter for residents. *Recreational Programs:* exercise, shopping, theatre, parties, entertainment, art classes, pet visiting, day trips, aquafit classes, Yoga, Tai Chi and Pilates.
OTHER SERVICES: *Housekeeping:* weekly. *Laundry:* linen & towel (included in fee); dry cleaning (extra cost). Transportation for group social activities. 24-hour security. Nightly security checks. Telephone (extra cost). Cable TV & Utilities (included in fee).
RENTAL INFORMATION: Rates may vary; prices are subject to change. Extra cost for 2nd person sharing suite ($700.00/month). Rent paid monthly. *Payment Options:* cheques, post-dated cheques, direct deposit and pre-authorized payments. Rent increases as per Provincial Tenancy Legislation, annual for resident with 3 months' notice given. Short-term respite and trial stays available.

◆ BARRIE ◆

BARRIE MANOR SENIOR LIVING

340 Blake Street, Barrie, ON L4M 1L3
Tel: (705) 722-3611 • Fax: (705) 722-4530
Email: **cheryl@barriemanor.ca**
Website: **www.barriemanor.ca**
Contact: **Cheryl Pritchard**
Capacity: **118 residents** • Subsidies: **none**
Price: **$1,995.00 - $2,999.00/month**

Barrie Manor Senior Living has been serving our community for 26 years. We specialize in a stroke recovery program and rehabilitation after surgery. We also offer a Day-Away Program to accommodate members of our community who like to socialize during the day. We are located steps away from Johnson Beach on beautiful Kempenfelt Bay!

RESIDENCE INFORMATION: 27 years in operation. *Near:* Blake Street and Johnson Street. Decorated in 2013. Handrails in hallways. 3 floors, 1 elevator. Wheelchair accessible. Central PA system. *Funding Base:* Corporate/for profit. Privately owned. 77 units. *Average Waiting Period*: varies. *Average Age*: 75. Can accommodate cognitively impaired people & physically challenged people (acceptance is determined through assessment). Residents have a dress code (must be appropriately dressed at mealtimes). Smoking allowed (outdoor patio smoking area). Alcohol allowed. *Procedures to leave the premises on a temporary basis...*Short-term: notify Nurse in Charge and Receptionist. *Languages:* English, French & Spanish. Will accept Public Guardian and Trustee clients. Main doors of residence secured at night only. *Close to:* Public Transit, Shopping, Churches, Seniors' Centre, Library and Local Hospital (Royal Victoria Regional Health Centre is 3.5 km from Barrie Manor). Licensed under the Retirement Homes Act.
STAFFING: *Available Staff/Services*: Pharmacy, Social Work, Recreation Therapy, Physiotherapy, Podiatry (CCAC), Chaplaincy, Speech Pathology (CCAC) and Foot Care Clinic. *External services arranged by:* family/resident. 24-hour nursing staff. RPNs and PSWs on staff. Visiting MD (1 day/week). Can retain own MD. Police Check or Vulnerable Person Screening is done for all new staff.
HEALTH SERVICES: Medication administration and/or supervision. Vitals monitored if required. Will accept and provide special assistance for residents who require oxygen, catheters and ostomies. Assistance with dressing available. Assistance with bathing available twice a week. Care plans done. Different levels of care available. Lab service (visiting, $20.00/visit). Residents can purchase outside resources and use agency of their choice. Clinic area for medical visits. Will help locate higher level of care if needed (Director of Care communicates with CCAC).
ACCOMMODATION: *Choice of suites available*: private (38), semi-private (34) & ward (5) units. *In all suites*: locks, storage, window coverings, light fixtures, linens, smoke detector, sprinkler, call bell, thermostats for heating, twin bed, dresser with mirror, nightstand and chair. Private bathrooms with call bells, tubs and showers. In-suite cable TV provided by residence (residence charges extra $69.00/month). Can have own phone number if resident arranges with phone company. Furnished suites available on request. *Restrictions on electrical appliances*: only microwaves and bar fridges permitted. Suites can be shared (by couples only), roommate picked by residence staff. No pets allowed.
DINING SERVICE: All meals included in fee and served in dining room daily. *Sittings per meal:* Breakfast: 1, Lunch: 1, Dinner: 1. *Menu choices available:* Breakfast: 2, Lunch: 2, Dinner: 2. *Guest Meals*: Breakfast $3.00, Lunch $4.00, Dinner $5.00. *Special Diets*: Vegetarian, Low Salt, Diabetic and Gluten Free. Tray service to room if ill (no charge as long as doctor orders). 3 snacks/day. Party facilities.

AMENITIES AND ACTIVITIES: Parking available (outdoor, for visitors: free and residents: $50.00/month). *2 lounges with:* TV (1) and piano (1). Guest suites available ($110.00/night). *Residence has a:* library, visiting library, chapel, barber/beauty shop and laundry room(s) (no cost). Banking services on premises (Monday to Friday). Mail delivered to main desk. *Recreation Facilities*: pool table, shuffleboard, exercise room, craft room, card room, internet café and dart board. Posted schedule of activities. Internal newsletter for residents. *Recreational Programs*: exercise, shopping, theatre, parties, entertainment, art classes, pet visiting, day trips, Happy Hour, bingo, Tai Chi, gardening and horseshoes.
OTHER SERVICES: *Housekeeping*: daily. *Laundry*: linen & towel (included in fee); personal ($15.00/week). Residents can do their own personal laundry for no charge. Transportation for group social activities (some activities require a small fee). Nightly security checks. Telephone & Cable TV (extra cost). Utilities ($15.00/month if resident has bar fridge & $150.00 annually if resident has an in-room air conditioner).
RENTAL INFORMATION: Rates may vary. Semi-private room $1,995.00/month; standard private - $2,295.00/month; large private - $2,999.00/month. Extra cost for 2nd person sharing suite ($975.00/month). Rent paid monthly. *Payment Options*: cheques, post-dated cheques and pre-authorized payments. Rent increases as per Provincial Tenancy Legislation, annual for resident with 3 months' notice given. Short-term respite and trial stays available (both $110.00/day).

SIMCOE TERRACE RETIREMENT CENTRE

44 Donald Street, Barrie, ON L4N 1E3
Tel: (705) 722-5750 • Fax: (705) 722-7041
Email: **info@simcoeterrace.com**
Website: **www.simcoeterrace.com**
Contact: **Michael Ayers**
Capacity: **120 residents**
Subsidies: **limited number semi-private;**
Ontario Works Domiciliary Care Program
Price: **$1,674.00 - $2,508.00/month**

If you're looking for a warm and friendly residence at an affordable rate, you will be happy to discover Simcoe Terrace - Barrie's best retirement value. With more than 20 years of experience and friendly staff, Simcoe Terrace is a warm and inviting place to call home. You will have opportunities to meet your neighbours, enjoy your interests and find good company with whom to share a cup of tea. Our innovative *Zest for Life™* signature service promotes the health and well-being of each resident by focusing on the needs of mind, body and spirit. We work with you one-on-one to connect you with activities and services that spark your particular interests. Come and explore Simcoe Terrace for yourself. If you are looking for a rewarding place to live and you too have a zest for life – our doors are open.

A Cozy and Affordable Residence – that's Simcoe Terrace.

RESIDENCE INFORMATION: 28 years in operation. *Near:* Anne Street and Dunlop Street. Decorated in 2011. Handrails in hallways. 2 floors, 1 elevator. Wheelchair accessible. Central PA system. *Owned by:* Simcoe Terrace Inc. *Managed by:* Specialty Care. 97 units. *Average Waiting Period*: varies. *Average Age*: 80. Can accommodate cognitively impaired people with restrictions (no risk of elopement or aggressive behaviour). Can accommodate physically challenged people with restrictions (by assessment). Smoking allowed (specified area outside residence only). *Procedures to leave the premises on a temporary basis...* Short-term & Overnight: notify staff, sign out in log book. Holidays: notify 4 days advance if medications required. *Languages:* English. Will accept Public Guardian and Trustee clients. Main doors of residence secured at night only. *Close to:* Public Transit, Shopping, Churches, Seniors' Centre, Library, Major Highway and Local Hospital (Royal Victoria Regional Health Centre). Member of ORCA. Licensed under the Retirement Homes Act.

STAFFING: *Available Staff/Services:* Pharmacy, Recreation Therapy, Occupational Therapy (CCAC), Visiting Dentist, Physiotherapy, Dietitian (CCAC), Podiatry (CCAC), Chaplaincy, Speech Pathology (CCAC), Foot Care and Social Worker. *External services arranged by:* residence and/or family/resident. Staff trained *re:* visually, hearing and cognitively impaired. 24-hour nursing and other staff. RNs, RPNs, HCAs, PSWs and UCPs on staff. Visiting MD (weekly). Can retain own MD. Police Check or Vulnerable Person Screening is done for all new staff.
HEALTH SERVICES: Medication administration (use dosette system with specified pharmacy) and/or supervision. Vitals monitored if required. Will accept (but not provide special assistance for) residents who require catheters. Will accept and provide special assistance for residents who require oxygen. Assistance with dressing available ($450.00/half hour). Weekly assistance with bathing available. *Extra baths:* $100.00/month. Care plans done. Different levels of care available. Assisted Living Care (extra cost). Lab service (visiting). Residents can purchase outside resources and use agency of their choice. Clinic area for medical visits. Will help locate higher level of care if needed (via CCAC & will assist if needed).
ACCOMMODATION: *Choice of suites available*: studio: semi-private or private units. *In all suites*: locks, storage, window coverings, light fixtures, smoke detector, call bell, air conditioning (window units - extra cost) and thermostats for heating. Common areas have heater/air conditioning units. Private bathrooms with call bells, grab bars and tubs. In-suite cable TV if resident arranges with cable company. Can have own phone number if resident arranges with phone company. Unfurnished suites, furnished suites available for short stays. *Restrictions on electrical appliances*: all electrical items must be checked by Administration. Suites can be shared (couples, family members or companion/friendship), roommate picked by resident & residence staff. Pets allowed (subject to approval of the General Manager).
DINING SERVICE: All meals included in fee and served in dining room daily. *Sittings per meal:* Breakfast: 2, Lunch: 2, Dinner: 2. *Menu choices available:* Breakfast: 2, Lunch: 2, Dinner: 2. *Guest Meals*: Breakfast $4.00, Lunch $6.00, Dinner $8.00. *Special Diets*: Vegetarian, Low Salt, Diabetic and Cholesterol Reduced. Tray service to room if ill (no charge for a maximum time of 3 days). 3 snacks/day. Party facilities. Coffee, tea & juice available 24-hours/day.
AMENITIES AND ACTIVITIES: Parking available (outdoor, for visitors and residents). *5 lounges with:* TVs (2) and pianos (2). Guest suites available ($85.00/night). *Residence has a:* library, visiting library, barber/beauty shop, visiting hairdresser, laundry room(s) (no cost), tuck/gift shop (open twice/week; hours vary). Resident can arrange newspaper delivery to main desk. Mail delivered to main desk. *Recreation Facilities*: pool table, exercise room, craft room and card room. Posted schedule of activities. Internal newsletter for residents. *Recreational Programs*: exercise, shopping, theatre, parties, art classes, entertainment, pet visiting, day trips, pub night with entertainment Thursday nights, horse races, horseshoes and bingo.
OTHER SERVICES: *Housekeeping*: weekly for Full Service; bi-weekly for Independent. *Laundry*: linen & towel (included in fee); personal (extra cost for Full Service & Independent). Transportation for group social activities (nominal cost). 24-hour security. Nightly security checks. Telephone & Cable TV (extra cost/external supplier). Utilities (included in fee).
RENTAL INFORMATION: Rates may vary. Extra cost for 2nd person sharing suite ($625.00/month). Rent paid monthly. *Payment Options*: post-dated cheques and pre-authorized payments. Rent increases as per Provincial Tenancy Legislation, reviewed annually with 3 months' notice given. Short-term respite ($85.00/day) and trial stays available.

Did you know?

The website for The Canadian Mental Health Association has information on caregiving and coping with aging parents. Visit **www.cmha.ca/mental_health/you-and-your-aging-parents/** to view their information.

WOODS PARK CARE CENTRE

110 Lillian Crescent, Barrie, ON L4N 5H7
Tel: (705) 739-6881 • Fax: (705) 739-0638
Email: **caron.wyers@woodspark.on.ca**
Website: **www.specialtyliving.ca**
Contact: **Caron Wyers**
Capacity: **59 residents** • Subsidies: **none**
Price: **$2,695.00/month and up**

Woods Park ranks highest in Ontario in resident satisfaction! (Survey conducted by Rice and Associates.) Woods Park offers a lifestyle all your own; spacious rooms including many with private courtyard access, professional, friendly staff and chef-inspired meals. There is a lot to keep you busy if you choose. Enjoy our signature *Zest for Life™* lifestyle programs, designed to engage your mind, body and spirit. We also offer private bus transportation for outings. Located adjacent to beautiful parklands in a well-established residential area, Woods Park offers a serene atmosphere with 3 spacious courtyards and a wide variety of wellness services to suit every lifestyle. We offer 55 retirement suites, 108 long-term care beds and 15 convalescent care beds.

RESIDENCE INFORMATION: 15 years in operation. *Near:* Bayfield Street and Cundles Avenue. Decorated in 2010. Handrails in hallways. 3 floors, 3 elevators. Wheelchair accessible. *Owned and managed by:* Specialty Care. 55 units. *Average Waiting Period*: varies. *Average Age*: 80. Can accommodate physically challenged people (fully accessible home; assessed individually). Smoke-free residence. Alcohol allowed. *Procedures to leave the premises on a temporary basis...*Short-term & Overnight: sign out and report leave to staff. Holidays: arrange with Director of Marketing and Resident Services. *Languages:* English. Will accept Public Guardian and Trustee clients. Main doors of residence secured at night only. *Close to:* Public Transit, Shopping, Churches, Seniors' Centre, Major Highway and Local Hospital (Royal Victoria Regional Health Centre). Member of ORCA. Member of OLTCA for adjoining long-term care home. Licensed under the Retirement Homes Act.
STAFFING: *Available Staff/Services*: Pharmacy, Social Work (CCAC), Recreation Therapy, Occupational Therapy (CCAC), Visiting Dentist, Denturist, Dietitian, Podiatry, Chaplaincy, Speech Pathology (CCAC), Chiropody, Audiology/Hearing Clinic, Hair Care, Massage Therapy and Physiotherapist (on-site). *External services arranged by:* residence and/or family/resident. Staff trained *re*: visually, hearing and cognitively impaired. RN's on-site 24-hours/day. RNs, RPNs, HCAs and PSWs on staff. Visiting MD (twice/week). Can retain own MD. Police Check or Vulnerable Person Screening is done for all new staff.
HEALTH SERVICES: Medication administered if required (extra fee). Vitals monitored if required. Will accept (but not provide special assistance for) residents who require ostomies. Will accept and provide special assistance for residents who require oxygen and catheters. Assistance with dressing available ($16.75/half hour). Weekly assistance with bathing available ($100.00/month). *Extra baths:* $15.00/half hour. Care plans done. Different levels of care available. Private Duty/Extra Care available ($33.50/hour). Assisted Living Area ($465.00/month; 6 - 12 months waiting period). Lab service (visiting, $25.00/visit). Residents can purchase outside resources and use agency of their choice. MD visits residents in their rooms/suites. Will help locate higher level of care if needed (staff arrange for CCAC assessment). Convalescent care through CCAC available in long-term care.
ACCOMMODATION: *Choice of suites available*: private studio (51) & 1-bedroom (5) suites. *In all suites*: locks, window coverings, light fixtures, fire alarm, smoke detector, sprinkler, call bell, air conditioning (individual built in each room) and thermostats for heating & cooling. Some rooms with walkouts, storage area & kitchenettes. Private bathrooms with call bells, grab bars, tubs and showers with non-slip surfaces. In-suite cable TV provided by residence (residence charges extra $43.00/month). Can have own phone number provided by residence (residence charges extra $31.00/month). Furnished & unfurnished suites available. *Restrictions on electrical appliances*: no toasters, toaster ovens, portable heaters; approval by

Administration needed. Suites can be shared (by couples only). Pets allowed (must be assessed prior to admission).
DINING SERVICE: All meals included in fee and served in dining room daily. *Sittings per meal:* Breakfast: 1, Lunch: 1, Dinner: 1. *Menu choices available:* Breakfast: 6, Lunch: 6, Dinner: 6. *Guest Meals*: Breakfast $7.00, Lunch $9.00, Dinner $11.00. *Special Diets*: Vegetarian, Low Salt and Diabetic. Healthy choices menu options identified. Tray service to room if ill (no charge for a maximum time of 3 days). 2 snacks/day and unlimited snacks available at any time. Party facilities. Open pantry. 24-hour self-serve café is made available to retirement home residents - items include: fresh fruit, coffee, tea and a variety of beverages, breads, cold & hot cereal.
AMENITIES AND ACTIVITIES: Parking available (outdoor, for visitors and residents). *7 lounges with:* TVs (4), fireplaces (2), piano and organ on each floor (1). *Residence has a:* library, visiting library, chapel, barber/beauty shop, visiting hairdresser, laundry room(s) (no cost) and tuck/gift shop (open daily; 10:00 a.m. - 5:00 p.m.). Resident can arrange newspaper delivery to individual suite. Mail delivered to individual suite. *Recreation Facilities*: pool table, shuffleboard, exercise room, craft room, card room, library, computer access, community room, massage centre and a wood working room. Posted schedule of activities. Internal newsletter for residents. *Recreational Programs*: exercise, shopping, theatre, parties, entertainment, art classes, pet visiting, day trips, computer classes and French lessons.
OTHER SERVICES: *Housekeeping*: weekly; additional can be purchased separately. *Laundry*: linen & towel (included in fee); personal (maximum 2 loads/week is $80.00/month) & dry cleaning (extra cost). Transportation for group social activities ($5.00/person for bus outings). 24-hour security. Nightly security checks. Telephone ($31.00/month). Cable TV ($43.00/month). Utilities (included in fee).
RENTAL INFORMATION: Rates may vary. Prices include meals and Basic Service Package. Extra cost for 2nd person sharing suite ($620.00/month). Rent paid monthly. *Payment Options*: cheques and pre-authorized payments. Rent increases as per Provincial Tenancy Legislation, annual for resident with 3 months' notice given. Short-term respite ($120.00/day) and trial stays ($100.00/day) can be accommodated based on availability.

◆ BELLEVILLE ◆

THE RICHMOND

175 North Front Street, Belleville, ON K8P 4Y8
Tel: (613) 966-4407 • Fax: (613) 967-0996
Email: **gm.therichmond@diversicare.ca**
Website: **www.richmondretirement.ca**
Contact: **Marketing Manager**
Capacity: **90 residents** • Subsidies: **none**
Price: **$2,024.00 - $4,894.50/month**

The Richmond Retirement Residence is centrally located in Belleville close to shopping, entertainment and transportation. With a strong focus on lifestyle and choice we are pleased to offer a safe, home-like environment with friendly, dedicated staff. Enjoy daily activities with your new friends or invite your old friends to stop by for tea at our bistro. All meals are provided along with nursing support should you require it. Accommodation ranges from studio to 1-bedroom suites and all suites have an Emergency Response System. Our outdoor patios and gardens are a wonderful way to enjoy the sunny weather. **The Richmond Retirement Residence is managed by Diversicare, who is the proud recipient of the 2003, 2006, 2009 and 2012 Order of Excellence Award given by Excellence Canada.** This award was received for the exceptional quality and customer service we provide to our residents every day.

RESIDENCE INFORMATION: 30 years in operation. *Near:* College Street and North Front Street. Decorated in 2011. Handrails in hallways. 4 floors, 1 elevator. Wheelchair accessible. Central PA system. *Funding Base:* Corporate/for profit. *Owned by:* Master Equity. *Managed by:* Diversicare Canada Management Services Co., Inc. 83 units. *Average Waiting Period*: varies. *Average Age*: 84. Can accommodate cognitively impaired people & physically challenged people with restrictions (assessment required). Smoke-free residence. Alcohol allowed (in suite only). *Procedures to leave the premises on a temporary basis...*sign out. *Languages:* English. Will accept Public Guardian and Trustee clients. Main doors of residence secured at night only. *Close to:* Public Transit, Shopping, Churches, Library, Major Highway and Local Hospital (Quinte Healthcare Corporation). Member of ORCA & Belleville Chamber of Commerce. Licensed under the Retirement Homes Act.

STAFFING: *Available Staff/Services*: Pharmacy, Social Work (CCAC), Recreation Therapy, Occupational Therapy (CCAC), Physiotherapy (CCAC), Dietitian (CCAC), Chaplaincy, Speech Pathology (CCAC) and Hair Salon. *External services arranged by:* residence and/or family/resident. Staff trained *re*: visually, hearing and cognitively impaired. 24-hour nursing and other staff. RPNs, HCAs, PSWs and UCPs on staff. Can retain own MD. Staff members are bonded. Police Check or Vulnerable Person Screening is done for all new staff.

HEALTH SERVICES: Medication administration (assessed by nurse) and/or supervision. Vitals monitored if required. Will accept (but not provide special assistance for) residents who require oxygen, catheters and ostomies. Assistance with dressing available ($8.50/half hour). Weekly assistance with bathing available ($10.00/half hour). *Extra baths:* $10.00/half hour. Care plans done. Different levels of care available. Lab service (visiting, $25.00/visit). Residents can purchase outside resources and use agency of their choice. MD visits residents in their rooms/suites. Clinic area for medical visits. Will help locate higher level of care if needed (liaise with CCAC).

ACCOMMODATION: *Choice of suites available*: studio (32), studio deluxe (33), 1-bedroom (11) & 1-bedroom deluxe (6) units. *In all suites*: locks, window coverings, light fixtures, linens, fire alarm, smoke detector, call bell, air conditioning (window units are negotiated on move in) and thermostats for heating. Some suites are equipped with kitchenettes. Private bathrooms with call bells, grab bars, tubs and showers with non-slip surfaces. In-suite cable TV if resident arranges with cable company. Can have own phone number if resident arranges with phone company. Unfurnished suites, furnished suites available for short stays. *Restrictions on electrical appliances*: all electrical appliances are checked for safety by Environmental Services. Suites can be shared (by couples only). Pets allowed (small to medium and must meet Guidelines).

DINING SERVICE: All meals included in fee and served in dining room daily. *Sittings per meal:* Breakfast: 2, Lunch: 2, Dinner: 2. *Menu choices available:* Breakfast: 1, Lunch: 2, Dinner: 2. *Guest Meals*: Breakfast $6.00, Lunch $8.00, Dinner $15.00. *Special Diets*: Vegetarian, Low Salt, Diabetic and Modified (Food Service and Nutrition Manager). Tray service to room if ill (no charge for a maximum time of 7 days). 2 snacks/day. Party facilities. Open pantry. Full Breakfast Daily - Eggs/Bacon or Sausage or Ham/Hot and Cold Cereal.

AMENITIES AND ACTIVITIES: Parking available (outdoor, for visitors and residents). *6 lounges with:* TVs (4), pianos (4), small outdoor terraces (2), covered and furnished terrace (1). Guest suites available ($55.00/night). *Residence has a:* visiting library, chapel, barber/beauty shop, visiting hairdresser and laundry room(s) (cost). Mail delivered to private mailbox with key. *Recreation Facilities*: craft room, card room and lounge with large screen TV. Posted schedule of activities. Internal newsletter for residents. *Recreational Programs*: exercise, shopping, theatre, parties, entertainment, art classes, pet visiting, day trips, Brain Gym® & More and Wine Tours with multiple special events.

OTHER SERVICES: *Housekeeping*: daily and weekly (included in fee; fresh towels twice weekly). *Laundry*: linen & towel (included in fee); personal & dry cleaning (extra cost). Bed linen provided for single beds only (included in fee). Transportation for group social activities. Nightly security checks. Telephone (resident arranges via Bell). Cable TV (resident arranges via Cogeco). Utilities (included in fee).

RENTAL INFORMATION: Rates may vary. Studio 1-room suite - $2,024.00/month; studio deluxe 1-room suite - $2,550.00/month; 2-room 1-bedroom - $3,479.00/month; 2-room 1-bedroom deluxe - $4,533.00/ month. Extra cost for 2nd person sharing suite ($700.00/month; Full Service Lifestyle Package offered). Rent paid monthly. *Payment Options*: cheques, post-dated cheques, direct deposit and pre-authorized payments. Rent increases indexed to inflation as per Provincial Tenancy Legislation, annual for resident with 3 months' notice given. Short-term respite and trial stays available ($75.00 to $142.00/day, price range relevant to suite size).

◆ BRAMPTON ◆

SOUTHBROOK RETIREMENT COMMUNITY

400 Ray Lawson Boulevard, Brampton, ON L6Y 4G4
Tel: (905) 456-3334 • Fax: (905) 456-2764
Email: **mail@southbrook.on.ca**
Website: **www.southbrook.on.ca**
Contact: **Sharon Raven**
Capacity: **117 units** • Subsidies: **none**
Price: **$2,135.17 - $5,025.17/month**

At Southbrook, everything we do makes life easier and more enjoyable. We offer a variety of spacious accommodations, carefree elegant dining, a variety of social and recreational programs as well as Independent and Assisted Living care services. We are located in a residential neighbourhood close to amenities. We are an accredited member of ORCA and licensed under the RHRA. *Southbrook is affordable luxury retirement living, for the best years of your life.*

RESIDENCE INFORMATION: 25 years in operation. *Near:* Highway 10 and Ray Lawson Boulevard. Decorated in 2013. Handrails in hallways. 2 floors, 2 elevators. Wheelchair accessible. Central PA system. *Funding Base:* Corporate/for profit. *Owned by:* Rice Development Corporation Inc. *Average Waiting Period*: 2 - 4 months. *Average Age*: 87. Can accommodate cognitively impaired & physically challenged people. Residents have a dress code (proper attire expected in the dining room). Smoke-free residence. *Restrictions around Visitors/Visiting Hours:* visitors before 9:00 a.m. and after 9:00 p.m. must be let in or out. All visitors must sign in. *Procedures to leave the premises on a temporary basis...*notify residence of dates away and request for medications. *Languages:* English. Main doors of residence secured at all times. *Close to:* Public Transit, Shopping, Churches, Seniors' Centre, Library, Major Highway and Local Hospitals (William Osler Health Centre - Brampton Civic Hospital Site and Trillium Health Partners - Credit Valley Hospital Site). Member of ORCA. Licensed under the Retirement Homes Act.
STAFFING: *Available Staff/Services*: Pharmacy, Social Work (CCAC), Recreation Therapy, Occupational Therapy (CCAC), Visiting Dentist, Physiotherapy, Denturist, Dietitian, Companions, Podiatry, Chaplaincy, Speech Pathology (CCAC), Audiology/Hearing Clinic and Oxygen Management Consultant/Service Provider. *External services arranged by:* residence and/or family/resident. Staff trained *re*: visually, hearing and cognitively impaired. 24-hour nursing staff. RNs, RPNs, HCAs and PSWs on staff. Visiting MD (on-site 3 half days/week & on call 24-hours). Can retain own MD. Police Check or Vulnerable Person Screening is done for all new staff.
HEALTH SERVICES: Medication administered if required. Vitals monitored if required. Will accept and provide special assistance for residents who require oxygen, catheters and ostomies. Assistance with dressing available (cost). Weekly assistance with bathing available ($65.00/month). *Extra baths:* $16.25/hour. Care plans done. Different levels of care available. Private Duty/Extra Care available ($8.15 to $36.00/hour). Assisted Living Area ($486.40 to $950.00/month; 6 - 12 month waiting period) is secured

to accommodate residents with dementia. Lab service (visiting). Residents can purchase outside resources and use agency of their choice. MD visits residents in their rooms/suites. Clinic area for medical visits. Will help locate higher level of care if needed (placement is coordinated with CCAC and family).
ACCOMMODATION: *Choice of suites available*: semi-private in Assisted Living Unit, bedsitting studio, 1-bedroom suite & deluxe 1-bedroom suite. *In all suites*: locks, kitchenette, storage, bar fridge, window coverings, light fixtures, linens, fire alarm, smoke detector, sprinkler, call bell, emergency response system with wearable pendant/bracelet, air conditioning (central & window units) and thermostats for heating & cooling. Private bathrooms (semi-private accommodations share a washroom) with call bells, grab bars, tubs and showers with non-slip surfaces. In-suite cable TV provided by residence. Can have own phone number if resident arranges with phone company. Unfurnished suites, furnished suites available for short stays. *Restrictions on electrical appliances*: must be in good working order. Suites can be shared (by couples or other relation, e.g. sisters). Pets allowed (on approval of Management and Pet Agreement signed).
DINING SERVICE: All meals included in fee and served in dining room daily. *Sittings per meal:* Breakfast: 2, Lunch: 2, Dinner: 2. *Menu choices available:* Lunch: 3, Dinner: 3. *Guest Meals*: Breakfast $4.00, Lunch $8.00, Dinner $11.25. *Special Diets*: Vegetarian, Low Salt, Diabetic, Minced, Pureed and Thickened Fluids. Tray service to room if ill (no charge as long as doctor orders). 2 snacks/day. Party facilities. Private dining room available. Morning continental breakfast & afternoon tea served daily.
AMENITIES AND ACTIVITIES: Parking available (outdoor, for visitors and residents). *4 lounges with:* TVs (4), pianos (2) and organ (1). Guest suites available ($100.00/night). *Residence has a:* library, visiting library, chapel, barber/beauty shop, visiting hairdresser, laundry room(s) (no cost) and Tuck Cart (Monday & Friday for 1 hour/day). Resident can arrange newspaper delivery to individual suite. Mail delivered to private mailbox with key. *Recreation Facilities*: pool table, billiards, shuffleboard, craft room, card room, exercise area and hobby kitchen. Posted schedule of activities. Internal newsletter for residents. *Recreational Programs*: exercise, shopping, theatre, parties, entertainment, art classes, pet visiting, day trips, church services, bingo and movies.
OTHER SERVICES: *Housekeeping*: daily. *Laundry*: linen & towel (included in fee); personal ($65.00/month; included in fee for Assisted Living residents). Dry cleaning (fee for service through outside service). Transportation for group social activities. 24-hour security. Nightly security checks. Cable TV & Utilities (included in fee).
RENTAL INFORMATION: Rates may vary. Extra cost for 2nd person sharing suite ($835.00/month). Rent paid monthly. *Payment Options*: cheques, post-dated cheques and pre-authorized payments. Rent increases as per Provincial Tenancy Legislation, annual for resident with 3 months' notice given. Short-term respite and trial stays available (both $100.00/day).

WOODHALL PARK RETIREMENT VILLAGE

10250 Kennedy Road, Brampton, ON L6Z 4N7
Tel: (905) 846-1441 • Fax: (905) 846-1451
Email: **postmaster@woodhallpark.ca**
Website: **www.woodhallpark.ca**
Contact: **Nancy Novak**
Capacity: **80 residents** • Subsidies: **none**
Price: **$2,917.00 - $4,150.00/month**

Woodhall Park opened in 1998 in order to assist seniors and their families live life to the fullest by providing individual care services and a happy worry free lifestyle.

RESIDENCE INFORMATION: 25 years in operation. *Near:* Bovaird Drive and Kennedy Road. Decorated in 2013. Handrails in hallways. 3 floors, 1 elevator. Wheelchair accessible. Central PA system. *Funding Base:* Corporate/for profit. 75 units. *Average Waiting Period*: less than 2 weeks. *Average Age*: 85. Can

accommodate cognitively impaired people (cannot accommodate wanderers). Can accommodate physically challenged people (as long as they can be managed by 1 person only). Smoking allowed (outside). Alcohol allowed. *Languages:* English. Will accept Public Guardian and Trustee clients. Main doors of residence secured at night only. *Close to:* Public Transit, Shopping, Churches, Seniors' Centre, Library, Major Highway and Local Hospital (William Osler Health Centre - Brampton Civic Hospital Site). Member of ORCA. Licensed under the Retirement Homes Act.

STAFFING: *Available Staff/Services*: Pharmacy, Social Work (CCAC), Recreation Therapy, Occupational Therapy (CCAC), Physiotherapy, Dietitian (CCAC), Companions, Podiatry, Chaplaincy, Speech Pathology (CCAC) and Chiropody. *External services arranged by:* family/resident. Staff trained *re*: visually, hearing and cognitively impaired. 24-hour nursing and other staff. RNs, RPNs, HCAs, PSWs and UCPs on staff. Visiting MD (2x/week or by phone daily). Can retain own MD. Police Check or Vulnerable Person Screening is done for all new staff.

HEALTH SERVICES: Medication administration and/or supervision. Vitals monitored if required. Will accept and provide special assistance for residents who require oxygen, catheters and feeding tubes. Assistance with dressing available. Weekly assistance with bathing available ($65.00/month). Care plans done. Different levels of care available. Lab service (visiting, $27.50/visit). Residents can purchase outside resources and use agency of their choice. MD visits residents in their rooms/suites. Clinic area for medical visits. Will help locate higher level of care if needed.

ACCOMMODATION: *Choice of suites available*: private, deluxe & couples. *In all suites*: locks, storage, window coverings, light fixtures, linens, smoke detector, sprinkler, call bell, air conditioning (central) and thermostats for heating & cooling. Private bathrooms with call bells, grab bars, tubs and showers with non-slip surfaces. In-suite cable TV provided by residence (residence charges extra $32.00/month). Can have own phone number if resident arranges with phone company. Furnished suites available on request. *Restrictions on electrical appliances*: NO cooking allowed in rooms. Suites can be shared; roommate picked by resident & residence staff. Pets allowed (birds and fish only).

DINING SERVICE: All meals included in fee and served in dining room daily. *Sittings per meal:* Breakfast: 1, Lunch: 1, Dinner: 1. *Menu choices available:* Breakfast: 4, Lunch: 2, Dinner: 2. *Guest Meals*: Lunch $7.00, Dinner $9.00. *Special Diets*: Vegetarian, Low Salt and Diabetic. Tray service to room if ill (no charge for a maximum time of 14 days). Unlimited snacks available at any time. All day snack stations. Party facilities. Open pantry.

AMENITIES AND ACTIVITIES: Parking available (outdoor, for visitors and residents). *7 lounges with:* TVs (2) and pianos (3). *Residence has a:* library, visiting library, barber/beauty shop, laundry room(s) (no cost) and tuck/gift shop (open 3 days). Residence provides newspaper delivery to individual suite. Mail delivered to individual suite. *Recreation Facilities*: shuffleboard, craft room, card room and auditorium. Posted schedule of activities. Internal newsletter for residents. *Recreational Programs*: exercise, shopping, theatre, parties, entertainment, art classes, pet visiting and day trips.

OTHER SERVICES: *Housekeeping*: daily (included in fee). *Laundry*: linen & towel (included in fee); personal (choose extra service or do your own). Transportation for group social activities. 24-hour security. Nightly security checks. Telephone & Cable TV (extra cost). Utilities (included in fee).

RENTAL INFORMATION: Rates may vary. Rent paid monthly. *Payment Options*: cheques and pre-authorized payments. Rent increases as per Provincial Tenancy Legislation, annual for resident with 3 months' notice given. Will help resident move into residence. Short-term respite and trial stays available.

Downsizing Tip

Take photos of items you treasure but must give away. Create a keepsake album with those photos in them and write stories to go with each item that remind you of their importance.

◆ BRANTFORD ◆

REVERA - CHARLOTTE VILLA

120 Darling Street, Brantford, ON N3T 5W6
Tel: (855) 573-8372 • Toll Free: (855) 573-8372
Email: **charlotte@reveraliving.com**
Website: **www.reveraliving.com/charlotte**
Contact: **Executive Director or Lifestyle Consultant**
Capacity: **73 residents** • Subsidies: **none**
Price: **$2,409.00/month and up**

At Charlotte Villa you'll find the range of services, amenities and choices that fit your lifestyle and requirements – all in a warm and safe environment. Our elegant residence is centrally located in Brantford, close to restaurants, entertainment, green space, and churches. At Charlotte Villa, everything is designed to enable you to maintain your independence and privacy, enjoy a full social life, and participate in a wide variety of activities offered. Our caring and friendly staff, along with beautiful accommodations, supports who you are and how you want to live. Explore what we have to offer, to keep you living in freedom and comfort. With retirement living at Charlotte Villa, you change your address, not your life. *Charlotte Villa is part of the Revera family, one of North America's leading and most trusted providers of seniors' accommodation, care and services since 1961.*

RESIDENCE INFORMATION: 39 years in operation. *On:* Charlotte Street and Dalhousie Street. Decorated in 2010. Handrails in hallways. 6 floors, 2 elevators. Wheelchair accessible. Central PA system. *Funding Base:* Corporate/for profit. *Owned and managed by:* Revera Inc. 80 units. *Average Waiting Period*: varies. *Average Age*: 82. Can accommodate cognitively impaired people. Can accommodate physically challenged people (cost of care is based on amount required). Smoking allowed (outside). Alcohol allowed. *Procedures to leave the premises on a temporary basis...*sign in/out; all departments notified. *Languages:* English, German, Dutch, Polish & Ukrainian. Will accept Public Guardian and Trustee clients. Main doors of residence secured at all times. *Close to:* Public Transit, Shopping, Churches, Seniors' Centre, Library, Major Highway and Local Hospital (The Brantford General Hospital). Member of ORCA & Chamber of Commerce. Licensed under the Retirement Homes Act.
STAFFING: *Available Staff/Services*: Social Work (CCAC), Recreation Therapy, Occupational Therapy (CCAC), Physiotherapy (CCAC), Dietitian (CCAC), Companions, Podiatry, Speech Pathology (CCAC), Audiology/Hearing Clinic, Pastoral Care and Recreation/Cultural Programs. *External services arranged by:* residence and/or family/resident. Staff trained *re*: visually, hearing and cognitively impaired. 24-hour nursing and other staff. RNs, RPNs, HCAs, PSWs and UCPs on staff. Visiting MD (only for new residents without an existing doctor). Can retain own MD. Police Check or Vulnerable Person Screening is done for all new staff.
HEALTH SERVICES: Medication administered if required. Vitals monitored if required. Will accept and provide special assistance for residents who require oxygen, catheters and ostomies. Assistance with dressing available (cost). Weekly assistance with bathing available (cost). Care plans done. Different levels of care available. Private Duty/Extra Care available. Assisted Living Area. Lab service (visiting). Residents can purchase outside resources and use agency of their choice. MD visits residents in their rooms/suites. Will help locate higher level of care if needed (CCAC).
ACCOMMODATION: *Choice of suites available*: private (66) & 2-room (7) suites. *In all suites*: locks, storage, window coverings, light fixtures, linens, smoke detector, sprinkler, call bell, air conditioning (central) and thermostats for heating. Each floor has a common kitchenette. Private bathrooms with call bells, grab bars, showers with non-slip surfaces and elevated toilet seats. In-suite cable TV provided by residence (residence charges extra). Can have own phone number provided by residence (residence

charges extra). Unfurnished suites, furnished suites available for short stays. *Restrictions on electrical appliances*: must pass inspection for safety. Suites can be shared (by couples only), roommate picked by resident. Pets allowed (adherence to Pet Policy).
DINING SERVICE: All meals included in fee and served in dining room daily. *Sittings per meal:* Breakfast: 1, Lunch: 2, Dinner: 2. *Menu choices available:* Breakfast: 2, Lunch: 2, Dinner: 2. *Guest Meals*: Available. *Special Diets*: Vegetarian, Low Salt, Diabetic, Renal, Low or High Fibre, Dental, Puree and Minced. Tray service to room if ill (no charge for a maximum time of 4 days). 2 snacks/day. Party facilities. Elegant and cheerful dining area.
AMENITIES AND ACTIVITIES: Parking available (outdoor, for visitors and residents). *5 lounges with:* TVs (4), piano (1), fireplaces (1) and organ (1). *Residence has a:* library, visiting library, chapel, barber/beauty shop, visiting hairdresser, laundry room(s) (no cost) and tuck/gift shop. Resident can arrange newspaper delivery to individual suite. Mail delivered to individual suite. *Recreation Facilities*: shuffleboard, exercise room, craft room and card room. Posted schedule of activities. Internal newsletter for residents. *Recreational Programs*: exercise, shopping, theatre, parties, entertainment, art classes, pet visiting, day trips, Musical performances, SKIP, cultural outings, Strawberry Social, cards and social hour.
OTHER SERVICES: *Housekeeping*: weekly (included in fee). *Laundry*: linen & towel (included in fee); personal (extra cost). Dry cleaning (extra cost/pick-up from service). Transportation to medical appointments and for group social activities (extra cost/taxi service & operation lift). 24-hour security. Nightly security checks. Telephone & Cable TV (extra cost). Utilities (included in fee).
RENTAL INFORMATION: Rates may vary. Studio and 1-bedroom suites available. Extra cost for 2nd person sharing suite. Rent paid monthly. *Payment Options*: pre-authorized payments. Rent increases as per Provincial Tenancy Legislation, annual for resident with 3 months' notice given. Will help resident move into residence. Short-term respite and trial stays available.

◆ BROOKLIN ◆

THE COURT AT BROOKLIN

5909 Anderson Street, Brooklin, ON L1M 2H1
Tel: (905) 655-7718 • Fax: (905) 655-9567
Email: **5143-manager@holidaytouch.com**
Website: **www.courtatbrooklin.com**
Contact: **Community Managers**
Capacity: **115 units** • Subsidies: **none**
Price: **$2,995.00/month and up (rates may vary)**

Holiday Retirement believes retirement living should be relaxing and carefree, spent doing the things you love. That's why our communities provide a unique independent retirement lifestyle in a warm and welcoming environment. In one affordable, all-inclusive month-to-month rent, residents enjoy 3 delicious chef-prepared meals daily, enriching activities to share with friendly neighbours, housekeeping service, complimentary transportation, and so much more. Each Holiday community also features 2 sets of compassionate, dedicated live-in Managers available 24/7 to ensure safety and security. We do not provide any health care services; however, residents are welcome to receive services from any outside home health care provider of their choice to help them continue enjoying life at our community. Discover the peace-of-mind, happiness and fulfillment you deserve. Contact us today to schedule your personal tour!

RESIDENCE INFORMATION: 11 years in operation. *Near:* Anderson Street and Winchester Avenue. Decorated in 2003. Handrails in hallways. 3 floors, 1 elevator. Wheelchair accessible. Central PA system.

Funding Base: Corporate/for profit. *Owned and managed by:* Holiday Retirement. *Average Waiting Period*: none. *Average Age*: 83. Can accommodate cognitively impaired people with restrictions. Can accommodate physically challenged people (wheelchairs, walkers, scooters are welcome). Residents have a dress code (casual, no sleepwear in common areas). Smoking allowed (in own apartment). Alcohol allowed (in own apartment). *Procedures to leave the premises on a temporary basis...*Overnight & Holidays: let office know. *Languages:* English. Will accept Public Guardian and Trustee clients. Main doors of residence secured at night only. *Close to:* Public Transit, Shopping, Churches, Seniors' Centre, Library, Major Highway and Local Hospital (Lakeridge Health – Oshawa General Hospital Site).
STAFFING: *External services arranged by:* family/resident. 24-hour staff. Can retain own MD. Staff members are bonded.
HEALTH SERVICES: Will accept (but not provide special assistance for) residents who require oxygen, catheters, ostomies and feeding tubes. Residents can purchase outside resources and use agency of their choice. Will help locate higher level of care if needed (information).
ACCOMMODATION: *Choice of suites available*: studio, 1-bedroom & 2-bedroom/2-bath units. *In all suites*: locks, kitchenette, storage, window coverings, light fixtures, linens, smoke detector, sprinkler, call bell, air conditioning (wall unit) and thermostats for heating & cooling. Most have patios/balconies. Private bathrooms with call bells, grab bars and showers with non-slip surfaces. In-suite cable TV provided by residence. Can have own phone number if resident arranges with phone company. Furnished & unfurnished suites available. *Restrictions on electrical appliances*: no hot plates. Suites can be shared, roommate picked by resident. Pets allowed.
DINING SERVICE: All meals included in fee and served in dining room daily. *Sittings per meal:* Breakfast: 1, Lunch: 1, Dinner: 1. *Menu choices available:* Breakfast: 5, Lunch: 6, Dinner: 5. *Guest Meals*: Breakfast $8.00, Lunch $10.00, Dinner $8.00. *Special Diets*: Vegetarian, Low Salt and Diabetic. Tray service to room if ill. 2 snacks/day. Party facilities. Large meal of day served at noon-time. Private Dining Area. Fresh fruit, coffee, tea & goodies available all day.
AMENITIES AND ACTIVITIES: Parking available (outdoor, for visitors and indoor & outdoor for residents). *4 lounges with:* TV (1), piano (1), computer kiosks (1) and pool table (1). Guest suites available ($65.00/night). *Residence has a:* library, chapel, barber/beauty shop and laundry room(s) (no cost). Resident can arrange newspaper delivery to individual suite. Mail delivered to private mailbox with key. *Recreation Facilities*: pool table, billiards, shuffleboard, exercise room, craft room and card room. Posted schedule of activities. Internal newsletter for residents. *Recreational Programs*: exercise, shopping, theatre, parties, entertainment, art classes, pet visiting, day trips and resident suggested.
OTHER SERVICES: *Housekeeping*: weekly (included in fee). *Laundry*: linen & towel (included in fee). Free laundry rooms for personal use. Transportation to medical appointments and for group social activities. 24-hour security. Cable TV & Utilities (included in fee).
RENTAL INFORMATION: Rates may vary. Rate listed above is based on single occupancy. Extra cost for 2nd person sharing suite (please call for specifics). Rent paid monthly. *Payment Options*: cheques, post-dated cheques and pre-authorized payments. Rent increases indexed to inflation as per Provincial Tenancy Legislation, annual for resident with 3 months' notice given. Will help resident move into residence. Trial stays available (see Managers).

Did you know?

If you served in World War II, the Korean War or were a part of the Canadian Commonwealth or Allied Forces you may be eligible for services and benefits through Veterans Affairs Canada. Call **(866) 522-2122** for more information. Their website is **www.veterans.gc.ca/eng/.**

♦ BURLINGTON ♦

BURLINGTON GARDENS

300 Plains Road West, Burlington, ON L7T 0A2
Tel: (905) 521-0888 • Fax: (905) 521-0843
Email: **5316-manager@holidaytouch.com**
Website: **www.burlington-gardens.net**
Contact: **Community Managers**
Capacity: **160 residents** • Subsidies: **none**
Price: **$2,645.00/month and up (rates may vary)**

Holiday Retirement believes retirement living should be relaxing and carefree, spent doing the things you love. That's why our communities provide a unique independent retirement lifestyle in a warm and welcoming environment. In one affordable, all-inclusive month-to-month rent, residents enjoy 3 delicious chef-prepared meals daily, enriching activities to share with friendly neighbours, housekeeping service, complimentary transportation, and so much more. Each Holiday community also features 2 sets of compassionate, dedicated live-in Managers available 24/7 to ensure safety and security. We do not provide any health care services; however, residents are welcome to receive services from any outside home health care provider of their choice to help them continue enjoying life at our community. Discover the peace-of-mind, happiness and fulfillment you deserve. Contact us today to schedule your personal tour!

RESIDENCE INFORMATION: 8 years in operation. *Near:* Waterdown Road and Plains Road. Decorated in 2006. Handrails in hallways. 3 floors, 1 elevator. Wheelchair accessible. Central PA system. *Funding Base:* Corporate/for profit. *Owned and managed by:* Holiday Retirement. 134 units. *Average Waiting Period*: varies. *Average Age*: 80. Can accommodate cognitively impaired people (discuss with Management). Can accommodate physically challenged people (wheelchairs, walkers, scooters are welcome). Residents have a dress code (casual, comfortable). Smoking allowed (in own suite). Alcohol allowed (resident managed). *Procedures to leave the premises on a temporary basis...*Overnight & Holidays: let Management know. *Languages:* English. Will accept Public Guardian and Trustee clients. Main doors of residence secured at night only. *Close to:* Public Transit, Shopping, Churches, Synagogues, Seniors' Centre, Library, Major Highway and Local Hospital (Joseph Brant Hospital & Hamilton Health Sciences Corporation - McMaster University Medical Centre Site).
STAFFING: *External services arranged by:* family/resident. Staff trained *re*: visually and hearing impaired. 24-hour staff. Can retain own MD. Staff members are bonded. Police Check or Vulnerable Person Screening is done for all new staff.
HEALTH SERVICES: Will accept (but not provide special assistance for) residents who require oxygen, catheters, ostomies and feeding tubes. Residents can purchase outside resources and use agency of their choice. Will help locate higher level of care if needed (See Managers or CCAC).
ACCOMMODATION: *Choice of suites available*: studio, 1 & 2-bedroom/2-bath apartments & 2-bedroom/2-bath cottages with attached garages. *In all suites*: locks, kitchenette, full-sized fridge with freezer, patio/balcony, storage, window coverings, light fixtures, linens, fire alarm, smoke detector, sprinkler, call bell, air conditioning (wall unit) and thermostats for heating & cooling. Private bathrooms with call bells, grab bars, tubs and showers with non-slip surfaces. In-suite cable TV provided by residence. Can have own phone number if resident arranges with phone company. Furnished & unfurnished suites available. *Restrictions on electrical appliances*: no hot plates/stoves. Suites can be shared, roommate picked by resident. Pets allowed.
DINING SERVICE: All meals included in fee and served in dining room daily. *Sittings per meal:* Breakfast: 1, Lunch: 1, Dinner: 1. *Menu choices available:* Breakfast: 5, Lunch: 6, Dinner: 5. *Guest Meals*: Breakfast

$8.00, Lunch $10.00, Dinner $8.00. *Special Diets*: Vegetarian, Low Salt and Diabetic. Ample choices give consideration to special diets. Tray service to room if ill (no charge or restrictions). Unlimited snacks available at any time. Party facilities. Open pantry. Snack area with coffee, tea, fruit & goodies.
AMENITIES AND ACTIVITIES: Parking available (outdoor, for visitors and indoor & outdoor for residents). *7 lounges with:* TVs (2), pianos (2), activities & fitness equipment (1) and chapel (1). Guest suites available ($65.00/night). *Residence has a:* library, chapel, barber/beauty shop and laundry room(s) (no cost). Resident can arrange newspaper delivery to individual suite. Mail delivered to private mailbox with key. *Recreation Facilities*: pool table, billiards, shuffleboard, exercise room, craft room, card room, community kitchen, walking path and full-time activity coordinator. Posted schedule of activities. Internal newsletter for residents. *Recreational Programs*: exercise, shopping, theatre, parties, entertainment, art classes, pet visiting, day trips, bridge, euchre, educational seminars, etc. and residents input for programs.
OTHER SERVICES: *Housekeeping*: weekly (included in fee). *Laundry*: linen & towel (included in fee; linens & towels provided & laundered weekly). Free laundry rooms on each floor for personal use. Transportation to medical appointments and for group social activities. 24-hour security. Telephone (resident has own phone service). Cable TV & Utilities (except telephone) including built in emergency call system (included in fee).
RENTAL INFORMATION: Rates may vary. Rate listed above is based on single occupancy. Extra cost for 2nd person sharing suite (please call for specifics). Rent paid monthly. *Payment Options*: cheques, post-dated cheques and pre-authorized payments. Rent increases indexed to inflation as per Provincial Tenancy Legislation, annual for resident with 3 months' notice given. Will help resident move into residence. Trial stays available.

HERITAGE PLACE RETIREMENT COMMUNITY

4151 Kilmer Drive, Burlington, ON L7M 5A9
Tel: (905) 315-2500 • Fax: (905) 319-6349
Email: **info@heritage-place.ca**
Website: **www.heritage-place.ca**
Contact: **Jan Harper**
Capacity: **200 residents** • Subsidies: **none**
Price: **$3,166.00 - $5,997.00/month**

Heritage Place is an independent retirement community in Burlington, with spacious studio, 1-bedroom & 2-bedroom suites with balconies, walk-in closets and kitchenettes. Also available are elegant, 2-bedroom maintenance-free bungalows with patios plus 5 appliances. Enjoy first-class dining in our beautiful dining room. A full complement of services is offered plus well-appointed amenity spaces; a theatre, piano lounge, library, wellness centre, chapel, hair salon and much more. 24-hour Emergency Response and on-site staffing provide peace-of-mind. Health support program with on-site nurse consultation is available 7 days/ week. Our signature lifestyle program, offers a wide range of activities that support the mind, body and spirit with everything from a choice of fitness classes and equipment, lectures, and entertainment, to travel opportunities. Our competitive rates offer a great lifestyle for the active senior. Respite stays available.

RESIDENCE INFORMATION: 9 years in operation. *Near:* Walkers Line and Upper Middle Road. Decorated in 2005. 4 floors, 2 elevators. Wheelchair accessible. *Funding Base:* Corporate/for profit. *Owned by:* Tobyn Park Homes. 132 units. *Average Waiting Period*: varies. *Average Age*: 85. Can accommodate cognitively impaired people with restrictions (assessment required). Can accommodate physically challenged people with restrictions (assessed individually). Smoking allowed (outdoor gazebo). Alcohol allowed. *Procedures to leave the premises on a temporary basis...*Short-term & Overnight: sign out with Front Desk. Holidays: notify Administration. *Languages:* English. Will accept Public Guardian and

Trustee clients. Main doors of residence secured at night only. *Close to:* Public Transit, Shopping, Churches, Seniors' Centre, Library, Major Highway and Local Hospital (Joseph Brant Hospital). Member of ORCA & Chamber of Commerce. Licensed under the Retirement Homes Act.

STAFFING: *Available Staff/Services*: Pharmacy, Social Work (CCAC), Recreation Therapy, Occupational Therapy (CCAC), Physiotherapy (on-site), Dietitian (CCAC), Companions, Podiatry (CCAC), Chaplaincy, Speech Pathology (CCAC), Chiropody, Audiology/Hearing Clinic and Professional Health Support Services Consultant (RN/RPN) (on-site). *External services arranged by:* residence and/or family/resident. Staff trained *re*: visually and hearing impaired. 24-hour staff. RNs, RPNs and PSWs on staff. Can retain own MD. Police Check or Vulnerable Person Screening is done for all new staff.

HEALTH SERVICES: Medication administration (extra fee) and/or supervision (extra fee). Vitals monitored if required. Will accept (but not provide special assistance for) residents who require oxygen. Assistance with dressing available (cost). Weekly assistance with bathing available (cost). Care plans done. Different levels of care available. Respite care subject to availability. Residents can purchase outside resources and use agency of their choice. Will help locate higher level of care if needed (information and referral to CCAC).

ACCOMMODATION: *Choice of suites available*: studio (36), 1-bedroom (58), 2-bedroom (12) & 2-bedroom bungalow (25). *In all suites*: locks, patio/balcony, storage, window coverings, light fixtures, fire alarm, smoke detector, sprinkler, emergency response system with wearable pendant/bracelet, air conditioning (central & window units) and thermostats for heating & cooling. Kitchenette or full-size kitchen with apartment-size fridge. Private bathrooms with grab bars, walk-in showers or tub shower combinations with non-slip surfaces and elevated toilet seats. In-suite satellite TV provided by residence. Can have own phone number provided by residence. Unfurnished suites, furnished suites available for short stays. *Restrictions on electrical appliances*: must be approved by Administration. Suites can be shared (couples, family members or friends), roommate picked by resident. Small pets allowed (with approval by Administration).

DINING SERVICE: All meals included in fee and served in dining room daily. *Sittings per meal:* Breakfast: 1, Lunch: 1, Dinner: 1. *Menu choices available:* Breakfast: 6, Lunch: 3, Dinner: 3. *Guest Meals*: Breakfast $7.00, Lunch $9.00, Dinner $13.00. *Special Diets*: Vegetarian, Low Salt, Diabetic and Healthy Choices. À la carte options available. Tray service to room if ill (no charge for a maximum time of 3 days). Unlimited snacks available at any time. Party facilities. Open pantry. Bistro/bar open daily for resident snacks, cocktail hours & wine service.

AMENITIES AND ACTIVITIES: Parking available (outdoor, for visitors and residents). *7 lounges with:* TVs (4), piano (1), double-sided fireplaces (2) and baker's kitchen (1). Guest suites available ($95.00/night). *Residence has a:* library, visiting library, chapel, barber/beauty shop, visiting hairdresser and tuck/gift shop. Mail delivered to private mailbox with key. *Recreation Facilities*: pool table, billiards, shuffleboard, exercise room, craft room, card room, surround sound movie theatre, baker's kitchen and fitness equipment. Posted schedule of activities. Internal newsletter for residents. *Recreational Programs*: exercise, shopping, theatre, parties, entertainment, art classes, day trips, bridge, euchre, lectures, slide shows, cruises, overnight get-aways and various lessons.

OTHER SERVICES: *Housekeeping*: weekly (included in fee; daily at an extra cost). *Laundry*: linen & towel (included in fee); personal (extra cost). Dry cleaning (delivery services as required, cost as posted). Transportation for group social activities. 24-hour security. Nightly security checks. Telephone, Cable TV & Utilities (included in fee). Access to High speed internet (fee applies) & resident computer.

RENTAL INFORMATION: Rates may vary. Extra cost for 2nd person sharing suite ($700.00/month). Rent paid monthly. *Payment Options*: pre-authorized payments. Rent increases as per Provincial Tenancy Legislation, annual for resident with 3 months' notice given. Short-term respite ($125.00/day) and trial stays ($95.00/day) available (includes 3 meals/day and all activities).

REVERA - APPLEBY PLACE

500 Appleby Line, Burlington, ON L7L 5Z6
Tel: (855) 573-8372 • Toll Free: (855) 573-8372
Email: **appleby@reveraliving.com**
Website: **www.reveraliving.com/appleby**
Contact: **Executive Director or Lifestyle Consultant**
Capacity: **100 residents** • Subsidies: **none**
Price: **$2,895.00/month and up**

Keep living your life, your way, at Appleby Place. You'll find the range of services, amenities and choices that fit your lifestyle and requirements – all in a warm and safe environment. Appleby Place is a three-storey residence, located in a sought-after area of south Burlington, just steps away from shopping, community services, and public transportation. Our residence exudes an atmosphere of friendliness and family, and offers a gorgeous landscaped courtyard. Everything is designed to enable you to maintain your independence and privacy, enjoy a full social life, and participate in the activities that you love. Our caring staff support who you are and how you want to live. With retirement living at Revera, you change your address, not your life. Explore what we have to offer, to keep you living in freedom and comfort. *Appleby Place is part of the Revera family, one of North America's leading and most trusted providers of seniors' accommodation, care and services since 1961.*

RESIDENCE INFORMATION: 24 years in operation. *Near:* New Street and Appleby Line. Decorated in 2010. Handrails in hallways. 3 floors, 2 elevators. Wheelchair accessible. Central PA system. *Funding Base:* Corporate/for profit. *Owned and managed by:* Revera Inc. 90 units. *Average Waiting Period*: 3 - 4 weeks. *Average Age*: 85. Can accommodate cognitively impaired & physically challenged people (assessed individually). Residents have a dress code (for dinner only). Smoke-free residence. Alcohol allowed. *Restrictions around Visitors/Visiting Hours:* all visitors are to sign in Guest Book at Reception Area. *Procedures to leave the premises on a temporary basis...*Short-term: inform staff only if a meal will be missed. Overnight & Holidays: inform staff. *Languages:* English. Will accept Public Guardian and Trustee clients. Main doors of residence secured at all times. *Close to:* Public Transit, Shopping, Churches, Synagogues, Seniors' Centre, Library, Major Highway and Local Hospital (Joseph Brant Hospital). Member of ORCA, Burlington Chamber of Commerce and Canadian Club. Licensed under the Retirement Homes Act.
STAFFING: *Available Staff/Services*: Pharmacy, Social Work (CCAC), Recreation Therapy, Occupational Therapy, Visiting Dentist, Physiotherapy (CCAC), Companions, Podiatry, Chaplaincy, Speech Pathology, Audiology/Hearing Clinic and Massage Therapist. *External services arranged by:* family/resident. Staff trained *re*: visually, hearing and cognitively impaired. 24-hour nursing and other staff. RNs, RPNs, HCAs, PSWs and UCPs on staff. Visiting MD (monthly and on call). Can retain own MD. Staff members are bonded. Police Check or Vulnerable Person Screening is done for all new staff.
HEALTH SERVICES: Medication administration and/or supervision. Vitals monitored if required. Will accept and provide special assistance for residents who require oxygen, catheters and ostomies. Assistance with dressing available. Weekly assistance with bathing available (cost). Care plans done. Different levels of care available. Assisted Living Area. Lab service (visiting). Residents can purchase outside resources and use agency of their choice. MD visits residents in their rooms/suites. Clinic area for medical visits. Will help locate higher level of care if needed (family conference arranged to determine future care needs).
ACCOMMODATION: *Choice of suites available*: spacious studio & 1-bedroom suites. *In all suites*: locks, kitchenette, bar fridge, storage, window coverings, light fixtures, fire alarm, smoke detector, sprinkler, call bell, air conditioning (central) and thermostats for heating & cooling. Private bathrooms with call bells, grab bars, showers with non-slip surfaces and elevated toilet seats. In-suite cable TV provided by residence (residence charges extra). Can have own phone number provided by residence (residence

charges extra). Furnished & unfurnished suites available. *Restrictions on electrical appliances*: no hot plates/toaster ovens. Suites can be shared (2nd person charge applies), roommate picked by resident. Pets allowed (cats, birds and small dogs with assessment).

DINING SERVICE: All meals included in fee and served in dining room daily. *Sittings per meal:* Breakfast: 2, Lunch: 2, Dinner: 2. *Menu choices available:* Breakfast: 3, Lunch: 3, Dinner: 3. *Guest Meals*: Available. *Special Diets*: Vegetarian, Low Salt, Diabetic and Heart Healthy Options. Tray service to room if ill (no charge as long as doctor orders). 2 snacks/day. Party facilities. Fresh fruit available throughout the day.

AMENITIES AND ACTIVITIES: Parking available (outdoor, for visitors and residents). *4 lounges with:* TVs (2), piano (1) and card lounge (1). Guest suites available. *Residence has a:* library, visiting library, barber/beauty shop, visiting hairdresser, laundry room(s) (no cost) and tuck/gift shop. Banking services on premises (weekly). Resident can arrange newspaper delivery to individual suite. Mail delivered to private mailbox with key. *Recreation Facilities*: exercise room, craft room, card room and Appleby Room for private parties with full kitchen. Posted schedule of activities. Internal newsletter for residents. *Recreational Programs*: exercise, shopping, theatre, parties, entertainment, art classes, pet visiting, day trips, weekly church service, bridge and euchre. Recreational programs based on residents' interests.

OTHER SERVICES: *Housekeeping*: weekly (included in fee; daily can be arranged at a fee). *Laundry*: linen & towel (included in fee); personal (extra cost). Laundry facilities free of charge for residents use. Transportation for group social activities. 24-hour security. Nightly security checks. Telephone (resident is responsible for their own telephone). Cable TV (extra cost). Utilities (included in fee). Access to high speed internet & computer in Lounge.

RENTAL INFORMATION: Rates vary depending on suite size and services chosen. Extra cost for 2nd person sharing suite. Rent paid monthly. *Payment Options*: pre-authorized payments. Rent increases as per Provincial Tenancy Legislation, annual for resident with 90 days' notice given notice given. Short-term respite and trial stays available (rates dependent on suite choice; monthly minimum).

THE VILLAGE OF TANSLEY WOODS

4100 Upper Middle Road, Burlington, ON L7W 4W8
Tel: (905) 336-9904 • Fax: (289) 636-1404
Email: **tanya.corkum@schlegelvillages.com**
Website: **www.schlegelvillages.com**
Contact: **Tanya Corkum**
Capacity: **250 residents** • Subsidies: **none**
Price: **$3,250.00 - $7,745.00/month**

In June of 2013, our existing long-term care home welcomed its Retirement Living Phase. The Village of Tansley Woods Retirement Phase is a full continuum of care in a village design, including Independent Living, Retirement Living, Full Service Retirement Living, Assisted Care and Memory Care.

RESIDENCE INFORMATION: New residence. *Near:* Upper Middle Road and Itabashi Way. Decorated in 2013. Handrails in hallways. 10 floors, 2 elevators. Wheelchair accessible. Central PA system. *Funding Base:* Corporate/for profit. *Owned and managed by:* Schlegel Villages. 225 units. *Average Waiting Period*: varies. *Average Age*: 76. Can accommodate cognitively impaired people (Memory Care Neighbourhood in Village). Can accommodate physically challenged people (Assisted Care Neighbourhood in Village). Residents have a dress code (smart casual). Smoke-free residence. Alcohol allowed. *Procedures to leave the premises on a temporary basis*...please inform Team Leader or Neighbourhood Coordinator. *Languages:* English, French, German, Croatian, Serbian, Polish, Ukrainian & Spanish. Will accept Public Guardian and Trustee clients. Main doors of residence secured at night only. *Close to:* Public Transit, Shopping, Churches, Seniors' Centre, Library, Major Highway and Local Hospital (Joseph Brant Hospital). Member of ORCA. Licensed under the Retirement Homes Act.

STAFFING: *Available Staff/Services*: Pharmacy, Social Work (CCAC), Recreation Therapy, Occupational Therapy (CCAC), Visiting Dentist, Physiotherapy, Denturist, Dietitian, Companions, Podiatry, Chaplaincy, Speech Pathology (CCAC), Chiropody, Audiology/Hearing Clinic and Visiting Optometry. *External services arranged by:* residence and/or family/resident. Staff trained *re*: visually, hearing and cognitively impaired. 24-hour nursing staff. RNs, RPNs, HCAs, PSWs and UCPs on staff. Visiting MD (Dr. Jerome Medical Practice is open 6 days/week). Can retain own MD. Staff members are bonded. Police Check or Vulnerable Person Screening is done for all new staff.
HEALTH SERVICES: Medication administration and/or supervision. Vitals monitored if required. Will accept and provide special assistance for residents who require oxygen, catheters, ostomies and feeding tubes. Assistance with dressing available ($27.00/hour). Weekly assistance with bathing available ($14.00/bath). *Extra baths:* $14.00/bath. Care plans done. Different levels of care available. Private Duty/Extra Care available ($27.00/hour). Assisted Living Area ($27.00/hour). Separate unit for residents with dementia. Lab service (visiting). Residents can purchase outside resources and use agency of their choice. MD visits residents in their rooms/suites. Clinic area for medical visits. Will help locate higher level of care if needed (The Village can accommodate most care levels. If specialized care is required, our Care Coordinator will work with you to find a suitable option.).
ACCOMMODATION: *Choice of suites available*: 2-bedroom, 1-bedroom + alcove, 1-bedroom & studio suites. *In all suites*: locks, kitchenette, bar fridge, storage, window coverings, light fixtures, fire alarm, smoke detector, sprinkler, call bell, emergency response system with wearable pendant/bracelet, air conditioning (central) and thermostats for heating & cooling. Washer/dryer in Retirement Apartments; modified kitchens in Retirement Apartments, Assisted Care Suites and dishwasher in Independent Living suites. Private bathrooms with call bells, grab bars, showers with non-slip surfaces and elevated toilet seats. In-suite cable TV provided by residence (residence charges extra $37.00/month). Can have own phone number provided by residence (residence charges extra $35.00/month). Unfurnished suites, furnished suites available for short stays. *Restrictions on electrical appliances*: auto shut-off appliances are recommended. Suites can be shared (by couples only), roommate picked by resident. Pets allowed.
DINING SERVICE: All meals included in fee and served in dining room daily. *Menu choices available:* Breakfast: 4, Lunch: 4, Dinner: 4. *Guest Meals*: Breakfast $7.00, Lunch $12.00, Dinner $15.00. *Special Diets*: Vegetarian, Low Salt, Diabetic and Gluten Free. À la carte menu available over and above the daily meal options. Tray service to room if ill (no charge as long as doctor orders). Unlimited snacks available at any time. Party facilities.
AMENITIES AND ACTIVITIES: Parking available (outdoor, for visitors: free and indoor for residents: $50.00/month). *Residence has a:* library, chapel, barber/beauty shop and laundry room(s) (no cost). Mail delivered to resident. *Recreation Facilities*: pool table, exercise room, greenhouse, craft room and card room. Posted schedule of activities. Internal newsletter for residents. *Recreational Programs*: exercise, shopping, theatre, parties, entertainment, art classes, pet visiting and day trips.
OTHER SERVICES: *Housekeeping*: daily and weekly. *Laundry*: linen & towel (included in fee); personal ($30.00/month) & dry cleaning (extra cost). Staff label clothing ($60.00 one-time fee). Transportation for group social activities. Telephone & Cable TV (extra cost). Utilities (included in fee).
RENTAL INFORMATION: Rates may vary. Starting Rates: Main Floor Suites - $3,250.00/month; Assisted Care Suites - $4,120.00/month; Memory Care Suites - $4,260.00/month; Retirement Apartments - $3,450.00/month; Independent Living - $3,200.00/month. Extra cost for 2nd person sharing suite (couples have rate per person). Option to purchase unit available (Condo Life Equity Units available). Rent paid monthly. *Payment Options*: cheques and pre-authorized payments. Rent increases as per Provincial Tenancy Legislation, annual for resident with 3 months' notice given.

Have you found our Guide helpful?

Please let the residences you contact know that you found them here!!!

♦ CALEDONIA ♦

RIVIERA RETIREMENT LODGE

339 Argyle Street South, Caledonia, ON N3W 1L7
Tel: (905) 765-5503 • Fax: (905) 765-5504
Email: **rrl.riviera@gmail.com**
Website: **www.rivieraretirement.ca**
Contact: **Florence Jarvis**
Capacity: **44 residents** • Subsidies: **none**
Price: **$2,540.00 - $3,799.00/month**

We have a beautifully landscaped enclosed courtyard.

RESIDENCE INFORMATION: 26 years in operation. *On:* Argyle Street and Haddington Street. Decorated in 2012. Handrails in hallways. 1 floor, no elevators. Wheelchair accessible. Central PA system. *Funding Base:* Corporate/for profit. *Owned by:* Villabar. 40 units. *Average Waiting Period*: varies. *Average Age*: 84. Can accommodate cognitively impaired people. Can accommodate physically challenged people with restrictions (must be able to walk in room to bathroom or w/c self). Smoking allowed (outside back door 30 feet away; no protection or sitting area). Alcohol allowed (night caps). *Procedures to leave the premises on a temporary basis...*Short-term: inform the Administrator. Overnight: inform Charge Nurse or Director of Nursing. Holidays: inform the Administrator. *Languages:* English. Will accept Public Guardian and Trustee clients. Main doors of residence secured at night only. *Close to:* Shopping, Churches, Library, Major Highway and Local Hospital (West Haldimand General Hospital, Hagersville). Member of ORCA. Licensed under the Retirement Homes Act.
STAFFING: *Available Staff/Services*: Pharmacy, Social Work, Recreation Therapy, Occupational Therapy, Physiotherapy, Dietitian, Podiatry, Chaplaincy, Speech Pathology and Audiology/Hearing Clinic. *External services arranged by:* residence and/or family/resident. Staff trained *re*: visually, hearing and cognitively impaired. 24-hour staff. RPNs, PSWs and UCPs on staff. Visiting MD (regularly visits, fax or phone). Can retain own MD. Police Check or Vulnerable Person Screening is done for all new staff.
HEALTH SERVICES: All residents must have TB test prior to admission. Medication administered if required. Vitals monitored if required. Will accept and provide special assistance for residents who require oxygen. Assistance with dressing available ($26.00/hour). Weekly assistance with bathing available ($13.00/half hour). *Extra baths:* $13.00/half hour. Care plans done. Different levels of care available. Private Duty/Extra Care available ($26.00/hour). Lab service (visiting, $25.00/visit). Residents can purchase outside resources and use agency of their choice. MD visits residents in their rooms/suites. Will help locate higher level of care if needed (CCAC).
ACCOMMODATION: *Choice of suites available*: private (40) units. *In all suites*: locks, window coverings, light fixtures, linens, smoke detector, call bell, emergency response system with wearable pendant/bracelet and thermostats for heating. Private bathrooms with call bells, grab bars, tubs and showers. In-suite cable/satellite TV if resident arranges with cable/satellite company. Can have own phone number if resident arranges with phone company. Furnished & unfurnished suites available. *Restrictions on electrical appliances*: only microwave and fridge and auto shut-off tea kettle are allowed. Suites can be shared (by couples only). Pets allowed (cats/dogs must be up to date on vaccinations and licenses; resident responsible for cleanliness).
DINING SERVICE: All meals included in fee and served in dining room daily. *Sittings per meal:* Breakfast: 1, Lunch: 1, Dinner: 1. *Menu choices available:* Breakfast: 2, Lunch: 2, Dinner: 2. *Guest Meals*: Breakfast $7.50, Lunch $7.50, Dinner $7.50. *Special Diets*: Vegetarian, Low Salt, Diabetic and Others (on request). Tray service to room if ill (no charge as long as doctor orders; charge of $5.00 if not for medical reasons). 3 snacks/day and unlimited snacks available at any time. Party facilities.

AMENITIES AND ACTIVITIES: Parking available (outdoor, for visitors and residents). *3 lounges with:* TVs (2) and piano (1). *Residence has a:* library, barber/beauty shop and visiting hairdresser. Mail delivered to individual suite. Posted schedule of activities. Internal newsletter for residents. *Recreational Programs*: exercise, shopping, parties, entertainment, pet visiting and day trips.
OTHER SERVICES: *Housekeeping*: daily (included in fee). *Laundry*: linen, towel & personal (included in fee). Transportation for group social activities (no charge for transportation in home's van). 24-hour security. Nightly security checks. Utilities (included in fee).
RENTAL INFORMATION: Rates may vary. Extra cost for 2nd person sharing suite ($675.00/month). Rent paid monthly. *Payment Options*: cheques and post-dated cheques. Rent increases as per Provincial Tenancy Legislation, annual for resident with 3 months' notice given. Short-term respite and trial stays available (both $95.00/day, plus one-time $50.00 Administration Fee).

♦ CAMPBELLFORD ♦

ISLAND PARK RETIREMENT COMMUNITY

18 Trent Drive, Campbellford, ON K0L 1L0
Tel: (705) 653-3100 • Fax: (705) 653-3823
Email: **cindy.mcmurray@specialtyliving.ca**
Website: **www.specialtyliving.ca**
Contact: **Cindy McMurray**
Capacity: **152 residents •** Subsidies: **none**
Price: **$2,295.00/month and up**

Island Park is a beautiful waterfront community surrounded by the Trent River, Trent Canal and Ferris Provincial Park, located in the picturesque town of Campbellford, Ontario. At Island Park you can expect extraordinary customer service and comfortable amenities at an affordable rate. Here you can do things your way – while continuing to enjoy things that matter – time with family, connections with friends and being involved in the community. Our innovative *Zest for Life™* signature service promotes the health and well-being of each resident by focusing on the needs of mind, body and spirit. We work with you one-on-one to connect you with activities and services that spark your particular interests. Come and explore Island Park for yourself. If you are looking for a rewarding place to live and you too have a zest for life – our doors are open!

RESIDENCE INFORMATION: 9 years in operation. *On:* Trent Drive and Highway 30. Decorated in 2012. 4 floors, 2 elevators. Wheelchair accessible. *Owned by:* Specialty Care. 85 units. *Average Waiting Period*: varies. *Average Age*: 85. Can accommodate cognitively impaired people with restrictions. Can accommodate physically challenged people with restrictions (unable to accommodate people requiring 2-person transfer). Residents have a dress code (residents dress for breakfast). Smoking allowed (designated smoking area outside only). Alcohol allowed. *Restrictions around Visitors/Visiting Hours:* after hours call system in front entrance. *Procedures to leave the premises on a temporary basis...*Short-term: Sign Out Book in Front Lobby. Overnight: inform staff and sign out. Holidays: notify Administration. *Languages:* English. Main doors of residence secured at night only. *Close to:* Public Transit, Shopping, Churches, Seniors' Centre, Library, Major Highway and Local Hospital (Campbellford Memorial Hospital). Member of ORCA & Chamber of Commerce. Licensed under the Retirement Homes Act.
STAFFING: *Available Staff/Services*: Pharmacy, Social Work (CCAC), Recreation Therapy, Occupational Therapy (CCAC), Physiotherapy, Denturist, Podiatry, Chaplaincy, Speech Pathology (CCAC), Audiology/Hearing Clinic and Hairdresser. *External services arranged by:* residence and/or family/resident. Staff

trained *re*: visually, hearing and cognitively impaired. 24-hour staff. RPNs, PSWs and UCPs on staff. Can retain own MD. Police Check or Vulnerable Person Screening is done for all new staff.

HEALTH SERVICES: Medication administration and/or supervision. Vitals monitored if required. Will accept (but not provide special assistance for) residents who require ostomies. Will accept and provide special assistance for residents who require oxygen and catheters. Assistance with dressing available (cost). Assistance with bathing available as needed (cost). Care plans done. Different levels of care available. Short- term and rest and recuperation stays available. Assisted Living Area ($450.00/month). Lab service (visiting). Residents can purchase outside resources and use agency of their choice. Clinic area for medical visits. Will help locate higher level of care if needed (will assist families in accessing the local CCAC).

ACCOMMODATION: *Choice of suites available*: studio, 1-bedroom & 1-bedroom + den suites. *In all suites*: locks, patio/balcony, storage, bar fridge, window coverings, light fixtures, fire alarm, smoke detector, sprinkler, emergency response system with wearable pendant/bracelet, air conditioning (units in each suite and central air in common areas) and thermostats for heating & cooling. Oversized suites, many with water views. Private bathrooms with grab bars, tubs and showers with non-slip surfaces. In-suite cable/satellite TV if resident arranges with cable/satellite company (residence charges extra). Can have own phone number if resident arranges with phone company (residence charges extra). Furnished & unfurnished suites available. *Restrictions on electrical appliances*: no hot plates; additional approval from General Manager. Suites can be shared (by couples/family members; Friendship Suites available). Pets allowed (approval from Administration needed).

DINING SERVICE: All meals included in fee and served in dining room daily. *Sittings per meal:* Breakfast: 3, Lunch: 3, Dinner: 3. *Menu choices available:* Breakfast: 5, Lunch: 8, Dinner: 8. *Guest Meals*: Breakfast $8.00, Lunch $10.00, Dinner $13.00. *Special Diets*: Vegetarian, Low Salt, Diabetic and Healthy Choices (options identified). Tray service to room if ill (no charge for a maximum time of 4 days). Unlimited snacks available at any time. Party facilities. Dining room opens up to a beautiful patio overlooking the Trent River. Private dining room available.

AMENITIES AND ACTIVITIES: Parking available (outdoor, for visitors and residents). *3 lounges with:* TV (1), piano (1), fireplaces (2) and resident kitchen (1). Guest suites available ($90.40/night). *Residence has a:* library, visiting library, chapel, barber/beauty shop, visiting hairdresser, laundry room(s) (no cost) and tuck/gift shop. Resident can arrange newspaper delivery to individual suite (extra cost). Mail delivered to individual suite. *Recreation Facilities*: shuffleboard, exercise room, craft room, card room, entertainment room, baking kitchen area, computer and walking paths. Posted schedule of activities. Internal newsletter for residents. *Recreational Programs*: exercise, shopping, theatre, parties, entertainment, art classes, pet visiting, day trips, bowling, physiotherapy and wellness programs.

OTHER SERVICES: *Housekeeping*: weekly (included in fee). *Laundry*: linen, towel, personal & dry cleaning (extra cost). Complimentary washer/dryer located on each floor. Transportation for group social activities (extra cost varies). 24-hour security. Telephone & Cable TV (extra cost). Utilities (included in fee).

RENTAL INFORMATION: Rates may vary. Extra cost for 2nd person sharing suite ($635.00/month). Rent paid monthly. *Payment Options*: pre-authorized payments. Rent increases as per Provincial Tenancy Legislation, annual for resident with 3 months' notice given. Will help resident move into residence (extra cost). Short-term respite ($108.00/day) and trial stays available.

CARLETON PLACE — **WATERSIDE – A V!VA RETIREMENT COMMUNITY**

Please see OTTAWA WEST (CARLETON PLACE) for information on this residence.

♦ CHATHAM ♦

CHATHAM RETIREMENT RESORT

25 Keil Drive North, Chatham, ON N7L 5J9
Tel: (519) 351-7777 • Fax: (519) 351-7447
Email: **bcaron@regallc.com**
Website: **www.regallc.com**
Contact: **Barb Caron**
Capacity: **194 residents** • Subsidies: **none**
Price: **$2,395.00 - $2,795.00/month**

Chatham Retirement Resort is located along the Thames River with 6 acres of beautifully landscaped grounds and gardens. Our residence features a spa, recreational area with hot tub, pool, sauna, in-house physiotherapy and senior-friendly exercise equipment. If you're looking for superb meals with no household burdens in a supportive, caring environment filled with activities and fun galore – look no further! Drop by for a tour anytime; we'd love to show you our home.

RESIDENCE INFORMATION: 25 years in operation. *Near:* Keil Drive and Grand Avenue. Decorated in 2012. Handrails in hallways. 2 floors, 2 elevators. Wheelchair accessible. Central PA system. *Funding Base:* Corporate/for profit. 173 units. *Average Waiting Period*: none. *Average Age*: 84. Can accommodate cognitively impaired people. Can accommodate physically challenged people. Smoking allowed (in resident's own room). Alcohol allowed. *Languages:* English, French, Dutch, Italian & Polish. Main doors of residence secured at night only. *Close to:* Public Transit, Shopping, Churches, Seniors' Centre, Library, Major Highway and Local Hospital (Chatham-Kent Health Alliance). Licensed under the Retirement Homes Act.
STAFFING: *Available Staff/Services*: Pharmacy, Social Work (CCAC), Recreation Therapy, Occupational Therapy (CCAC), Physiotherapy (CCAC), Denturist, Dietitian (CCAC), Companions, Podiatry, Chaplaincy, Speech Pathology (CCAC), Chiropody and Audiology/Hearing Clinic. *External services arranged by:* residence and/or family/resident. Staff trained *re*: visually, hearing and cognitively impaired. 24-hour nursing staff. RNs, RPNs, HCAs and PSWs on staff. Visiting MD (weekly and called for emergencies). Can retain own MD. Police Check or Vulnerable Person Screening is done for all new staff.
HEALTH SERVICES: Medication administration and/or supervision. Vitals monitored if required. Will accept and provide special assistance for residents who require oxygen, catheters, ostomies and feeding tubes. Assistance with dressing available ($160.00/month). Weekly assistance with bathing available. *Extra baths:* $95.00/month. Care plans done. Different levels of care available. Lab service ($20.00/visit). Residents can purchase outside resources and use agency of their choice. MD visits residents in their rooms/suites. Clinic area for medical visits. Will help locate higher level of care if needed (meeting with family and arrangements made with CCAC).
ACCOMMODATION: *Choice of suites available*: private units (133) & apartments (40). *In all suites*: locks, storage, bar fridge, window coverings, light fixtures, linens, fire alarm, smoke detector, emergency response system with wearable pendant/bracelet, air conditioning (central) and thermostats for heating & cooling. Private bathrooms with grab bars, tubs and showers with non-slip surfaces. In-suite cable TV provided by residence. Can have own phone number provided by residence (residence charges extra $31.00/month). Furnished & unfurnished suites available. *Restrictions on electrical appliances*: auto shut-off preferred. Suites can be shared (pending availability of beds), roommate picked by residence staff. Pets allowed (Pet Policy must be signed).
DINING SERVICE: All meals included in fee and served in dining room daily. *Sittings per meal:* Breakfast: 1, Lunch: 1, Dinner: 1. *Menu choices available:* Breakfast: 2, Lunch: 2, Dinner: 2. *Guest Meals*: Breakfast $5.00, Lunch $5.00, Dinner $7.00. *Special Diets*: Vegetarian, Low Salt and Diabetic. Tray service to room if

ill (no charge for a maximum time of 7 days). 3 snacks/day. 4 snack areas are located throughout the building. Party facilities. Open pantry.
AMENITIES AND ACTIVITIES: Parking available (outdoor, for visitors and residents). *5 lounges with:* TVs (2) and pianos (2). Guest suites available ($40.00/night). *Residence has a:* library, chapel, barber/beauty shop, laundry room(s) (no cost) and tuck/gift shop (open 3:30 p.m. - 6:30 p.m.). Banking services on premises (monthly). Residence provides newspaper delivery to individual suite (extra cost). Mail delivered to private mailbox with key. *Recreation Facilities*: pool table, billiards, shuffleboard, exercise room, craft room, card room, swimming pool, outdoor garden and raised flower boxes. Posted schedule of activities. Internal newsletter for residents. *Recreational Programs*: exercise, shopping, parties, entertainment, art classes, pet visiting, day trips, card parties, barbecues and chapel mass (held daily).
OTHER SERVICES: *Housekeeping*: weekly. *Laundry*: linen & towel (included in fee); personal (included for all rooms/suites; extra cost for apartment tenants (service packages)) & dry cleaning (extra cost). Staff label clothing. 24-hour security. Nightly security checks. Telephone (extra cost). Cable TV & Utilities (included in fee).
RENTAL INFORMATION: Rates may vary. $78.73 to $91.89/day depending on room. Extra cost for 2nd person sharing suite ($650.00/month). Rent paid monthly. *Payment Options*: pre-authorized payments. Rent increases as per Provincial Tenancy Legislation, annual for resident with 3 months' notice given. Short-term respite and trial stays available (both $91.89/day, minimum stay is 14 days).

MAPLE CITY RETIREMENT RESIDENCE

97 McFarlane Avenue, Chatham, ON N7L 4V6
Tel: (519) 354-7111 • Fax: (519) 351-5780
Email: **gm.maplecity@diversicare.ca**
Website: **www.diversicare.ca**
Contact: **Marketing Manager**
Capacity: **52 residents •** Subsidies: **none**
Price: **$1,757.17 - $2,848.17/month**

Located on a quiet residential street close to shopping and amenities, our one-storey retirement residence offers a wide range of suite options with affordable, competitive pricing. Outdoors, you'll find 2 attractive courtyards and ample parking; indoors, you'll experience daily fine dining, plenty of recreational activities and an attentive, compassionate staff devoted to making residents feel special. The additional support of laundry services, housekeeping and medication management means a worry-free lifestyle that brings peace of mind for residents and families alike. We welcome permanent residency, respite stays, and vacation/seasonal stays. *For over 30 years, we've been Caring for People you Love!* **Maple City is owned/managed by Diversicare, who is the proud recipient of the 2003, 2006, 2009 and 2012 Order of Excellence Award given by Excellence Canada**. This award was received for the exceptional quality and customer service we provide to our residents every day.

RESIDENCE INFORMATION: 36 years in operation. *Near:* St. Clair Street and McNaughton Avenue. Decorated in 2010. Handrails in hallways. 1 floor, no elevators. Wheelchair accessible. Central PA system. *Funding Base:* Corporate/for profit. *Owned and managed by:* Diversicare Canada Management Services Co., Inc. 45 units. *Average Waiting Period*: varies. *Average Age*: 82. Can sometimes accommodate cognitively impaired people (assessment required by RPN). Can accommodate physically challenged people (assessment required by RPN). Residents have a dress code (appropriate dress in public areas within the residence). Smoking allowed (outside smoking shelter). Alcohol allowed. *Procedures to leave the premises on a temporary basis*...inform Reception. *Languages:* English. Will accept Public Guardian and Trustee clients. Main doors of residence secured at night only. *Close to:* Public Transit, Shopping, Churches, Seniors' Centre, Library, Major Highway and Local Hospital (Chatham-Kent Health Alliance - Chatham Campus). Member of ORCA. Licensed under the Retirement Homes Act.

STAFFING: *Available Staff/Services*: Pharmacy, Social Work (CCAC), Recreation Therapy, Occupational Therapy (CCAC), Physiotherapy (CCAC), Dietitian (CCAC), Companions, Podiatry (CCAC), Chaplaincy, Speech Pathology (CCAC), Chiropody, Audiology/Hearing Clinic, Hair Salon Services, Foot Care and Massage Therapy. *External services arranged by:* residence and/or family/resident. Staff trained *re*: visually, hearing and cognitively impaired. 24-hour staff. RPNs, HCAs, PSWs and UCPs on staff. Visiting MD (weekly & on call). Can retain own MD. Police Check or Vulnerable Person Screening is done for all new staff.
HEALTH SERVICES: Medication administration and/or supervision. Vitals monitored if required. Will accept and provide special assistance for residents who require oxygen and catheters. Assistance with dressing available. Weekly assistance with bathing available. Care plans done. Different levels of care available. Private Duty/Extra Care available ($18.00 to $24.00/hour). Lab service (visiting, $20.00/visit). Residents can purchase outside resources and use agency of their choice. MD visits residents in their rooms/suites. Will help locate higher level of care if needed (resident is referred to CCAC caseworker).
ACCOMMODATION: *Choice of suites available*: semi-private, luxury semi-private, small, medium, large & luxury large private units. *In all suites*: locks, storage, window coverings, light fixtures, linens, smoke detector, call bell and thermostats for heating. Private bathrooms (semi-privates share bathroom) with call bells, grab bars, non-slip surfaces and elevated toilet seats. In-suite cable/satellite TV if resident arranges with cable/satellite company (residence charges extra $40.00/month). Can have own phone number if resident arranges with phone company. Furnished & unfurnished suites available. *Restrictions on electrical appliances*: all electrical appliances must be inspected by Maintenance. Suites can be shared (appointed suites to accommodate), roommate picked by resident & residence staff. Small pets only allowed (must be able to care for their pet).
DINING SERVICE: All meals included in fee and served in dining room daily. *Sittings per meal:* Breakfast: 1, Lunch: 1, Dinner: 1. *Menu choices available:* Breakfast: 2, Lunch: 2, Dinner: 2. *Guest Meals*: Breakfast $6.00, Lunch $7.50, Dinner $8.50. *Special Diets*: Vegetarian, Low Salt, Diabetic, Food Allergies and Lactose Intolerance. Tray service to room if ill (no charge as long as doctor orders). 3 snacks/day and unlimited snacks available at any time. Self-serve beverage & snack area outside meal-time. Party facilities. Walk-out to dining room patio.
AMENITIES AND ACTIVITIES: Parking available (outdoor, for visitors and residents). *4 lounges with:* TVs (2), piano (1), private dining (2) and access to courtyard gardens (1). Guest suites available ($40.00/night). *Residence has a:* library, visiting library, chapel, barber/beauty shop, laundry room(s) (no cost) and tuck/gift shop (open weekly). Resident can arrange newspaper delivery to individual suite. Mail delivered to individual suite. *Recreation Facilities*: shuffleboard, exercise room, craft room, card room, 2 outdoor courtyards for gardening and movie lounge. Posted schedule of activities. Internal newsletter for residents. *Recreational Programs*: exercise, shopping, theatre, parties, entertainment, art classes, pet visiting, day trips, Brain Gym® & More program, Reading Circle, bingo, Pamper Days, Friendship Teas, casino visits and card parties.
OTHER SERVICES: *Housekeeping*: daily (included in fee). *Laundry*: linen, towel & personal (included in fee); dry cleaning (extra cost). Staff label clothing ($20.00/100 labels). Transportation for group social activities. 24-hour security. Nightly security checks (no cost - every 2 hours). Utilities (included in fee). Telephone & Cable TV Hook up.
RENTAL INFORMATION: Rates may vary. Extra cost for 2nd person sharing suite ($700.00/month; $2,848.17 to $3,548.17/couple/month). Rent paid monthly. *Payment Options*: cheques, post-dated cheques, direct deposit, pre-authorized payments and bank drafts. Rent increases as per Provincial Tenancy Legislation, annual for resident with 3 months' notice given. Will help resident move into residence. Short-term respite and trial stays available (both $68.00/day, depending on personal choice of suite & availability).

♦ COBOURG ♦

PALISADE GARDENS

240 Chapel Street, Cobourg, ON K9A OE3
Tel: (905) 372-1150 • Fax: (905) 372-1157
Email: **mmclean@palisadegardens.ca**
Website: **www.palisadegardens.ca**
Contact: **Mrs. Micki McLean**
Capacity: **175 residents** • Subsidies: **none**
Price: **$2,422.00/month and up**

Palisade Gardens Independent Living Retirement Residence is situated on a quiet, leafy street in Cobourg's heritage district, within walking distance to downtown shopping and the waterfront park. Palisade Gardens offers exceptional quality, yet affordable retirement living in elegant surroundings. A full range of customized service options can be tailored to best suite individual requirements. Services include flexible meal plans, housekeeping, laundry, 24-hour nursing care and emergency response, plus a host of programs and activities to ensure an enjoyable, stress-free lifestyle! The property features an on-site Wellness Centre complete with a health management team, spa services, meeting and lecture room, movie theatre, library, craft room and exercise room. 1-bedroom & 2-bedroom suites are available, each complete with kitchen and balcony or patio. Complimentary meal and tour available.

RESIDENCE INFORMATION: 6 years in operation. *Near:* Darcy Street and King Street. Decorated in 2008. Handrails in hallways. 4 floors, 3 elevators. Wheelchair accessible. *Funding Base:* Corporate/for profit. *Owned and managed by:* Retirement Life Communities. 118 units. *Average Waiting Period*: none. *Average Age*: 75. Can accommodate cognitively impaired people with restrictions. Can accommodate physically challenged people (we are wheelchair accessible). Smoking allowed (condominium section only). Alcohol allowed (in residents' suites & during special events). *Procedures to leave the premises on a temporary basis...*residents sign in & out. *Languages:* English. Will accept Public Guardian and Trustee clients. Main doors of residence secured at all times. *Close to:* Public Transit, Shopping, Churches, Seniors' Centre, Library, Major Highway and Local Hospital (Northumberland Hills Hospital). *Predominant Cultural Group:* Canadian. Licensed under the Retirement Homes Act.
STAFFING: *Available Staff/Services*: Pharmacy, Social Work (CCAC), Recreation Therapy, Occupational Therapy (CCAC), Physiotherapy (CCAC), Dietitian (CCAC), Podiatry, Chaplaincy, Chiropody, Audiology/Hearing Clinic and Meditation. *External services arranged by:* residence and/or family/resident. Staff trained *re*: hearing and cognitively impaired. 24-hour nursing and other staff. RNs, RPNs, HCAs, PSWs and UCPs on staff. Visiting MD (has a clinic within the residence). Can retain own MD. Police Check or Vulnerable Person Screening is done for all new staff.
HEALTH SERVICES: Medication administration and/or supervision. Vitals monitored if required. Will accept and provide special assistance for residents who require oxygen, catheters, ostomies and feeding tubes. Assistance with dressing available (cost). Assistance with bathing available as needed. *Extra baths:* $15.00/bath. Care plans done. Different levels of care available. Lab service (visiting, $20.00/visit). Residents can purchase outside resources and use agency of their choice. MD visits residents in their rooms/suites. Clinic area for medical visits. Will help locate higher level of care if needed (Director of Care will assist).
ACCOMMODATION: *Choice of suites available*: 1-bedroom & 2-bedroom rental or condominium suites. *In all suites*: locks, kitchenette, microwave, stove, patio/balcony, storage, light fixtures, smoke detector, sprinkler, emergency response system with wearable pendant/bracelet, air conditioning (central) and thermostats for heating & cooling. Window coverings provided in rental suites. Private bathrooms with grab bars, tubs and showers with non-slip surfaces and elevated toilet seats. In-suite satellite TV

provided by residence. Can have own phone number if resident arranges with phone company. Furnished & unfurnished suites available. Suites can be shared (by couples only). Pets allowed (one small dog or cat per suite).

DINING SERVICE: Meals/service packages as per service plans purchased. Breakfast & 8 additional meals are included in Basic Service Package. *Sittings per meal:* Breakfast: 1, Lunch: 1, Dinner: 2. *Menu choices available:* Lunch: 2, Dinner: 2. *Guest Meals*: Breakfast $6.00, Lunch $12.00, Dinner $17.00. *Special Diets*: Vegetarian, Low Salt, Diabetic and Gluten Free. Tray service to room if ill (no charge as long as doctor orders). 2 snacks/day. Party facilities. Beautifully decorated dining room with private family dining area.

AMENITIES AND ACTIVITIES: Parking available (outdoor, for visitors and indoor & outdoor for residents). *5 lounges with:* TV (1), piano (1), theatre (1) and lounge (1). Guest suites available ($75.00/night). *Residence has a:* library, chapel, barber/beauty shop, visiting hairdresser, laundry room(s) (no cost) and tuck/gift shop. Residence provides newspaper delivery to main desk. Mail delivered to private mailbox with key. *Recreation Facilities*: billiards, shuffleboard, exercise room, greenhouse, craft room, card room, beauty salon, games room, wellness centre and theatre. Posted schedule of activities. Internal newsletter for residents. *Recreational Programs*: exercise, shopping, theatre, parties, entertainment, art classes, pet visiting and day trips with shuttle bus.

OTHER SERVICES: *Housekeeping*: depends on service package purchased. *Laundry*: linen & towel (extra cost); personal (extra cost depends on service package). Dry cleaning (local dry cleaner picks up and delivers 2x/weekly). In-suite laundry for condominiums. Transportation to medical appointments and for group social activities. 24-hour security. Telephone (extra cost). Cable TV & Utilities (included in fee). Amenities vary based on service package purchased.

RENTAL INFORMATION: Rates may vary. Option to rent or buy - purchase price of condominiums suites range from (1-bedroom) $179,000 to (2-bedroom) $270,000. Basic Service Package included with rental suites may vary from condominium package. Basic Service Package fees are: Condominium - $1,000.00/month, 2nd occupant - $853.00/month. Rental - $732.00/month, 2nd occupant $650.00/month. Extra cost for 2nd person sharing suite. Option to purchase unit available (2-bedroom condominiums for sale). Rent paid monthly. *Payment Options*: cheques, post-dated cheques and pre-authorized payments. Rent increases as per Provincial Tenancy Legislation, annual for resident with 3 months' notice given. Will help resident move into residence (extra cost). Trial stays available (cost to be determined).

◆ COLLINGWOOD ◆

BAY HAVEN SENIOR CARE COMMUNITY

499 Hume Street, Collingwood, ON L9Y 4H8
Tel: (705) 445-6501 • Fax: (705) 445-6506
Email: **cynthia@bayhaven.com**
Website: **www.bayhaven.com**
Contact: **Cynthia Strandholt**
Capacity: **50 residents** • Subsidies: **none**
Price: **$2,300.00 - $3,300.00/month**

We are a family owned and operated home located on the banks of the Pretty River. Bay Haven, which is all on one level with no stairs to climb and no elevators to navigate, has an inviting landscape with beautiful grounds including courtyards and walking paths for leisurely strolls. Conveniently located on the bus route, Bay Haven is in close proximity to the community hospital and has professional nursing staff available 24-hours/day. The retirement home services are all inclusive; there are no extra charges for medication administration, nurse call systems, personalized housekeeping and laundry service. Additional

à la carte services include activity programs, hairdresser, manicure services, therapeutic foot care services and visiting physiotherapists.

RESIDENCE INFORMATION: 45 years in operation. *Near:* Hume Street and Pretty River Parkway. Decorated in 2011. Handrails in hallways. 1 floor, no elevators. Wheelchair accessible. Central PA system. *Funding Base:* Corporate/for profit. Family owned and operated. 41 units. *Average Waiting Period*: varies. *Average Age*: 83. Can accommodate physically challenged people with restrictions. Smoke-free residence. Alcohol allowed (within limitations). *Procedures to leave the premises on a temporary basis*...residents are free to leave; after 7 days, charge is for rent portion only. *Languages:* English. Main doors of residence secured at night only. *Close to:* Public Transit, Shopping and Local Hospital (Collingwood General and Marine). Member of ORCA & OLTCA. Licensed under the Retirement Homes Act.
STAFFING: *Available Staff/Services*: Pharmacy, Recreation Therapy, Occupational Therapy, Visiting Dentist, Physiotherapy, Dietitian, Chaplaincy, Speech Pathology and Chiropody. *External services arranged by:* residence and/or family/resident. Staff trained *re*: visually, hearing and cognitively impaired. 24-hour nursing and other staff. RNs, RPNs, HCAs and PSWs on staff. Visiting MD (weekly or as needed). Can retain own MD. Police Check or Vulnerable Person Screening is done for all new staff.
HEALTH SERVICES: Medication administration and/or supervision. Vitals monitored if required. Will accept and provide special assistance for residents who require oxygen. Weekly assistance with bathing available. Care plans done. Different levels of care available. Lab service (visiting, $25.00/visit). Residents can purchase outside resources and use agency of their choice. MD visits residents in their rooms/suites.
ACCOMMODATION: *Choice of suites available*: private with varying sizes and amenities. *In all suites*: locks, window coverings, light fixtures, linens, fire alarm, call bell, air conditioning (window units) and thermostats for heating & cooling. Private bathrooms with call bells, grab bars, showers with non-slip surfaces and elevated toilet seats. In-suite cable TV provided by residence (residence charges extra $35.00/month). Can have own phone number if resident arranges with phone company. Unfurnished suites, furnished suites available for short stays. *Restrictions on electrical appliances*: quality and age of items are reviewed. Suites can be shared (by couples only). Pets allowed (depending on resident's independence and size of pet).
DINING SERVICE: All meals included in fee and served in dining room daily. *Sittings per meal:* Breakfast: 1, Lunch: 1, Dinner: 1. *Menu choices available:* Breakfast: 2, Lunch: 2, Dinner: 2. *Guest Meals*: Breakfast $5.50, Lunch $5.50, Dinner $7.75. *Special Diets*: Vegetarian and Low Salt. All diets are available. Tray service to room if ill (no charge for a maximum time of 3 days). Unlimited snacks available at any time. The food is prepared in-house & residents quite enjoy their meals and dining experience.
AMENITIES AND ACTIVITIES: Parking available (outdoor, for visitors and residents). *2 lounges with:* TV (1) and piano (1). *Residence has a:* library, visiting library, barber/beauty shop, visiting hairdresser and laundry room(s) (no cost). Resident can arrange newspaper delivery to individual suite. Mail delivered to individual suite. *Recreation Facilities*: card room. Mature grounds with walking path and courtyards. Posted schedule of activities. Internal newsletter for residents. *Recreational Programs*: exercise, shopping, theatre, parties, entertainment, art classes and day trips. Activities are based on residents' requests.
OTHER SERVICES: *Housekeeping*: weekly (included in fee). *Laundry*: linen, towel & personal (included in fee); dry cleaning (extra cost - as requested). Staff label clothing (included in fee). Laundry is washed with resident's clothing not mixed in with the entire population's laundry. Transportation to medical appointments (extra cost) and for group social activities. 24-hour security. Nightly security checks. Telephone (arranged via resident). Cable TV (extra cost). Utilities (included in fee).
RENTAL INFORMATION: Rates may vary. Extra cost for 2nd person sharing suite. Rent paid monthly. *Payment Options*: cheques, post-dated cheques, direct deposit, pre-authorized payments and telephone/ internet banking. Rent increases as per Provincial Tenancy Legislation, annual for resident with 3 months' notice given. Short-term respite and trial stays available (both $105.00/day).

COURTICE **WHITE CLIFFE TERRACE**

Please see OSHAWA (COURTICE) for information on this residence.

DORCHESTER **LIFESTYLE OASIS DORCHESTER**

Please see LONDON (DORCHESTER) for information on this residence.

◆ DRESDEN ◆

PARK STREET PLACE

650 Park Street, Dresden, ON N0P 1M0
Tel: (519) 683-4474 • Fax: (519) 683-4555
Email: **rec.parkstreet@diversicare.ca**
Website: **www.diversicare.ca**
Contact: **Marketing Manager**
Capacity: **50 residents** • Subsidies: **none**
Price: **$2,065.00 - $3,342.17/month**

Park Street Place is a charming retirement residence located on 6 acres and is beautifully landscaped with flowers and trees. We offer Independent and Full Service Lifestyle Packages to meet your needs. Our accommodations include 2-room suites, private studio suites, as well as semi-private suites. Our caring, professional staff are available 24-hours/day to provide you with the assistance you may need. Come and enjoy wonderful country hospitality, convenience and personal comfort under one roof. Please ask about our respite stays, and vacation/seasonal stays. Bring your family to our family! **Park Street Place is owned/managed by Diversicare, who is the proud recipient of the 2003, 2006, 2009 and 2012 Order of Excellence Award given by Excellence Canada.** This award was received for the exceptional quality and customer service we provide to our residents every day.

RESIDENCE INFORMATION: 26 years in operation. *On:* Park Street and North Street. Decorated in 2010. Handrails in hallways. 1 floor, no elevator. Wheelchair accessible. Central PA system. *Funding Base:* Corporate/for profit. *Owned and managed by:* Diversicare Canada Management Services Co., Inc. 49 units. *Average Waiting Period*: none. *Average Age*: 84. Can accommodate cognitively impaired people with restrictions (assessment required by RN). Can accommodate physically challenged people with restrictions (assessment required). Residents have a dress code (appropriate dress in public areas within the residence). Smoking allowed (outside smoking shelter). Alcohol allowed. *Procedures to leave the premises on a temporary basis...*inform Reception. *Languages:* English. Will accept Public Guardian and Trustee clients. Main doors of residence secured at night only. *Close to:* Public Transit, Shopping, Churches, Seniors' Centre, Library, Major Highway and Local Hospital (Chatham-Kent Health Alliance - Sydenham District Hospital, Wallaceburg). Member of ORCA, Better Business Bureau of Windsor & Southwestern Ontario, Wallaceburg & District Chamber of Commerce. Licensed under the Retirement Homes Act. **STAFFING:** *Available Staff/Services*: Pharmacy, Social Work (CCAC), Recreation Therapy, Occupational Therapy (CCAC), Visiting Dentist, Physiotherapy (CCAC), Dietitian, Companions, Podiatry, Chaplaincy, Speech Pathology (CCAC), Audiology/Hearing Clinic and Hair Salon Services. *External services arranged by:* residence and/or family/resident. Staff trained *re*: visually, hearing and cognitively impaired. 24-hour nursing staff. RPNs, HCAs, PSWs and UCPs on staff. Visiting MD (weekly). Can retain own MD. Staff members are bonded. Police Check or Vulnerable Person Screening is done for all new staff.

HEALTH SERVICES: Medication administration and/or supervision. Vitals monitored if required. Will accept and provide special assistance for residents who require oxygen, catheters and ostomies. Assistance with dressing available. Weekly assistance with bathing available. *Extra baths:* $7.00/half hour. Care plans done. Different levels of care available. Private Duty/Extra Care available ($24.00/hour). Lab service (visiting, $22.00/visit). Residents can purchase outside resources and use agency of their choice. MD visits residents in their rooms/suites. Will help locate higher level of care if needed (resident is referred to CCAC caseworker).
ACCOMMODATION: *Choice of suites available*: double-room, luxury private, private & semi-private suites. *In all suites*: locks, storage, window coverings, light fixtures, smoke detector, call bell and thermostats for heating. Private bathrooms with call bells and grab bars. In-suite cable TV if resident arranges with cable company. Can have own phone number if resident arranges with phone company. Unfurnished suites, furnished suites available for short stays. *Restrictions on electrical appliances*: all electrical appliances to be inspected by Maintenance. Suites can be shared (depending on suite to be accommodated), roommate picked by resident & residence staff. Small pets only allowed (must be able to care for own pet).
DINING SERVICE: All meals included in fee and served in dining room daily. *Sittings per meal:* Breakfast: 1, Lunch: 1, Dinner: 1. *Menu choices available:* Breakfast: 2, Lunch: 2, Dinner: 2. *Guest Meals*: Breakfast $6.00, Lunch $8.00, Dinner $10.00. *Special Diets*: Vegetarian, Low Salt, Diabetic, Food Allergies and Lactose Intolerance. Tray service to room if ill (no charge or restrictions). 3 snacks/day and unlimited snacks available at any time (self-serve beverage & snack area outside meal-time). Party facilities. Beautiful, centrally located, extra-large dining room can accommodate special private functions for resident/family.
AMENITIES AND ACTIVITIES: Parking available (outdoor, for visitors and residents). *4 lounges with:* TVs (2), independent recreation area (1) and pool table (1). Guest suites available ($70.00/night). *Residence has a:* library, visiting library, chapel, barber/beauty shop and tuck/gift shop. Resident can arrange newspaper delivery to individual suite. Mail delivered to individual suite. *Recreation Facilities*: pool table, craft room and card room. Posted schedule of activities. Internal newsletter for residents. *Recreational Programs*: exercise, shopping, parties, entertainment, art classes, pet visiting, day trips, Brain Gym® & More, gardening, church services/bible study, Pamper Days and discussion groups.
OTHER SERVICES: *Housekeeping*: daily and weekly. *Laundry*: linen, towel & personal (included in fee). Transportation for group social activities. 24-hour security. Nightly security checks. Telephone & Cable TV (extra cost). Utilities (included in fee). Phone & Cable Hook Up Fee.
RENTAL INFORMATION: Rates may vary. Discount available for couples! Extra cost for 2nd person sharing suite ($750.00/month). Rent paid monthly. *Payment Options*: cheques, post-dated cheques, direct deposit and pre-authorized payments. Rent increases as per Provincial Tenancy Legislation, annual for resident with 3 months' notice given. Will help resident move into residence. Short-term respite and trial stays available (both $85.00/day, depending on personal choice of suite & availability).

Downsizing Tip

Before starting to pack things up or deciding what to take with you, make sure you have everything you will need handy - boxes, tape, coloured stickers, pen and paper. Use different coloured stickers for things you are taking, things you are giving away and things you are selling. Keeping a list of items (and where they are going) is also helpful and allows you an opportunity to organize yourself and keep track of what is happening with all of your possessions.

◆ ELORA ◆

HERITAGE RIVER RETIREMENT RESIDENCE

25 Wellington Drive, Elora, ON N0B 1S0
Tel: (519) 846-5350 • Fax: (519) 846-0911
Toll Free: (877) 746-5350
Email: **svandyke@heritageriver.ca**
Website: **www.heritageriver.ca**
Contact: **Marketing Manager**
Capacity: **120 residents** • Subsidies: **none**
Price: **$2,695.00 - $4,750.00/month**

Heritage River is situated on 7 acres manicured grounds, including flower gardens and walking paths. We are very close to the centre of town and accessible to amenities and services in the community of Elora. Our staff are nurturing and sensitive to our residents' needs and often go beyond the call of duty to assist. We also have a Supportive Care Package to provide extra care when needed the most. **Heritage River is managed by Diversicare, who is the recipient of the 2003, 2006, 2009 and 2012 Order of Excellence Award given by Excellence Canada**. This award was received for the exceptional quality and customer service we provide to our residents every day.

RESIDENCE INFORMATION: 6 years in operation. *Near:* Colborne Street and Cuthbert Street. Decorated in 2008. Handrails in hallways. 3 floors, 2 elevators. Wheelchair accessible. *Funding Base:* Corporate/for profit. *Owned by:* Bob and Lynn Cameron. *Managed by:* Diversicare Canada Management Services Co., Inc. 101 units. *Average Waiting Period*: varies. *Average Age*: 82. Can accommodate cognitively impaired people with restrictions (mild cognitive impairment). Can accommodate physically challenged people (wheelchair accessible suites). Smoking allowed (patios located in front of home/walk-outs off selected suites). Alcohol allowed. *Languages:* English. Will accept Public Guardian and Trustee clients. Main doors of residence secured at night only. *Close to:* Shopping, Churches, Seniors' Centre, Library and Local Hospital (Groves Memorial Community Hospital, Fergus ON). Member of ORCA. Licensed under the Retirement Homes Act.
STAFFING: *Available Staff/Services*: Pharmacy, Social Work, Recreation Therapy, Occupational Therapy, Visiting Dentist, Physiotherapy, Dietitian, Podiatry, Chaplaincy, Speech Pathology, Audiology/Hearing Clinic and Massage Therapy. *External services arranged by:* residence and/or family/resident. Staff trained *re*: visually, hearing and cognitively impaired. 24-hour staff. RNs, RPNs, PSWs and UCPs on staff. Visiting MD (bi-weekly clinical visits). Can retain own MD. Staff members are bonded. Police Check or Vulnerable Person Screening is done for all new staff.
HEALTH SERVICES: Medication administration and/or supervision. Vitals monitored if required. Will accept (but not provide special assistance for) residents who require oxygen, catheters and ostomies. Assistance with dressing available (cost). Assistance with bathing available twice a week (cost). *Extra baths:* $12.00/half hour. Care plans done. Different levels of care available. Private Duty/Extra Care available ($365.00/month). Assisted Living Area. Residents can purchase outside resources and use agency of their choice. Clinic area for medical visits. Will help locate higher level of care if needed (CCAC – long-term care options).
ACCOMMODATION: *Choice of suites available*: private suites (101). Bedsitting studio, large 1-bedroom, balconies and terraces available on selected suites. *In all suites*: locks, kitchenette, bar fridge, storage, window coverings, light fixtures, fire alarm, smoke detector, sprinkler, emergency response system with wearable pendant/bracelet, air conditioning (central) and thermostats for heating & cooling. Private bathrooms with call bells, grab bars, showers and elevated toilet seats. In-suite cable/satellite TV if resident arranges with cable/satellite company (residence charges extra). Can have own phone number

ed by residence. Unfurnished suites, furnished suites available for short stays. Restrictions on ical appliances. Suites can be shared (by couples only). Small indoor pets allowed.
ING SERVICE: All meals included in fee and served in dining room daily. *Sittings per meal:* Breakfast: Lunch: 1, Dinner: 1. *Menu choices available:* Breakfast: 1, Lunch: 5, Dinner: 5. *Guest Meals*: Lunch $8.00, Dinner $12.00. *Special Diets*: Vegetarian, Low Salt and Diabetic. Tray service to room if ill (no charge as long as doctor orders). Unlimited snacks available at any time. Party facilities.
AMENITIES AND ACTIVITIES: Parking available (outdoor, for visitors and residents). *6 lounges with:* TVs (2) and pianos (2). Guest suites available ($85.00/night). *Residence has a:* library, visiting library, chapel, barber/beauty shop, visiting hairdresser, laundry room(s) (no cost) and tuck/gift shop (open Monday to Saturday; 10:00 -11:00 a.m.). Banking services on premises (1 x/week). Resident can arrange newspaper delivery to individual suite. Mail delivered to private mailbox with key. *Recreation Facilities*: pool table, exercise room, craft room and card room. Posted schedule of activities. Internal newsletter for residents. *Recreational Programs*: exercise, shopping, theatre, parties, entertainment, art classes, day trips & Brain Gym® & More programs.
OTHER SERVICES: *Housekeeping*: weekly (included in fee). *Laundry*: linen & towel (included in fee); personal (extra cost) & dry cleaning (extra expense to our residents). Personal laundry can be done in our complimentary washers and dryers located on each floor. Transportation to medical appointments and for group social activities. 24-hour security. Nightly security checks. Cable TV ($29.99/month). Telephone & Utilities (included in fee).
RENTAL INFORMATION: Rates may vary. Extra cost for 2nd person sharing suite ($600.00/month). Rent paid monthly. *Payment Options*: cheques, post-dated cheques and pre-authorized payments. Rent increases as per Provincial Tenancy Legislation, annual for resident with 3 months' notice given. Will help resident move into residence. Short-term respite and trial stays available (both $105.00/day, 2nd occupant is $20.00/day).

ETOBICOKE

DELMANOR PRINCE EDWARD
HEARTHSTONE BY THE BAY
REVERA – CENTENNIAL PARK
REVERA – KINGSWAY
TAPESTRY AT VILLAGE GATE WEST
THE VILLAGE OF HUMBER HEIGHTS

Please see TORONTO (ETOBICOKE) for information on these residences.

◆ FORT ERIE ◆

REVERA - GARRISON PLACE

373 Garrison Road, Fort Erie, ON L2A 1N1
Tel: (855) 573-8372 • Toll Free: (855) 573-8372
Email: **garrison@reveraliving.com**
Website: **www.reveraliving.com/garrison**
Contact: **Executive Director or Lifestyle Consultant**
Capacity: **81 residents** • Subsidies: **none**
Price: **$2,423.00/month and up**

Keep living your life, your way, at Garrison Place. Here, you'll find the range of services, amenities and choices that fit your lifestyle and requirements – all in a warm and safe environment. With retirement living at Garrison Place, you change your address, not your life. We're located off the main road in Fort

Erie, in a beautiful park-like setting, full of wildlife, flower beds and a charming courtyard with gazebo. There is easy access to shopping, entertainment and banking. Everything is designed to enable you to maintain your independence and privacy, enjoy a full social life, and participate in the activities that you love. Our caring and friendly staff, along with appealing accommodations, support who you are and how you want to live. Explore what we have to offer, to keep you living in freedom and comfort. *Garrison Place is part of the Revera family, one of North America's leading and most trusted providers of seniors' accommodation, care and services since 1961.*

RESIDENCE INFORMATION: 27 years in operation. *Near:* Concession Road and Highway 3. Decorated in 2012. Handrails in hallways. 2 floors, 1 elevator. Wheelchair accessible. *Funding Base:* Corporate/for profit. *Owned and managed by:* Revera Inc. 80 units. *Average Waiting Period*: none. *Average Age*: 85. Can accommodate cognitively impaired people with restrictions (physician's assessment required). Can accommodate physically challenged people (assessment required). Smoking allowed (exterior designated areas). Alcohol allowed. *Procedures to leave the premises on a temporary basis...*Short-term: sign out at front desk. Overnight & Holidays: sign out at Front Desk; notify Nurse if staff administers medications. *Languages:* English. Will accept Public Guardian and Trustee clients. Main doors of residence secured at all times. *Close to:* Public Transit, Shopping, Churches, Seniors' Centre, Library, Major Highway and Local Hospital (Niagara Health System - Douglas Memorial Site). Member of ORCA & Chamber of Commerce. Licensed under the Retirement Homes Act.
STAFFING: *Available Staff/Services*: Pharmacy, Social Work (CCAC), Recreation Therapy, Occupational Therapy (CCAC), Physiotherapy (CCAC), Dietitian (CCAC), Podiatry, Chaplaincy, Speech Pathology (CCAC), Chiropody and Audiology/Hearing Clinic. *External services arranged by:* family/resident. Staff trained *re*: visually, hearing and cognitively impaired. 24-hour nursing and other staff. RPNs, PSWs and UCPs on staff. Visiting MD (all physicians visit and are available by phone 24/7). Can retain own MD. Police Check or Vulnerable Person Screening is done for all new staff.
HEALTH SERVICES: Medication administration and/or supervision. Vitals monitored if required. Will accept and provide special assistance for residents who require oxygen, catheters and ostomies. Assistance with dressing available. Weekly assistance with bathing available. Care plans done. Different levels of care available. Lab service (visiting). Residents can purchase outside resources and use agency of their choice. MD visits residents in their rooms/suites. Will help locate higher level of care if needed (family conference arranged to determine future care needs).
ACCOMMODATION: *Choice of suites available*: private suites (70) & 1-bedroom (5) units. *In all suites*: locks, window coverings, light fixtures, linens, smoke detector, sprinkler, emergency response system with wearable pendant/bracelet, thermostats for heating and bay window. Private bathrooms with call bells, grab bars and showers with non-slip surfaces. In-suite cable TV provided by residence (residence charges extra). Can have own phone number provided by residence (residence charges extra). Unfurnished suites, furnished suites available for short stays. *Restrictions on electrical appliances*: must be checked by Maintenance personnel before use. Suites can be shared (by couples only), roommate picked by resident. Pets allowed (with assessment).
DINING SERVICE: All meals included in fee and served in dining room daily. *Sittings per meal:* Breakfast: 2, Lunch: 2, Dinner: 2. *Menu choices available:* Breakfast: 3, Lunch: 2, Dinner: 3. *Guest Meals*: Available. *Special Diets*: Vegetarian, Low Salt, Diabetic and Physician Ordered. Tray service to room if ill (no charge as long as doctor orders). 3 snacks/day. Party facilities.
AMENITIES AND ACTIVITIES: Parking available (outdoor, for visitors and residents). *5 lounges with:* TVs (3), piano (1) and quiet areas (2). Guest suites available. *Residence has a:* library and barber/beauty shop. Residence provides newspaper delivery to individual suite. Mail delivered to resident. *Recreation Facilities*: pool table, exercise room, card room and Dakim Mind Gym System. Posted schedule of activities. Internal newsletter for residents. *Recreational Programs*: exercise, shopping, theatre, parties, entertainment, pet visiting and day trips.

. **SERVICES:** *Housekeeping*: weekly (daily tidy and garbage pick-up). *Laundry*: linen, towel & ..nal (included in fee). All laundry done separately. Transportation for group social activities (van for ..ent outings). 24-hour security. Nightly security checks. Telephone (extra cost - Revera phone ..tem). Cable TV (extra cost - bulk cable available). Utilities (included in fee).
.ENTAL INFORMATION: Rates may vary. Private - $2,423.00/month & up. Extra cost for 2nd person sharing suite. Rent paid monthly. *Payment Options*: post-dated cheques and pre-authorized payments. Rent increases as per Provincial Tenancy Legislation, annual for resident with 3 months' notice given. Short-term respite and trial stays available (assessment required for short-term stays; additional care cost may apply).

◆ GEORGETOWN ◆

MOUNTAINVIEW RESIDENCE

222 Mountainview Road North, Georgetown, ON L7G 3R2
Tel: (905) 877-1800 • Fax: (905) 873-9083
Email: **info@mountainviewresidence.com**
Website: **www.mountainviewresidence.com**
Contact: **Christoph Summer**
Capacity: **90 residents** • Subsidies: **none**
Price: **$2,965.00 - $5,425.00/month**

Privately owned and operated by the Summer family. Located in a residential area, the Residence is set on 5.66 acres of land close to picturesque Glen Williams. Enjoy the raised gardens for easy gardening, outside walkways, gazebos, water features, flower gardens and a wooded area. Available too, is a computer along with internet access in the rooms.

RESIDENCE INFORMATION: 14 years in operation. *Near:* Mountainview Road and Guelph Street. Decorated in 2012. Handrails in hallways. 2 floors, 1 elevator. *Funding Base:* Corporate/for profit. *Owned by:* Ursula & Christoph Summer. 81 units. *Average Waiting Period*: varies. *Average Age*: 87. Can accommodate cognitively impaired people with restrictions (early stage only; can't accommodate wanderers, exit-seekers & aggressive behavior). Can accommodate physically challenged people with restrictions (must be ambulatory without supervision). Smoke-free residence. Alcohol allowed. *Procedures to leave the premises on a temporary basis...*Short-term: notify Receptionist. Overnight & Holidays: notify Nurse. *Languages:* English & German. Will accept Public Guardian and Trustee clients. Main doors of residence secured at night only. *Close to:* Shopping, Churches, Seniors' Centre, Library, Major Highway and Local Hospital (Halton Healthcare Services Corporation – Georgetown and District Site). Member of ORCA. Licensed under the Retirement Homes Act.
STAFFING: *Available Staff/Services*: Pharmacy, Social Work (CCAC), Recreation Therapy, Occupational Therapy (CCAC), Physiotherapy, Denturist, Dietitian (CCAC), Chaplaincy, Speech Pathology (CCAC), Audiology/Hearing Clinic, Hairdresser and Foot Care. *External services arranged by:* residence and/or family/resident. Staff trained *re*: visually, hearing and cognitively impaired. 24-hour nursing staff. RPNs and PSWs on staff. Visiting MD (on call in emergency). Can retain own MD. Police Check or Vulnerable Person Screening is done for all new staff.
HEALTH SERVICES: Medication administered if required (must use our pharmacy). Vitals monitored if required. Will accept and provide special assistance for residents who require oxygen, catheters, ostomies and feeding tubes. Assistance with dressing available ($24.50/hour). Weekly assistance with bathing available. *Extra baths:* $12.25/half hour. Care plans done. Different levels of care available. Private Duty/Extra Care available ($24.50/hour). Lab service (on-site). Residents can purchase outside

resources and use agency of their choice. Clinic area for medical visits. Will help locate higher level of care if needed.
ACCOMMODATION: *Choice of suites available*: 81 private bed/sitting rooms and 1-bedroom units in a variety of sizes. All rooms have a private bathroom, 76 have walk-in showers, 5 have baths. Larger rooms/1-bedroom suites have kitchenettes. *In all suites*: locks, storage, window coverings, light fixtures, linens, fire alarm, smoke detector, sprinkler, call bell, air conditioning, thermostats for heating & cooling (individual suite air conditioner & heater), telephone outlets and high speed internet. Private bathrooms with call bells, grab bars, showers with non-slip surfaces and elevated toilet seats. In-suite cable TV provided by residence. Can have own phone extension number provided by residence. Unfurnished suites, furnished suites available for short stays. *Restrictions on electrical appliances*: electric kettles must have automatic shut-off. Suites can be shared (by couples only). No pets allowed.
DINING SERVICE: All meals included in fee and served in dining room daily. *Sittings per meal:* Breakfast: 1, Lunch: 1, Dinner: 1. *Menu choices available:* Breakfast: 6, Lunch: 4, Dinner: 2. *Guest Meals*: Lunch $8.00, Dinner $12.00. *Special Diets*: Vegetarian, Low Salt, Diabetic, Soft, Renal and Diverticulitis. Tray service to room if ill (no charge as long as doctor orders). Unlimited snacks available at any time. Snacks available throughout the day in the French Provincial Café. Party facilities. All meals prepared on-site. Gourmet nights twice/month.
AMENITIES AND ACTIVITIES: Parking available (outdoor, for visitors and residents). *5 lounges with:* TV (1), pianos (2), computer (1) and card/sunroom lounge (1). *Residence has a:* library, visiting library, chapel, barber/beauty shop, visiting hairdresser, laundry room(s) (no cost) and tuck/gift shop (open Wednesday 3:00 p.m. – 4:00 p.m.; Saturday 10:00 a.m. – 11:00 a.m.). Banking services on premises (if needed). Resident can arrange newspaper delivery to individual suite (extra cost). Mail delivered to main desk. *Recreation Facilities*: pool table, billiards, shuffleboard, exercise room, craft room, 2 sunrooms, theatre, activities kitchen, computer lounge and exercise pool. Posted schedule of activities. Internal newsletter for residents. *Recreational Programs*: exercise, shopping, theatre, parties, entertainment, pet visiting, day trips, church services, scheduled outings, cards, bowling, discussion groups, crafts, bingo and computer class.
OTHER SERVICES: *Housekeeping*: daily and weekly (included in fee). *Laundry*: linen, towel & personal (included in fee). Dry cleaning (charges are residents' responsibility). Transportation for group social activities. 24-hour security. Nightly security checks. Telephone, Cable TV & Utilities (included in fee). All meals & snacks. Basic Care Package.
RENTAL INFORMATION: Rates may vary. A Suite: $2,965.00 to $2,990.00/month; B Suite: $3,265.00 to $3,315.00/month; information on larger suites available on our website. Extra cost for 2nd person sharing suite ($715.00/month). Rent paid monthly. *Payment Options*: cheques and pre-authorized payments. Rent increases as per Provincial Tenancy Legislation, annual for resident with 3 months' notice given.

Did you know?

Advance Care Planning gives you more control over your health and personal care choices if you should become incapable of making decisions in the future. Public education and training sessions on this topic includes information on who makes decisions for you if you become incapable, what a substitute decision-maker is, what they do and who you should choose to be yours. For information on seminars in your area contact your local Alzheimer's chapter or the Alzheimer Society of Ontario at **(416) 967-5900.**

From: **www.seniors.gov.on.ca/en/seminars/advancedcare.php** October 2013

...NTAINVIEW TERRACE

...ountainview Road North, Georgetown, ON L7G 3R2
...(905) 877-1800 • Fax: (905) 873-9083
...ail: **info@mountainviewterrace.ca**
...ebsite: **www.mountainviewterrace.ca**
Contact: **Christoph Summer**
Capacity: **72 residents** • Subsidies: **none**
Price: **$2,650.00 - $3,735.00/month**

The Terrace, independent living with apartment-style suites, opened in late 2010. Privately owned and operated by the Summer family. Located in a residential area close to picturesque Glen Williams, it is set on 5.66 acres of land. Enjoy the raised gardens for easy gardening, outside walkways, gazebos, water features, flower gardens, roof-top patio and a wooded area. Available too, are computers along with internet access in the rooms and an exercise pool.

RESIDENCE INFORMATION: 4 years in operation. *Near:* Mountainview Road and Guelph Street. 4 floors, 1 elevator. *Funding Base:* Corporate/for profit. *Owned by:* Ursula & Christoph Summer. 60 units. *Average Waiting Period*: varies. Can accommodate physically challenged people with restrictions (must be ambulatory without supervision). Smoke-free residence. Alcohol allowed. *Procedures to leave the premises on a temporary basis...*Short-term: sign in/out book. Overnight & Holidays: notify Nurse & sign in/out book. *Languages:* English & German. Main doors of residence secured at night only. *Close to:* Shopping, Churches, Seniors' Centre, Library, Major Highway and Local Hospital (Halton Healthcare Services Corporation – Georgetown and District Site). Member of ORCA.
STAFFING: *Available Staff/Services*: Pharmacy, Social Work (CCAC), Recreation Therapy, Occupational Therapy (CCAC), Physiotherapy, Denturist, Dietitian (CCAC), Chaplaincy, Speech Pathology (CCAC), Audiology/Hearing Clinic and Hairdresser & Foot Care. *External services arranged by:* family/resident. Staff trained *re*: visually and hearing impaired. 24-hour nursing staff. RPNs and PSWs on staff. Can retain own MD. Physician in town will accept new patients if moving to Terrace. Police Check or Vulnerable Person Screening is done for all new staff.
HEALTH SERVICES: Medication administered if required ($345.00/month & must use our pharmacy). Vitals monitored if required. Will accept (but not provide special assistance for) residents who require oxygen. Weekly assistance with bathing available ($50.00/month). Lab service (on-site, $25.00/visit). Clinic area for medical visits. Will help locate higher level of care if needed.
ACCOMMODATION: *Choice of suites available*: 60 private 1 & 2-bedroom units, some 1-bedroom units with den. *In all suites*: locks, kitchenette, microwave, apartment-size fridge, storage, walk-in closet, window coverings, light fixtures, linens, fire alarm, smoke detector, sprinkler, call bell, air conditioning and thermostats for heating & cooling (individual suite air conditioner & heater). Private bathrooms with call bells, grab bars, showers with non-slip surfaces and elevated toilet seats. In-suite cable TV provided by residence. Can have own phone extension number provided by residence. Unfurnished suites. *Restrictions on electrical appliances*: electric kettles must have automatic shut-off. Suites can be shared (by couples only). No pets allowed.
DINING SERVICE: Lunch and Dinner included in fee and served in dining room daily. *Sittings per meal:* Lunch: 1, Dinner: 1. *Menu choices available:* Lunch: 4, Dinner: 2. *Guest Meals*: Lunch $8.00, Dinner $12.00. *Special Diets*: Vegetarian, Low Salt, Diabetic, Soft, Renal and Diverticulitis. Tray service to room if ill (no charge as long as doctor orders). Party facilities. Snacks available in the afternoon and evening in the café. All meals prepared on-site. Gourmet nights twice/month.
AMENITIES AND ACTIVITIES: Parking available (outdoor, for visitors: free and indoor for residents: $60.00/month). *8 lounges with:* TV (1), piano (1), computer (1) and multi-use (5). *Residence has a:* library, visiting library, chapel, barber/beauty shop, visiting hairdresser, laundry room(s) (no cost) and tuck/gift shop (open Wednesday, 3:00 p.m. – 4:00 p.m.; Saturday, 10:00 a.m. -11:00 a.m.). Banking services on

premises (if needed). Resident can arrange newspaper delivery to individual suite (extra cost). Mail delivered to main desk. *Recreation Facilities*: pool table, billiards, shuffleboard, exercise room, craft room, card room and exercise pool. Posted schedule of activities. Internal newsletter for residents. *Recreational Programs*: exercise, shopping, parties, entertainment, pet visiting, day trips, church service cards, bowling, discussion groups, crafts, bingo, computer class and physiotherapy.

OTHER SERVICES: *Housekeeping*: weekly (included in fee). *Laundry*: linen & towel (included in fee if Mountainview linens & towels are used); personal ($85.00/month) & dry cleaning (extra cost). Transportation for group social activities. Telephone, Cable TV & Utilities (included in fee).

RENTAL INFORMATION: Rates may vary. Logan Suite - $2,650.00 to $2,725.00/month; Glen Suite - $2,860.00 to $ 2,935.00/month; Terra Cotta Suite - $3,290.00 to $3,530.00/month; Esquesing Suite - $3,660.00 to $3,735.00/month. Extra cost for 2nd person sharing suite ($415.00/month). Rent paid monthly. *Payment Options*: cheques and pre-authorized payments. Rent increases as per Provincial Tenancy Legislation, annual for resident with 3 months' notice given.

♦ GODERICH ♦

GODERICH PLACE RETIREMENT RESIDENCE

30 Balvina Drive East, Goderich, ON N7A 4L5
Tel: (519) 524-4243 • Fax: (519) 524-8173
Email: **salesgp@hurontel.on.ca**
Website: **www.goderichplace.com**
Contact: **Sue LeBeau**
Capacity: **110 residents** • Subsidies: **none**
Price: **$2,130.00 - $3,780.00/month**

Goderich Place is unique to the region and just minutes from beautiful Lake Huron. Goderich Place offers private rooms with bath as well as self-contained 1-bedroom and 2-bedroom suites. There is an extended fireside lounge, an elegant dining room as well as many varied social, recreational and educational activities. Goderich Place offers optional personal support and nursing assistance as well as 24-hour security and emergency response system to ensure peace of mind. Residents have a varied choice of dining services and menus. There are a number of active social and cultural programs, including outings by our shuttle bus. The community includes a hair salon, private whirlpool spa, and laundry facilities. Housekeeping and linen services are included. Phase II Offers 30 spacious newly built 1-bedroom and 2-bedroom apartments ranging from 596 - 760 square feet. Each unit is equipped with a kitchen, walk-in shower, individually controlled heat/air conditioning and lovely, brand new decor!

RESIDENCE INFORMATION: 26 years in operation. *On:* Balvina Drive and South Street. Decorated in 2013. Handrails in hallways. 3 floors, 2 elevators. Wheelchair accessible. Central PA system. *Funding*

RIC

ɔrate/for profit. *Owned and managed by:* Retirement Life Communities. 96 units. *Average* *riod*: varies. *Average Age*: 82. Can sometimes accommodate cognitively impaired & physically l people (situation must be evaluated). Smoking allowed (outside areas). Alcohol allowed ıs re: safety for self & others). *Procedures to leave the premises on a temporary basis*...sign ɔok, only for safety purposes. *Languages:* English, French, Dutch & Danish (spoken only by ɩs). Main doors of residence secured at night only. *Close to:* Public Transit, Shopping, Churches, s' Centre, Library, Major Highway and Local Hospital (Alexandra Marine and General Hospital). ɩsed under the Retirement Homes Act.

ɩFFING: *Available Staff/Services*: Pharmacy, Social Work (CCAC), Recreation Therapy, Occupational ɩerapy (CCAC), Physiotherapy (in-house & CCAC), Dietitian (CCAC), Companions, Podiatry, Chaplaincy, ɔhiropody and Audiology/Hearing Clinic. *External services arranged by:* residence and/or family/resident. Staff trained *re*: visually, hearing and cognitively impaired. 24-hour nursing and other staff. RPNs, HCAs, PSWs and UCPs on staff. Visiting MD (twice/month - in house clinic). Can retain own MD. Police Check or Vulnerable Person Screening is done for all new staff.

HEALTH SERVICES: Medication administration and/or supervision. Vitals monitored if required. Will accept and provide special assistance for residents who require oxygen and catheters. Assistance with dressing available. Weekly assistance with bathing available ($60.00/month). *Extra baths:* $15.00/bath. Care plans done. Different levels of care available. Private Duty/Extra Care available ($17.50 to $35.00/hour). Residents can purchase outside resources and use agency of their choice. Clinic area for medical visits. Will help locate higher level of care if needed (via CCAC).

ACCOMMODATION: *Choice of suites available*: private, 1-bedroom & 2-bedroom suites. *In all suites*: locks, window coverings, light fixtures, fire alarm, smoke detector, air conditioning (central & window units), call bell and thermostats for heating. Private bathrooms with call bells, grab bars, tubs and showers with non-slip surfaces. In-suite cable TV if resident arranges with cable company. Can have own phone number if resident arranges with phone company. Unfurnished suites, furnished suites available for short stays. Suites can be shared, roommate picked by resident. Small pets only allowed (one per suite).

DINING SERVICE: Dinner included in fee and served in dining room daily. *Sittings per meal:* Breakfast: 1, Lunch: 2, Dinner: 2. *Menu choices available:* Breakfast: 2, Lunch: 2, Dinner: 2. *Special Diets*: Vegetarian, Low Salt, Diabetic, Gluten Free and Lactose Intolerant. Tray service to room if ill (no charge for a maximum time of 3 days). 3 snacks/day. Fresh fruit, tea, coffee, orange/apple/cranberry/prune juices and snacks available at all times. Party facilities.

AMENITIES AND ACTIVITIES: Parking available (outdoor, for visitors and indoor & outdoor for residents). *3 lounges with:* TV (1), piano (1), stationary bike (1), computer (1) and organ (1). Guest suites available ($60.00/night). *Residence has a:* library, visiting library, chapel, barber/beauty shop, laundry room(s) (no cost) and tuck/gift shop. Resident can arrange newspaper delivery to main desk. Mail delivered to private mailbox with key. *Recreation Facilities*: exercise room, craft room, card room and entertainment lounge. Posted schedule of activities. Internal newsletter for residents. *Recreational Programs*: exercise, shopping, theatre, parties, entertainment, art classes, day trips, Yoga, Happy Hour, Gardening Club, Literature Club and Computer Club, etc.

OTHER SERVICES: *Housekeeping*: daily and weekly. *Laundry*: linen & towel (included in fee); personal (available & included on some levels). Dry cleaning (extra cost by local dry cleaning agency). Transportation for group social activities. 24-hour security. Nightly security checks. Utilities (included in fee).

RENTAL INFORMATION: Rates may vary. Prices include service package. Extra cost for 2nd person sharing suite ($839.00/month depending which unit/level of care). Rent paid monthly. *Payment Options*: cheques, post-dated cheques and pre-authorized payments. Rent increases are a set percentage as per Provincial Tenancy Legislation, annual for resident with 3 months' notice given. Trial stays available (short-term respite cost depends on service level).

Pricing information for homes listed in *The Guide* may vary slightly. Please verify rates with the residences you are interested in directly.

◆ GRIMSBY ◆

LINCOLN PARK RETIREMENT COMMUNITY

265 Main Street East, Grimsby, ON L3M 1P7
Tel: (905) 309-0055 • Fax: (905) 309-0053
Email: **terri.mcbean@specialtyliving.ca**
Website: **www.specialtyliving.ca**
Contact: **Terri McBean**
Capacity: **120 residents** • Subsidies: **none**
Price: **$2,995.00/month and up**

Lincoln Park has redefined Retirement Living with a thoughtfully designed home that offers great value and impressive services. Here you can do things your way – while continuing to enjoy things that matter – time with family, connections with friends and being involved in the community. Our innovative *Zest for Life™* signature service promotes the health and well-being of each resident by focusing on the needs of mind, body and spirit. We work with you one-on-one to connect you with activities and services that spark your particular interests. Come and explore Lincoln Park for yourself. If you are looking for a rewarding place to live and you too have a zest for life – our doors are open!

RESIDENCE INFORMATION: 8 years in operation. *Near:* Bartlett Avenue and Main Street. Decorated in 2006. 4 floors, 2 elevators. Wheelchair accessible. *Owned by:* Specialty Care. 70 units. *Average Waiting Period*: varies. *Average Age*: 80. Can accommodate cognitively impaired people with restrictions (no risk of elopement or aggressive behaviour). Can accommodate physically challenged people with restrictions (no lift policy). Residents have a dress code (appropriate social dress code out of suite). Smoke-free residence. Alcohol allowed. *Procedures to leave the premises on a temporary basis...*Short-term & Overnight: sign in/out. Holidays: notify Administration. *Languages:* English. Main doors of residence secured at night only. *Close to:* Shopping, Churches, Seniors' Centre, Library, Major Highway and Local Hospital (West Lincoln Memorial Hospital). Member of ORCA & Chamber of Commerce. Licensed under the Retirement Homes Act.
STAFFING: *Available Staff/Services*: Pharmacy, Social Work (CCAC), Recreation Therapy, Occupational Therapy (CCAC), Visiting Dentist, Denturist, Dietitian (CCAC), Chaplaincy, Chiropody, Audiology/Hearing Clinic, Full Salon Services and Physiotherapy (on-site). Respite Care available. *External services arranged by:* residence and/or family/resident. Staff trained *re*: visually and hearing impaired. 24-hour staff. RPNs and PSWs on staff. Can retain own MD (several community physicians visit Lincoln Park). Police Check or Vulnerable Person Screening is done for all new staff.
HEALTH SERVICES: Medication administration (extra fee) and/or supervision. Vitals monitored if required. Will accept and provide special assistance for residents who require oxygen, catheters and ostomies. Assistance with dressing available (cost). Assistance with bathing available as needed (cost). Care plans done. Different levels of care available. Lab service (visiting). Residents can purchase outside resources and use agency of their choice. MD visits residents in their rooms/suites. Will help locate higher level of care if needed (options provided to families with contact information for CCAC).
ACCOMMODATION: *Choice of suites available*: studio & 1-bedroom suites. *In all suites*: locks, kitchenette, bar fridge, storage, window coverings, light fixtures, fire alarm, smoke detector, sprinkler, call bell, emergency response system with wearable pendant/bracelet, air conditioning (wall mounted and controlled in each suite), thermostats for heating & cooling and Patio/balcony units available on 1st & 2nd floor. Private bathrooms with shower or tub with grab bars. In-suite cable TV if resident arranges with cable company. Can have own phone number if resident arranges with phone company. Furnished & unfurnished suites available. *Restrictions on electrical appliances*: Maintenance must approve and safety check. Suites can

be shared (Friendship Suites available), roommate picked by resident & residence staff. Small pets only allowed (must be approved by Administration).

DINING SERVICE: All meals included in fee and served in dining room daily. *Sittings per meal:* Breakfast: 2, Lunch: 3, Dinner: 3. *Menu choices available:* Breakfast: 5, Lunch: 15, Dinner: 15. *Guest Meals*: Breakfast $7.00, Lunch $9.00, Dinner $12.00. *Special Diets*: Vegetarian, Low Salt, Diabetic and Healthy Choices (menu options identified). Innovative à la carte menu provides unparalleled choice. Tray service to room if ill (no charge for a maximum time of 3 days). Unlimited snacks available at any time. Open pantry. Party facilities.

AMENITIES AND ACTIVITIES: Parking available (outdoor, for visitors and residents). *4 lounges with:* TVs (2), piano (1), billiards table (1) and bistro bar (1). Guest suites available ($85.00/night). *Residence has a:* library, visiting library, barber/beauty shop and laundry room(s) (no cost). Residence provides newspaper delivery to individual suite. Mail delivered to individual suite. *Recreation Facilities*: pool table, billiards, exercise room, craft room, card room, activity/hobby room and home theatre room. Posted schedule of activities. Internal newsletter for residents. *Recreational Programs*: exercise, shopping, day trips, theatre, parties, entertainment, wellness programs and physiotherapy.

OTHER SERVICES: *Housekeeping*: weekly (included in fee). *Laundry*: linen, towel & personal (extra cost - weekly). Free laundry facilities on every floor. Transportation for group social activities (some trips included). 24-hour security. Telephone & Cable TV (arranged with outside provider for extra cost). Utilities (included in fee).

RENTAL INFORMATION: Rates may vary. Extra cost for 2nd person sharing suite ($620.00/month). Rent paid monthly. *Payment Options*: pre-authorized payments. Rent increases as per Provincial Tenancy Legislation, annual for resident with 3 months' notice given. Will help resident move into residence (extra cost). Short-term respite (respite rates: $88.00/day - no care; $108.00/day with 30 minutes of care; add $10.00/day for double occupancy) and trial stays ($88.00/day) available.

REVERA - MAPLECREST VILLAGE

85 Main Street East, Grimsby, ON L3M 1N6
Tel: (855) 573-8372 • Toll Free: (855) 573-8372
Email: **maplecrest@reveraliving.com**
Website: **www.reveraliving.com/maplecrest**
Contact: **Executive Director or Lifestyle Consultant**
Capacity: **80 residents** • Subsidies: **none**
Price: **$2,195.00/month and up**

Keep living your life, your way, at Maplecrest Village. You'll find the range of services, amenities and choices that fit your lifestyle and requirements – all in a warm and safe environment. Maplecrest Village is conveniently located in the heart of Grimsby, just steps from downtown shops and cafés, and amenities. Everything here is designed to enable you to maintain your independence and privacy, enjoy a full social life, and participate in the activities that you love. Our caring and friendly staff, along with appealing accommodations, support who you are and how you want to live in freedom and comfort. With retirement living at Maplecrest Village, you change your address, not your life. *Maplecrest Village is part of the Revera family, one of North America's leading and most trusted providers of seniors' accommodation, care and services since 1961.*

RESIDENCE INFORMATION: 23 years in operation. *Near:* Maple Avenue and Main Street East. Decorated in 2012. Handrails in hallways. 3 floors, 2 elevators. Wheelchair accessible. Central PA system. *Funding Base:* Corporate/for profit. *Owned and managed by:* Revera Inc. 71 units. *Average Waiting Period*: none. *Average Age*: 86. Can accommodate cognitively impaired people with restrictions (based on assessment; not a secured environment). Can accommodate physically challenged people (walkers, wheelchairs, scooters). Smoke-free residence. Alcohol allowed. *Procedures to leave the premises on a temporary*

basis...Short-term: sign in/out at Reception. Overnight & Holidays: inform staff when leaving and expected time of return. *Languages:* English. Main doors of residence secured at night only. *Close to:* Public Transit, Shopping, Churches, Seniors' Centre, Library, Major Highway and Local Hospital (West Lincoln Memorial Hospital). Member of ORCA. Licensed under the Retirement Homes Act.
STAFFING: *Available Staff/Services*: Pharmacy, Social Work (CCAC), Recreation Therapy, Occupational Therapy (CCAC), Physiotherapy (CCAC), Denturist, Dietitian (CCAC), Podiatry (CCAC), Chaplaincy, Speech Pathology (CCAC), Chiropody, Audiology/Hearing Clinic, Hearing Aide Care, Foot Care and Hairdresser (on-site). *External services arranged by:* residence and/or family/resident. 24-hour nursing and other staff. RNs, RPNs, HCAs, PSWs and UCPs on staff. Can retain own MD. Police Check or Vulnerable Person Screening is done for all new staff.
HEALTH SERVICES: Medication administration (additional monthly fee) and/or supervision. Vitals monitored if required. Will accept and provide special assistance for residents who require oxygen, catheters and ostomies. Assistance with dressing available (cost). Weekly assistance with bathing available (cost). Care plans done. Different levels of care available. Lab service (visiting). Residents can purchase outside resources and use agency of their choice. MD visits residents in their rooms/suites. Will help locate higher level of care if needed.
ACCOMMODATION: *Choice of suites available*: 1-bedroom with kitchenette (12) & studios varying sizes (62). *In all suites*: locks, window coverings, light fixtures, linens, smoke detector, carbon monoxide detector, sprinkler, wireless call bell, air conditioning (PTAC Units) and thermostats for heating & cooling. Private bathrooms with call bells, grab bars, tubs and showers with non-slip surfaces. In-suite cable & satellite TV provided by residence (residence charges extra). Can have own phone number provided by residence (residence charges extra). Unfurnished suites, furnished suites available for short stays. *Restrictions on electrical appliances*: all must comply with CSA standards and Handyman must inspect. Suites can be shared (by couples only), roommate picked by resident. Pets allowed (with assessment - cats and birds only).
DINING SERVICE: All meals included in fee and served in dining room daily. *Sittings per meal:* Breakfast: 1, Lunch: 2, Dinner: 2. *Menu choices available:* Lunch: 2, Dinner: 5. *Guest Meals*: Breakfast $5.00, Lunch $6.50, Dinner $7.50. *Special Diets*: Low Salt and Diabetic. Tray service to room if ill (no charge for a maximum time of 4 days). 3 snacks/day. Party facilities. Private dining space is available.
AMENITIES AND ACTIVITIES: Parking available (outdoor, for visitors and residents). *4 lounges with:* TVs (2) and piano (1). Guest suites available. *Residence has a:* library, visiting library, barber/beauty shop, visiting hairdresser, laundry room(s) (no cost) and tuck/gift shop. Resident can arrange newspaper delivery to main desk. Mail delivered to main desk. *Recreation Facilities*: pool table, billiards, shuffleboard, exercise room, craft room and card room. Posted schedule of activities. Internal newsletter for residents. *Recreational Programs*: exercise, shopping, parties, entertainment, pet visiting, day trips, music therapy and games.
OTHER SERVICES: *Housekeeping*: weekly. *Laundry*: linen & towel (included in fee); personal (extra cost). Dry cleaning is at the expense of the resident. Transportation to medical appointments (schedule set by Recreation Department) and for group social activities. Nightly security checks (extra cost). Telephone & Cable TV (extra cost). Utilities (included in fee).
RENTAL INFORMATION: Rates may vary. Studios - $2,295.00/month & up; 1-bedrooms - $3,631.00/month & up. Extra cost for 2nd person sharing suite ($500.00/month). Rent paid monthly. *Payment Options*: cheques, post-dated cheques and pre-authorized payments. Rent increases as per Provincial Tenancy Legislation, annual for resident with 3 months' notice given. Will help resident move into residence. Short-term respite and trial stays available (cost dependent upon care level).

♦ GUELPH ♦

REVERA - STONE LODGE

165 Cole Road, Guelph, ON N1G 4N9
Tel: (855) 573-8372 • Toll Free: (855) 573-8372
Email: **stonelodge@reveraliving.com**
Website: **www.reveraliving.com/stonelodge**
Contact: **Lifestyle Consultant or Executive Director**
Capacity: **109 residents** • Subsidies: **none**
Price: **$1,750.00/month and up**

Keep living your life, your way, at Stone Lodge. Here, you'll find the range of services, amenities and choices that fit your lifestyle and requirements – all in a warm and safe environment. Our charming one-storey residence is located on 3 acres of land, close to Stone Road Mall and amenities like, churches, the library, theatre, public transportation, and more. Everything is designed to enable you to maintain your independence and privacy, enjoy a full social life, and participate in in a wide range of activities offered. Our caring and friendly staff, along with appealing accommodations, support who you are and how you want to live in freedom and comfort. With retirement living at Stone Lodge, you change your address, not your life. *Stone Lodge is part of the Revera family, one of North America's leading and most trusted providers of seniors' accommodation, care and services since 1961.*

RESIDENCE INFORMATION: 25 years in operation. *Near:* Stone Road and Scottsdale Drive. Decorated in 2012. Handrails in hallways. 1 floor, no elevators. Wheelchair accessible. Central PA system. *Funding Base:* Corporate/for profit. *Owned and managed by:* Revera Inc. 94 units. *Average Waiting Period*: varies. *Average Age*: 83. Can sometimes accommodate cognitively impaired people (assessment required). Can accommodate physically challenged people with restrictions (assessment required). Smoking allowed (designated areas - outside only). Alcohol allowed. *Procedures to leave the premises on a temporary basis...*Short-term: sign out sheet at Front Desk. Overnight: sign out sheet at Front Desk & nursing staff. Holidays: sign out and provide enough notice to get medications. *Languages:* English, German, Polish, Spanish, French, Italian & Hungarian. Will accept Public Guardian and Trustee clients. Main doors of residence secured at night only. *Close to:* Public Transit, Shopping, Churches, Library, Major Highway and Local Hospital (Guelph General Hospital). Member of ORCA. Licensed under the Retirement Homes Act.
STAFFING: *Available Staff/Services*: Pharmacy, Social Work (CCAC), Recreation Therapy, Occupational Therapy (CCAC), Physiotherapy (CCAC), Dietitian (CCAC), Companions, Podiatry, Chaplaincy, Speech Pathology (CCAC) and Audiology/Hearing Clinic. *External services arranged by:* residence and/or family/resident. Staff trained *re*: visually, hearing and cognitively impaired. 24-hour nursing staff. RPNs, HCAs, PSWs and UCPs on staff. Visiting MD (available weekly). Can retain own MD. Police Check or Vulnerable Person Screening is done for all new staff.
HEALTH SERVICES: Medication administration and/or supervision. Vitals monitored if required. Will accept and provide special assistance for residents who require oxygen, catheters, ostomies and feeding tubes. Assistance with dressing available (cost). Weekly assistance with bathing available (cost). Care plans done. Different levels of care available. Assisted Living Area. Lab service (visiting). Residents can purchase outside resources and use agency of their choice. MD visits residents in their rooms/suites. Clinic area for medical visits. Will help locate higher level of care if needed (CCAC).
ACCOMMODATION: *Choice of suites available*: various studio & suite sizes. *In all suites*: locks, storage, window coverings, light fixtures, linens, fire alarm, smoke detector, sprinkler, emergency response system with wearable pendant/bracelet, air conditioning (residents can have window units; common areas have central air conditioning) and thermostats for heating. Private bathrooms with call bells, grab bars and

showers with non-slip surfaces. In-suite cable TV provided by residence (residence charges extra). Can have own phone number if resident arranges with phone company (residence charges extra). Unfurnished suites, furnished suites available for short stays. *Restrictions on electrical appliances*: must be approved. Suites can be shared (by couples only). Pets allowed (assessment required).
DINING SERVICE: All meals included in fee and served in dining room daily. *Sittings per meal:* Breakfast: 2, Lunch: 2, Dinner: 2. *Menu choices available:* Breakfast: 2, Lunch: 2, Dinner: 2. *Guest Meals*: Breakfast $4.00, Lunch $5.00, Dinner $7.00. *Special Diets*: Vegetarian, Low Salt, Diabetic and Gluten Free. Tray service to room if ill (no charge as long as doctor orders). 3 snacks/day. Party facilities. Meals are home-cooked and delicious.
AMENITIES AND ACTIVITIES: Parking available (outdoor, for visitors and residents). *4 lounges with:* TVs (2) and piano (1). Guest suites available. *Residence has a:* library, visiting library, barber/beauty shop, laundry room(s) (no cost), tuck/gift shop (open Tuesday & Friday; 11:30 a.m. - 1:00 p.m.). Residence provides newspaper delivery to individual suite (extra cost). Mail delivered to resident. *Recreation Facilities*: pool table, shuffleboard, exercise room, craft room, card room, library, computer with internet, Dakim and sunroom. Posted schedule of activities. Internal newsletter for residents. *Recreational Programs*: exercise, shopping, theatre, parties, entertainment, art classes, pet visiting, day trips, casino trips, boat cruises and restaurant visits.
OTHER SERVICES: *Housekeeping*: weekly (included in fee). *Laundry*: linen & towel (included in fee); personal ($80.00/month). Transportation for group social activities. 24-hour security. Nightly security checks. Utilities (included in fee).
RENTAL INFORMATION: Rates may vary. Studios - 2,395.00/month & up; suites - $3,300.00/month & up; large studio - $2,700.00/month & up; 1-bedroom - $3,250.00/month & up. Extra cost for 2nd person sharing suite ($670.00/month). Rent paid monthly. *Payment Options*: post-dated cheques and pre-authorized payments. Rent increases as per Provincial Tenancy Legislation, annual for resident with 3 months' notice given. Short-term respite ($100.00/day) and trial stays available (care assessment required).

THE VILLAGE OF ARBOUR TRAILS

32 Bayberry Drive, Guelph, ON N1G 0A2
Tel: (226) 251-3065
Email: **kelly.meeussen@schlegelvillages.com**
Website: **www.schlegelvillages.com**
Contact: **Kelly Meeussen**
Capacity: **211 units** • Subsidies: **none**
Price: **$3,294.58 - $5,260.10/month**

The Village of Arbour Trails is located within the adult lifestyle community of the Village by the Arboretum making this village a true continuum of care neighbourhood. Our residences are modern and attractive, set on beautifully landscaped grounds, without the institutional feeling of nursing and retirement homes of the past. Our internal Main Street offers the conveniences of a small town without having to go outside: winter, summer, rain or shine! Four levels of care are offered at Arbour Trails: Retirement Apartments, Full Service Retirement Suites, Assisted Care and Memory Care.

RESIDENCE INFORMATION: New residence. *Near:* Gordon Street and Stone Road. Decorated in 2013. Handrails in hallways. 3 floors, 2 elevators. Wheelchair accessible. Central PA system. *Funding Base:* Corporate/for profit. *Owned by:* Reid's Heritage Homes. *Managed by:* Schlegel Villages. *Average Waiting Period*: none. Can accommodate cognitively impaired & physically challenged people. Smoke-free residence. Alcohol allowed. *Procedures to leave the premises on a temporary basis*...advise Neighbourhood Coordinator. *Languages:* English. Main doors of residence secured at night only. *Close to:* Public Transit, Shopping, Churches, Seniors' Centre, Library and Local Hospital. Licensed under the Retirement Homes Act.

STAFFING: *Available Staff/Services*: Pharmacy, Recreation Therapy, Occupational Therapy, Physiotherapy, Dietitian, Companions and Chaplaincy. *External services arranged by:* residence and/or family/resident. Staff trained *re*: visually, hearing and cognitively impaired. 24-hour nursing staff. RPNs and PSWs on staff. Can retain own MD. Police Check or Vulnerable Person Screening is done for all new staff.
HEALTH SERVICES: Medication administered if required. Vitals monitored if required. Will accept (but not provide special assistance for) residents who require catheters and ostomies. Will accept and provide special assistance for residents who require oxygen. Assistance with dressing available. Weekly assistance with bathing available. *Extra baths:* $27.00/hour. Care plans done. Different levels of care available. Assisted Living Area. Residents can purchase outside resources and use agency of their choice. Clinic area for medical visits.
ACCOMMODATION: *Choice of suites available*: studio, 1-bedroom & 1-bedroom + den. *In all suites*: locks, storage, bar fridge, window coverings, light fixtures, smoke detector, sprinkler, emergency response system with wearable pendant/bracelet, air conditioning (central) and thermostats for heating & cooling. Private bathrooms with call bells, grab bars, showers and elevated toilet seats. In-suite cable TV provided by residence (residence charges extra $37.00/month). Can have own phone number provided by residence (residence charges extra $35.00/month). Unfurnished suites, furnished suites available for short stays. Suites can be shared, roommate picked by resident. Pets allowed (based on approval of General Manager).
DINING SERVICE: All meals included in fee and served in dining room daily. *Sittings per meal:* Breakfast: 1, Lunch: 1, Dinner: 1. *Guest Meals*: Available. Tray service to room if ill (no charge as long as doctor orders). Unlimited snacks available at any time. Party facilities.
AMENITIES AND ACTIVITIES: Parking available (outdoor, for visitors and residents). *Residence has a:* library, chapel, barber/beauty shop, laundry room(s) (no cost) and tuck/gift shop. Mail delivered to individual suite. *Recreation Facilities*: pool table, billiards, exercise room, greenhouse, craft room and card room. Posted schedule of activities. Internal newsletter for residents. *Recreational Programs*: exercise, shopping, theatre, parties, entertainment, art classes, pet visiting and day trips.
OTHER SERVICES: *Housekeeping*: weekly (included in fee). *Laundry*: linen (included in fee) & towel (included in fee - in certain suites); personal ($30.00/month) & dry cleaning (extra cost). Staff label clothing (one-time charge of $60.00). Transportation for group social activities. Telephone ($35.00/month). Cable TV ($37.00/month). Utilities (included in fee).
RENTAL INFORMATION: Rates may vary. Starting Rates: Retirement Suites $3,294.00/month; Assisted Care - $3,952.00/month; Memory Care - $4,090.00/month. Extra cost for 2nd person sharing suite. Rent paid monthly. *Payment Options*: cheques, post-dated cheques and pre-authorized payments. Rent increases as per Provincial Tenancy Legislation, annual for resident with 3 months' notice given. Short-term respite and trial stays available.

THE VILLAGE OF RIVERSIDE GLEN

60 Woodlawn Road East, Guelph, ON N1H 8M8
Tel: (519) 822-5272 • Fax: (519) 822-5520
Email: **gillian.james@schlegelvillages.com**
Website: **www.schlegelvillages.com**
Contact: **Gillian James**
Capacity: **195 units** • Subsidies: **none**
Price: **$3,340.00/month and up**

The Village of Riverside Glen provides Guelph with a unique continuum of care concept for seniors - offering multiple levels of care and support allows residents to stay in the Village that has become home. Our residences are modern and attractive, set on beautifully landscaped grounds, without the institutional feeling of nursing and retirement homes of the past. Our signature indoor Main Street has the conveniences of a small town - available to our residents in winter, summer, rain or shine! Residents, both singles and couples, can choose from cozy studios that emphasize care to generous 1-bedroom apartments that

emphasize independence. Four levels of care are offered - Full Service Retirement Living, Assisted Care, Memory Care and Long-Term Care.

RESIDENCE INFORMATION: 16 years in operation. *Near:* Woodlawn Road and Woolwich Street. Handrails in hallways. 2 floors, 5 elevators. Wheelchair accessible. Central PA system. *Funding Base:* Corporate/for profit. *Owned and managed by:* Schlegel Villages. *Average Waiting Period*: none. Can accommodate cognitively impaired people (we have a Memory Care Neighbourhood). Can accommodate physically challenged people. Smoke-free residence. Alcohol allowed. *Procedures to leave the premises on a temporary basis*...inform Director of Retirement Care or Neighbourhood Coordinator. *Languages:* English. Will accept Public Guardian and Trustee clients. Main doors of residence secured at night only. *Close to:* Public Transit, Shopping, Churches, Seniors' Centre, Library, Major Highway and Local Hospital. Member of ORCA. Licensed under the Retirement Homes Act.
STAFFING: *Available Staff/Services*: Pharmacy, Social Work (CCAC), Recreation Therapy, Occupational Therapy (CCAC), Visiting Dentist, Physiotherapy, Dietitian, Podiatry, Chaplaincy, Speech Pathology (CCAC) and Chiropody. *External services arranged by:* residence and/or family/resident. Staff trained *re*: visually, hearing and cognitively impaired. 24-hour nursing and other staff. RNs, RPNs, HCAs, PSWs and UCPs on staff. Visiting MD. Can retain own MD. Police Check or Vulnerable Person Screening is done for all new staff.
HEALTH SERVICES: Medication administration and/or supervision. Vitals monitored if required. Will accept and provide special assistance for residents who require oxygen, catheters and ostomies. Assistance with dressing available. Weekly assistance with bathing available. *Extra baths:* $27.00/hour. Care plans done. Different levels of care available. Assisted Living Area. Separate unit for residents with dementia. Lab service (visiting). Residents can purchase outside resources and use agency of their choice. Will help locate higher level of care if needed (guidance can be provided by our Director of Retirement Care).
ACCOMMODATION: *Choice of suites available*: studios, 1-bedroom suites & 2-room suites. *In all suites*: locks, kitchenette, bar fridge, storage, window coverings, light fixtures, linens, fire alarm, smoke detector, sprinkler, call bell, emergency response system with wearable pendant/bracelet, air conditioning (central) and thermostats for heating & cooling. Suites on our main floor have walk-out patios. Private bathrooms with call bells, grab bars, showers with non-slip surfaces and elevated toilet seats. In-suite cable TV provided by residence (residence charges extra $36.50/month). Can have own phone number if resident arranges with phone company (residence charges extra). Unfurnished suites, furnished suites available for short stays. Suites can be shared, roommate picked by resident. Pets allowed.
DINING SERVICE: All meals included in fee and served in dining room daily. *Sittings per meal:* Breakfast: 1, Lunch: 1, Dinner: 1. *Guest Meals*: Breakfast $8.00, Lunch $10.00, Dinner $12.00. Tray service to room if ill. Unlimited snacks available at any time. Party facilities.
AMENITIES AND ACTIVITIES: Parking available (outdoor, for visitors and residents). *Residence has a:* library, chapel, barber/beauty shop, laundry room(s) ($1.00/washer load, $1.00/dryer load) and tuck/gift shop. Mail delivered to resident. *Recreation Facilities*: pool table, exercise room, greenhouse, craft room and card room. Posted schedule of activities. Internal newsletter for residents. *Recreational Programs*: exercise, shopping, parties, entertainment, art classes, pet visiting and day trips.
OTHER SERVICES: *Housekeeping*: weekly unless otherwise stated (included in fee). *Laundry*: linen & towel (included in fee); personal ($30.00/month) & dry cleaning (extra cost). Staff label clothing ($60.00 one-time fee). Transportation for group social activities. Telephone & Cable TV (extra cost), Utilities (included in fee). Additional Care levels offered in $27.00/hour increments spread throughout a 24-hour period.
RENTAL INFORMATION: Rates may vary. Starting Rates: Full Service Retirement Suites - $3,340.00/month; Assisted Care - $3,976.00/month; Memory Care - $3,944.00/month. Extra cost for 2nd person sharing suite. Rent paid monthly. *Payment Options*: cheques and pre-authorized payments. Rent increases are a set percentage as per Provincial Tenancy Legislation, annual for resident with 3 months' notice given. Short-term respite and trial stays available.

◆ HAMILTON ◆

ABERDEEN GARDENS

330 Dundurn Street South, Hamilton, ON L8P 4L6
Tel: (905) 529-3163 • Fax: (905) 529-3214
Email: **btozer@aberdeengardens.com**
Website: **www.aberdeengardens.com**
Contact: **Brenda Tozer**
Capacity: **100 residents** • Subsidies: **none**
Price: **$2,250.00 - $2,850.00/month**

Aberdeen Gardens is located off Highway 403 on Dundurn Street South, thus we have very easy access. We have warm and caring team members, and great space for all the great activities in house. We have a van for trips and appointments and lots of parking for visitors. With Assisted Living support, our professional staff can handle resident needs 24-hours/day. Our location and the many services we have make us a great choice for retirement living in Hamilton today. Please call for lunch and a tour.

RESIDENCE INFORMATION: 16 years in operation. *Near:* Aberdeen Street and Dundurn Street South. Decorated in 2010. Handrails in hallways. 3 floors, 2 elevators. Wheelchair accessible. Central PA system. *Funding Base:* Corporate/for profit. *Managed by:* Greenwood Retirement Communities. 86 units. *Average Waiting Period*: none. *Average Age*: 80. Can accommodate cognitively impaired people (we cannot accommodate wandering residents). Can accommodate physically challenged people (need to be able to transfer with 1-person assist). Residents have a dress code (for eating in dining room - no pyjamas). Smoking allowed (outside - 9 meters from building). Alcohol allowed. *Procedures to leave the premises on a temporary basis...*sign out sheet. *Languages:* English, French, Polish & Romanian. Will accept Public Guardian and Trustee clients. Main doors of residence secured at night only. *Close to:* Public Transit, Shopping, Churches, Synagogues, Seniors' Centre, Major Highway and Local Hospital (St. Joseph's Health Care System - Hamilton). Member of ORCA. Licensed under the Retirement Homes Act.
STAFFING: *Available Staff/Services*: Pharmacy, Social Work, Recreation Therapy, Occupational Therapy (CCAC), Physiotherapy, Dietitian, Companions, Podiatry, Chaplaincy, Speech Pathology (CCAC), Chiropody, Audiology/Hearing Clinic and Van with Driver (for doctor's appointments). *External services arranged by:* residence and/or family/resident. Staff trained *re*: visually, hearing and cognitively impaired. 24-hour nursing and other staff. RNs, RPNs, PSWs and UCPs on staff. Visiting MD (office across the road; comes in every 5 - 6 weeks). Can retain own MD. Police Check or Vulnerable Person Screening is done for all new staff. Some staff have been working at Aberdeen since it opened.
HEALTH SERVICES: Medication administration (we use our own pharmacy) and/or supervision (we do not do sliding scale insulin). Vitals monitored if required. Will accept and provide special assistance for residents who require oxygen, catheters and ostomies. Assistance with dressing available ($20.00/hour). Weekly assistance with bathing available. *Extra baths:* $10.00/half hour. Care plans done. Different levels of care available. If extra care services are needed we assess with CCAC first before charging for extra care. Private Duty/Extra Care available ($20.00 to $40.00/hour). Lab service (visiting, $25.00/visit). Residents can purchase outside resources and use agency of their choice. MD visits residents in their rooms/suites. Clinic area for medical visits. Will help locate higher level of care if needed (we work with families and CCAC to find a solution if we are unable to care for the resident).
ACCOMMODATION: *Choice of suites available*: 4 sizes of studio apartments & 2 styles of 1-bedroom units. *In all suites*: locks, storage, window coverings, light fixtures, smoke detector, sprinkler, call bell, emergency response system with wearable pendant/bracelet, air conditioning (window units) and thermostats for heating & cooling. Private bathrooms with call bells, grab bars, tubs and showers with non-slip surfaces. In-suite cable TV provided by residence (residence charges extra $45.00/month). Can

have own phone extension number provided by residence (residence charges extra $35.00/month). Unfurnished suites, furnished suites available for short stays. *Restrictions on electrical appliances*: should utilize power bar to ensure safety. Suites can be shared (by couples only). Pets allowed (an Agreement must be signed).

DINING SERVICE: All meals included in fee and served in dining room daily. *Sittings per meal:* Breakfast: 1, Lunch: 1, Dinner: 1. *Menu choices available:* Breakfast: 3, Lunch: 4, Dinner: 4. *Guest Meals*: Breakfast $5.00, Lunch $5.00, Dinner $10.00. *Special Diets*: Vegetarian, Low Salt, Diabetic, Cut-Up, Minced and Pureed. Tray service to room if ill (no charge for a maximum time of 5 days). Unlimited snacks available at any time. Open pantry. Café in-house open 24-hours. Full stove and microwave available to residents and families in café. Party facilities.

AMENITIES AND ACTIVITIES: Parking available (outdoor, for visitors and residents). *5 lounges with:* TV (1), piano (1), pool table (1) and library (1). *Residence has a:* library, visiting library, chapel and barber/ beauty shop. Resident can arrange newspaper delivery to individual suite. Mail delivered to private mailbox (no key). *Recreation Facilities*: pool table, exercise room, craft room, card room, chapel, café, games room, puzzle area and library. Van available for trips & doctor visits. Posted schedule of activities. Internal newsletter for residents. *Recreational Programs*: exercise, shopping, theatre, parties, entertainment, art classes, pet visiting and day trips.

OTHER SERVICES: *Housekeeping*: weekly (included in fee; daily is possible if needed for extra cost). *Laundry*: linen, towel & personal (extra cost if more than once/week). Transportation to medical appointments (by appointment 3 days/week) and for group social activities (ticket portion of outings paid by residents). 24-hour security. Nightly security checks. Telephone ($35.00/month). Cable TV ($45.00/month). Utilities (included in fee). Daily costs for extra services can be arranged.

RENTAL INFORMATION: Rates may vary. Extra cost for 2nd person sharing suite. Rent paid monthly. *Payment Options*: cheques, post-dated cheques and pre-authorized payments. Rent increases as per Provincial Tenancy Legislation, annual for resident with 3 months' notice given. Will help resident move into residence ($20.00/hour). Short-term respite ($90.00/day) and trial stays ($100.00/day) available.

CAROLINE PLACE RETIREMENT RESIDENCE

118 Market Street, Hamilton, ON L8R 3P9
Tel: (905) 548-7660
Email: **info@caroline-place.com**
Website: **www.caroline-place.com**
Contact: **Madelaine Steller Cain**
Capacity: **108 residents** • Subsidies: **none**
Price: **$2,595.00 - $4,500.00/month**

We are the newest retirement residence located in the heart Hamilton, steps away from shopping and entertainment: We are elegant yet amazingly affordable. We offer large studios, 1-bedroom & 2-bedroom suites all with fully equipped kitchens. We have an indoor pool, fitness centre and a physiotherapy instructor all at no additional cost.

RESIDENCE INFORMATION: 4 years in operation. *Near:* Bay Street and Caroline Street. Decorated in 2010. 3 floors, 2 elevators. Wheelchair accessible. *Funding Base:* Corporate/for profit. *Managed by:* Greenwood Retirement Communities. 108 units. *Average Waiting Period*: none. *Average Age*: 87. Can accommodate physically challenged people. Residents have a dress code (casual dress). Smoking allowed (outside). Alcohol allowed. *Procedures to leave the premises on a temporary basis...*sign out. *Languages:* English, Croatian, German, French & Polish. Main doors of residence secured at night only. *Close to:* Public Transit, Shopping, Churches, Synagogues, Seniors' Centre, Library, Major Highway and Local Hospital (St. Joseph's Health Care System-Hamilton). Member of ORCA. Licensed under the Retirement Homes Act.

STAFFING: *Available Staff/Services*: Pharmacy, Social Work (CCAC), Recreation Therapy, Occupational Therapy (CCAC), Physiotherapy, Dietitian (CCAC), Chaplaincy, Speech Pathology (CCAC) and Chiropody. *External services arranged by:* residence and/or family/resident. Staff trained *re*: visually and hearing impaired. 24-hour nursing and other staff. RNs, RPNs, PSWs and UCPs on staff. Can retain own MD. Police Check or Vulnerable Person Screening is done for all new staff.
HEALTH SERVICES: Medication administration and/or supervision. Vitals monitored if required. Will accept (but not provide special assistance for) residents who require catheters, ostomies and feeding tubes. Will accept and provide special assistance for residents who require oxygen. Assistance with dressing available ($25.00/hour). Assistance with bathing available as needed ($25.00/hour). Care plans done. Private Duty/Extra Care available ($25.00/hour). Lab service (visiting, $30.00/visit). Residents can purchase outside resources and use agency of their choice. MD visits residents in their rooms/suites. Clinic area for medical visits. Will help locate higher level of care if needed.
ACCOMMODATION: *Choice of suites available*: private, studios, 1-bedroom & 2-bedroom suites. *In all suites*: locks, kitchenette, full-size fridge, cooktop , microwave, dishwasher, window coverings, light fixtures, stove, fire alarm, smoke detector, sprinkler, emergency response system with wearable pendant/bracelet, air conditioning (window units) and thermostats for heating & cooling. Private bathrooms with grab bars, tubs and showers. In-suite satellite TV provided by residence (residence charges extra $50.00/month). Can have own phone number provided by residence (residence charges extra $35.00/month). Furnished & unfurnished suites available. *Restrictions on electrical appliances*: must be in good condition. Suites can be shared. Pets allowed (resident has to be able to take care of their own pet).
DINING SERVICE: Lunch and Dinner included in fee and served in dining room daily. *Sittings per meal:* Lunch: 1, Dinner: 1. *Menu choices available:* Lunch: 3, Dinner: 3. *Guest Meals*: Breakfast $5.00, Lunch $8.00, Dinner $10.00. *Special Diets*: Vegetarian, Low Salt, Diabetic, Gluten Free, Lactose Intolerant and Renal. 3 snacks/day and unlimited snacks available at any time. Party facilities. All meals are freshly prepared daily. Large variety. 3 course meals. Sunday dinner buffet monthly.
AMENITIES AND ACTIVITIES: Parking available (outdoor, for visitors: free and residents: $25.00/month). *2 lounges with:* TVs (2) and piano (1). Guest suites available. *Residence has a:* barber/beauty shop, visiting hairdresser and laundry room(s) (no cost). Banking services on premises. Mail delivered to main desk. *Recreation Facilities*: exercise room, craft room, card room, café and indoor swimming pool. Posted schedule of activities. Internal newsletter for residents. *Recreational Programs*: exercise, shopping, theatre, parties, entertainment, art classes, pet visiting and day trips.
OTHER SERVICES: *Housekeeping*: weekly (included in fee). *Laundry*: linen & towel (included in fee); personal ($50.00/month, 2 loads/week) & dry cleaning (extra cost). Transportation for group social activities. 24-hour security. Nightly security checks. Telephone ($35.00/month). Cable TV ($50.00/month). Utilities (included in fee).
RENTAL INFORMATION: Rates may vary. Studios - $2,595.00 to $3,100.00/month, depending on size; 1-bedroom suites - $3,900.00/month; 2-bedroom suites - $4,500.00/month. Extra cost for 2nd person sharing suite ($500.00/month). Rent paid monthly. *Payment Options*: pre-authorized payments. Rent increases annual for resident with 3 months' notice given. Short-term respite and trial stays available (both $89.00/day).

Downsizing Tip

Consider involving your children and grandchildren in your decluttering process. Suggest they choose something special from your mementos that you are willing to part with. Take the opportunity to share your stories around the items they have chosen. You can also ask them to organize a Garage Sale in the summer and allow them to keep the money for items sold.

DURAND RESIDENCE

10 Herkimer Street, Hamilton, ON L8P 2G2
Tel: (905) 525-0338 • Fax: (905) 524-5948
Email: **durandresidenceadmin@bellnet.ca**
Website: **www.durandresidence.com**
Contact: **Barbara Shaw**
Capacity: **83 residents •** Subsidies: **none**
Price: **$1,855.00 - $3,920.00/month**

Our residents enjoy the cheerful atmosphere, the friendly people and a full range of amenities. The Durand is nestled at the foot of Hamilton Mountain in the historic Durand neighborhood - a perfect setting; you're only steps away from churches, shops, restaurants, and medical offices. Just a short walk from the GO Train terminal.

RESIDENCE INFORMATION: 31 years in operation. *Near:* James Street on Herkimer Street. Decorated in 2012. Handrails in hallways. 3 floors, 2 elevators. Wheelchair accessible. *Funding Base:* Corporate/for profit. 74 units. *Average Waiting Period*: less than 2 weeks. *Average Age*: 86. Can sometimes accommodate cognitively impaired & physically challenged people. Smoke-free residence. Alcohol allowed. *Procedures to leave the premises on a temporary basis...*Short-term: sign out book in Office. Overnight & Holidays: let staff know return date & take medications for the time away. *Languages:* English, Italian, German, Polish, Lithuanian & Filipino. Will accept Public Guardian and Trustee clients. Main doors of residence secured at night only. *Close to:* Public Transit, Shopping, Churches, Seniors' Centre, Library, Major Highway and Local Hospital (St. Joseph's Health Care System - Hamilton). *Predominant Cultural Group:* White Anglo-Saxon. Member of ORCA. Licensed under the Retirement Homes Act.
STAFFING: *Available Staff/Services*: Pharmacy, Social Work (CCAC), Recreation Therapy, Occupational Therapy (CCAC), Visiting Dentist, Physiotherapy (CCAC), Dietitian, Companions, Chaplaincy, Speech Pathology (CCAC) and Audiology/Hearing Clinic. *External services arranged by:* residence and/or family/resident. Staff trained *re*: visually, hearing and cognitively impaired. 24-hour nursing and other staff. RNs, RPNs, HCAs, PSWs and UCPs on staff. Visiting MD (monthly). Can retain own MD. Staff members are bonded. Police Check or Vulnerable Person Screening is done for all new staff.
HEALTH SERVICES: Medication administration and/or supervision. Vitals monitored if required. Will accept (but not provide special assistance for) residents who require catheters and ostomies. Will accept and provide special assistance for residents who require oxygen. Assistance with dressing available ($25.00/hour). Weekly assistance with bathing available. *Extra baths:* $25.00/half hour. Care plans done. Different levels of care available. Private Duty/Extra Care available ($25.00/hour). Lab service (visiting, $25.00/visit). Residents can purchase outside resources and use agency of their choice. MD visits residents in their rooms/suites. Clinic area for medical visits. Will help locate higher level of care if needed (will liaise with CCAC).
ACCOMMODATION: *Choice of suites available*: small, medium, large or 2-room private suites, all with ensuite bath. *In all suites*: locks, bar fridge, window coverings, light fixtures, linens, fire alarm, smoke detector, sprinkler, call bell, emergency response system with wearable pendant/bracelet, air conditioning (central & window units) and thermostats for heating & cooling. Private bathrooms with call bells and grab bars. In-suite cable TV provided by residence (residence charges extra). Can have own phone number provided by residence (residence charges extra). Furnished & unfurnished suites available. *Restrictions on electrical appliances*: no hot plates, irons. Suites can be shared, roommate picked by resident. Pets allowed.
DINING SERVICE: All meals included in fee and served in dining room daily. *Sittings per meal:* Breakfast: 1, Lunch: 1, Dinner: 1. *Menu choices available:* Breakfast: 5, Lunch: 5, Dinner: 5. *Guest Meals*: Breakfast $5.00, Lunch $7.00, Dinner $10.00. *Special Diets*: Vegetarian, Low Salt, Diabetic and Soft/Minced. Tray service to room if ill (no charge as long as doctor orders). 3 snacks/day. Party facilities. Open pantry.

AMENITIES AND ACTIVITIES: Parking available (outdoor, for visitors and residents). *4 lounges with:* TVs (2) and piano (1). Guest suites available. *Residence has a:* library, chapel, barber/beauty shop and visiting hairdresser. Residence provides newspaper delivery to individual suite. Mail delivered to dining room. *Recreation Facilities*: exercise room, craft room, library and bistro. Posted schedule of activities. Internal newsletter for residents. *Recreational Programs*: exercise, shopping, theatre, parties, entertainment, art classes, pet visiting, day trips, Yoga and Reflexology.
OTHER SERVICES: *Housekeeping*: daily (included in fee). *Laundry*: linen, towel & personal (included in fee). Transportation for group social activities (extra cost). 24-hour security. Nightly security checks. Telephone & Cable TV (extra cost). Utilities (included in fee).
RENTAL INFORMATION: Rates may vary. Extra cost for 2nd person sharing suite ($600.00/month). Rent paid monthly. *Payment Options*: cheques, post-dated cheques and pre-authorized payments. Rent increases as per Provincial Tenancy Legislation, annual for resident with 3 months' notice given. Will help resident move into residence. Short-term respite ($85.00 to $110.00/day depending on the level of care) and trial stays available ($85.00/day). Trial stays can be negotiated on a monthly basis.

KINGSBERRY PLACE

1221 Limeridge Road East, Hamilton, ON L8W 1Y1
Tel: (905) 318-3815 • Fax: (905) 318-8734
Email: **doris.kingsberry@gmail.com**
Website: **www.kingsberryplace.ca**
Contact: **Doris Dollar**
Capacity: **32 residents** • Subsidies: **none**
Price: **$2,295.00 - $3,495.00/month**

We have a one floor plan that makes it easy for residents as well as a house doctor on-site.

RESIDENCE INFORMATION: 9 years in operation. *Near:* Upper Ottawa Street and Limeridge Road. Decorated in 2010. 1 floor, no elevators. Wheelchair accessible. *Owned by:* 1221 Limeridge Inc. 32 units. *Average Waiting Period*: 1 - 2 months. *Average Age*: 83. Can sometimes accommodate cognitively impaired people (memory loss or Stage 1 Alzheimer's). Can sometimes accommodate physically challenged people (wheelchairs, but must be independent with transfers). Residents have a dress code (must be dressed appropriately for dining room). Smoke-free residence. Alcohol allowed (suites only). *Procedures to leave the premises on a temporary basis*...sign in/out and staff must be informed. *Languages:* English. Main doors of residence secured at night only. *Close to:* Public Transit, Shopping, Churches, Seniors' Centre, Library, Major Highway and Local Hospital (Hamilton Health Sciences Corporation – Juravinski Hospital Site). Licensed under the Retirement Homes Act.
STAFFING: *Available Staff/Services*: Pharmacy, Social Work, Recreation Therapy, Occupational Therapy, Visiting Dentist, Physiotherapy, Denturist, Dietitian, Podiatry, Chaplaincy, Speech Pathology, Chiropody, Audiology/Hearing Clinic and Hair Salon (on-site) and Family Physician. *External services arranged by:* residence and/or family/resident. Staff trained *re*: visually and cognitively impaired. 24-hour nursing staff. RPNs and PSWs on staff. Visiting MD (24-hours). Can retain own MD. Police Check or Vulnerable Person Screening is done for all new staff.
HEALTH SERVICES: Medication administration and/or supervision. Vitals monitored if required. Will accept (but not provide special assistance for) residents who require catheters. Will accept and provide special assistance for residents who require oxygen and ostomies. Assistance with dressing available. Weekly assistance with bathing available. Lab service (visiting, $30.00/visit). Residents can purchase outside resources and use agency of their choice. MD visits residents in their rooms/suites. Clinic area for medical visits. Will help locate higher level of care if needed (assistance provided through CCAC).
ACCOMMODATION: *Choice of suites available*: all private rooms with 1 double room available. *In all suites*: locks, kitchenette, bar fridge, microwave, storage, window coverings, light fixtures, linens, fire

alarm, emergency response system with wearable pendant/bracelet, air conditioning (central & window units) and thermostats for heating & cooling. Private 4-piece bathrooms with grab bars, tubs and showers with non-slip surfaces and elevated toilet seats. In-suite cable TV provided by residence (residence charges extra). Can have own phone number if resident arranges with phone company (residence charges extra). Furnished & unfurnished suites available. *Restrictions on electrical appliances*: no toasters or toaster ovens. Suites can be shared (by couples only). No pets allowed.
DINING SERVICE: All meals included in fee and served in dining room daily. *Sittings per meal:* Breakfast: 1, Lunch: 1, Dinner: 1. *Menu choices available:* Breakfast: 2, Lunch: 2, Dinner: 2. *Guest Meals*: Breakfast $5.00, Lunch $5.00, Dinner $8.00. *Special Diets*: Vegetarian, Low Salt, Diabetic and Gluten Free (will accommodate other requests). Tray service to room if ill (no charge or restrictions). 3 snacks/day and unlimited snacks available at any time.
AMENITIES AND ACTIVITIES: Parking available (outdoor, for visitors and residents). *2 lounges with:* TV (1) and piano (2). Guest suites available ($95.00/night). *Residence has a:* visiting library, barber/beauty shop and visiting hairdresser. Residence provides newspaper delivery to individual suite. Mail delivered to dining room. Posted schedule of activities. *Recreational Programs*: exercise, shopping, parties, art classes, entertainment and day trips.
OTHER SERVICES: *Housekeeping*: weekly (included in fee). *Laundry*: linen, towel & personal (included in fee); dry cleaning (residents/family responsible). 24-hour security. Nightly security checks. Telephone & Cable TV (extra cost). Utilities (included in fee).
RENTAL INFORMATION: Rates may vary. Extra cost for 2nd person sharing suite ($500.00/month). Rent paid monthly. *Payment Options*: cheques and post-dated cheques. Rent increases as per Provincial Tenancy Legislation, annual for resident with 3 months' notice given. Short-term respite and trial stays available (both $95.00/day).

THE COURT AT RUSHDALE

1360 Upper Sherman Avenue, Hamilton, ON L8W 3Z6
Tel: (905) 575-6832 • Fax: (905) 575-2842
Email: **5144-manager@holidaytouch.com**
Website: **www.courtatrushdale.com**
Contact: **Community Managers**
Capacity: **115 units** • Subsidies: **none**
Price: **$2,700.00/month and up (rates may vary)**

Holiday Retirement believes retirement living should be relaxing and carefree, spent doing the things you love. That's why our communities provide a unique independent retirement lifestyle in a warm and welcoming environment. In one affordable, all-inclusive month-to-month rent, residents enjoy 3 delicious chef-prepared meals daily, enriching activities to share with friendly neighbours, housekeeping service, complimentary transportation, and so much more. Each Holiday community also features 2 sets of compassionate, dedicated live-in Managers available 24/7 to ensure safety and security. We do not provide any health care services; however, residents are welcome to receive services from any outside home health care provider of their choice to help them continue enjoying life at our community. Discover the peace-of-mind, happiness and fulfillment you deserve. Contact us today to schedule your personal tour!

RESIDENCE INFORMATION: 12 years in operation. *On:* Stone Church Street and Upper Sherman Avenue. Handrails in hallways. 3 floors, 1 elevator. Wheelchair accessible. Central PA system. *Funding Base:* Corporate/for profit. *Owned and managed by:* Holiday Retirement. *Average Waiting Period*: none. *Average Age*: 83. Can accommodate cognitively impaired people with restrictions. Can accommodate physically challenged people (must be independent). Residents have a dress code (casual, no sleepwear in common areas). Smoking allowed (In own apartment). Alcohol allowed (in own apartment). *Procedures*

*to leave the premises on a temporary basis...*Overnight & Holidays: inform Front Office. *Languages:* English. Will accept Public Guardian and Trustee clients. Main doors of residence secured at night only. *Close to:* Public Transit, Shopping, Churches, Synagogues, Seniors' Centre, Library, Major Highway and Local Hospital (Hamilton Health Sciences Corporation – Juravinski Hospital Site).
STAFFING: *External services arranged by:* family/resident. 24-hour staff. Can retain own MD. Staff members are bonded.
HEALTH SERVICES: Will accept (but not provide special assistance for) residents who require oxygen, catheters, ostomies and feeding tubes. Residents can purchase outside resources and use agency of their choice. Will help locate higher level of care if needed (information available from Front Office and local government health agencies).
ACCOMMODATION: *Choice of suites available*: studios, 1-bedroom & 2-bedroom units. *In all suites*: locks, kitchenette, storage, window coverings, light fixtures, linens, fire alarm, smoke detector, sprinkler, call bell, air conditioning (wall unit) and thermostats for heating & cooling. Most have patios/balconies. Private bathrooms with call bells and showers with non-slip surfaces. In-suite cable TV provided by residence. Can have own phone number if resident arranges with phone company. Furnished & unfurnished suites available. *Restrictions on electrical appliances*: no hot plates or stoves. Suites can be shared, roommate picked by resident. Pets allowed.
DINING SERVICE: All meals included in fee and served in dining room daily. *Sittings per meal:* Breakfast: 1, Lunch: 1, Dinner: 1. *Menu choices available:* Breakfast: 5, Lunch: 6, Dinner: 5. *Guest Meals*: Breakfast $8.00, Lunch $10.00, Dinner $8.00. *Special Diets*: Vegetarian, Low Salt and Diabetic. Tray service to room if ill. 2 snacks/day. Party facilities. Private Dining Area. Large meal served at noon-time. Fresh fruit, coffee, tea & goodies available all day.
AMENITIES AND ACTIVITIES: Parking available (outdoor, for visitors and indoor & outdoor for residents). *4 lounges with:* TV (1), piano (1), computer kiosks (1) and library (1). Guest suites available ($75.00/night). *Residence has a:* library, chapel, barber/beauty shop and laundry room(s) (no cost). Resident can arrange newspaper delivery to individual suite. Mail delivered to private mailbox with key. *Recreation Facilities*: pool table, billiards, exercise room, craft room and card room. Posted schedule of activities. Internal newsletter for residents. *Recreational Programs*: exercise, shopping, theatre, parties, entertainment, art classes, pet visiting, day trips and resident suggested activities.
OTHER SERVICES: *Housekeeping*: weekly. *Laundry*: linen & towel (included in fee). Free laundry rooms for personal use. Transportation to medical appointments and for group social activities. 24-hour security. Cable TV & Utilities (included in fee).
RENTAL INFORMATION: Rates may vary. Rate listed above is based on single occupancy. Extra cost for 2nd person sharing suite (please call for specifics). Rent paid monthly. *Payment Options*: cheques, post-dated cheques and pre-authorized payments. Rent increases indexed to inflation as per Provincial Tenancy Legislation, annual for resident with 3 months' notice given. Will help resident move into residence. Trial stays available.

Did you know?

The Retirement Homes Regulatory Authority (RHRA) regulates, educates, oversees and enforces the regulations and care standards established by the government to protect seniors in retirement residences across Ontario. For additional information and to view the Public Register of homes visit **www.rhra.ca** or call **(855) ASK-RHRA (275-7472).**

THE WELLINGTON

1430 Upper Wellington Street, Hamilton, ON L9A 5H3
Tel: (905) 385-2111 • Fax: (905) 385-2110
Toll Free: (866) 385-2111
Email: **dderosa@thewellington.ca**
Website: **www.thewellington.ca**
Contact: **Doretta DeRosa**
Capacity: **102 residents** • Subsidies: **none**
Price: **$2,430.00 - $4,142.00/month**

Our first and second floors are independent living and our third floor offers more living assistance, with attendants to aid our seniors in daily living activities. Our residence also has a 102 bed long-term care home attached. This is a totally separate facility but is available to residents that require more assistance than can be provided in our retirement residence. Our 'Living Tapestry' program creates a comfortable home where residents can put up their feet, surround themselves in children's laughter and the companionship of animals within a framework of vibrant greenery.....

RESIDENCE INFORMATION: 23 years in operation. *On:* Upper Wellington Street and Stonechurch Avenue. Decorated in 2011. Handrails in hallways. 3 floors, 1 elevator. Wheelchair accessible. Central PA system. *Funding Base:* Corporate/for profit. *Owned by:* Mr. Daniel Scully - Barton Retirement Inc. 79 units. *Average Waiting Period*: varies. *Average Age*: 85. Can accommodate cognitively impaired people (on our 3rd floor Personal Service Unit). Can sometimes accommodate physically challenged people (on our 3rd floor Personal Service Unit). Residents have a dress code (must be appropriately dressed for mealtimes in the dining room). Smoke-free residence. Alcohol allowed. *Procedures to leave the premises on a temporary basis...*sign out and inform Nurse Manager. *Languages:* English, Italian, Portuguese, Polish, German, Filipino & Spanish. Will accept Public Guardian and Trustee clients. Main doors of residence secured at night only. *Close to:* Public Transit, Shopping, Churches, Seniors' Centre, Library, Major Highway and Local Hospitals (St. Joseph's Health Care System -Hamilton, Hamilton Health Sciences Corporation – Juravinski Hospital Site, General Hospital Site & McMaster University Medical Centre Site). Member of ORCA & OLTCA. Licensed under the Retirement Homes Act.
STAFFING: *Available Staff/Services*: Pharmacy, Social Work, Recreation Therapy, Occupational Therapy, Visiting Dentist, Physiotherapy, Denturist, Dietitian, Companions, Podiatry, Chaplaincy, Speech Pathology, Chiropody, Audiology/Hearing Clinic, Financial Planners and Massage Therapy. *External services arranged by:* residence and/or family/resident. Staff trained *re*: visually, hearing and cognitively impaired. 24-hour nursing staff. RNs, RPNs, HCAs and PSWs on staff. Visiting MD (every other Friday and on an as needed basis). Can retain own MD. Police Check or Vulnerable Person Screening is done for all new staff.
HEALTH SERVICES: Medication administered if required. Vitals monitored if required. Will accept and provide special assistance for residents who require oxygen, catheters and ostomies. Assistance with dressing available ($315.00/month). Weekly assistance with bathing available ($45.00/month). *Extra baths:* $11.25/half hour. Care plans done. Different levels of care available. Private Duty/Extra Care available ($25.00/hour). Assisted Living Area ($445.00/month) is secured to accommodate residents with dementia. Lab service (visiting, $25.00/visit). Residents can purchase outside resources and use agency of their choice. Will help locate higher level of care if needed (with the help of Nurse Manager, Social Worker, CCAC, Marketing Manager and our own long-term care home).
ACCOMMODATION: *Choice of suites available*: private (65) & 2-room (12) suites. *In all suites*: locks, kitchenette, bar fridge, window coverings, light fixtures, linens, fire alarm, smoke detector, sprinkler, air conditioning (window units) and thermostats for heating & cooling. Private bathrooms with call bells, grab bars, tubs and showers with non-slip surfaces. In-suite cable TV if resident arranges with cable company. Can have own phone extension number provided by residence (residence charges extra

$28.00/month). Unfurnished suites, furnished suites available for short stays. Suites can be shared (pending availability of beds), roommate picked by resident & residence staff. No pets allowed.
DINING SERVICE: All meals included in fee and served in dining room daily. *Sittings per meal:* Breakfast: 2, Lunch: 2, Dinner: 2. *Menu choices available:* Breakfast: 2, Lunch: 2, Dinner: 2. *Guest Meals*: Breakfast $4.00, Lunch $7.00, Dinner $10.00. *Special Diets*: Vegetarian, Low Salt and Diabetic. Tray service to room if ill. 3 snacks/day. Party facilities. Home-cooked meals on premises. Elegant dining room with fireplace.
AMENITIES AND ACTIVITIES: Parking available (outdoor, for visitors and residents). *4 lounges with:* TV (1) and piano (1). Guest suites available ($85.00/night). *Residence has a:* library, visiting library, barber/beauty shop, laundry room(s) (no cost), tuck/gift shop (open at mealtimes & as needed). Residence provides newspaper delivery to individual suite. Mail delivered to private mailbox with key. *Recreation Facilities*: craft room and card room. Posted schedule of activities. Internal newsletter for residents. *Recreational Programs*: exercise, shopping, theatre, parties, entertainment, art classes, pet visiting, day trips, monthly Diner's Club, cottage rental for a weekend for interested residents, planting and fundraisers.
OTHER SERVICES: *Housekeeping*: daily. *Laundry*: linen & towel (included in fee); personal ($45.00/ month/person). Staff label clothing ($20.50/40 Labels). Transportation for group social activities (mini-bus for weekly planned activities). 24-hour security. Nightly security checks. Telephone ($28.00/month). Cable TV (resident to arrange with Cable Company). Utilities (included in fee). 24-hour nursing care. Medication supervision.
RENTAL INFORMATION: Rates may vary. Small studio - $2,430.00/month; large studio - $2,989.00/month; suite - $3,660.00/month; suite with 2 bathrooms - $4,142.00/month. Extra cost for 2nd person sharing suite ($675.00/month). Rent paid monthly. *Payment Options*: cheques, post-dated cheques and pre-authorized payments. Rent increases as per Provincial Tenancy Legislation, annual for resident with 3 months' notice given. Short-term respite ($95.00/day) and trial stays ($85.00/day) available ($95.00/day for the Supportive Care Unit).

VILLA ITALIA RETIREMENT RESIDENCE

530 Upper Paradise Road, Hamilton, ON L9C 7W2
Tel: (905) 388-4552 • Fax: (905) 540-3736
Email: **abiscak@villaitalia.ca**
Website: **www.villaitalia.ca**
Contact: **Anita Biscak**
Capacity: **130 residents**
Subsidies: **call for information/through an application process**
Price: **$2,665.00 - $3,625.00/month**

Villa Italia Retirement Residence caters to seniors from the Italian community as well as non-Italian seniors who enjoy a European lifestyle. We have gracious lounges and libraries, a wellness room with physiotherapy equipment, an entertainment studio and a fountained serenity courtyard.

RESIDENCE INFORMATION: 11 years in operation. *On:* Upper Paradise Road and south of Mohawk Road West. Decorated in 2012. Handrails in hallways. 3 floors, 3 elevators. Wheelchair accessible. Central PA system. *Funding Base:* Not-for-profit. *Owned by:* The Sons of Italy Hamilton Charitable Corporation. 123 units. *Average Waiting Period*: varies. *Average Age*: 82. Can accommodate cognitively impaired & physically challenged people. Smoke-free residence. Alcohol allowed (responsible drinking). *Procedures to leave the premises on a temporary basis*...sign out process to inform Nurses. *Languages:* English & Italian. Will accept Public Guardian and Trustee clients. Main doors of residence secured at night only. *Close to:* Public Transit, Shopping, Churches, Seniors' Centre, Library and Major Highway. *Predominant Cultural Group:* Italian. Member of ORCA. Licensed under the Retirement Homes Act.

STAFFING: *Available Staff/Services*: Pharmacy, Social Work (CCAC), Recreation Therapy, Occupational Therapy (CCAC), Physiotherapy, Dietitian, Chaplaincy and Speech Pathology (CCAC). *External services arranged by:* residence and/or family/resident. Staff trained *re*: visually, hearing and cognitively impaired. 24-hour nursing and other staff. RNs, RPNs and PSWs on staff. Can retain own MD. Staff members are bonded. Police Check or Vulnerable Person Screening is done for all new staff.
HEALTH SERVICES: Medication administration and/or supervision. Vitals monitored if required. Will accept (but not provide special assistance for) residents who require catheters, ostomies and feeding tubes. Will accept and provide special assistance for residents who require oxygen. Assistance with dressing available (cost). Weekly assistance with bathing available. Care plans done. Different levels of care available. Private Duty/Extra Care available. Lab service (on-site). Residents can purchase outside resources and use agency of their choice. Clinic area for medical visits. Will help locate higher level of care if needed (Director of Care works with families & referral source to assist family & resident).
ACCOMMODATION: *Choice of suites available*: standard studio, deluxe studio, grand studio, deluxe 1-bedroom & grand 1-bedroom units. *In all suites*: locks, kitchenette, bar fridge, microwave, storage, window coverings, light fixtures, fire alarm, smoke detector, sprinkler, call bell, air conditioning (central) and thermostats for heating & cooling. Private bathrooms with call bells, grab bars and showers with non-slip surfaces. In-suite cable TV if resident arranges with cable company. Can have own phone number provided by residence (residence charges extra $30.00/month). Unfurnished suites, furnished suites available for short stays. Pets allowed.
DINING SERVICE: All meals included in fee and served in dining room daily. *Sittings per meal:* Breakfast: 2, Lunch: 2, Dinner: 2. *Menu choices available:* Breakfast: 2, Lunch: 2, Dinner: 2. *Guest Meals*: Breakfast $5.00, Lunch $6.00, Dinner $10.00. *Special Diets*: Vegetarian, Low Salt, Diabetic, Celiac and Lactose Free. Tray service to room if ill. 3 snacks/day. Open pantry. Party facilities (private dining room). Dining room faces out to a beautiful courtyard.
AMENITIES AND ACTIVITIES: Parking available (outdoor, for visitors and residents). *6 lounges with:* TVs (2), piano (1) and pool table (1). Guest suites available. *Residence has a:* library, visiting library, chapel, barber/beauty shop, visiting hairdresser, laundry room(s) (no cost) and tuck/gift shop (open Monday to Saturday, 9:00 a.m. – 5:00 p.m.). Residence provides newspaper delivery to individual suite. Mail delivered to private mailbox with key. *Recreation Facilities*: pool table, billiards, shuffleboard, exercise room, craft room, card room and raised garden. Posted schedule of activities. Internal newsletter for residents. *Recreational Programs*: exercise, shopping, theatre, parties, entertainment, art classes, pet visiting, day trips and Aromatherapy.
OTHER SERVICES: *Housekeeping*: weekly (included in fee). *Laundry*: linen, towel & personal (included in fee). Laundry savings apply if resident/family does the personal laundry. Either staff or resident label clothing (extra fee if staff to apply name labels). Transportation to medical appointments (extra cost) and for group social activities (transportation to planned outings is included). 24-hour security. Nightly security checks. Telephone ($30.00/month). Cable TV (resident responsible). Utilities (included in fee). Medication administration. Weekly bathing assistance.
RENTAL INFORMATION: Rates may vary. Extra cost for 2nd person sharing suite ($745.00/month). Rent paid monthly. *Payment Options*: cheques and pre-authorized payments. Rent increases as per Provincial Tenancy Legislation, reviewed annually with 3 months' notice given. Short-term respite and trial stays available (care packages available).

Did you know?

There is an array of online publications about Arthritis, including general information, health and wellness tips, medication options as well as many other valuable tools available on the website of the Arthritis Society. Look in the *Education* section of **www.arthritis.ca.**

WESTMOUNT TERRACE

723 Rymal Road West, Hamilton, ON L9B 2W1
Tel: (905) 318-3090 • Fax: (905) 318-3091
Email: **westmount.terrace@gmail.com**
Website: **www.westmountterrace.ca**
Contact: **Melissa Oakes or Debbie Piett**
Capacity: **51 residents** • Subsidies: **none**
Price: **$2,485.00 - $2,694.00/month**

At Westmount Terrace, we care. Your comfort is our utmost concern. Our home is your home. Located on Hamilton's West Mountain, our intimate family environment provides a full range of services and amenities. We invite you to come and enjoy our inviting lounges and activity areas. Or perhaps, afternoon tea with a friend or a stroll around our garden. Whatever your choice, you are sure to enjoy the variety of activities, new friendships, and facilities available to you. At Westmount Terrace we offer short-stay accommodation and services. Join us at the Terrace for a short-stay to recuperate from or following a hospitalization, surgery or illness. Our residence is ideal if you are in need of extra care, while your family is away or if you want a change of scenery or if you just want a trial stay in our comfortable and elegant home. Our short stay suite is fully furnished with all the services provided. We offer this enhanced program on a daily rate basis.

RESIDENCE INFORMATION: 13 years in operation. *Near:* Upper Paradise Road and Rymal Road. Decorated in 2009. 2 floors, 2 elevators. Wheelchair accessible. *Funding Base:* Corporate/for profit. *Owned by:* Westmount Terrace I Inc. 51 units. *Average Waiting Period*: varies. *Average Age*: 85. Can sometimes accommodate cognitively impaired people (mild and must not wander). Can sometimes accommodate physically challenged people. Residents have a dress code (residents must be dressed to attend meals). Smoking allowed (outside on front or back patio). Alcohol allowed (not in public areas unless part of activity). *Restrictions around Visitors/Visiting Hours:* visitors are to sign in & out; all entries are locked 8:00 p.m., intercom for visitors after hours. *Procedures to leave the premises on a temporary basis...*Short-term: sign in/out. Overnight: staff member must be notified. Holidays: staff member must be notified and dates given. *Languages:* English. Will accept Public Guardian and Trustee clients. Main doors of residence secured at night only. *Close to:* Public Transit, Shopping, Churches and Major Highway. Licensed under the Retirement Homes Act.
STAFFING: *Available Staff/Services*: Pharmacy, Social Work, Recreation Therapy, Occupational Therapy (CCAC), Physiotherapy (CCAC), Denturist, Dietitian, Podiatry, Speech Pathology (CCAC), Chiropody, Audiology/Hearing Clinic, Dentist, X-Ray/Ultrasound and GP & Specialty Clinics. *External services arranged by:* residence and/or family/resident. Staff trained *re*: visually, hearing and cognitively impaired. 24-hour nursing and other staff. RNs, RPNs and PSWs on staff. Can retain own MD. Police Check or Vulnerable Person Screening is done for all new staff.
HEALTH SERVICES: Medication administration (must be administered over 85 years of age) and/or supervision. Vitals monitored if required. Will accept (but not provide special assistance for) residents who require ostomies. Will accept and provide special assistance for residents who require oxygen and catheters. Assistance with dressing available. Weekly assistance with bathing available. Care plans done. Different levels of care available. Lab service (visiting). Residents can purchase outside resources and use agency of their choice. Clinic area for medical visits. Will help locate higher level of care if needed (Administrator assists family and resident through CCAC).
ACCOMMODATION: *Choice of suites available*: all private. *In all suites*: locks, kitchenette, bar fridge, storage, window coverings, light fixtures, linens, smoke detector, sprinkler, emergency response system with wearable pendant/bracelet, air conditioning (terminal air conditioner) and thermostats for heating & cooling. Private bathrooms with grab bars, tubs and showers with non-slip surfaces. In-suite cable TV if resident arranges with cable company. Can have own phone number if resident arranges with phone

company. Unfurnished suites, furnished suites available for short stays. *Restrictions on electrical appliances*: kettles must have an automatic shut-off, toasters & irons are not permitted in suites. No pets allowed.
DINING SERVICE: All meals included in fee and served in dining room daily. *Sittings per meal:* Breakfast: 2, Lunch: 1, Dinner: 1. *Menu choices available:* Breakfast: 2, Lunch: 2, Dinner: 2. *Guest Meals*: Breakfast $5.00, Lunch $5.00, Dinner $7.00. *Special Diets*: Low Salt, Diabetic, Celiac and Lactose Free. Tray service to room if ill. 3 snacks/day. Fruit available in dining room and refreshment available on request.
AMENITIES AND ACTIVITIES: Parking available (outdoor, for visitors and residents). *3 lounges with:* TVs (2) and piano (1). *Residence has a:* library, visiting library, barber/beauty shop, visiting hairdresser and laundry room(s) (no cost). Resident can arrange newspaper delivery to individual suite. Mail delivered to individual suite. Posted schedule of activities. Internal newsletter for residents. *Recreational Programs*: exercise, shopping, parties, entertainment, art classes, day trips, baking & cooking class, happy hour, social tea, regular games, outings and fundraisers.
OTHER SERVICES: *Housekeeping*: weekly (included in fee). *Laundry*: linen, towel & personal (included in fee). Transportation to medical appointments (first come, first serve basis) and for group social activities. 24-hour security. Nightly security checks. Telephone & Cable TV (resident responsible). Utilities (included in fee).
RENTAL INFORMATION: Rates may vary. Rent paid monthly. *Payment Options*: cheques and post-dated cheques. Rent increases as per Provincial Tenancy Legislation, annual for resident with 3 months' notice given. Short-term respite and trial stays available (both $90.00/day).

♦ HAMILTON (ANCASTER) ♦

CARRINGTON PLACE RETIREMENT RESIDENCE

75 Dunham Drive, Ancaster, ON L9G 1X7
Tel: (905) 648-0343 • Fax: (905) 648-9581
Email: **paulakamula.carringtonplace@gmail.com**
Website: **www.carringtonplaceretirement.ca**
Contact: **Paula Kamula**
Capacity: **65 residents** • Subsidies: **none**
Price: **$2,400.00 - $4,350.00/month**

Nestled in the heart of Ancaster, Carrington Place offers security and peace of mind. A beautiful location off the main roads but close to shopping. Our residents enjoy a short walk to all the amenities including local churches. Our relaxed and caring staff provide a nurturing environment for our seniors in which to thrive. A full complement of social activities, entertainment and outings is tailored by our Activity Director based on input from the Residents' Council. We offer in-house physiotherapy, manicures & pedicures, a full exercise program and visiting pastoral care provided by different denominations in the local community. In addition to our nutritional home-style meals, we offer a tailor-made menu for those with varying health considerations. Carrington Place is elegant, clean and bright. We take pride in our home, because we want to make it yours.

RESIDENCE INFORMATION: 23 years in operation. *Near:* Highway 2 and Wilson Road. Decorated in 2004. Handrails in hallways. 3 floors, 1 elevator. Central PA system. *Funding Base:* Corporate/for profit. *Owned by:* Villabar. 64 units. *Average Waiting Period*: varies. *Average Age*: 85. Can sometimes accommodate cognitively impaired & physically challenged people. Residents have a dress code. Smoking allowed (smoking area is on the back patio at the west end). Alcohol allowed (with doctors permission, Happy Hour twice/week, otherwise no alcohol in public areas). *Restrictions around Visitors/Visiting Hours:* entries are locked at 9:00 p.m. & visitors must ring the buzzer; visitors are required to sign in/out. *Procedures to leave the premises on a temporary basis...*Short-term: sign out

sheets at front desk. Overnight: inform Charge Nurse. Holidays: specify in writing to Manager, length of time away and dates; after 7 days away, resident pays rent. *Languages:* English, Latvian, German, French & Dutch. Will accept Public Guardian and Trustee clients. Main doors of residence secured at night only. *Close to:* Public Transit, Shopping, Churches, Seniors' Centre, Library, Major Highway and Local Hospital (Hamilton Health Sciences Corporation – McMaster University Medical Centre Site). *Predominant Cultural Group:* Anglo-Saxon. Licensed under the Retirement Homes Act.

STAFFING: *Available Staff/Services*: Pharmacy, Social Work (CCAC), Recreation Therapy, Occupational Therapy (CCAC), Physiotherapy (CCAC), Dietitian (CCAC), Companions, Podiatry (CCAC), Chaplaincy, Speech Pathology (CCAC), Chiropody, Audiology/Hearing Clinic, Nails, Pet Therapy and Volunteer Companions. *External services arranged by:* residence and/or family/resident. Staff trained *re*: visually, hearing and cognitively impaired. 24-hour staff. RNs, RPNs, HCAs, PSWs and UCPs on staff. Can retain own MD. Nurses will assist in finding doctors as needed. Staff members are bonded. Police Check or Vulnerable Person Screening is done for all new staff.

HEALTH SERVICES: Medication administered if required. Vitals monitored if required. Will accept (but not provide special assistance for) residents who require catheters and ostomies. Will accept and provide special assistance for residents who require oxygen. Weekly assistance with bathing available. *Extra baths:* $15.00/half hour. Care plans done. Different levels of care available. Private Duty/Extra Care available ($25.00/hour). Lab service (visiting, $25.00/visit). Residents can purchase outside resources and use agency of their choice. Physiotherapy is provided 5 days/week free with a referral from physician. Will help locate higher level of care if needed (via CCAC).

ACCOMMODATION: *Choice of suites available*: Addisson, Bentley & Carlyle or adjoining rooms. Kitchenettes and walk-in showers available. *In all suites*: locks, storage, window coverings, light fixtures, linens, fire alarm, smoke detector, sprinkler, call bell, emergency response system with wearable pendant/bracelet, air conditioning (cooling system for public areas/corridors; window units in suites) and thermostats for heating. Air conditioning window units available ($300.00/season). Private bathrooms with call bells, grab bars, tubs and showers with non-slip surfaces. In-suite cable TV if resident arranges with cable company. Can have own phone number if resident arranges with phone company. Unfurnished suites, furnished suites available for short stays. Restrictions on electrical appliances. Suites can be shared (by spouses or friends only), roommate picked by resident. Pets allowed (cats only - in suites located on the lower level; immunization records must be provided).

DINING SERVICE: All meals included in fee and served in dining room daily. *Sittings per meal:* Breakfast: 1, Lunch: 1, Dinner: 1. *Menu choices available:* Breakfast: 2, Lunch: 2, Dinner: 2. *Guest Meals*: Breakfast $7.00, Lunch $9.00, Dinner $7.00. *Special Diets*: Vegetarian, Low Salt, Diabetic, Celiac's and Medical Diets. Tray service to room if ill (no charge as long as doctor orders). Unlimited snacks available at any time. Snacks are available 24-hours/day as well as coffee, tea, and hot drinks in the dining room so that residents may help themselves at any time. Party facilities.

AMENITIES AND ACTIVITIES: Parking available (outdoor, for visitors and residents). *2 lounges with:* TV (1), pianos (2), DVD & VCR (1) and gas fireplace (1). Guest suites available ($50.00/night). *Residence has a:* library, visiting library, chapel, barber/beauty shop, visiting hairdresser and laundry room(s) (no cost). Banking services on premises (Monday to Friday, 9:00 a.m. - 4:30 p.m.). Resident can arrange newspaper delivery to breakfast table (extra cost). Mail delivered to main desk. *Recreation Facilities*: shuffleboard, exercise room, craft room, card room, garden and puzzle area. Posted schedule of activities. Internal newsletter for residents. *Recreational Programs*: exercise, shopping, theatre, parties, entertainment, Horticultural Club, Happy Hour, social tea, Residents' Council, art classes, pet visiting, day trips and van outings.
OTHER SERVICES: *Housekeeping*: daily and weekly (included in fee). *Laundry*: linen, & personal (extra cost for Independent Package; included for Full Service); dry cleaning (resident invoiced 10% discount). Facilities available for those who wish to do their own laundry. Transportation to medical appointments (extra cost - taxi service/private duty) and for group social activities. 24-hour security. Nightly security checks (no cost). Telephone & Cable TV (arranged by resident/family). Utilities (included in fee). Seasonal air conditioner provided for a minimal cost.
RENTAL INFORMATION: Rates may vary. Extra cost for 2nd person sharing suite ($675.00/month). Rent paid monthly. *Payment Options*: cheques and post-dated cheques. Rent increases as per Provincial Tenancy Legislation, annual for resident with 3 months' notice given. Short-term respite and trial stays available (both $95.00/day).

HIGHGATE RESIDENCE

325 Fiddler's Green Road, Ancaster, ON L9G 1W9
Tel: (905) 648-8399 • Fax: (905) 648-5190
Email: **info@highgateresidence.com**
Website: **www.highgateresidence.com**
Contact: **Christoph Summer and Paula Wiggins**
Capacity: **45 residents** • Subsidies: **none**
Price: **$3,045.00 - $4,600.00/month**

Privately owned and operated by the Summer family. Located in the scenic town of Ancaster, this friendly home environment is surrounded by history and tradition, while only minutes away from shopping, entertainment, the finest recreational facilities and the nearby city of Hamilton. The residence is encircled by beautifully landscaped lawns and gardens with walking paths, gazebo and patios.

RESIDENCE INFORMATION: 25 years in operation. *Near:* Fiddler's Green Road and Highway 403. Decorated in 2012. Handrails in hallways. 2 floors, 1 elevator. *Funding Base:* Corporate/for profit. *Owned by:* Christoph, Ursula, Gord & Eva Summer. 40 units. *Average Waiting Period*: varies. *Average Age*: 88. Can accommodate cognitively impaired people (early stage only, can't accommodate wanderers, exit-seekers & aggressive behavior). Can accommodate physically challenged people (must be ambulatory without supervision). Smoke-free residence. Alcohol allowed. *Procedures to leave the premises on a temporary basis*...Short-term: notify receptionist. Overnight & Holidays: notify nurse. *Languages:* English & German. Will accept Public Guardian and Trustee clients. Main doors of residence secured at night only. *Close to:* Public Transit, Shopping, Churches, Seniors' Centre, Library, Major Highway and Local Hospital (Hamilton Health Sciences Corporation—McMaster University Medical Centre Site). Member of ORCA. Licensed under the Retirement Homes Act.
STAFFING: *Available Staff/Services*: Pharmacy, Social Work (CCAC), Recreation Therapy, Occupational Therapy (CCAC), Physiotherapy, Dietitian (CCAC), Chaplaincy, Speech Pathology (CCAC), Chiropody and Hairdresser. *External services arranged by:* residence and/or family/resident. Staff trained *re*: visually, hearing and cognitively impaired. 24-hour nursing staff. RPNs and PSWs on staff. Visiting MD. Can retain own MD. Police Check or Vulnerable Person Screening is done for all new staff.

HEALTH SERVICES: Medication administered if required (must use our pharmacy). Vitals monitored if required. Will accept and provide special assistance for residents who require oxygen, catheters, ostomies and feeding tubes. Assistance with dressing available ($12.25/half hour). Weekly assistance with bathing available. *Extra baths:* $12.25/half hour. Care plans done. Different levels of care available. Private Duty/Extra Care available ($24.50/hour). Residents can purchase outside resources and use agency of their choice. MD visits residents in their rooms/suites. Will help locate higher level of care if needed.
ACCOMMODATION: *Choice of suites available*: 40 private bed/sitting rooms and 1-bedroom units in a variety of sizes. All rooms have a private 4-piece bathroom. Larger rooms have kitchenettes. *In all suites*: locks, storage, window coverings, light fixtures, linens, smoke detector, call bell, air conditioning (individual suite air conditioner & heater with thermostat control), telephone outlets and high speed internet. Private bathrooms with call bells, grab bars and tubs with non-slip surfaces. In-suite cable TV if resident arranges with cable company (residence charges extra). Can have own phone number if resident arranges with phone company (residence charges extra). Unfurnished suites, furnished suites available for short stays. *Restrictions on electrical appliances*: electric kettles must have automatic shut-off. Suites can be shared (by couples only). No pets allowed.
DINING SERVICE: All meals included in fee and served in dining room daily. *Sittings per meal:* Breakfast: 1, Lunch: 1, Dinner: 1. *Menu choices available:* Breakfast: 6, Lunch: 4, Dinner: 2. *Guest Meals*: Lunch $7.00, Dinner $10.00. *Special Diets*: Vegetarian, Low Salt, Diabetic, Soft, Renal and Diverticulitis. Tray service to room if ill (no charge as long as doctor orders). Unlimited snacks available at any time. Party facilities. All meals prepared on-site.
AMENITIES AND ACTIVITIES: Parking available (outdoor, for visitors and residents). *5 lounges with:* TV (1), piano (1), kitchenette lounges (2) and crafts & games lounge (1). *Residence has a:* library, chapel, barber/beauty shop and visiting hairdresser. Resident can arrange newspaper delivery to main desk (extra cost). Mail delivered to main desk. *Recreation Facilities*: shuffleboard, exercise room, craft room, card room, sunroom and private dining room. Posted schedule of activities. *Recreational Programs*: exercise, shopping, theatre, parties, entertainment, day trips, physiotherapy, fashion shows, bingo, cards, slide shows, resident plays and gardening.
OTHER SERVICES: *Housekeeping*: weekly (included in fee). *Laundry*: linen, towel & personal (included in fee); dry cleaning (extra cost). Transportation to medical appointments (chauffeur service within Ancaster area) and for group social activities. Nightly security checks. Telephone & Cable TV (extra cost). Utilities (included in fee).
RENTAL INFORMATION: Rates may vary. A Suite - $3,045.00/month; B Suite -$3,915.00/month; C Suite - $3,915.00/month; D Suite - $4,400.00/month; E Suite - $4,600.00/month. Extra cost for 2nd person sharing suite ($700.00/month). Rent paid monthly. *Payment Options*: cheques and pre-authorized payments. Rent increases as per Provincial Tenancy Legislation, annual for resident with 3 months' notice given.

THE MEADOWLANDS RETIREMENT RESIDENCE

1248 Mohawk Road, Ancaster, ON L9K 1P5
Tel: (905) 304-1968 • Fax: (905) 304-1949
Email: **dcarlesso@meadowlandsretirement.com**
Website: **www.meadowlandsretirement.com**
Contact: **Donna Carlesso**
Capacity: **181 residents** • Subsidies: **none**
Price: **$3,150.00 - $4,950.00/month**

As lovely as its name implies, The Meadowlands Retirement Residence offers independent retirement living with the peace-of-mind of knowing professional nursing is available 24-hours/day. Well-appointed spacious 1-bedroom & 2-bedroom suites with kitchenette. Three expertly prepared meals/day. Daily housekeeping. Various recreational programs. Beautifully appointed amenity areas including a well-stocked library with fireplace, several espresso bars, heated aquatic indoor swimming pool, fitness

centre, home theatre room and horticultural centre. Close proximity to Ancaster town centre shops, theatre and community services. Luxury and comfort await you. *Who could ask for anything more?*

RESIDENCE INFORMATION: 12 years in operation. *Near:* Lincoln Alexander Parkway and Mohawk Road. Decorated in 2010. 4 floors, 6 elevators. Wheelchair accessible. Central PA system. *Funding Base:* Corporate/for profit. *Owned by:* Mohawk Seniors Incorporated. *Managed by:* V!VA Retirement Communities. 168 units. *Average Waiting Period*: varies. *Average Age*: 83. Can accommodate physically challenged people with restrictions (post-surgery - e.g. hip or knee replacement). Smoke-free residence. Alcohol allowed (In suites, not in common areas). *Procedures to leave the premises on a temporary basis...*notification of departure and return. *Languages:* English, Italian, Polish, Spanish & German. Will accept Public Guardian and Trustee clients. Main doors of residence secured at night only. *Close to:* Public Transit, Shopping, Churches, Seniors' Centre, Library, Major Highway and Local Hospital (Hamilton Health Sciences Corporation – McMaster University Medical Centre Site). Licensed under the Retirement Homes Act.

STAFFING: *Available Staff/Services*: Pharmacy, Social Work (CCAC), Recreation Therapy, Occupational Therapy, Visiting Dentist, Physiotherapy, Dietitian, Podiatry, Chaplaincy, Speech Pathology (CCAC), Chiropody, Beauty & Barber, Chiropractic and Massage Therapy. *External services arranged by:* residence and/or family/resident. 24-hour nursing and other staff. RPNs and PSWs on staff. Visiting MD (weekly). Can retain own MD. Police Check or Vulnerable Person Screening is done for all new staff.

HEALTH SERVICES: Medication administration (at nurse's office, residence has contracted pharmacy) and/or supervision. Vitals monitored if required. Will accept (but not provide special assistance for) residents who require catheters and ostomies. Will accept and provide special assistance for residents who require oxygen. Assistance with bathing available twice/week ($80.00/month). Extra baths: $10.00/bath. Care plans done. Lab service (visiting, $25.00/visit). Residents can purchase outside resources and use agency of their choice. Clinic area for medical visits. Will help locate higher level of care if needed (CCAC).

ACCOMMODATION: *Choice of suites available*: all private suites, 2-bedroom (13), 1-bedroom (150) & bachelor (3) units. *In all suites*: locks, kitchenette, bar fridge, microwave, storage, window coverings, light fixtures, linens, fire alarm, smoke detector, sprinkler, call bell, air conditioning (central) and thermostats for heating & cooling. Private bathrooms with call bells, grab bars, tubs and showers with non-slip surfaces and elevated toilet seats. In-suite cable TV if resident arranges with cable company. Can have own phone number if resident arranges with phone company. Unfurnished suites, furnished suites available for short stays. *Restrictions on electrical appliances*: toaster, kettle, coffee maker only allowed. Suites can be shared (couples, family members). No pets allowed.

DINING SERVICE: All meals included in fee and served in dining room daily. *Sittings per meal:* Breakfast: 2, Lunch: 2, Dinner: 2. *Menu choices available:* Breakfast: 3, Lunch: 5, Dinner: 5. *Guest Meals*: Breakfast $5.00, Lunch $8.50, Dinner $14.00. *Special Diets*: Low Salt and Diabetic. Tray service to room if ill (no charge for a maximum time of 4 days). 3 snacks/day and unlimited snacks available at any time. Open pantry. Private dining room will seat 12 and party facilities available.

AMENITIES AND ACTIVITIES: Parking available (outdoor, for visitors and residents). *15 lounges with:* TVs (5) and pianos (2). *Residence has a:* library, visiting library, barber/beauty shop, visiting hairdresser, laundry room(s) (no cost), tuck/gift shop (open Monday, Wednesday & Saturday). Resident can arrange newspaper delivery to individual suite. Mail delivered to private mailbox with key. *Recreation Facilities*: pool table, billiards, shuffleboard, exercise room, greenhouse, craft room, card room, swimming pool and air hockey table. Posted schedule of activities. Internal newsletter for residents. *Recreational Programs*: exercise, shopping, theatre, parties, entertainment, art classes, pet visiting, day trips, pool activities and pool fitness programs.

OTHER SERVICES: *Housekeeping*: weekly (included in fee). *Laundry*: linen & towel (included in fee); personal ($80.00/month) & dry cleaning (extra cost - arrangements for pick-up and delivery). Laundry

facilities available on all floors. Transportation for group social activities. Nightly security checks. Telephone & Cable TV (arranged with local provider). Utilities (included in fee).
RENTAL INFORMATION: Rates may vary. 1-bedroom (468 sq. ft.- 633 sq. ft.) - $3,150.00 to $4,950.00/month; 2-bedroom (768 sq. ft. - sq. ft.) - $4,300.00 to $4,800.00/month. Extra cost for 2nd person sharing suite ($750.00/month). Rent paid monthly. *Payment Options*: pre-authorized payments. Rent increases as per Provincial Tenancy Legislation, annual with 3 months' notice given. Short-term respite and trial stays available (both $125.00/day; $150.00/couple/day).

KANATA **THE ROYALE – KANATA**

Please see OTTAWA WEST (KANATA) for information on this residence.

♦ KESWICK ♦

CEDARVALE LODGE RETIREMENT COMMUNITY

121 Morton Avenue, Keswick, ON L4P 3T5
Tel: (905) 476-2656 • Fax: (905) 476-5689
Email: **donna.taylor@specialty-care.com**
Website: **www.specialtyliving.ca**
Contact: **Donna Taylor**
Capacity: **200 residents** • Subsidies: **none**
Price: **$2,695.00/month and up**

Located near Lake Simcoe - Cedarvale Lodge has redefined Retirement Living with a thoughtfully designed Home that offers great value and impressive services. Here you can do things your way – while continuing to enjoy things that matter – time with family, connections with friends and being involved in the community. Our innovative *Zest for Life™* signature service promotes the health and well-being of each resident by focusing on the needs of mind, body and spirit. We work with you one-on-one to connect you with activities and services that spark your particular interests. Come and explore Cedarvale Lodge for yourself. If you are looking for a rewarding place to live and you too have a zest for life – our doors are open!

RESIDENCE INFORMATION: 24 years in operation. *Near:* Woodbine Avenue and Morton Avenue. Decorated in 2012. Handrails in hallways. 3 floors, 2 elevators. Wheelchair accessible. Central PA system. *Owned and managed by:* Specialty Care. 130 units. *Average Waiting Period*: varies. *Average Age*: 80. Can accommodate cognitively impaired people with restrictions (no risk of elopement or aggressive behaviour). Can accommodate physically challenged people with restrictions (assess individually). Smoking allowed (designated outdoor area). Alcohol allowed. *Procedures to leave the premises on a temporary basis...*Short-term & Overnight: sign in/out book. Holidays: notify Administration. *Languages:* English. Will accept Public Guardian and Trustee clients. Main doors of residence secured at night only. *Close to:* Shopping, Churches, Seniors' Centre, Library, Major Highway and Local Hospital (Southlake Regional Health Centre). Member of ORCA & Georgina Chamber of Commerce and East Gwillimbury. Licensed under the Retirement Homes Act.
STAFFING: *Available Staff/Services*: Pharmacy, Social Work (CCAC), Recreation Therapy, Occupational Therapy, Visiting Dentist, Physiotherapy, Denturist, Dietitian, Companions, Podiatry, Chaplaincy, Speech Pathology (CCAC), Chiropody, Audiology/Hearing Clinic and Ontario Telemedicine Link to Southlake Regional Health Centre. *External services arranged by:* residence and/or family/resident. Staff trained *re:*

visually, hearing and cognitively impaired. 24-hour nursing and other staff. RPNs, PSWs and UCPs on staff. Visiting MD (weekly). Can retain own MD. Police Check or Vulnerable Person Screening is done for all new staff.

HEALTH SERVICES: Medication administration and/or supervision. Vitals monitored if required. Will accept and provide special assistance for residents who require oxygen, catheters and ostomies. Assistance with dressing available (cost). Weekly assistance with bathing available (cost). Care plans done. Different levels of care available. Private Duty/Extra Care available ($33.50/hour). Assisted Living Area ($465.00/month; 1 - 2 months waiting period). Lab service (visiting). Residents can purchase outside resources and use agency of their choice. MD visits residents in their rooms/suites. Clinic area for medical visits. Will help locate higher level of care if needed (staff arrange for CCAC assessment).

ACCOMMODATION: *Choice of suites available*: studio, deluxe studio, 1-bedroom & 2-bedroom suites. *In all suites*: locks, storage, window coverings, light fixtures, fire alarm, smoke detector, sprinkler, call bell, emergency response system with wearable pendant/bracelet, air conditioning (incremental units) and thermostats for heating & cooling. New addition offers kitchenettes, walk-in closets, some in-suite laundry, electric fireplaces, balconies and dens. Private bathrooms with call bells, grab bars, tubs and showers. In-suite cable TV provided by residence (residence charges extra). Can have own phone number provided by residence (residence charges extra). Furnished & unfurnished suites available. *Restrictions on electrical appliances*: no hot plates; Maintenance approval and safety check during move-in. Suites can be shared (pending availability of beds). Pets allowed (small animals, approved by Administration).

DINING SERVICE: All meals included in fee and served in dining room daily. *Sittings per meal:* Breakfast: 3, Lunch: 3, Dinner: 3. *Menu choices available:* Breakfast: 3, Lunch: 8, Dinner: 8. *Guest Meals*: Breakfast $7.25, Lunch $9.25, Dinner $11.50. *Special Diets*: Vegetarian, Low Salt, Diabetic and Healthy Choices (menu options identified). Tray service to room if ill (no charge for a maximum time of 3 days). Unlimited snacks available at any time. Open pantry. There is a café available with use of a full kitchen and seating area. Party facilities.

AMENITIES AND ACTIVITIES: Parking available (outdoor, for visitors and residents). *8 lounges with:* TVs (5), piano (1), café /kitchen (2) and card/games room (2). Guest suites available. *Residence has a:* library, visiting library, chapel, barber/beauty shop, visiting hairdresser, laundry room(s) (no cost) and tuck/gift shop (open Monday to Friday, 9:00 a.m.- 5:00 p.m.; Saturday & Sunday, 11:30 a.m. - 5:00 p.m.). Resident can arrange newspaper delivery to main desk (extra cost). Mail delivered to private mailbox with key. *Recreation Facilities*: pool table, billiards, shuffleboard, exercise room, craft room, card room, large community party room and private dining room. Bus for outings. Posted schedule of activities. Internal newsletter for residents. *Recreational Programs*: exercise, shopping, theatre, parties, entertainment, art classes, pet visiting and day trips. Full calendar of programs 7 days/week.

OTHER SERVICES: *Housekeeping*: daily and weekly (included in fee, daily & weekly in Assisted Living: weekly in new addition). *Laundry*: linen, towel & personal (full laundry service included in Assisted Living; for Independent, linen laundry service weekly; personal is extra); dry cleaning (sent out, price list is provided in home). Staff label clothing (included in fee). 24-hour security. Nightly security checks. Telephone & Cable TV (hook up and monthly cost). Utilities (included in fee).

RENTAL INFORMATION: Rates may vary. Extra cost for 2nd person sharing suite ($675.00/month). Rent paid monthly. *Payment Options*: pre-authorized payments. Rent increases as per Provincial Tenancy Legislation, annual for resident with 3 months' notice given. Short-term respite and trial stays available (based on room availability).

Did you know?

The Government of Ontario has produced several publications for seniors on various important topics. To read or download any or all of these publications visit **www.seniors.gov.on.ca.** Look under the *Publications* section.

◆ KINGSTON ◆

KINGSDALE CHATEAU

520 Kingsdale Avenue, Kingston, ON K7M 9B6
Tel: (613) 547-4884 • Fax: (613) 547-5897
Email: **5158-manager@holidaytouch.com**
Website: **www.kingsdalechateau.com**
Contact: **Community Managers**
Capacity: **114 units** • Subsidies: **none**
Price: **$2,895.00/month and up (rates may vary)**

Holiday Retirement believes retirement living should be relaxing and carefree, spent doing the things you love. That's why our communities provide a unique independent retirement lifestyle in a warm and welcoming environment. In one affordable, all-inclusive month-to-month rent, residents enjoy 3 delicious chef-prepared meals daily, enriching activities to share with friendly neighbours, housekeeping service, complimentary transportation, and so much more. Each Holiday community also features 2 sets of compassionate, dedicated live-in Managers available 24/7 to ensure safety and security. We do not provide any health care services; however, residents are welcome to receive services from any outside home health care provider of their choice to help them continue enjoying life at our community. Discover the peace-of-mind, happiness and fulfillment you deserve. Contact us today to schedule your personal tour!

RESIDENCE INFORMATION: 15 years in operation. *Near:* Centennial Drive and Kingsdale Avenue. Decorated in 2013. Handrails in hallways. 3 floors, 1 elevator. Wheelchair accessible. Central PA system. *Funding Base:* Corporate/for profit. *Owned and managed by:* Holiday Retirement. *Average Waiting Period*: varies. *Average Age*: 82. Can accommodate cognitively impaired people with restrictions. Can accommodate physically challenged people (must be independent; wheelchairs, walkers, scooter are welcome). Residents have a dress code (casual, no sleepwear in common areas). Smoking allowed (in own apartments). Alcohol allowed (in own apartments). *Procedures to leave the premises on a temporary basis...*Overnight & Holidays: let Front Office know. *Languages:* English. Will accept Public Guardian and Trustee clients. Main doors of residence secured at night only. *Close to:* Public Transit, Shopping, Churches, Seniors' Centre, Library, Major Highway and Local Hospital (Kingston General Hospital).
STAFFING: *External services arranged by:* family/resident. 24-hour staff. Can retain own MD. Staff members are bonded. Police Check or Vulnerable Person Screening is done for all new staff.
HEALTH SERVICES: Will accept (but not provide special assistance for) residents who require oxygen, catheters, ostomies and feeding tubes. Residents can purchase outside resources and use agency of their choice. Will help locate higher level of care if needed (Information available from Front Office and local government health agencies).
ACCOMMODATION: *Choice of suites available*: studio, 1-bedroom & 2-bedroom suites. *In all suites*: locks, kitchenette, bar fridge, window coverings, light fixtures, linens, fire alarm, smoke detector, sprinkler, call bell, air conditioning (through the wall) and thermostats for heating & cooling. Most have patios/balconies. Private bathrooms with call bells, grab bars, tubs and showers with non-slip surfaces. In-suite cable TV provided by residence. Can have own phone number if resident arranges with phone company. Furnished & unfurnished suites available. *Restrictions on electrical appliances*: no hot plates or stoves. Suites can be shared, roommate picked by resident. Pets allowed.
DINING SERVICE: All meals included in fee and served in dining room daily. *Sittings per meal:* Breakfast: 1, Lunch: 1, Dinner: 1. *Menu choices available:* Breakfast: 5, Lunch: 6, Dinner: 5. *Guest Meals*: Breakfast $8.00, Lunch $10.00, Dinner $8.00. *Special Diets*: Vegetarian, Low Salt and Diabetic. Tray service to room if ill. 2 snacks/day. Party facilities. Private Dining Area. Large meal of day served at noon-time. Fresh fruit, coffee, tea & goodies available all day.

AMENITIES AND ACTIVITIES: Parking available (outdoor, for visitors and indoor & outdoor for residents). *4 lounges with:* TV (1), piano (1), computer kiosks (1) and fitness equipment (1). Guest suites available ($75.00/night). *Residence has a:* library, chapel, barber/beauty shop and laundry room(s) (no cost). Resident can arrange newspaper delivery to individual suite. Mail delivered to private mailbox with key. *Recreation Facilities*: pool table, billiards, shuffleboard, exercise room, craft room and card room. Posted schedule of activities. Internal newsletter for residents. *Recreational Programs*: exercise, shopping, theatre, parties, entertainment, art classes, pet visiting, day trips and resident suggested activities.
OTHER SERVICES: *Housekeeping*: weekly (included in fee). *Laundry*: linen & towel (included in fee). Free laundry rooms for personal use. Transportation to medical appointments and for group social activities. 24-hour security. Cable TV & Utilities (included in fee). Charge for garage parking.
RENTAL INFORMATION: Rates may vary. Rate listed above is based on single occupancy. Extra cost for 2nd person sharing suite ($685.00/month; please call for specifics). Rent paid monthly. *Payment Options*: cheques, post-dated cheques and pre-authorized payments. Rent increases indexed to inflation as per Provincial Tenancy Legislation, annual for resident with 3 months' notice given. Will help resident move into residence. Trial stays available (see Managers).

THE ROSEWOOD RETIREMENT RESIDENCE

833 Sutton Mills Court, Kingston, ON K7P 2N9
Tel: (613) 384-7131 • Fax: (613) 634-3247
Email: **rhonda.jarvis@specialty-care.com**
Website: **www.specialtyliving.ca**
Contact: **Rhonda Jarvis**
Capacity: **70 residents** • Subsidies: **none**
Price: **$3,044.00/month and up**

The Rosewood has built a reputation for providing exceptional care, comfort and quality services. Our innovative *Zest for Life™* signature service promotes the health and well-being of each resident by focusing on the needs of mind, body and spirit. We work with you one-on-one to connect you with activities and services that spark your particular interests. Come and explore The Rosewood for yourself. If you are looking for a rewarding place to live and you too have a zest for life – our doors are open!

RESIDENCE INFORMATION: 26 years in operation. *On:* Sutton Mills Court and Ridley Street. Decorated in 2009. Handrails in hallways. 1 floor, no elevators. Wheelchair accessible. Central PA system. *Owned by:* Kingstown Investments Inc. *Managed by:* Specialty Care. 65 units. *Average Waiting Period*: varies. *Average Age*: 86. Can sometimes accommodate cognitively impaired & physically challenged people (assessed individually). Smoke-free residence. Alcohol allowed. *Procedures to leave the premises on a temporary basis*...notify the Office. *Languages:* English. Will accept Public Guardian and Trustee clients. Main doors of residence secured at night only. *Close to:* Public Transit, Shopping, Churches, Seniors' Centre, Library, Major Highway and Local Hospitals (Hotel Dieu & Kingston General Hospitals). Member of ORCA & Kingston Chamber of Commerce. Licensed under the Retirement Homes Act.
STAFFING: *Available Staff/Services*: Pharmacy, Social Work (CCAC), Recreation Therapy, Dietitian (CCAC), Podiatry, Chaplaincy, Speech Pathology (CCAC), Relaxation Massage Therapy and Physiotherapy (on-site). *External services arranged by:* residence and/or family/resident. Staff trained *re*: visually, hearing and cognitively impaired. 24-hour nursing staff. RPNs, HCAs and PSWs on staff. Visiting MD (in home Wednesday mornings and on call). Can retain own MD. Police Check or Vulnerable Person Screening is done for all new staff.
HEALTH SERVICES: Medication administration (extra fee) and/or supervision. Vitals monitored if required. Will accept and provide special assistance for residents who require oxygen, catheters and ostomies. Assistance with dressing available ($450.00/month). Weekly assistance with bathing available

($25.75/half hour). Care plans done. Different levels of care available. Several health care services available through CCAC. Private Duty/Extra Care available. Lab service (visiting). Residents can purchase outside resources and use agency of their choice. MD visits residents in their rooms/suites. Will help locate higher level of care if needed (appointment made with CCAC for eligibility assessment).
ACCOMMODATION: *Choice of suites available*: studio & 1-bedroom units. *In all suites*: locks, storage, window coverings, light fixtures, smoke detector, call bell, emergency response system with wearable pendant/bracelet, air conditioning (units in some of the suites) and thermostats for heating. Kitchenettes in some suites. Private bathrooms with grab bars, tubs and showers. In-suite cable TV if resident arranges with cable company. Can have own phone extension number provided by residence (residence charges extra $35.00/month). Unfurnished suites, furnished suites available for short stays. *Restrictions on electrical appliances*: no hot plates, toaster ovens, auto shut-off kettles allowed; approval needed from Administration. Suites can be shared (by couples only), roommate picked by resident. Pets allowed (under 30 lbs. with Administrator's approval).
DINING SERVICE: All meals included in fee and served in dining room daily. *Sittings per meal:* Breakfast: 1, Lunch: 2, Dinner: 2. *Menu choices available:* Breakfast: 5, Lunch: 2, Dinner: 2. *Guest Meals*: Breakfast $8.00, Lunch $10.50, Dinner $11.50. *Special Diets*: Healthy Choices (menu options identified). Tray service to room if ill (no charge for a maximum time of 3 days). Unlimited snacks available at any time. Open pantry. Kitchenette available with fruit, cookies, crackers, milk, juices, tea and coffee 24-hours/day. In the evening hours sandwiches, cheese and crackers are available for residents. Party facilities.
AMENITIES AND ACTIVITIES: Parking available (outdoor, for visitors and residents). *4 lounges with:* TVs (3), piano (1), exercise equipment (1) and views of the gardens (1). *Residence has a:* library, chapel, barber/beauty shop, visiting hairdresser, laundry room(s) (no cost) and tuck/gift shop (hours vary). Resident can arrange newspaper delivery to dining room. Mail delivered to dining room. *Recreation Facilities*: shuffleboard, exercise room, craft room, card room, gazebo and library with computer. Posted schedule of activities. Internal newsletter for residents. *Recreational Programs*: exercise, shopping, theatre, parties, entertainment, art classes, pet visiting and day trips.
OTHER SERVICES: *Housekeeping*: daily and weekly. *Laundry*: linen & towel (included in fee); personal (extra cost) & dry cleaning (extra cost - staff can arrange if requested). Transportation to medical appointments (extra cost - through Bryden Transportation) and for group social activities (nominal fee to cover costs of residence bus). 24-hour security. Nightly security checks. Telephone (extra cost). Cable TV (extra cost - third party billing with Cogeco). Utilities (included in fee).
RENTAL INFORMATION: Rates may vary. Extra cost for 2nd person sharing suite ($675.00/month). Rent paid monthly. *Payment Options*: pre-authorized payments. Rent increases as per Provincial Tenancy Legislation, annual for resident with 3 months' notice given. Will help resident move into residence. Short-term respite ($115.00/day; if extra care is needed rate is $125.00/day) and trial stays ($100.00/day) available.

THE ROYALE - KINGSTON

2485 Princess Street, Kingston, ON K7M 3G1
Tel: (613) 634-5900
Email: **Kingston@theroyale.ca**
Website: **www.theroyale.ca**
Contact: **Community Relations Manager**
Capacity: **136 units** • Subsidies: **none**
Price: **$2,460.00 - $5,475.00/month**

This new state-of-the-art residence offers amenities, features and benefits that are unsurpassed. With the largest selection of 1-bedroom & 2-bedroom retirement suite/apartments in Kingston, these suites boast complete kitchens with stainless steel fridge, microwave and cooktop, hardwood flooring and spacious

bathrooms that will allow you to feel refreshed and relaxed from the moment you step in the door. Offering both Independent and Assisted Living lifestyles this is truly *Aging in Place*. With a saltwater pool, on-site theatre, demonstration kitchen, wine bar and library, this is living life to its fullest.

RESIDENCE INFORMATION: 5 years in operation. *Near:* Princess Street and Gardiners Avenue. Decorated in 2009. Handrails in some of the hallways. 5 floors, 3 elevators. Wheelchair accessible. *Funding Base:* Corporate/for profit. *Owned by:* Leisureworld Senior Care Corporation. *Average Waiting Period*: none. *Average Age*: 82. Can sometimes accommodate cognitively impaired people. Can accommodate physically challenged people. Smoke-free residence. Alcohol allowed. *Languages:* English. Will accept Public Guardian and Trustee clients. Main doors of residence secured at all times. *Close to:* Public Transit, Shopping, Churches, Seniors' Centre, Library, Major Highway and Local Hospital (Kingston General Hospital). Member of ORCA. Licensed under the Retirement Homes Act.
STAFFING: *Available Staff/Services*: Pharmacy, Social Work (CCAC), Recreation Therapy, Occupational Therapy (CCAC), Visiting Dentist, Physiotherapy, Dietitian (CCAC), Companions, Podiatry (CCAC) and Speech Pathology (CCAC). *External services arranged by:* residence and/or family/resident. Staff trained *re*: visually, hearing and cognitively impaired. 24-hour staff. RPNs and PSWs on staff. Can retain own MD. Police Check or Vulnerable Person Screening is done for all new staff.
HEALTH SERVICES: Medication administered if required. Vitals monitored if required. Will accept (but not provide special assistance for) residents who require oxygen, catheters, ostomies and feeding tubes. Assistance with dressing available (cost). Weekly assistance with bathing available (cost). Care plans done. Different levels of care available. Private Duty/Extra Care available. Residents can purchase outside resources and use agency of their choice. Will help locate higher level of care if needed.
ACCOMMODATION: *Choice of suites available*: studio, 1-bedroom & 2-bedroom units. *In all suites*: locks, kitchenette, bar fridge, microwave, cooktop, patio/balcony, storage, light fixtures, fire alarm, smoke detector, sprinkler, call bell, emergency response system with wearable pendant/bracelet, air conditioning (central) and thermostats for heating & cooling. Private bathrooms with call bells, tubs and showers with non-slip surfaces. In-suite cable TV provided by residence (residence charges extra $45.00/month). Can have own phone number provided by residence (residence charges extra $35.00/month). Unfurnished suites, furnished suites available for short stays. Suites can be shared (by couples only). Small pets welcome (dog walking service available).
DINING SERVICE: All meals included in fee and served in dining room daily. *Menu choices available:* Breakfast: 5, Lunch: 6, Dinner: 6. *Guest Meals*: Available. *Special Diets*: Vegetarian, Low Salt and Diabetic. Tray service to room if ill (no charge as long as doctor orders). 2 snacks/day. Party facilities.
AMENITIES AND ACTIVITIES: Parking available (outdoor, for visitors and indoor & outdoor for residents). Guest suites available ($99.00/night). *Residence has a:* library, visiting library, chapel, barber/beauty shop, visiting hairdresser, laundry room(s) (no cost) and tuck/gift shop. Resident can arrange newspaper delivery to individual suite. Mail delivered to private mailbox with key. *Recreation Facilities*: pool table, billiards, exercise room, card room, swimming pool, demonstration kitchen, outdoor mini-putt, spa, sauna and workshop. Posted schedule of activities. Internal newsletter for residents. *Recreational Programs*: exercise, shopping, theatre, parties, entertainment, art classes, pet visiting and day trips.
OTHER SERVICES: *Housekeeping*: weekly (included in fee). *Laundry*: linen, towel, personal & dry cleaning (extra cost). Transportation to medical appointments and for group social activities (extra cost). 24-hour security. Nightly security checks (available for a fee). Telephone & Cable TV (extra cost). Utilities (included in fee).
RENTAL INFORMATION: Rates may vary. Extra cost for 2nd person sharing suite ($600.00/month). Rent paid monthly. *Payment Options*: cheques, post-dated cheques, direct deposit and pre-authorized payments. Rent increases are a set percentage indexed to inflation as per Provincial Tenancy Legislation, annual for resident with 3 months' notice given. Short-term respite ($125.00/day) and trial stays ($99.00/day) available.

TRILLIUM RIDGE RETIREMENT COMMUNITY

800 Edgar Street, Kingston, ON K7M 8S4
Tel: (613) 547-7003 • Fax: (613) 547-7020
Email: **jane.bray@specialty-care.com**
Website: **www.specialtyliving.ca**
Contact: **Jane Bray**
Capacity: **48 residents**
Subsidies: **Department of Veterans Affairs subsidies may apply**
Price: **$2,995.00/month and up**

Trillium Ridge provides a comfortable home-like environment centrally located in an established neighbourhood. Here you can do things your way – while continuing to enjoy things that matter – time with family, connections with friends and being involved in the community. Our innovative *Zest for Life™* signature service promotes the health and well-being of each resident by focusing on the needs of mind, body and spirit. We work with you one-on-one to connect you with activities and services that spark your particular interests. Come and explore Trillium Ridge for yourself. If you are looking for a rewarding place to live and you too have a zest for life – our doors are open!

RESIDENCE INFORMATION: 22 years in operation. *Near:* Taylor Kidd Boulevard and Princess Street. Decorated in 2010. Handrails in hallways. 1 floor, no elevators. Wheelchair accessible. *Owned by:* Specialty Care. 41 units. *Average Waiting Period*: varies. *Average Age*: 85. Can accommodate cognitively impaired people with restrictions (assessed individually). Can accommodate physically challenged people (wheelchairs, walkers are permitted; assessed individually). Smoking allowed (in designated outdoor area). Alcohol allowed. *Procedures to leave the premises on a temporary basis...*Short-term & Overnight: sign out with staff. Holidays: notify Administration. *Languages:* English. Will accept Public Guardian and Trustee clients. Main doors of residence secured at night only. *Close to:* Public Transit, Shopping, Churches, Synagogues, Seniors' Centre, Library, Major Highway and Local Hospitals (Kingston General Hospital, Providence Care Centre - St. Mary's of the Lake Hospital Site & Hotel Dieu Hospital). Member of ORCA, Seniors Association of Kingston, & OLTCA for long-term care building. Licensed under the Retirement Homes Act.
STAFFING: *Available Staff/Services*: Pharmacy, Social Work (CCAC), Recreation Therapy, Occupational Therapy (CCAC), Physiotherapy (CCAC), Dietitian (CCAC), Companions, Podiatry (CCAC), Chaplaincy, Speech Pathology (CCAC), Chiropody and Audiology/Hearing Clinic. *External services arranged by:* residence and/or family/resident. Staff trained *re*: visually, hearing and cognitively impaired. 24-hour nursing and other staff. RNs, RPNs and PSWs on staff. Visiting MD (weekly). A Physician Assistant and a Nurse Practitioner are available 5 days/week. Can retain own MD. Police Check or Vulnerable Person Screening is done for all new staff.
HEALTH SERVICES: Medication administration (extra cost) and/or supervision (Assisted Living Package for extra cost). Vitals monitored if required. Will accept and provide special assistance for residents who require oxygen, catheters and ostomies. Assistance with dressing available (cost). Weekly assistance with bathing available (cost). Care plans done. Different levels of care available. Private Duty/Extra Care available. Lab service (visiting). Residents can purchase outside resources and use agency of their choice. MD visits residents in their rooms/suites. Will help locate higher level of care if needed (Care Coordinator through CCAC attached to the home).
ACCOMMODATION: *Choice of suites available*: suite &1-bedroom suites. *In all suites*: locks, patio/balcony, storage, window coverings, light fixtures, smoke detector, sprinkler, call bell, air conditioning (central & window units) and thermostats for heating & cooling. Private bathrooms with call bells, grab bars, tubs and showers with non-slip surfaces and elevated toilet seats. In-suite cable TV if resident arranges with cable company. Can have own phone number provided by residence (residence charges extra). Furnished & unfurnished suites available. *Restrictions on electrical appliances*: no hot plates or

stoves; appliances require approval by Administration. Suites can be shared (couples, family members or friends). Pets allowed (with Administrator's approval).
DINING SERVICE: All meals included in fee and served in dining room daily. *Sittings per meal:* Breakfast: 1, Lunch: 1, Dinner: 1. *Menu choices available:* Breakfast: 6, Lunch: 10, Dinner: 10. *Guest Meals*: Breakfast $8.00, Lunch $11.00, Dinner $12.50. *Special Diets*: Vegetarian, Low Salt, Diabetic, Renal and Healthy Choices (menu choices identified). Tray service to room if ill (no charge for a maximum time of 4 days). Unlimited snacks available at any time. Open pantry. Bistro café. Party facilities.
AMENITIES AND ACTIVITIES: Parking available (outdoor, for visitors and residents). *4 lounges with:* TV (1), piano (1), outdoor patio (1) and fitness equipment (1). Guest suites available ($91.96/night). *Residence has a:* library, chapel, barber/beauty shop, visiting hairdresser, laundry room(s) (no cost) and tuck/gift shop. Resident can arrange newspaper delivery to main desk (extra cost). Mail delivered to dining room. *Recreation Facilities*: exercise room, craft room, card room and bus for scheduled outings. Posted schedule of activities. Internal newsletter for residents. *Recreational Programs*: exercise, shopping, theatre, parties, entertainment, art classes, pet visiting and day trips.
OTHER SERVICES: *Housekeeping*: weekly (included in fee; daily service available for extra fee). *Laundry*: linen & towel (included in fee); personal (extra cost) & dry cleaning (external provider). 24-hour security. Nightly security checks. Telephone (extra cost). Cable TV (extra cost - through Cogeco). Utilities (included in fee).
RENTAL INFORMATION: Rates may vary. Extra cost for 2nd person sharing suite ($675.00/month). Rent paid monthly. *Payment Options*: direct deposit and pre-authorized payments. Rent increases as per Provincial Tenancy Legislation, annual for resident with 3 months' notice given. Will help resident move into residence (extra cost). Short-term respite ($125.00/day) and trial stays ($96.10/day to $142.52/day depending on the room size) available.

♦ KITCHENER ♦

BAYBRIDGE - DOON VILLAGE RETIREMENT RESIDENCE

868 Doon Village Road, Kitchener, ON N2P 3A4
Tel: (519) 896-3338 • Fax: (519) 896-5145
Email: **marketing@doonvillage.ca**
Website: **www.doonvillage.ca**
Contact: **Deb Stanson**
Capacity: **115 residents •** Subsidies: **none**
Price: **$2,695.00 - $4,225.00/month**

Award winning Doon Village Retirement Residence is a gracious, full service retirement community, providing the optimum in private, independent living. 3 home-style meals served in an elegant dining room from 7:00 a.m. to 7:00 p.m. Special diets will be accommodated. Additional costs may apply.

RESIDENCE INFORMATION: 10 years in operation. *On:* Doon Village Road and Bechtel Street. Decorated in 2012. Handrails in hallways. 4 floors, 3 elevators. Wheelchair accessible. *Funding Base:* Corporate/for profit. *Owned and managed by:* BayBridge Senior Living. 97 units. *Average Waiting Period*: 2 - 4 months. *Average Age*: 82. Can accommodate cognitively impaired people with restrictions (with the addition of family/private outside care). Can accommodate physically challenged people with restrictions (e.g. wheelchair bound, as long as they are independent with their Activities of Daily Living). Residents have a dress code (must wear street clothes when leaving suite). Smoking allowed (smoking gazebo at side of building). Alcohol allowed (cocktails are from 4:00 p.m.- 5:00 p.m. daily). *Procedures to leave the premises on a temporary basis...*Short-term & Overnight: sign out at Reception Desk. Holidays: notify

Reception. *Languages:* English, German & French. Will accept Public Guardian and Trustee clients. Main doors of residence secured at night only. *Close to:* Public Transit, Shopping, Churches, Synagogues, Seniors' Centre, Library, Major Highway and Local Hospitals (St. Mary's General Hospital, Grand River Hospital Corporation & Freeport Health Centre). Member of ORCA. Licensed under the Retirement Homes Act.

STAFFING: *Available Staff/Services*: Pharmacy, Social Work (CCAC), Recreation Therapy, Occupational Therapy (CCAC), Physiotherapy (CCAC), Dietitian (CCAC), Companions, Podiatry (CCAC), Chaplaincy, Speech Pathology (CCAC) and Audiology/Hearing Clinic. *External services arranged by:* residence and/or family/resident. Staff trained *re*: visually, hearing and cognitively impaired. 24-hour nursing and other staff. RNs, RPNs, HCAs and PSWs on staff. Visiting MD (on-site twice monthly; on call 24/7). Can retain own MD. Police Check or Vulnerable Person Screening is done for all new staff.

HEALTH SERVICES: Medication administration (additional cost may apply) and/or supervision (additional cost may apply). Vitals monitored if required. Will accept and provide special assistance for residents who require oxygen, catheters, ostomies and feeding tubes. Assistance with dressing available (cost). Weekly assistance with bathing available (cost). Care plans done. Different levels of care available. Lab service (visiting). Residents can purchase outside resources and use agency of their choice. MD visits residents in their rooms/suites. Clinic area for medical visits. Will help locate higher level of care if needed.

ACCOMMODATION: *Choice of suites available*: all private: studio (59), 1-bedroom, (34) & 2-bedroom (4) units. *In all suites*: locks, storage, bar fridge, window coverings, light fixtures, linens, fire alarm, smoke detector, sprinkler, emergency response system with wearable pendant/bracelet, air conditioning (central) and thermostats for heating & cooling. Kitchenettes in most suites. Private bathrooms with grab bars, showers with non-slip surfaces and elevated toilet seats. Can have own phone number provided by residence. Unfurnished suites, furnished suites available for short stays. *Restrictions on electrical appliances*: no toasters or toaster ovens; others must have auto shut-off. Suites can be shared. No pets allowed.

DINING SERVICE: All meals included in fee and served in dining room daily. *Sittings per meal:* Breakfast: 1, Lunch: 1, Dinner: 1. *Menu choices available:* Breakfast: 2, Lunch: 2, Dinner: 2. *Guest Meals*: Breakfast $5.00, Lunch $8.00, Dinner $12.00. *Special Diets*: Low Salt and Diabetic. Tray service to room if ill. Party facilities.

AMENITIES AND ACTIVITIES: Parking available (outdoor, for visitors and residents). *5 lounges with:* TVs (2), piano (1), putting green (1), billiards, darts and shuffleboard (1). Guest suites available. *Residence has a:* library, visiting library, chapel, barber/beauty shop, visiting hairdresser, laundry room(s) (no cost) and tuck/gift shop (open 8:00 a.m. - 8:00 p.m.). Resident can arrange newspaper delivery to individual suite. Mail delivered to private mailbox with key. *Recreation Facilities*: pool table, billiards, shuffleboard, exercise room, craft room and card room. Posted schedule of activities. Internal newsletter for residents. *Recreational Programs*: exercise, shopping, theatre, parties, entertainment, art classes, pet visiting and day trips.

OTHER SERVICES: *Housekeeping*: weekly (included in fee). *Laundry*: linen & towel (included in fee); personal (extra cost or included in care packages) & dry cleaning (resident can arrange). Laundry rooms on each floor (no cost). Transportation to medical appointments (extra cost) and for group social activities (cost varies). 24-hour security (no extra charge). Nightly security checks. Telephone (extra cost for Long Distance; local included in fee). Cable TV (extra cost; basic cable, telephone and high speed internet $60.00/month). Utilities (included in fee). Spa treatments available.

RENTAL INFORMATION: Rates may vary. Extra cost for 2nd person sharing suite ($600.00/month for food & services). Rent paid monthly. *Payment Options*: cheques and pre-authorized payments. Rent increases as per Provincial Tenancy Legislation, annual for resident with 3 months' notice given. Will help resident move into residence. Short-term respite and trial stays available (both $85.00/day, additional care charges may apply if required upon assessment).

CONESTOGA LODGE

55 Hugo Crescent, Kitchener, ON N2M 5J1
Tel: (519) 576-2140 • Fax: (519) 576-1790
Email: **sbarkshire@thecaringnetwork.ca**
Website: **www.thecaringnetwork.ca**
Contact: **Sandy Barkshire**
Capacity: **87 residents •** Subsidies: **none**
Price: **$2,403.00 - $4,200.00/month**

RESIDENCE INFORMATION: 27 years in operation. *Near:* Heiman Street and Highland Avenue. Handrails in hallways. 3 floors, 1 elevator. Wheelchair accessible. Central PA system. *Funding Base:* Corporate/for profit. *Owned by:* Deem Management. 79 units. *Average Waiting Period*: none. *Average Age*: 80. Can accommodate cognitively impaired people. Can accommodate physically challenged people. Smoking allowed (outside patio area). Alcohol allowed. *Procedures to leave the premises on a temporary basis...*Short-term: sign out at Front Desk. Overnight & Holidays: alert Charge Nurse/sign out at Front Desk. *Languages:* English & German. Will accept Public Guardian and Trustee clients. Main doors of residence secured at night only. *Close to:* Public Transit, Shopping, Churches and Local Hospital (St. Mary's General Hospital). Member of ORCA. Licensed under the Retirement Homes Act.
STAFFING: *Available Staff/Services*: Pharmacy, Social Work (CCAC), Recreation Therapy, Occupational Therapy (CCAC), Physiotherapy, Denturist, Dietitian and Resident Care Attendants. *External services arranged by:* family/resident. Staff trained *re*: visually, hearing and cognitively impaired. 24-hour nursing staff. RPNs on staff. Visiting MD (weekly). Police Check or Vulnerable Person Screening is done for all new staff.
HEALTH SERVICES: Medication administration and/or supervision. Vitals monitored if required. Will accept (but not provide special assistance for) residents who require catheters and ostomies. Will accept and provide special assistance for residents who require oxygen. Weekly assistance with bathing available. *Extra baths:* $20.00/hour. Care plans done. Different levels of care available. Private Duty/Extra Care available ($20.00/hour). Lab service (visiting, $10.90/visit). Residents can purchase outside resources and use agency of their choice. MD visits residents in their rooms/suites.
ACCOMMODATION: Choice of suites available. *In all suites*: locks, kitchenette, bar fridge, storage, window coverings, light fixtures, linens, smoke detector, sprinkler and thermostats for heating. Private bathrooms with call bells, grab bars, tubs and showers. In-suite cable TV provided by residence (residence charges extra $40.00/month). Can have own phone extension number provided by residence (residence charges extra $15.00/month). Furnished & unfurnished suites available. Suites can be shared, roommate picked by residence staff. No pets allowed.
DINING SERVICE: All meals included in fee and served in dining room daily. *Sittings per meal:* Breakfast: 1, Lunch: 1, Dinner: 1. *Menu choices available:* Breakfast: 1, Lunch: 2, Dinner: 2. *Guest Meals*: Breakfast $3.00, Lunch $5.00, Dinner $4.00. *Special Diets*: Vegetarian, Low Salt and Diabetic. Tray service to room if ill (no charge as long as doctor orders). Unlimited snacks available at any time. Party facilities.
AMENITIES AND ACTIVITIES: Parking available (outdoor, for visitors and residents). *3 lounges with:* TVs (2) and piano (1). *Residence has a:* library, visiting library, chapel, barber/beauty shop, visiting hairdresser, laundry room(s) (no cost) and tuck/gift shop. Residence provides newspaper delivery to individual suite. Mail delivered to dining room. *Recreation Facilities*: pool table, shuffleboard, exercise room, craft room and card room. Posted schedule of activities. Internal newsletter for residents. *Recreational Programs*: exercise, shopping, theatre, parties, entertainment, art classes, pet visiting and day trips.
OTHER SERVICES: *Housekeeping*: daily and weekly. *Laundry*: linen & towel (included in fee); personal ($4.00/load). Transportation for group social activities. 24-hour security. Nightly security checks. Telephone ($15.00/month). Cable TV ($40.00/month). Utilities (included in fee).

RENTAL INFORMATION: Rates may vary. Extra cost for 2nd person sharing suite. Rent paid monthly. *Payment Options*: cheques, post-dated cheques, direct deposit and pre-authorized payments. Rent increases as per Provincial Tenancy Legislation, annual for resident with 3 months' notice given. Short-term respite and trial stays available (both $70.00/day).

EMMANUEL VILLAGE

1250 Weber Street East, Kitchener, ON N2A 4E1
Tel: (519) 748-4814 • Fax: (519) 748-4840
Email: **Sarah.gurney@emmanuelvillage.com**
Website: **www.emmanuelvillage.com**
Contact: **Sarah Gurney**
Capacity: **138 residents** • Subsidies: **none**
Price: **$2,490.00 - $5,175.00/month**

An extraordinary enclave where residents have all the conveniences and genuine comforts of home. A place to call your own, with all the best features such as fine dining, and social and cultural programs. Savour your privacy or participate in the array of available amenities and activities. Emmanuel Village encourages you to create an active, independent lifestyle where you can truly enjoy your retirement years.

RESIDENCE INFORMATION: 11 years in operation. *Near:* Franklin Street and Weber Street. Decorated in 2011. Handrails in hallways. 5 floors, 2 elevators. Wheelchair accessible. Central PA system. *Funding Base:* Corporate/for profit. *Owned by:* Bryan Hunking. 102 units. *Average Waiting Period*: varies. *Average Age*: 85. Can accommodate cognitively impaired people with restrictions (no locked unit/residents with early dementia). Can accommodate physically challenged people. Residents have a dress code (must be dressed appropriately for meals and functions). Smoking allowed (outside). Alcohol allowed. *Restrictions around Visitors/Visiting Hours:* sign in/out at the Front Desk. *Procedures to leave the premises on a temporary basis*...Short-term: notify staff and sign out. *Languages:* English & German. Will accept Public Guardian and Trustee clients. Main doors of residence secured at night only. *Close to:* Public Transit, Shopping, Churches, Synagogues, Seniors' Centre, Library, Major Highway and Local Hospitals (St. Mary's General Hospital & Grand River Hospital Corporation). *Predominant Cultural Group:* German. Licensed under the Retirement Homes Act.
STAFFING: *Available Staff/Services*: Pharmacy, Social Work (CCAC), Recreation Therapy, Occupational Therapy (CCAC), Visiting Dentist, Physiotherapy (CCAC), Denturist, Dietitian (CCAC), Companions, Podiatry (CCAC), Chaplaincy, Speech Pathology (CCAC), Chiropody and Audiology/Hearing Clinic. *External services arranged by:* residence and/or family/resident. Staff trained *re*: visually, hearing and cognitively impaired. 24-hour staff. RPNs, HCAs, PSWs and UCPs on staff. Visiting MD (weekly). Can retain own MD. Police Check or Vulnerable Person Screening is done for all new staff.
HEALTH SERVICES: Medication administration (use of Emmanuel Village pharmacy) and/or supervision (if requested). Vitals monitored if required. Will accept and provide special assistance for residents who require oxygen, catheters, ostomies and feeding tubes. Assistance with dressing available ($28.00/hour). Assistance with bathing available as needed ($28.00/hour). Care plans done. Different levels of care available. Lab service (visiting, $11.00/visit). Residents can purchase outside resources and use agency of their choice. Clinic area for medical visits. Will help locate higher level of care if needed (CCAC for long-term care papers).
ACCOMMODATION: *Choice of suites available*: studio (68) & 1-bedroom (35) suites. *In all suites*: locks, kitchenette, bar fridge, microwave, window coverings, light fixtures, linens, fire alarm, smoke detector, sprinkler, call bell, emergency response system with wearable pendant/bracelet, air conditioning (central) and thermostats for heating & cooling. Private bathrooms with call bells, grab bars and showers with non-slip surfaces. In-suite cable & satellite TV provided by residence (residence charges extra). Can have own phone number provided by residence (residence charges extra). Unfurnished suites, furnished suites

available for short stays. *Restrictions on electrical appliances*: toaster oven/hot plates/crock pots. Suites can be shared (by couples only), roommate picked by resident & residence staff. Pets allowed (one-time fee required).

DINING SERVICE: All meals included in fee and served in dining room daily. *Sittings per meal:* Breakfast: 1, Lunch: 1, Dinner: 2. *Menu choices available:* Breakfast: 3, Lunch: 3, Dinner: 5. *Guest Meals*: Breakfast $8.00, Lunch $13.00, Dinner $16.50. *Special Diets*: Vegetarian, Low Salt, Diabetic, Fluid Restrictions, Renal Diet and Celiac. Tray service to room if ill. 3 snacks/day. Party facilities.

AMENITIES AND ACTIVITIES: Parking available (outdoor, for visitors and residents). *12 lounges with:* TVs (2) and piano (1). Guest suites available ($85.00/night). *Residence has a:* library, visiting library, chapel, barber/beauty shop, laundry room(s) (no cost), tuck/gift shop (open Monday & Wednesday, 3:00 p.m. – 4:00 p.m.; Saturday, 10:00 a.m. – 11:00 a.m.). Banking services on premises (monthly). Mail delivered to private mailbox with key. *Recreation Facilities*: pool table, billiards, exercise room, craft room, card room and library/banquet hall. Posted schedule of activities. Internal newsletter for residents. *Recreational Programs*: exercise, shopping, theatre, parties, entertainment, art classes, pet visiting and day trips.

OTHER SERVICES: *Housekeeping*: weekly (included in fee). *Laundry*: linen & towel (included in fee); personal ($15.00/load). Laundry Room on each floor. Transportation for group social activities (with Activity Coordinator). Nightly security checks. Telephone ($30.00 to $40.00/month). Cable TV ($40.00 to $60.00/month). Utilities (included in fee).

RENTAL INFORMATION: Rates may vary. Extra cost for 2nd person sharing suite. Life Lease Option is available (42 units on the property). Rent paid monthly. *Payment Options*: pre-authorized payments. Rent increases are a set percentage indexed to inflation as per Provincial Tenancy Legislation, annual for resident with 3 months' notice given. Short-term respite and trial stays available (both $75.00/day; respite and trial stays do not include nursing care - additional $28.00/hour).

LANARK PLACE RETIREMENT RESIDENCE

44 Lanark Crescent, Kitchener, ON N2N 2Z8
Tel: (519) 743-0121 • Fax: (519) 743-8901
Email: **lanarkplace@srgroup.ca**
Website: **www.srgroup.ca**
Contact: **Karen Church**
Capacity: **110 residents** • Subsidies: **none**
Price: **$2,524.00 - $4,469.00/month**

At Lanark Place it's all about choice...you can enjoy the independence of Willow's bright airy suites or receive extra assistance from Linden's professional caregivers. Both areas enjoy their own elegant dining rooms while sharing numerous comfortable lounges featuring fireplaces and tranquil views. Activities to stimulate both mind and body are offered along with fun trips. *It's your life, live it the way you want to.*

RESIDENCE INFORMATION: 26 years in operation. *Near:* Fischer Hallman Road and Queens Boulevard. Decorated in 2013. Handrails in hallways. 2 floors, 1 elevator. Wheelchair accessible. *Funding Base:* Corporate/for profit. *Owned by:* Steeves and Rozema. 100 units. *Average Waiting Period*: varies. *Average Age*: 85. Can accommodate cognitively impaired people with restrictions (open concept building with ease of access). Can accommodate physically challenged people. Residents have a dress code (fully dressed in common areas). Smoke-free residence. Alcohol allowed. *Procedures to leave the premises on a temporary basis*...Short-term: advise Reception. Overnight & Holidays: advise Reception/Wellness Staff. *Languages:* English, Romanian & Serbian. Main doors of residence secured at night only. *Close to:* Shopping, Churches, Synagogues, Seniors' Centre, Library, Major Highway and Local Hospitals (St. Mary's General Hospital, Grand River Hospital Corporation & Freeport Hospital). Member of ORCA & Waterloo Gerontology Interest Group. Licensed under the Retirement Homes Act.

STAFFING: *Available Staff/Services*: Pharmacy, Social Work (CCAC), Occupational Therapy, Physiotherapy, Dietitian (CCAC), Chaplaincy, Speech Pathology (CCAC), Beauty Salon, Esthetics, Massage Therapy and Foot Care. *External services arranged by:* residence and/or family/resident. Staff trained *re*: visually, hearing and cognitively impaired. 24-hour staff. RNs, RPNs, PSWs and UCPs on staff. Visiting MD (twice weekly clinic; on call for emergencies). Can retain own MD. Specialized customer service programs and training in place for all staff. Police Check or Vulnerable Person Screening is done for all new staff.
HEALTH SERVICES: Medication administration (as per personal physician) and/or supervision. Vitals monitored if required. Will accept and provide special assistance for residents who require oxygen. Assistance with dressing available ($175.00/month). Weekly assistance with bathing available. *Extra baths:* $95.00/month. Care plans done. Different levels of care available. Private Duty/Extra Care available ($25.00 to $700.00/month). Lab service (visiting, $25.00/visit). Residents can purchase outside resources. Clinic area for medical visits. Will help locate higher level of care if needed (we support the work of CCAC & the endeavors of the family/resident). Lanark Place is partnered with and physically linked with Lanark Heights Long-Term Care.
ACCOMMODATION: *Choice of suites available*: private (88), studio + den (3) & 2-room (7) suites. *In all suites*: locks, window coverings, light fixtures, linens, fire alarm, smoke detector, nurse call system, air conditioning (central & window units) and thermostats for heating & cooling. Private bathrooms with call bells, grab bars, tubs and showers with non-slip surfaces. In-suite cable TV if resident arranges with cable company. Can have own phone number if resident arranges with phone company. Furnished & unfurnished suites available. *Restrictions on electrical appliances*: only ULC/CSA approved. Suites can be shared (by couples only). No pets allowed.
DINING SERVICE: All meals included in fee and served in dining room daily. *Sittings per meal:* Breakfast: 1, Lunch: 1, Dinner: 1. *Menu choices available:* Breakfast: 1, Lunch: 2, Dinner: 2. *Guest Meals*: Breakfast $6.00, Lunch $10.25, Dinner $14.00. *Special Diets*: Vegetarian, Low Salt, Diabetic and Healthy Heart. Tray service to room if ill (no charge for a maximum time of 4 days). Unlimited snacks available at any time. Snacks are available in kitchenette lounges 24-hours/day. Party facilities. There are 2 main dining rooms and guest dining.
AMENITIES AND ACTIVITIES: Parking available (outdoor, for visitors and residents). *9 lounges with:* TV (1), piano (1) and fireplaces (6). Guest suites available ($65.00/night). *Residence has a:* library, visiting library, chapel, barber/beauty shop, laundry room(s) (no cost) and tuck/gift shop (open daily weekdays; 11:00 a.m. - 12:00 noon). Resident can arrange newspaper delivery to main desk (extra cost). Mail delivered to main desk. *Recreation Facilities*: exercise room, craft room, card room, spa, wellness centre, baking kitchen, theatre lounge, computer lounge and 2 outdoor courtyards. Posted schedule of activities. Internal newsletter for residents. *Recreational Programs*: exercise, shopping, theatre, parties, entertainment, art classes, pet visiting, day trips, educational classes, baking, crafts, card games and group/individual physiotherapy.
OTHER SERVICES: *Housekeeping*: daily and weekly (included based on program selected). *Laundry*: linen & towel (included in fee); personal (extra cost; included based on program selected) & dry cleaning (as arranged privately). Either staff or resident label clothing (included in fee, based on program selected). Transportation for group social activities (ticket prices vary according to events booked). 24-hour security. Nightly security checks. Telephone & Cable TV (resident makes arrangement with service provider). Utilities (included in fee).
RENTAL INFORMATION: Rates may vary. Extra cost for 2nd person sharing suite ($599.00/month). Rent paid monthly. *Payment Options*: pre-authorized payments. Rent increases as per Provincial Tenancy Legislation, annual for resident with 3 months' notice given. Short-term respite ($95.00/day) and trial stays ($85.00/day) available (daily cost may change based on care required).

Pricing information for homes listed in *The Guide* may vary slightly.
Please verify rates with the residences you are interested in directly.

REVERA - FERGUS PLACE

164 Fergus Avenue, Kitchener, ON N2A 2H2
Tel: (855) 573-8372 • Toll Free: (855) 573-8372
Email: **Fergus@reveraliving.com**
Website: **www.reveraliving.com/fergus**
Contact: **Executive Director or Lifestyle Consultant**
Capacity: **65 residents** • Subsidies: **none**
Price: **$1,647.00/month and up**

Keep living your life, your way, at Fergus Place. Here, you'll find the range of services, features and choices that fit your lifestyle and requirements – all in a warm and safe environment. With retirement living at Fergus Place, you change your address, not your life. Everything is designed to enable you to maintain your independence and privacy, enjoy a full social life, and participate in the activities that you love. Fergus Place is located on beautiful grounds in a lovely residential neighbourhood, close to shopping malls, local amenities and the highway. Our caring and friendly staff, along with appealing accommodations and convenient one-storey layout, support who you are and how you want to live. Explore what we have to offer, to keep you living in freedom and comfort. *Fergus Place is part of the Revera family, one of North America's leading and most trusted providers of seniors' accommodation, care and services since 1961.*

RESIDENCE INFORMATION: 36 years in operation. *Near:* Weber Street and Franklin Avenue. Decorated in 2009. Handrails in hallways. 1 floor, no elevators. Wheelchair accessible. Central PA system. *Funding Base:* Corporate/for profit. *Owned and managed by:* Revera Inc. 50 units. *Average Waiting Period*: none. *Average Age*: 80. Can accommodate cognitively impaired & physically challenged people with restrictions (assessment required). Smoking allowed (outdoors). *Procedures to leave the premises on a temporary basis...*sign in/out. *Languages:* English, French & Italian. Will accept Public Guardian and Trustee clients. Main doors of residence secured at all times. *Close to:* Public Transit, Shopping, Churches, Seniors' Centre, Library, Major Highway and Local Hospitals (Grand River Hospital Corporation & St. Mary's General Hospital). Member of ORCA & Chamber of Commerce. Licensed under the Retirement Homes Act.
STAFFING: *Available Staff/Services*: Pharmacy, Social Work (CCAC), Recreation Therapy, Occupational Therapy (CCAC), Physiotherapy (CCAC), Denturist, Dietitian (CCAC), Companions, Podiatry, Chaplaincy, Speech Pathology (CCAC) and Hair Salon/Barber. *External services arranged by:* residence and/or family/resident. Staff trained *re*: visually, hearing and cognitively impaired. 24-hour nursing and other staff. RNs, RPNs, HCAs and PSWs on staff. Visiting MD (weekly and on call). Can retain own MD. Police Check or Vulnerable Person Screening is done for all new staff.
HEALTH SERVICES: Medication administration and/or supervision. Vitals monitored if required. Will accept and provide special assistance for residents who require oxygen, catheters and ostomies. Assistance with dressing available. Weekly assistance with bathing available. Care plans done. Different levels of care available. Lab service (visiting). Residents can purchase outside resources and use agency of their choice. Clinic area for medical visits. Will help locate higher level of care if needed (via CCAC).
ACCOMMODATION: *Choice of suites available*: private & semi-private as needed. *In all suites*: locks, storage, window coverings, light fixtures, linens, smoke detector, sprinkler, call bell, emergency response system with wearable pendant/bracelet, air conditioning (central) and thermostats for heating & cooling. Private bathrooms with grab bars and showers with non-slip surfaces. In-suite cable TV provided by residence (residence charges extra $46.90/month). Can have own phone number provided by residence (residence charges extra $35.00/month). Furnished & unfurnished suites available. *Restrictions on electrical appliances*: must be checked by Maintenance staff on move in. Suites can be shared, roommate picked by residence staff. Pets allowed (Pet Policy).

DINING SERVICE: All meals included in fee and served in dining room daily. *Sittings per meal:* Breakfast: 2, Lunch: 2, Dinner: 2. *Menu choices available:* Breakfast: 2, Lunch: 2, Dinner: 2. *Guest Meals*: Available. *Special Diets*: Vegetarian, Low Salt, Diabetic, Cardiac, Renal and High Calorie. Tray service to room if ill (no charge as long as doctor orders). 2 snacks/day. Party facilities.
AMENITIES AND ACTIVITIES: Parking available (outdoor, for visitors and residents). *1 lounge with:* TV (1) and piano (1). Guest suites available. *Residence has a:* visiting library, barber/beauty shop, visiting hairdresser and tuck/gift shop (hours vary). Mail delivered to dining room. *Recreation Facilities*: exercise room, craft room, card room and relaxing spa room. Posted schedule of activities. Internal newsletter for residents. *Recreational Programs*: exercise, shopping, parties, entertainment, art classes, pet visiting, day trips and adult education.
OTHER SERVICES: *Housekeeping*: weekly (included in fee). *Laundry*: linen, towel & personal (included in fee). Transportation for group social activities. 24-hour security. Nightly security checks. Telephone & Cable TV (extra cost). Utilities (included in fee).
RENTAL INFORMATION: Rates may vary. Semi-private - $1,647.00/month & up; private - $2,677.00/month & up. Extra cost for 2nd person sharing suite ($567.00/month). Rent paid monthly. *Payment Options*: cheques and pre-authorized payments. Rent increases as per Provincial Tenancy Legislation, annual for resident with 3 months' notice given. Will help resident move into residence (extra cost). Short-term respite and trial stays available.

REVERA - HIGHLAND PLACE

20 Fieldgate Street, Kitchener, ON N2M 5K3
Tel: (855) 573-8372 • Toll Free: (855) 573-8372
Email: **Highland@reveraliving.com**
Website: **www.reveraliving.com/highland**
Contact: **Executive Director or Lifestyle Consultant**
Capacity: **89 residents** • Subsidies: **none**
Price: **$2,879.00/month and up**

Keep living your life, your way, at Highland Place. You'll find the range of services, amenities and choices that fit your lifestyle and requirements – all in a warm and safe environment. Our recently renovated single-storey residence is conveniently located close to shopping, churches, recreation centres, medical services, public transportation, and more. Everything here is designed to enable you to maintain your independence and privacy, enjoy a full social life, and participate in the activities that you love. Our caring and friendly staff, along with appealing accommodations, support who you are and how you want to live in freedom and comfort. With retirement living at Highland Place, you change your address, not your life. *Highland Place is part of the Revera family, one of North America's leading and most trusted providers of seniors' accommodation, care and services since 1961.*

RESIDENCE INFORMATION: 26 years in operation. *On:* Highland Road and Westmount Road. Decorated in 2010. Handrails in hallways. 1 floor, no elevators. Wheelchair accessible. Central PA system. *Funding Base:* Corporate/for profit. *Owned and managed by:* Revera Inc. 84 units. *Average Waiting Period*: varies. *Average Age*: 83. Can accommodate cognitively impaired people (early dementia). Can accommodate physically challenged people (a variety of challenges accommodated). Residents have a dress code (daytime wear to be worn outside suite except early breakfast). Smoking allowed (outside in designated area). Alcohol allowed (in suite only; special occasion at residence). *Procedures to leave the premises on a temporary basis...*Short-term: sign in/out book. Overnight: sign in/out book, let Nursing know. Holidays: sign in/out book, let Nursing know length of time so medications can be ordered and taken. *Languages:* English, German, Romanian, Polish & Spanish. Will accept Public Guardian and Trustee clients. Main doors of residence secured at all times. *Close to:* Public Transit, Shopping, Churches,

Synagogues, Seniors' Centre, Library, Major Highway and Local Hospitals (Grand River Hospital Corporation & St. Mary's General Hospital). Member of ORCA, Chamber of Commerce, Alzheimer Society & Elder Abuse Committee. Licensed under the Retirement Homes Act.
STAFFING: *Available Staff/Services*: Pharmacy, Social Work (CCAC), Recreation Therapy, Occupational Therapy (CCAC), Physiotherapy (CCAC), Denturist, Dietitian (CCAC), Companions, Podiatry, Chaplaincy, Speech Pathology (CCAC) and Audiology/Hearing Clinic. *External services arranged by:* residence and/or family/resident. Staff trained *re*: visually, hearing and cognitively impaired. 24-hour nursing and other staff. RPNs, HCAs, PSWs and UCPs on staff. Visiting MD (weekly). Can retain own MD. Police Check or Vulnerable Person Screening is done for all new staff.
HEALTH SERVICES: Medication administration and/or supervision. Vitals monitored if required. Will accept and provide special assistance for residents who require oxygen, catheters and ostomies. Assistance with dressing available (cost). Weekly assistance with bathing available (cost). Care plans done. Different levels of care available. Lab service (visiting). Residents can purchase outside resources and use agency of their choice. MD visits residents in their rooms/suites. Clinic area for medical visits. Will help locate higher level of care if needed (CCAC).
ACCOMMODATION: *Choice of suites available*: private (80) & 2-bedroom (4) units. *In all suites*: locks, window coverings, light fixtures, linens, fire alarm, smoke detector, heat detectors, sprinkler, call bell, emergency response system with wearable pendant/bracelet, air conditioning (central) and thermostats for heating & cooling. Private bathrooms with call bells, grab bars and showers with non-slip surfaces. In-suite cable TV provided by residence (residence charges extra). Furnished & unfurnished suites available. *Restrictions on electrical appliances*: must be CSA approved and checked by Maintenance Department. Suites can be shared (by couples only). Pets allowed (resident must be able to provide total care and keep pet in suite except for toileting dogs).
DINING SERVICE: All meals included in fee and served in dining room daily. *Sittings per meal:* Breakfast: 2, Lunch: 2, Dinner: 2. *Menu choices available:* Breakfast: 2, Lunch: 3, Dinner: 3. *Guest Meals*: Available. *Special Diets*: Vegetarian, Low Salt, Diabetic, Renal, Heart Smart and Textured. Tray service to room if ill (no charge for a maximum time of 4 days). 2 snacks/day. 24-hour tea & coffee and filtered water available. Party facilities.
AMENITIES AND ACTIVITIES: Parking available (outdoor, for visitors and residents). *5 lounges with:* TVs (2), piano (1), fireplaces (2) and library/card tables & computer (1). Guest suites available. *Residence has a:* library, visiting library, chapel, barber/beauty shop, visiting hairdresser, laundry room(s) (no cost), tuck/gift shop (open Monday & Thursday 3:30 p.m.). Resident can arrange newspaper delivery to individual suite (extra cost). Mail delivered to individual suite. *Recreation Facilities*: shuffleboard, exercise room, craft room, card room and horse shoe pits. Posted schedule of activities. Internal newsletter for residents. *Recreational Programs*: exercise, shopping, theatre, parties, entertainment, art classes, pet visiting, day trips, Tim Horton's coffee & Timbits, BBQ's, theme parties and Canada Day Fireworks.
OTHER SERVICES: *Housekeeping*: weekly included; daily additional charge. *Laundry*: linen & towel (included in fee); personal (extra cost). Washer & dryer available for residents if they wish to do own laundry at no cost. Transportation for group social activities. 24-hour security. Nightly security checks. Telephone & Cable TV (extra cost). Utilities (included in fee).
RENTAL INFORMATION: Rates may vary. Private - $2,879.00/month & up; 1-bedroom suite - $3,703.00/month & up. Extra cost for 2nd person sharing suite. Rent paid monthly. *Payment Options*: pre-authorized payments. Rent increases as per Provincial Tenancy Legislation, annual for resident with 3 months' notice given. Will help resident move into residence. Short-term respite and trial stays available (additional care package if assessment deems necessary).

REVERA - VICTORIA PLACE

290 Queen Street South, Kitchener, ON N2G 1W3
Tel: (855) 573-8372 • Toll Free: (855) 573-8372
Email: **victoria@reveraliving.com**
Website: **www.reveraliving.com/victoria**
Contact: **Executive Director or Lifestyle Consultant**
Capacity: **91 residents** • Subsidies: **none**
Price: **$2,461.00/month and up**

Keep living your life, your way, at Victoria Place. You'll find the full range of services, amenities and choices that fit your lifestyle and requirements – all in a warm and safe environment. Victoria Place is Kitchener's only downtown retirement residence, offering Independent and Assisted Living. We are ideally located close to hospitals, shopping, public transportation, and more. Everything here is designed to enable you to maintain your independence and privacy, enjoy a full social life, and participate in the activities that you love. Our caring and friendly staff, along with appealing accommodations, support who you are and how you want to live in freedom and comfort. With retirement living at Victoria Place, you change your address, not your life. *Victoria Place is part of the Revera family, one of North America's leading and most trusted providers of seniors' accommodation, care and services since 1961.*

RESIDENCE INFORMATION: 32 years in operation. *Near:* Courtland Street and Queen Street. Decorated in 2013. Handrails in hallways. 7 floors, 2 elevators. Wheelchair accessible. Central PA system. *Funding Base:* Corporate/for profit. *Owned and managed by:* Revera Inc. 87 units. *Average Waiting Period*: varies. *Average Age*: 86. Can accommodate cognitively impaired people (Assisted Care floors). Can accommodate physically challenged people (will accept residents who are a 1-person transfer). Residents have a dress code (no bedclothes on the main floor; residents must dress in an appropriate manner in all common areas). Smoking allowed (outdoors). Alcohol allowed (appropriate use). *Procedures to leave the premises on a temporary basis...*Short-term: must sign out when leaving. Overnight & Holidays: must advise Director of Health and Wellness/Administration & sign out. *Languages:* English, French, German & Polish. Will accept Public Guardian and Trustee clients. Main doors of residence secured at all times. *Close to:* Public Transit, Shopping, Churches, Seniors' Centre, Library, Major Highway and Local Hospitals (St. Mary's General Hospital & Grand River Hospital Corporation). Member of ORCA & Greater Kitchener Waterloo Chamber of Commerce. Licensed under the Retirement Homes Act.
STAFFING: *Available Staff/Services*: Social Work (CCAC), Recreation Therapy, Occupational Therapy, Visiting Dentist, Physiotherapy (CCAC), Denturist, Dietitian (CCAC), Companions, Chaplaincy, Speech Pathology (CCAC), Audiology/Hearing Clinic, Foot Care, Optometrist and Geriatric Clinic. *External services arranged by:* residence and/or family/resident. Staff trained *re*: visually, hearing and cognitively impaired. 24-hour nursing staff. RNs, RPNs, PSWs and UCPs on staff. Visiting MD (1 day/week and on-call as required). Can retain own MD. Police Check or Vulnerable Person Screening is done for all new staff.
HEALTH SERVICES: Medication administration (as ordered by doctor) and/or supervision. Vitals monitored if required. Will accept and provide special assistance for residents who require oxygen, catheters, ostomies and feeding tubes. Assistance with dressing available (cost). Weekly assistance with bathing available (cost). Care plans done. Different levels of care available. Private Duty/Extra Care available. Assisted Living Area is secured to accommodate residents with dementia. Lab service (visiting). Residents can purchase outside resources and use agency of their choice. MD visits residents in their rooms/suites. Clinic area for medical visits. Will help locate higher level of care if needed (will assist with CCAC communication). Subject to assessment, higher level of care is available.
ACCOMMODATION: *Choice of suites available*: private (74) & 2-room (13) suites. *In all suites*: locks, window coverings, light fixtures, linens, smoke detector, sprinkler, call bell system, air conditioning (central) and thermostats for heating & cooling. Furniture if required (bed, dresser with hutch, desk &

chair/lounge chair - any or all can be supplied), Private bathrooms with call bells, grab bars and walk-in showers with non-slip surfaces. In-suite cable TV provided by residence (residence charges extra). Furnished & unfurnished suites available. *Restrictions on electrical appliances*: bar fridges, appliances with auto shut-off feature are allowed. Suites can be shared (by couples only). Pets allowed (adherence to Pet Policy).

DINING SERVICE: All meals included in fee and served in dining room daily. *Sittings per meal:* Breakfast: 1, Lunch: 2, Dinner: 2. *Menu choices available:* Breakfast: 5, Lunch: 2, Dinner: 2. *Guest Meals*: Available. *Special Diets*: Vegetarian, Low Salt, Diabetic, Heart Smart, Fluid Restricted, Renal and Diabetic. Tray service to room if ill (no charge as long as doctor orders). Unlimited snacks available at any time. Party facilities. Coffee, tea, juice, fresh fruit and water available 24-hours/day.

AMENITIES AND ACTIVITIES: Parking available (outdoor, for visitors and residents). *8 lounges with:* TVs (6) and pianos (2). *Residence has a:* library, visiting library, chapel, barber/beauty shop, laundry room(s) (no cost) and tuck/gift shop. Resident can arrange newspaper delivery to individual suite. Mail delivered to main desk. *Recreation Facilities*: shuffleboard, exercise room, craft room, card room, gazebo and library. Posted schedule of activities. Internal newsletter for residents. *Recreational Programs*: exercise, shopping, theatre, parties, entertainment, art classes, pet visiting, day trips, bingo, discussion groups, Dinner Club, travelogue and poker night.

OTHER SERVICES: *Housekeeping*: weekly (daily at extra cost). *Laundry*: linen & towel (included in fee); personal (extra cost; included in Enhanced and Secure Living) & dry cleaning (sent out and returned at prevailing costs). Transportation for group social activities. 24-hour security. Nightly security checks. Telephone & Cable TV (extra cost - set up with Administrative Staff). Utilities (included in fee). Personal Safety Pendant (included in fee).

RENTAL INFORMATION: Rates may vary. Independent Living - $2,461.00/month & up; Assisted Living - $2,776.00/month & up. Extra cost for 2nd person sharing suite. Rent paid monthly. *Payment Options*: pre-authorized payments. Rent increases as per Provincial Tenancy Legislation, annual for resident with 3 months' notice given. Will help resident move into residence (extra cost). Short-term convalescent/ respite (depending on care needs), vacation and trial stays available.

THE VILLAGE OF WINSTON PARK

695 Blockline Road, Kitchener, ON N2E 3K1
Tel: (519) 576-2430
Email: **lianne.parkhill@schlegelvillages.com**
Website: **www.schlegelvillages.com**
Contact: **Lianne Parkhill**
Capacity: **215 units** • Subsidies: **none**
Price: **$2,464.00/month and up**

The Village of Winston Park is Kitchener's unique continuum of care, offering Full Service Retirement Living, Assisted Care, Memory Care, Independent Living and Long- Term Care. Our residences are well designed and attractive, set on beautifully landscaped grounds, without the institutional feeling of nursing and retirement homes of the past. Our signature indoor Main Street offers the conveniences of a small town - accessible by our residents in winter, summer, rain or shine! Residents, both singles and couples, can choose from cozy studios that emphasize care to generous 1 or 2-bedroom apartments that emphasize independence. Multiple levels of care are offered at Winston Park, enabling residents to age in place in the Village that has become home.

RESIDENCE INFORMATION: 23 years in operation. *Near:* Blockline Road and Westmount Road. Decorated in 2012. Handrails in hallways. 5 floors, 3 elevators. Wheelchair accessible. Central PA system. *Funding Base:* Corporate/for profit. *Owned and managed by:* Schlegel Villages. *Average Waiting Period*: none. Can accommodate cognitively impaired people (Memory Care Neighbourhood). Can accommodate

physically challenged people (Assisted Care Neighbourhood). Smoke-free residence. Alcohol allowed. *Procedures to leave the premises on a temporary basis*...please inform the Director of Retirement Care or the Neighbourhood Coordinator. *Languages:* English. Will accept Public Guardian and Trustee clients. Main doors of residence secured at night only. *Close to:* Public Transit, Shopping, Churches, Library, Major Highway and Local Hospital. Member of ORCA. Licensed under the Retirement Homes Act.
STAFFING: *Available Staff/Services*: Pharmacy, Social Work (CCAC), Recreation Therapy, Occupational Therapy (CCAC), Visiting Dentist, Physiotherapy, Dietitian, Companions, Podiatry, Chaplaincy, Speech Pathology (CCAC), Chiropody and Audiology/Hearing Clinic. *External services arranged by:* residence and/or family/resident. Staff trained *re*: visually, hearing and cognitively impaired. 24-hour nursing and other staff. RNs, RPNs, HCAs, PSWs and UCPs on staff. Visiting MD. Can retain own MD. Police Check or Vulnerable Person Screening is done for all new staff.
HEALTH SERVICES: Medication administration and/or supervision. Will accept and provide special assistance for residents who require oxygen, catheters and ostomies. Assistance with dressing available. Weekly assistance with bathing available. *Extra baths:* $27.00/hour. Care plans done. Different levels of care available. Assisted Living Area. Separate unit for residents with dementia. Lab service (visiting). Residents can purchase outside resources and use agency of their choice. Will help locate higher level of care if needed (guidance can be provided by the Director of Retirement Care).
ACCOMMODATION: *Choice of suites available*: studio with walk-out patio, studio, 1-bedroom, 1-bedroom + den & 2-bedroom suites. *In all suites*: locks, storage, bar fridge, window coverings, light fixtures, linens, fire alarm, smoke detector, sprinkler, call bell, emergency response system with wearable pendant/ bracelet, air conditioning (central) and thermostats for heating & cooling. Apartments have full kitchens. Full Service Retirement Suites have kitchenettes. No kitchenettes in Memory Care Suites. Private bathrooms with call bells, grab bars, showers with non-slip surfaces and elevated toilet seats. Can have own phone number if resident arranges with phone company. Unfurnished suites, furnished suites available for short stays. Pets allowed.
DINING SERVICE: Apartments - one meal/day is included in base rate, Full Service Retirement Living/ Assisted Care/ Memory Care - 3 meals/day are included in the base rate. All meals served in dining room daily. *Guest Meals*: Available. *Special Diets*: Vegetarian, Low Salt and Diabetic. Tray service to room if ill. Unlimited snacks available at any time. Party facilities.
AMENITIES AND ACTIVITIES: Parking available (outdoor, for visitors and indoor & outdoor for residents). *Residence has a:* library, visiting library, chapel, barber/beauty shop, laundry room(s) (no cost) and tuck/gift shop. Banking services on premises. Residence provides newspaper delivery to individual suite. Mail delivered to resident. *Recreation Facilities*: pool table, exercise room, greenhouse, craft room and card room. Posted schedule of activities. Internal newsletter for residents. *Recreational Programs*: exercise, shopping, theatre, parties, entertainment, art classes, pet visiting and day trips.
OTHER SERVICES: *Housekeeping*: weekly (included in fee unless otherwise stated). *Laundry*: linen & towel (included in fee); personal & dry cleaning (extra cost). Staff label clothing ($60.00 one-time fee). Transportation for group social activities. Telephone & Cable TV (extra cost). Utilities (included in fee). Additional Levels of Care offered in $27.00/hour increments spread throughout a 24-hour period.
RENTAL INFORMATION: Rates may vary. Starting Rates: Full Service Retirement Living - $2,464.00/month; Assisted Care - $4,446.00/month; Memory Care - $4,173.00/month; Independent Apartments - $3,963.00/month. Extra cost for 2nd person sharing suite. Rent paid monthly. *Payment Options*: cheques and pre-authorized payments. Rent increases as per Provincial Tenancy Legislation, annual for resident with 3 months' notice given. Short-term respite and trial stays available.

Did you know?

For information on Government of Canada programs and services you can call **(800) 622-6232** or visit **www.servicecanada.gc.ca.**

♦ LEAMINGTON ♦

ERIE GLEN MANOR RETIREMENT RESIDENCE

119 Robson Road; R. R. #1, Leamington, ON N8H 3V4
Tel: (519) 322-2384 • Fax: (519) 322-1411
Email: **info.egm@diversicare.ca**
Website: **www.diversicare.ca**
Contact: **Marketing Manager**
Capacity: **75 residents**
Subsidies: **yes - via Social Services**
Price: **$2,076.17 - $3,279.38/month**

Erie Glen Manor is a uniquely designed one-storey residence with an enclosed, secure courtyard. Situated near the shores of Lake Erie and close proximity to golf /shopping and marina. We are a member of the Leamington District Chamber of Commerce and accredited by the Ontario Retirement Communities Association (ORCA). Accommodations include private suites and apartments. Respite care/vacation and trial stays offered upon availability. A retirement community where the comfort, service & security is our commitment to our residents. **Erie Glen Manor is owned/managed by Diversicare, who is the proud recipient of the 2003, 2006, 2009, and 2012 Order of Excellence Award given by Excellence Canada.** This award was received for the exceptional quality and customer service we provide to our residents every day.

RESIDENCE INFORMATION: 25 years in operation. *On:* Leamington Marina and Doc Lake Erie and Robson Road. Decorated in 2011. Handrails in hallways. 1 floor, no elevator. Wheelchair accessible. *Funding Base:* Corporate/for profit. *Owned and managed by:* Diversicare Canada Management Services Co., Inc. 75 units. *Average Waiting Period*: varies. *Average Age*: 88. Can accommodate cognitively impaired people. Can accommodate physically challenged people. Smoking allowed (by law non-smoking residence - designated areas outside residence). Alcohol allowed. *Procedures to leave the premises on a temporary basis...*sign out book at Reception. *Languages:* English, German, Spanish, Portuguese & Ukrainian. Will accept Public Guardian and Trustee clients. Main doors of residence secured at all times. *Close to:* Public Transit, Shopping, Churches, Seniors' Centre, Library, Major Highway and Local Hospital (Leamington District Memorial Hospital). Member of ORCA & Leamington District Chamber of Commerce/Friendly to Seniors. Licensed under the Retirement Homes Act.
STAFFING: *Available Staff/Services*: Pharmacy, Social Work, Recreation Therapy, Occupational Therapy (CCAC), Physiotherapy, Dietitian (CCAC), Companions, Chaplaincy, Speech Pathology, Chiropody and Audiology/Hearing Clinic. *External services arranged by:* residence. Staff trained *re*: visually, hearing and cognitively impaired. 24-hour nursing and other staff. RPNs, HCAs, PSWs and UCPs on staff. Visiting MD (regular schedule). Can retain own MD. Staff members are bonded. Police Check or Vulnerable Person Screening is done for all new staff.
HEALTH SERVICES: Medication administration and/or supervision. Vitals monitored if required. Will accept and provide special assistance for residents who require oxygen, catheters and ostomies. Assistance with dressing available. Weekly assistance with bathing available. *Extra baths:* $10.00/bath. Care plans done. Different levels of care available. Private Duty/Extra Care available ($300.00 to $1,100.00/ month). Lab service (on-site, $8.00/visit). Residents can purchase outside resources and use agency of their choice. MD visits residents in their rooms/suites. Will help locate higher level of care if needed.
ACCOMMODATION: *Choice of suites available*: privates: large and small, 2-room luxury suites & apartments. *In all suites*: locks, window coverings, light fixtures, linens, fire alarm, smoke detector, sprinkler, call bell, air conditioning (in common areas only), thermostats for heating and ceiling fans.

Private bathrooms with call bells, grab bars, tubs and showers with non-slip surfaces. In-suite cable TV provided by residence (residence charges extra $30.00/month). Can have own phone number if resident arranges with phone company. Unfurnished suites, furnished suites available for short stays. *Restrictions on electrical appliances*: upon approval of Maintenance Supervisor. Suites can be shared (pending availability of beds), roommate picked by resident. Pets allowed (resident responsible for care/maintenance - Pet Policy in place).
DINING SERVICE: All meals included in fee and served in dining room daily. *Sittings per meal:* Breakfast: 1, Lunch: 1, Dinner: 1. *Menu choices available:* Lunch: 2, Dinner: 2. *Guest Meals*: Breakfast $6.00, Lunch $7.00, Dinner $8.00. *Special Diets*: Vegetarian, Low Salt, Diabetic and Others upon direction of medical professional. Tray service to room if ill (no charge as long as doctor orders). 3 snacks/day and unlimited snacks available at any time. Open pantry. Beverages and snacks are available daily. Party facilities.
AMENITIES AND ACTIVITIES: Parking available (outdoor, for visitors and residents). *3 lounges with:* TVs (2), piano (1) and pool table/shuffleboard (1). Guest suites available ($60.00/night). *Residence has a:* library, chapel, barber/beauty shop, visiting hairdresser, laundry room(s) (no cost) and tuck/gift shop (open daily). Resident can arrange newspaper delivery to individual suite. Mail delivered to individual suite. *Recreation Facilities*: pool table, shuffleboard, exercise room, craft room and card room. Posted schedule of activities. Internal newsletter for residents. *Recreational Programs*: exercise, shopping, theatre, parties, entertainment, art classes, pet visiting, day trips & Brain Gym® & More programs.
OTHER SERVICES: *Housekeeping*: daily. *Laundry*: linen, towel & personal (included in fee). Dry cleaning is resident's cost/responsibility. Transportation for group social activities. 24-hour security. Nightly security checks. Cable TV ($30.00/month). Utilities (included in fee).
RENTAL INFORMATION: Rates may vary. Extra cost for 2nd person sharing suite ($600.00/month). Rent paid monthly. *Payment Options*: cheques, post-dated cheques and pre-authorized payments. Rent increases as per Provincial Tenancy Legislation, annual for resident with 3 months' notice given. Short-term respite and trial stays available (both $80.00/day, cost depends on room availability).

◆ LINDSAY ◆

ADELAIDE PLACE

84 Adelaide Street South, Lindsay, ON K9V 0G6
Tel: (705) 340-4000
Email: **info@adelaideplace.com**
Website: **www.adelaideplace.com**
Contact: **Diane Bray**
Capacity: **150 residents** • Subsidies: **none**
Price: **$3,300.00 - $4,800.00/month**

Adelaide Place Retirement Community offers affordable elegance in the heart of Lindsay. Unique features such as heated indoor therapeutic pool, movie theatre, chapel, and 24-hour café set Adelaide Place apart, and foster an active aging approach to Retirement Living.

RESIDENCE INFORMATION: 4 years in operation. *On:* Adelaide Street near Mary Street. Decorated in 2010. 4 floors, 2 elevators. Wheelchair accessible. Central PA system. *Funding Base:* Corporate/for profit. *Managed by:* Greenwood Retirement Communities. 125 units. *Average Waiting Period*: none. *Average Age*: 85. Can sometimes accommodate cognitively impaired people (we ensure residents dignity and safety are a top priority). Can accommodate physically challenged people (wheelchair accessible and 24-hour care support). Smoking allowed (outdoor only). Alcohol allowed. *Procedures to leave the premises on a temporary basis*...Short-term & Overnight: sign out with Concierge at Front Desk.

Holidays: some discounts may apply. *Languages:* English. Main doors of residence secured at night only. *Close to:* Public Transit, Shopping, Churches, Seniors' Centre, Library and Local Hospital (Ross Memorial Hospital less than 5 minutes away). Member of Chamber of Commerce, United Way and Silver Connections. Licensed under the Retirement Homes Act.
STAFFING: *Available Staff/Services*: Pharmacy, Social Work, Recreation Therapy, Occupational Therapy (CCAC), Visiting Dentist, Physiotherapy, Denturist, Dietitian, Companions, Podiatry, Speech Pathology and Physiotherapy. *External services arranged by:* residence and/or family/resident. Staff trained *re*: hearing impaired. 24-hour staff. RPNs and PSWs on staff. Visiting MD (weekly by appointment). Can retain own MD. Police Check or Vulnerable Person Screening is done for all new staff.
HEALTH SERVICES: Medication administration (Medication Management is included in monthly fee) and/or supervision. Vitals monitored if required. Will accept and provide special assistance for residents who require oxygen, catheters and ostomies. Assistance with bathing available as needed ($9.00/half hour). Care plans done. Different levels of care available. Residents can purchase outside resources and use agency of their choice. Clinic area for medical visits. Will help locate higher level of care if needed (our Director of Wellness will assist with transfers).
ACCOMMODATION: *Choice of suites available*: 1-bedroom, 1-bedroom + den & 2-bedroom suites. *In all suites*: locks, kitchenette, bar fridge, storage, window coverings, light fixtures, fire alarm, smoke detector, sprinkler, emergency response system with wearable pendant/bracelet/ Lifeline, air conditioning (central – forced air heating and cooling), thermostats for heating & cooling and granite sinks. Private bathrooms with call bells, heat lamps, grab bars, showers with non-slip surfaces and elevated toilet seats. Unfurnished suites, furnished suites available for short stays. Suites can be shared (by couples only), roommate picked by resident. Pets allowed (weight restriction may apply for dogs).
DINING SERVICE: All meals included in fee and served in dining room daily. *Sittings per meal:* Breakfast: 1, Lunch: 1, Dinner: 1. Flexible seating times daily. *Menu choices available:* Breakfast: 10, Lunch: 2, Dinner: 2. *Guest Meals*: Breakfast $7.00, Lunch $7.00, Dinner $9.00. *Special Diets*: Vegetarian, Low Salt, Diabetic and Additional menu items available at every meal. Tray service to room if ill (no charge or restrictions). Unlimited snacks available at any time. Party facilities.
AMENITIES AND ACTIVITIES: Parking available (outdoor, for visitors: free and residents: $25.00/month). *3 lounges with:* TVs (3) and piano (1). Guest suites available ($80.00/night). *Residence has a:* library, chapel, barber/beauty shop, laundry room(s) (no cost) and tuck/gift shop (TBD). Resident can arrange newspaper delivery to individual suite (extra cost). Mail delivered to private mailbox with key. *Recreation Facilities*: pool table, exercise room, craft room, card room, swimming pool and movie theatre/chapel. Posted schedule of activities. Internal newsletter for residents. *Recreational Programs*: exercise, shopping, theatre, parties, entertainment, art classes, pet visiting, day trips and pool fitness/therapy.
OTHER SERVICES: *Housekeeping*: weekly (included in fee). *Laundry*: linen & towel (included in fee); personal ($50.00/month for a weekly load) & dry cleaning (local vendor arranged). Laundry room and cart on each floor. Transportation for group social activities. 24-hour security. Nightly security checks (as requested). Telephone & Cable TV (included in fee). Utilities (included in fee).
RENTAL INFORMATION: Rates may vary. Extra cost for 2nd person sharing suite ($500.00/month). Rent paid monthly. *Payment Options*: pre-authorized payments. Rent increases as per Provincial Tenancy Legislation, annual for resident with 3 months' notice given. Short-term respite and trial stays available (both $90.00/day).

Did you know?

The Government of Canada has a website with information on resources for Persons with Disabilities including information on tax and financial benefits, transportation, housing and a host of other things. For detailed information, visit **www.pwd-online.ca/pwdhome.jsp?lang=en.**

REVERA - WILLIAM PLACE

140 William Street North, Lindsay, ON K9V 5R4
Tel: (855) 573-8372 • Toll Free: (855) 573-8372
Email: **williamplace@reveraliving.com**
Website: **www.reveraliving.com/williamplace**
Contact: **Executive Director or Lifestyle Consultant**
Capacity: **83 residents •** Subsidies: **none**
Price: **$2,295.00/month and up**

Keep living your life, your way, at William Place. You'll find the range of services, amenities and choices that fit your lifestyle and requirements – all in a warm and safe environment. William Place is situated on the banks of the Trent Severn Waterway in a quiet residential neighbourhood, within walking distance to downtown Lindsay. This picturesque location offers suites with a lovely view of the river and is conveniently close to shopping, churches, a seniors' centre, medical services, theatre, highway, public transportation, and more. Everything here is designed to enable you to maintain your independence and privacy, enjoy a full social life, and participate in the activities that you love. With retirement living at William Place, you change your address, not your life. *William Place is part of the Revera family, one of North America's leading and most trusted providers of seniors' accommodation, care and services since 1961.*

RESIDENCE INFORMATION: 27 years in operation. *Near:* William Street and Colbourne Street. Decorated in 2010. Handrails in hallways. 3 floors, 1 elevator. Wheelchair accessible. Central PA system. *Funding Base:* Corporate/for profit. *Owned and managed by:* Revera Inc. 73 units. *Average Waiting Period*: varies. *Average Age*: 83. Can accommodate cognitively impaired people with restrictions. Can accommodate physically challenged people (wheelchair accessible). Smoking allowed (outdoor smoking patio). Alcohol allowed. *Restrictions around Visitors/Visiting Hours:* Guest Registration Book at Reception Desk. *Procedures to leave the premises on a temporary basis...*residents sign in/out at Reception Desk. *Languages:* English. Will accept Public Guardian and Trustee clients. Main doors of residence secured at night only. *Close to:* Public Transit, Shopping, Churches, Seniors' Centre, Library, Major Highway and Local Hospital (Ross Memorial Hospital). Member of ORCA. Associated with Chamber of Commerce, Alzheimer Society, Canadian Cancer's Society's - Relay For Life. Licensed under the Retirement Homes Act.
STAFFING: *Available Staff/Services*: Social Work (CCAC), Recreation Therapy, Occupational Therapy (CCAC), Physiotherapy (CCAC), Dietitian (CCAC), Companions, Podiatry (CCAC), Chaplaincy, Speech Pathology (CCAC), Chiropody and Audiology/Hearing Clinic. *External services arranged by:* residence and/or family/resident. Staff trained *re*: visually, hearing and cognitively impaired. 24-hour nursing and other staff. RPNs, HCAs, PSWs and UCPs on staff. Visiting MD (weekly). Can retain own MD. Police Check or Vulnerable Person Screening is done for all new staff.
HEALTH SERVICES: Medication administration and/or supervision. Vitals monitored if required. Will accept and provide special assistance for residents who require oxygen, catheters and ostomies. Assistance with dressing available (cost). Weekly assistance with bathing available (cost). Care plans done. Different levels of care available. Private Duty/Extra Care available. Assisted Living Area is secured to accommodate residents with dementia. Lab service (visiting). Residents can purchase outside resources and use agency of their choice. MD visits residents in their rooms/suites. Will help locate higher level of care if needed (Community Care Access Centre for assistance with long-term care options).
ACCOMMODATION: *Choice of suites available*: private studio, 1-bedroom with kitchenette & studio with pantry kitchen. *In all suites*: locks, window coverings, light fixtures, smoke detector, sprinkler, call bell, air conditioning (all common areas are air conditioned; residents may have window units installed) and thermostats for heating. Private bathrooms with call bells, grab bars and showers with non-slip surfaces. In-suite cable TV provided by residence (residence charges extra). Can have own phone number provided by residence (residence charges extra). Unfurnished suites, furnished suites available for short

stays. *Restrictions on electrical appliances*: bar fridges & kettles with auto shut-off feature are allowed. Pets allowed (as per Pet Policy within Tenancy Agreement).

DINING SERVICE: All meals included in fee and served in dining room daily. *Sittings per meal:* Breakfast: 2, Lunch: 2, Dinner: 2. *Menu choices available:* Breakfast: 2, Lunch: 2, Dinner: 2. *Guest Meals*: Available. *Special Diets*: Vegetarian, Low Salt, Diabetic and All Therapeutic Diets. Fresh salad bar with lunch. Tray service to room if ill (no charge for a maximum time of 4 days). 3 snacks/day. Party facilities. Open pantry.

AMENITIES AND ACTIVITIES: Parking available (outdoor, for visitors and residents). *7 lounges with:* TV (1), piano (1), kitchenette (5) and activity room (1). Guest suites available. *Residence has a:* library, barber/beauty shop and laundry room(s) (no cost). Resident can arrange newspaper delivery to individual suite. Mail delivered to resident. *Recreation Facilities*: pool table, billiards, craft room and card room. Posted schedule of activities. Internal newsletter for residents. *Recreational Programs*: exercise, shopping, theatre, parties, entertainment, art classes, pet visiting, day trips, variety of educational seminars, travelogue, intergenerational programs, therapeutic swim and bowling.

OTHER SERVICES: *Housekeeping*: weekly. *Laundry*: linen, towel & personal (included in fee). Resident pays for dry cleaning; staff will arrange for item pick up. Transportation for group social activities. 24-hour security. Nightly security checks (extra cost). Telephone & Cable TV (extra cost). Utilities (included in fee).

RENTAL INFORMATION: Rates may vary. Private studio - $2,295.00/month & up. Extra cost for 2nd person sharing suite. Rent paid monthly. *Payment Options*: cheques and pre-authorized payments. Credit card for deposits for short-term stays. Rent increases as per Provincial Tenancy Legislation, annual for resident with 3 months' notice given. Will help resident move into residence. Short-term respite and trial stays available ($85.00/day & up, depending on care needs).

◆ LONDON ◆

BAYBRIDGE - MASONVILLE MANOR

350 North Centre Road, London, ON N6G 5G3
Tel: (519) 663-0220 • Fax: (519) 663-4154
Email: **MasonvilleManorCSL@BaybridgeSeniorLiving.ca**
Website: **www.masonvillemanor.com**
Contact: **Ingrid Posthumus**
Capacity: **123 residents** • Subsidies: **none**
Price: **$2,200.00 - $4,570.00/month**

At Masonville Manor we believe retirement living should be relaxing and carefree, spent doing the things you love. That's why our community provides a unique independent retirement lifestyle in a warm and welcoming environment. In one affordable, all-inclusive month-to-month rent, residents enjoy 3 delicious chef-prepared meals daily, enriching activities to share with friendly neighbours, housekeeping service, complimentary transportation, and so much more. We do not provide any health care services; however, residents are welcome to receive services from any outside home health care provider of their choice to help them continue enjoying life independently at our community. Discover the peace-of-mind, happiness and fulfillment you deserve. Contact us today to schedule your personal tour!

RESIDENCE INFORMATION: 16 years in operation. *Near:* Fanshaw Park Road and North Centre Road. Decorated in 2010. Handrails in hallways. 3 floors, 1 elevator. Wheelchair accessible. Central PA system. *Funding Base:* Corporate/for profit. *Owned and managed by:* BayBridge Senior Living. 112 units. *Average Waiting Period*: varies. *Average Age*: 83. Can sometimes accommodate cognitively impaired people. Can accommodate physically challenged people (must be independent: wheelchair, walkers,

scooters are welcome). Residents have a dress code (casual, no sleepwear in common areas). Smoking allowed (outdoor patios/balconies only). Alcohol allowed (in own apartments and dining room). *Procedures to leave the premises on a temporary basis*...book at Office. *Languages:* English. Will accept Public Guardian and Trustee clients. Main doors of residence secured at night only. *Close to:* Public Transit, Shopping, Churches, Synagogues, Seniors' Centre, Library, Major Highway and Local Hospital (St. Joseph's Health Care & London Health Sciences Centre).

STAFFING: *Available Staff/Services*: Social Work, Recreation Therapy, Occupational Therapy, Visiting Dentist, Physiotherapy, Denturist, Companions, Chaplaincy, Audiology/Hearing Clinic, Little Sewing Basket (sewing) and Robertson Brown Lab. *External services arranged by:* family/resident. Staff trained *re*: visually impaired. Can retain own MD. Staff members are bonded. Police Check or Vulnerable Person Screening is done for all new staff.

HEALTH SERVICES: Will accept (but not provide special assistance for) residents who require oxygen, catheters, ostomies and feeding tubes. Lab service (visiting, $10.00/visit). Residents can purchase outside resources and use agency of their choice. MD visits residents in their rooms/suites. Will help locate higher level of care if needed (information available from Front Office and local government health agencies).

ACCOMMODATION: *Choice of suites available*: studio, 1-bedroom & 2-bedroom suites. *In all suites*: locks, kitchenette, apartment-size fridge, storage, window coverings, light fixtures, linens, fire alarm, smoke detector, sprinkler, call bell, air conditioning (individual controls in apartments & central in common areas) and thermostats for heating & cooling. 3 emergency responses in apartment. Most have patios/balconies. Private bathrooms with call bells, grab bars, tubs and showers with non-slip surfaces and elevated toilet seats. In-suite cable TV provided by residence. Can have own phone number if resident arranges with phone company. Furnished & unfurnished suites available. *Restrictions on electrical appliances*: no hot plates or stoves. Suites can be shared, roommate picked by resident. Pets allowed (dogs on Ground Level).

DINING SERVICE: All meals included in fee and served in dining room daily. *Sittings per meal:* Breakfast: 1, Lunch: 1, Dinner: 1. *Menu choices available:* Breakfast: 5, Lunch: 6, Dinner: 5. *Guest Meals*: Breakfast $10.00, Lunch $12.00, Dinner $10.00. *Special Diets*: Vegetarian, Low Salt and Diabetic. Tray service to room if ill (no charge for a maximum time of 7 days). Unlimited snacks available at any time. Large meal served at noon. Fresh fruit, coffee, tea & goodies available all day. Party facilities. Private Dining Area.

AMENITIES AND ACTIVITIES: Parking available (outdoor, for visitors: free and indoor for residents: $85.00/month). *4 lounges with:* TV (1), piano (1), computer kiosks (1) and pool table (1). *Residence has a:* library, visiting library, chapel, barber/beauty shop, visiting hairdresser and laundry room(s) (no cost). Banking services on premises (once/ week). Resident can arrange newspaper delivery to individual suite. Mail delivered to private mailbox with key. *Recreation Facilities*: pool table, billiards, shuffleboard, exercise room and activity room. Posted schedule of activities. Internal newsletter for residents. *Recreational Programs*: exercise, shopping, theatre, parties, entertainment, pet visiting, day trips and educational seminars.

OTHER SERVICES: *Housekeeping*: weekly (included in fee). *Laundry*: linen & towel (included in fee); personal (extra cost; can pay outside services) & dry cleaning (extra cost - local dry cleaner comes once/week). Free use of laundry rooms. Transportation to medical appointments and for group social activities. 24-hour security. Nightly security checks. Cable TV & Utilities (included in fee). Garage parking (extra cost).

RENTAL INFORMATION: Rates may vary. Rate listed above is based on single occupancy. Extra cost for 2nd person sharing suite ($550.00/month; please call for specifics). Rent paid monthly. *Payment Options*: cheques, post-dated cheques, direct deposit and pre-authorized payments. Rent increases indexed to inflation as per Provincial Tenancy Legislation, annual for resident with 3 months' notice given. Will help resident move into residence. Short-term respite ($80.00/day) and trial stays available (please see Management Team).

CHELSEY PARK RETIREMENT COMMUNITY

312 Oxford Street West, London, ON N6H 4N7
Tel: (519) 432-1845 • Fax: (519) 432-7548
Website: **www.chelseypark.com**
Contact: **Diane Pope**
Capacity: **120 residents •** Subsidies: **none**
Price: **$2,242.00 - $4,044.00/month (based on single occupancy)**

Chelsey Park provides a full complement of choices, featuring comfortable retirement residence accommodations, well-appointed apartments, an accredited long-term care home and a wide variety of programs and first class services. Located across the street from a fully complemented shopping centre. While assistance and companionship are never more than a few feet away, privacy and independence are always respected.

RESIDENCE INFORMATION: 38 years in operation. *On:* Oxford Street West and Cherryhill Circle. Decorated in 2013. Handrails in hallways. 5 floors, 3 elevators. Wheelchair accessible. *Funding Base:* Corporate/for profit. 96 units. *Average Waiting Period*: none. *Average Age*: 86. Can accommodate cognitively impaired people (with assessment). Can accommodate physically challenged people (with assessment). Residents have a dress code (residents must be dressed in public areas). Smoking allowed (in their own suite or outside). Alcohol allowed (residents can purchase from dining lounge or have alcohol in their suites). *Procedures to leave the premises on a temporary basis...*notify the Health Services Office. *Languages:* English, some staff speak Dutch, Polish & German. Main doors of residence secured at night only. *Close to:* Public Transit, Shopping, Churches, Seniors' Centre, Library, Major Highway and Local Hospital (London Health Sciences Centre – University Site). Member of ORCA. Licensed under the Retirement Homes Act.
STAFFING: *Available Staff/Services*: Pharmacy, Social Work (CCAC), Recreation Therapy, Occupational Therapy (CCAC), Visiting Dentist, Denturist, Dietitian (CCAC), Companions, Podiatry (CCAC), Chaplaincy and Physiotherapy (on-site through CCAC). *External services arranged by:* residence and/or family/resident. Staff trained *re*: visually, hearing and cognitively impaired. 24-hour nursing staff. RPNs, HCAs, PSWs and UCPs on staff. Can retain own MD. Police Check or Vulnerable Person Screening is done for all new staff before hiring.
HEALTH SERVICES: Medication administration and/or supervision (extra charge for more than 4 times/day). Vitals monitored if required. Will accept (but not provide special assistance for) residents who require catheters and ostomies. Will accept and provide special assistance for residents who require oxygen. Assistance with dressing available ($16.55/half hour). Weekly assistance with bathing available. *Extra baths:* $22.20/bath. Care plans done. Different levels of care available. Private Duty/Extra Care available ($30.00/hour). Lab service (visiting). Residents can purchase outside resources and use agency of their choice. MD can visit residents in their suites. Will help locate higher level of care if needed (Care Conferences and CCAC).
ACCOMMODATION: *Choice of suites available*: bedsitting (35) & apartment (63) suites. *In all suites*: locks, kitchenette, fridge/bar fridge, storage, light fixtures, smoke detector, call bell, air conditioning (provided in Retirement Suites only; Apartments can bring own/rent) and thermostats for heating & cooling. Most have patio/balcony. Private bathrooms with call bells, grab bars, tubs and showers (tubs can be converted to walk-in shower) with non-slip surfaces. In-suite cable TV if resident arranges with cable company. Can have own phone number if resident arranges with phone company. Furnished & unfurnished suites available. *Restrictions on electrical appliances*: no hot plates. Suites can be shared (couples, mother/son, mother/daughter, etc.), roommate picked by resident. Pets allowed (Pet Rules and Regulations apply).
DINING SERVICE: All meals included in fee and served in dining room daily. *Sittings per meal:* Breakfast: 1, Lunch: 1, Dinner: 2. *Menu choices available:* Breakfast: 2, Lunch: 2, Dinner: 2. *Guest Meals*: Breakfast

$6.00, Lunch $11.00, Dinner $15.00. *Special Diets*: Vegetarian, Low Salt, Diabetic and Texture Modified. Tray service to room if ill (no charge for a maximum time of 7 days). Open pantry. Snacks put out 3 times/day in the dining lounge. Party facilities.
AMENITIES AND ACTIVITIES: Parking available (outdoor, for visitors and residents). *6 lounges with:* TVs (2) and pianos (2). Guest suites available ($80.00/night). *Residence has a:* library, visiting library, chapel, barber/beauty shop, laundry room(s) ($2.00/washer load, $2.00/dryer load) and tuck/gift shop (open Monday to Friday, 9:30 a.m. - 3:00 p.m.; Saturday, 10:00 a.m. – 2:00 p.m.). Banking services on premises (twice/month). Resident can arrange newspaper delivery to individual suite. Mail delivered to private mailbox with key. *Recreation Facilities*: pool table, billiards, shuffleboard, exercise room, craft room, card room, computer café, heated saltwater pool, whirlpool and sauna. Posted schedule of activities. Internal newsletter for residents. *Recreational Programs*: exercise, shopping, theatre, parties, entertainment, art classes, pet visiting and day trips.
OTHER SERVICES: *Housekeeping*: daily (included in fee). *Laundry*: linen, towel & personal (included in fee); dry cleaning (available to purchase at the Store). Laundry is done individually. Transportation for group social activities. Nightly security checks (available if ordered by physician). Telephone & Cable TV (extra cost). Utilities (included in fee). Parking (reserved parking only for residents who are actively driving - covered reserved $32.55/month; underground reserved - $43.05/month).
RENTAL INFORMATION: Rates may vary. Single Occupancy: studio - $2,242.00/month; bedsitting - $2,584.00/month; standard 1-bedroom suite - $3,709.00/month; large suite - $4,044.00/month; large 2-bedroom suite - $4,292.00/month. Double Occupancy: standard suite - $5,167.00/month; large 1-bedroom suite - $5,501.00/month; large 2-bedroom suite - $5,749.00/month. Extra cost for 2nd person sharing suite. Rent paid monthly. *Payment Options*: cheques, post-dated cheques and pre-authorized payments. Rent increases as per Provincial Tenancy Legislation, annual for resident with 3 months' notice given. Short-term respite and trial stays available (both $80.00/day). Vacation stays also available.

GRAND WOOD PARK APARTMENTS & RETIREMENT RESIDENCE

81 Grand Avenue, London, ON N6C 1M2
Tel: (519) 432-1162 • Fax: (519) 432-4005
Email: **jgirvin@regallc.com**
Website: **www.grandwoodpark.ca**
Contact: **Jaclynn Girvin**
Capacity: **157 residents** • Subsidies: **none**
Price: **$1,770.00 - $3,500.00/month**

This charming and gracious retirement home in Old South London is nestled amid 6 ½ acres of majestic trees, floral gardens and beautifully-groomed lawns with paved walkways throughout. Enjoy the best of life with our *Art of Living Program* for the mind, body and soul.

RESIDENCE INFORMATION: 27 years in operation. *Near:* Wellington Road and Commissioners Road. Decorated in 2012. Handrails in hallways. 3 floors, 3 elevators. Wheelchair accessible. Central PA system. *Funding Base:* Corporate/for profit. 131 units. *Average Waiting Period*: varies. *Average Age*: 83. Can accommodate cognitively impaired people with restrictions (some restrictions apply, no secure area available). Can accommodate physically challenged people (with assessment). Smoking allowed (outdoors). Alcohol allowed. *Procedures to leave the premises on a temporary basis...*notify Receptionist or staff. *Languages:* English, Polish (staff), Spanish (staff), Hungarian (staff), Arabic (staff) & Portuguese (staff). Will accept Public Guardian and Trustee clients. Main doors of residence secured at night only. *Close to:* Public Transit, Shopping, Churches, Seniors' Centre, Library, Major Highway and Local Hospitals (St. Joseph's Health Care - Parkwood Site and London Health Sciences Centre – Victoria and Westminster Sites). Licensed under the Retirement Homes Act.
STAFFING: *Available Staff/Services*: Pharmacy, Social Work (CCAC), Recreation Therapy, Occupational Therapy (CCAC), Visiting Dentist, Physiotherapy, Denturist, Dietitian, Companions, Chaplaincy, Speech

Pathology (CCAC), Chiropody, Audiology/Hearing Clinic and Spa. *External services arranged by:* residence and/or family/resident. Staff trained *re*: visually, hearing and cognitively impaired. 24-hour nursing and other staff. RNs, RPNs, HCAs, PSWs and UCPs on staff. Can retain own MD. Police Check or Vulnerable Person Screening is done for all new staff.

HEALTH SERVICES: Medication administration and/or supervision. Vitals monitored if required. Will accept and provide special assistance for residents who require oxygen, catheters and ostomies. Assistance with dressing available (cost). Weekly assistance with bathing available. *Extra baths:* $80.00/month. Care plans done. Different levels of care available. Private Duty/Extra Care available ($22.00 to $24.00/hour). Lab service (visiting, $25.00/visit). Residents can purchase outside resources and use agency of their choice. Will help locate higher level of care if needed (help with application forms).

ACCOMMODATION: *Choice of suites available*: private rooms with private 4-piece bathroom – various sizes (115) & 1-2-3 room apartments. *In all suites*: locks, storage, window coverings, light fixtures, linens, smoke detector, emergency response system with wearable pendant/bracelet, air conditioning (central) and thermostats for heating & cooling. Apartments available with full kitchenettes; microwaves & bar fridges supplied by resident. Sprinkler system in apartment units. Private bathrooms with grab bars, tubs and showers with non-slip surfaces. In-suite cable TV provided by residence (residence charges extra $30.00/month). Furnished & unfurnished suites available. *Restrictions on electrical appliances*: must be new equipment with auto shut-off features. Suites can be shared (by couples or family members), roommate picked by resident. Pets allowed (fish, birds, dogs and cats as per Pet Policy).

DINING SERVICE: All meals included in fee and served in dining room daily. *Sittings per meal:* Breakfast: 1, Lunch: 1, Dinner: 1. *Menu choices available:* Breakfast: 2, Lunch: 2, Dinner: 2. *Guest Meals*: Breakfast $6.00, Lunch $8.00, Dinner $10.00. *Special Diets*: Vegetarian, Low Salt, Diabetic, Renal, Gluten Free and Modified Textures. Tray service to room if ill (no charge for a maximum time of 3 days). 3 snacks/day and unlimited snacks available at any time. Party facilities. Open pantry. Private dining room available. 2 cafés in the Retirement Residence and 1 in the Apartments.

AMENITIES AND ACTIVITIES: Parking available (outdoor, for visitors and residents). *9 lounges with:* TVs (3), pianos (2) and café (1). Guest suites available ($50.00/night). *Residence has a:* library, visiting library, chapel, barber/beauty shop, visiting hairdresser, laundry room(s) (no cost) and tuck/gift shop (open Monday to Saturday). Banking services on premises (7 days/week). Resident can arrange newspaper delivery to individual suite (extra cost). Mail delivered to individual suite. *Recreation Facilities*: shuffleboard, exercise room, greenhouse, craft room, card room, gazebo and auditorium with TV & piano. Posted schedule of activities. Internal newsletter for residents. *Recreational Programs*: exercise, shopping, theatre, parties, entertainment, art classes, pet visiting, day trips and computer & cooking workshops.

OTHER SERVICES: *Housekeeping*: weekly. *Laundry*: linen & towel (included in fee); personal (extra cost; personal laundry in Retirement Residence) & dry cleaning (extra cost). Complimentary laundry facilities in both the Retirement Residence and the apartments. Either staff or resident label clothing. Transportation for group social activities. 24-hour security. Telephone (extra cost). Cable TV ($30.00/month). Utilities (included in fee).

RENTAL INFORMATION: Rates may vary. Extra cost for 2nd person sharing suite ($625.00/month). Rent paid monthly. *Payment Options*: cheques and pre-authorized payments. Rent increases indexed to inflation as per Provincial Tenancy Legislation, annual for resident with 3 months' notice given. Will help resident move into residence ($50.00/hour). Short-term respite ($115.00/day) and trial stays available ($1,770.00/month & up, depending on size of suite & additional care requirements).

Just a Reminder ....

Pricing information for homes listed in the *Guide* may vary slightly. Please verify rates with the residences you are interested in directly.

HIGHVIEW RESIDENCES

35 & 41 Capulet Walk, London, ON N6H 3E6
Tel: (519) 472-8882 • Fax: (519) 472-7947
Email: **info@highviewres.com**
Website: **www.highviewres.com**
Contact: **Kirk Summers, Chief Operating Officer**
Capacity: **48 units** • Subsidies: **none**
Price: **$5,395.00/month**

Highview Residences specializes in providing permanent and respite care to individuals with Alzheimer's disease and related dementia, and to the frail elderly. We are committed to creating a home for our residents which is inviting and comfortable, strengthening feelings of belonging and security while reducing feelings of loneliness and confusion. We understand how important these feelings are to our residents and their loved ones. Highview is committed to creating a quality of care that meets each resident's physical, social, spiritual and emotional needs.

RESIDENCE INFORMATION: 18 years in operation. Handrails in hallways. 1 floor, no elevator. Wheelchair accessible. *Funding Base:* Corporate/for profit. *Average Waiting Period*: varies. Can accommodate cognitively impaired people (specialize in Alzheimer's and dementia care). Smoke-free residence. *Languages:* English. Main doors of residence secured at all times. *Close to:* Public Transit, Shopping, Churches, Library and Local Hospital. Licensed under the Retirement Homes Act.
STAFFING: *Available Staff/Services*: Pharmacy, Physiotherapy, Dietitian, Companions, Podiatry, Chaplaincy, Music Therapy and Art Therapy. *External services arranged by:* residence and/or family/resident. Staff trained *re*: visually, hearing and cognitively impaired. 24-hour staff. RNs, RPNs and PSWs on staff. Can retain own MD. Police Check or Vulnerable Person Screening is done for all new staff.
HEALTH SERVICES: Medication administration and/or supervision. Vitals monitored if required. Will accept and provide special assistance for residents who require oxygen. Assistance with dressing available. Daily assistance with bathing available. Care plans done. Different levels of care available. Assisted Living Area is secured to accommodate residents with dementia. Lab service (visiting).
ACCOMMODATION: *Choice of suites available*: 48 private rooms. *In all suites*: window coverings, light fixtures, linens, fire alarm, smoke detector, sprinkler and air conditioning (central). Private bathrooms with grab bars, showers with non-slip surfaces and elevated toilet seats. In-suite cable TV if resident arranges with cable company. Can have own phone number if resident arranges with phone company. Furnished & unfurnished suites available. Suites can be shared (by couples only). Pets allowed (at Director's approval).
DINING SERVICE: All meals included in fee and served in dining room daily. *Guest Meals*: Available. *Special Diets*: Vegetarian, Low Salt and Diabetic. 3 snacks/day.
AMENITIES AND ACTIVITIES: Parking available (outdoor, for visitors and residents). *Residence has a:* visiting library and visiting hairdresser. Resident can arrange newspaper delivery to individual suite. Mail delivered to resident. Posted schedule of activities. Internal newsletter for residents.
OTHER SERVICES: *Housekeeping*: daily (included in fee). *Laundry*: linen, towel & personal (included in fee). Nightly security checks.
RENTAL INFORMATION: Rates may vary. Extra cost for 2nd person sharing suite. Rent paid monthly. *Payment Options*: cheques, post-dated cheques and direct deposit. Rent increases are a set percentage, annual for resident with 3 months' notice given. Will help resident move into residence. Short-term respite and trial stays available (both $177.00/day).

For updated and new information on homes that joined us after we went to press visit **www.senioropolis.com**

INSPIRIT RESIDENCES

81 Base Line Road West, London, ON N6Y 4Y5
Tel: (519) 675-0500 • Fax: (519) 675-9781
Email: **info@inspiritres.com**
Website: **www.inspiritres.com**
Contact: **Jane Zwaan, Director**
Capacity: **43 units** • Subsidies: **none**
Price: **$3,600.00 - $4,300.00/month**

Inspirit Residences offers you an exceptional opportunity to experience retirement living. Your independent lifestyle is accommodated by full-sized apartments and a full range of services that are available to you if needed. Inspirit is designed to assist you in maintaining a life that is in balance in all aspects of living; physical, mental, emotional and spiritual.

RESIDENCE INFORMATION: 15 years in operation. Decorated in 2009. 6 floors, 2 elevators. Wheelchair accessible. *Funding Base:* Corporate/for profit. *Owned by:* Ross & Cathy Chapin. *Average Waiting Period*: varies. *Average Age*: 84. Can sometimes accommodate physically challenged people. Smoke-free residence. *Languages:* English. Main doors of residence secured at all times. *Close to:* Public Transit, Shopping and Churches. Licensed under the Retirement Homes Act.
STAFFING: *Available Staff/Services*: Pharmacy, Recreation Therapy, Physiotherapy and Chaplaincy. 24-hour staff. RNs, RPNs and PSWs on staff. Can retain own MD. Police Check or Vulnerable Person Screening is done for all new staff.
HEALTH SERVICES: Medication administration and/or supervision. Vitals monitored if required. Will accept (but not provide special assistance for) residents who require oxygen. Assistance with dressing available. Weekly assistance with bathing available. Care plans done. Different levels of care available. Lab service (visiting).
ACCOMMODATION: Choice of suites available. *In all suites*: locks, kitchenette, stove, patio/balcony, storage, window coverings, fire alarm, smoke detector, sprinkler, air conditioning (central) and thermostats for heating & cooling. Shared bathrooms. In-suite cable TV provided by residence. Can have own phone number if resident arranges with phone company. Unfurnished suites. Suites can be shared (by couples only). Pets allowed.
DINING SERVICE: All meals included in fee and served in dining room daily. *Sittings per meal:* Breakfast: 1, Lunch: 1, Dinner: 1. *Guest Meals*: Available. *Special Diets*: Available. Tray service to room if ill. Party facilities.
AMENITIES AND ACTIVITIES: Parking available (outdoor, for visitors and residents). *3 lounges with:* TV (1). *Residence has a:* library, chapel, barber/beauty shop, visiting hairdresser and laundry room(s) (no cost). Banking services on premises. Residence provides newspaper delivery to individual suite. Mail delivered to private mailbox with key. *Recreation Facilities*: exercise room. Posted schedule of activities. Internal newsletter for residents. *Recreational Programs*: exercise, shopping, theatre, entertainment, art classes and day trips.
OTHER SERVICES: *Housekeeping*: daily. Telephone & Cable TV (extra cost). Utilities (included in fee).
RENTAL INFORMATION: Rates may vary. No cost for sharing suite. Rent paid monthly. *Payment Options*: cheques, direct deposit and pre-authorized payments. Rent increases as per Provincial Tenancy Legislation, annual for resident with 3 months' notice given. Will help resident move into residence.

Did you know?

There are many products that can assist visually impaired seniors maintain independence in their daily lives. Visit **www.cnib.ca** for information on various products and services.

KENSINGTON VILLAGE

1340 Huron Street, London, ON N5V 3R3
Tel: (519) 455-3910 • Fax: (519) 455-1570
Email: **sbrooks@kensingtonvillage.org**
Website: **www.svch.ca**
Contact: **Sharron Brooks**
Capacity: **144 residents** • Subsidies: **none**
Price: **$2,713.00 - $4,490.00/month**

There are many reasons why our residents have chosen to live in a Sharon Village Care Home. For some, it's the benefit of living together in a safe caring environment. For others, it's access to discrete Assisted Living Services in a continuum of care model. Whatever the reason, Sharon Village Care Homes is committed to enriching the mental and physical welfare of our residents through the comforts of home.

RESIDENCE INFORMATION: 30 years in operation. *Near:* Highbury Street on Huron Street. Decorated in 2010. Handrails in hallways. 1 floor, no elevators. Wheelchair accessible. Central PA system. *Funding Base:* Corporate/for profit. *Managed by:* Sharon Village Care Homes. 138 units. *Average Waiting Period*: varies. *Average Age*: 86. Can accommodate cognitively impaired people (Early Memory Loss Special Care Secure Unit). Can accommodate physically challenged people (all rooms and bathrooms are totally wheelchair accessible). Residents have a dress code (pyjamas & housecoat allowed in dining room for breakfast only). Smoking allowed (outdoor designated area only). Alcohol allowed. *Procedures to leave the premises on a temporary basis...*Short-term: sign out book. Overnight & Holidays: sign out book and advise staff. *Languages:* English, Polish, German, Spanish, Italian & Dutch. Will accept Public Guardian and Trustee clients. Main doors of residence secured at night only. *Close to:* Public Transit, Shopping, Churches, Synagogues, Library, Major Highway and Local Hospital (London Health Sciences Centre – University Site). Member of ORCA. Licensed under the Retirement Homes Act.
STAFFING: *Available Staff/Services*: Pharmacy, Social Work, Recreation Therapy, Occupational Therapy, Visiting Dentist, Physiotherapy, Dietitian, Companions, Chaplaincy, Speech Pathology, Chiropody and Hairdresser. *External services arranged by:* family/resident. Staff trained *re*: visually, hearing and cognitively impaired. 24-hour nursing staff. RNs, RPNs and PSWs on staff. Visiting MD (weekly & on call). Can retain own MD. Police Check or Vulnerable Person Screening is done for all new staff.
HEALTH SERVICES: Medication administration and/or supervision (physician's order required for resident to self-administer medications). Vitals monitored if required. Will accept and provide special assistance for residents who require oxygen and ostomies. Assistance with dressing available ($13.85/half hour). Weekly assistance with bathing available. *Extra baths:* $10.00/bath. Care plans done. Different levels of care available. Assisted Living Area ($13.85/day). Separate unit for residents with dementia. Lab service (visiting, $25.00/visit). Residents can purchase outside resources and use agency of their choice. Clinic area for medical visits. Will help locate higher level of care if needed (will assist through CCAC).
ACCOMMODATION: *Choice of suites available*: 2-room (3), semi-private (10), couple suite (15) & private (110) units. *In all suites*: locks, window coverings, light fixtures, linens, smoke detector, sprinkler, call bell and air conditioning (central & window units). Kitchenettes & showers in Independent areas. Private bathrooms with call bells and grab bars. In-suite cable TV if resident arranges with cable company. Can have own phone number if resident arranges with phone company. Unfurnished suites, furnished suites available for short stays. *Restrictions on electrical appliances*: CSA/UCLA approved. Suites can be shared, roommate picked by resident. No pets allowed.
DINING SERVICE: All meals included in fee and served in dining room daily. *Sittings per meal:* Breakfast: 1, Lunch: 1, Dinner: 1. *Menu choices available:* Breakfast: 2, Lunch: 2, Dinner: 2. *Guest Meals*: Breakfast $5.00, Lunch $6.00, Dinner $8.00. *Special Diets*: Vegetarian, Low Salt, Diabetic, Celiac and Renal. Tray service to room if ill (no charge as long as doctor orders). Unlimited snacks available at any time. Party facilities. Open pantry. Three dining rooms and café stocked with tea, coffee, juice, cookies, fruit bowls available 24/7.

SVCH
SHARON VILLAGE
CARE HOMES
THE BEST YEARS ARE STILL TO COME.
Long-Term Care, Seniors Housing
and Retirement Homes.
www.svch.ca
Our Properties
Kensington Village | Earls Court Village (Opening in 2014)
Saugeen Valley Nursing Home | Strathcona Village Homes
Tyndall Seniors Village

AMENITIES AND ACTIVITIES: Parking available (outdoor, for visitors and residents). *6 lounges with:* TVs (3), piano (1) and fireplaces (2). Guest suites available. *Residence has a:* library, visiting library, chapel, barber/beauty shop, laundry room(s) ($0.75/washer load, $0.25/dryer load), tuck/gift shop (open mornings & afternoons). Banking services on premises (monthly). Residence provides newspaper delivery to individual suite. Mail delivered to resident. *Recreation Facilities*: pool table, shuffleboard, craft room and card room. Posted schedule of activities. Internal newsletter for residents. *Recreational Programs*: exercise, shopping, theatre, parties, entertainment, art classes, pet visiting, day trips, creative writing, bingo/games and monthly birthday party.
OTHER SERVICES: *Housekeeping*: daily (included in fee). *Laundry*: linen & towel (included in fee); personal ($46.00/week). Staff label clothing (one-time charge of $54.00 + $.20 per label). Transportation for group social activities (extra cost may or may not apply). Nightly security checks. Telephone & Cable TV (extra cost). Utilities (included in fee).
RENTAL INFORMATION: Rates may vary. Private, Independent - $2,713.00/month & up; Supportive Living - $2,933.00/month & up. Extra cost for 2nd person sharing suite (discount/special pricing for couples). Rent paid monthly. *Payment Options*: cheques, post-dated cheques and pre-authorized payments. Rent increases as per Provincial Tenancy Legislation, annual for resident with 3 months' notice given. Short-term respite and trial stays available (cost varies).

QUEENS VILLAGE FOR SENIORS

518 Queens Avenue, London, ON N6B 1Y7
Tel: (519) 433-4066 • Fax: (519) 433-0731
Toll Free: (866) 433-4066
Email: **francine@queensvillage.ca**
Website: **www.queensvillage.ca**
Contact: **Francine Lacroix**
Capacity: **75 residents** • Subsidies: **none**
Price: **$1,800.00 - $4,000.00/month**

- We have an Alzheimer's Care Program - Memory Lane is a retirement community in a secured home-like setting geared towards seniors suffering from the early to mid-stages of Alzheimer Disease or dementia.

- We also have a Daycare Program and Respite Care in order to give caregivers a break. In addition, we provide post-surgery care and physiotherapy.
- This charming and prestigious property has been one of London's landmarks since 1872 and has been restored to its original state.
- It is also the home of The Classic Spa where you will get total body care for her and him – **(519) 432-0169.**

RESIDENCE INFORMATION: 10 years in operation. *On:* Queens Avenue and West of Adelaide Street. Decorated in 2008. Handrails in hallways. 4 floors, 2 elevators. Wheelchair accessible. Central PA system. *Funding Base:* Corporate/for profit. *Owned by:* Village Partners. 67 units. *Average Waiting Period*: none. *Average Age*: 82. Can accommodate cognitively impaired people (Alzheimer's Disease & dementia). Can accommodate physically challenged people (wheelchair dependent). Residents have a dress code (no pyjamas in dining room and common areas). Smoking allowed (indoor designated smoking area). Alcohol allowed (staff monitor use). *Restrictions around Visitors/Visiting Hours:* from 10:00 a.m. to 10:00 p.m. *Procedures to leave the premises on a temporary basis...*sign out and advise nursing staff of destination and expected return. *Languages:* English, French, Italian & Portuguese. Will accept Public Guardian and Trustee clients. Main doors of residence secured at night only. *Close to:* Public Transit, Shopping, Churches, Synagogues, Seniors' Centre, Library and Local Hospital (London Health Sciences Centre - South Street Site). Member of ORCA, Alzheimer's Society of London & Middlesex, Council For London Seniors & Woodfield Residents Association. Licensed under the Retirement Homes Act.
STAFFING: *Available Staff/Services*: Pharmacy, Social Work, Recreation Therapy, Occupational Therapy, Visiting Dentist, Physiotherapy, Denturist, Dietitian (CCAC), Companions, Podiatry, Chaplaincy, Speech Pathology (CCAC), Chiropody, Foot Care, Driving Service and The Classic Spa. *External services arranged by:* residence and/or family/resident. Staff trained *re*: visually, hearing and cognitively impaired. 24-hour nursing and other staff. RNs, RPNs, HCAs, PSWs and UCPs on staff. Visiting MD (every 2 weeks & on call). Can retain own MD. Police Check or Vulnerable Person Screening is done for all new staff. Strict policy on confidentiality.
HEALTH SERVICES: Medication administration and/or supervision. Vitals monitored if required. Will accept and provide special assistance for residents who require oxygen, catheters, ostomies and feeding tubes. Assistance with dressing available. Weekly assistance with bathing available. *Extra baths:* $12.00/ half hour. Care plans done. Different levels of care available. Private Duty/Extra Care available ($20.00/ hour). Assisted Living Area is secured to accommodate residents with dementia. Lab service (visiting, $25.00/visit). Residents can purchase outside resources and use agency of their choice. MD visits residents in their rooms/suites. Will help locate higher level of care if needed (we put families in contact with our CCAC representative).
ACCOMMODATION: *Choice of suites available*: all suites are private with bathrooms; 1-bedroom, 2-bedroom, studio & 2 semi-private suites. *In all suites*: locks, window coverings, light fixtures, linens, fire alarm, smoke detector, sprinkler, call bell, emergency response system with wearable pendant/bracelet and air conditioning (common areas & some units have central air and heat). Some units have own heating and air conditioning thermostats. Some units have kitchenettes with bar fridges, fireplace & patio. Private bathrooms (except for 2 suites that share 1 bathroom) with grab bars, tubs and showers with non-slip surfaces and elevated toilet seats. In-suite cable TV if resident arranges with cable company. Can have own phone extension number provided by residence (residence charges extra $35.00/month). Furnished & unfurnished suites available. *Restrictions on electrical appliances*: no toasters, no kettles, no electric blankets/pads. Suites can be shared (pending availability of beds), roommate picked by resident & residence staff. Pets allowed (resident must be able to provide total care).
DINING SERVICE: All meals included in fee and served in dining room daily. *Sittings per meal:* Breakfast: 1, Lunch: 1, Dinner: 1. *Menu choices available:* Breakfast: 2, Lunch: 2, Dinner: 2. *Guest Meals*: Breakfast $3.50, Lunch $5.00, Dinner $8.50. *Special Diets*: Vegetarian, Low Salt, Diabetic, Renal and Lactose Intolerance. Tray service to room if ill (no charge or restrictions). 3 snacks/day. Party facilities. Juice, coffee, tea, cookies & fruit are always available.

AMENITIES AND ACTIVITIES: Parking available (outdoor, for visitors and residents). *4 lounges with:* TVs (3), piano (1) and organ (1). Guest suites available ($50.00/night). *Residence has a:* library, visiting library, barber/beauty shop and Tuck Cart (twice/week). Banking services on premises (daily on request). Resident can arrange newspaper delivery to individual suite. Mail delivered to individual suite. *Recreation Facilities*: exercise room, craft room, card room and raised gardens. Posted schedule of activities. Internal newsletter for residents. *Recreational Programs*: exercise, shopping, theatre, parties, entertainment, art classes, pet visiting, day trips, gardening and total body care spa services.
OTHER SERVICES: *Housekeeping*: weekly (included in fee; curtains and windows twice a year). *Laundry*: linen, towel & personal (included in fee); dry cleaning (extra cost - pick-up and delivery). Either staff or resident label clothing (included in fee). Seamstress and alterations (extra cost). Transportation to medical appointments ($0.40/km) and for group social activities (limousine service; no extra cost). 24-hour security. Nightly security checks. Telephone ($35.00/month + $0.07/min long distance). Cable TV (extra cost according to package). Utilities (included in fee). Hair/barber salon. The Classic Spa full body care services.
RENTAL INFORMATION: Rates may vary. Small studio - $1,800.00/month; 2-bedroom apartment - $4,000.00/month. Extra cost for 2nd person sharing suite ($600.00/month). Rent paid monthly. *Payment Options*: cheques and post-dated cheques. Rent increases as per Provincial Tenancy Legislation, annual for resident with 3 months' notice given. Will help resident move into residence. Short-term respite and trial stays available (both $80.00 to $125.00/day up to 90 days).

REVERA - HORIZON PLACE

760 Horizon Drive, London, ON N6H 5G3
Tel: (855) 573-8372 • Toll Free: (855) 573-8372
Email: **horizonplace@reveraliving.com**
Website: **www.reveraliving.com/horizon**
Contact: **Executive Director or Lifestyle Consultant**
Capacity: **84 residents •** Subsidies: **none**
Price: **$2,795.00/month and up**

Keep living your life, your way, at Horizon Place. Here, you'll find the range of services, features and choices that fit your lifestyle and requirements – all in a warm, relaxed and safe environment. With retirement living at Horizon Place, you change your address, not your life. We're close to amenities and public transit, and everything in our one-storey residence is designed to enable you to maintain your independence and privacy, enjoy a full social life, and participate in the activities that you love. Our caring and friendly staff, along with appealing accommodations, support who you are and how you want to live. Explore what we have to offer, to keep you living in freedom and comfort. *Horizon Place is part of the Revera family, one of North America's leading and most trusted providers of seniors' accommodation, care and services since 1961.*

RESIDENCE INFORMATION: 24 years in operation. *Near:* Oxford Street and Wonderland Road. Decorated in 2011. Handrails in hallways. 1 floor, no elevators. Wheelchair accessible. *Funding Base:* Corporate/for profit. *Owned and managed by:* Revera Inc. 78 units. *Average Waiting Period*: varies. *Average Age*: 85. Can accommodate cognitively impaired people (Alzheimer's Disease, age-related dementias and memory impaired). Can accommodate physically challenged people. Smoking allowed (outside to the side of front entrance). Alcohol allowed. *Procedures to leave the premises on a temporary basis...*Short-term: sign out at Front Desk. Overnight & Holidays: inform Nursing and Administration. *Languages:* English, Spanish, Dutch, Polish, Filipino, French & Italian. Will accept Public Guardian and Trustee clients. Main doors of residence secured at all times. *Close to:* Public Transit, Shopping, Churches, Synagogues, Seniors' Centre, Library, Major Highway and Local Hospital (London Health Sciences Centre – University Site). Member of ORCA. Licensed under the Retirement Homes Act.

STAFFING: *Available Staff/Services*: Social Work (CCAC), Recreation Therapy, Occupational Therapy (CCAC), Visiting Dentist, Physiotherapy (CCAC), Dietitian (CCAC), Companions, Podiatry (CCAC), Chaplaincy, Speech Pathology (CCAC), Audiology/Hearing Clinic, Hair Salon and Foot Care Clinic. *External services arranged by:* residence and/or family/resident. Staff trained *re*: visually, hearing and cognitively impaired. 24-hour nursing and other staff. RPNs, PSWs and UCPs on staff. Visiting MD (weekly & on call for permanent residents). Can retain own MD. Police Check or Vulnerable Person Screening is done for all new staff.
HEALTH SERVICES: Medication administration and/or supervision. Vitals monitored if required. Will accept (but not provide special assistance for) residents who require ostomies. Will accept and provide special assistance for residents who require oxygen and catheters. Assistance with dressing available (cost). Assistance with bathing available as needed (cost). Care plans done. Different levels of care available. Private Duty/Extra Care available. Assisted Living Area. Lab service (visiting). Residents can purchase outside resources and use agency of their choice. MD visits residents in their rooms/suites. Will help locate higher level of care if needed (contact CCAC).
ACCOMMODATION: *Choice of suites available*: private suites (78). *In all suites*: locks, storage, window coverings, light fixtures, linens, fire alarm, smoke detector, sprinkler, call bell, emergency response system with wearable pendant/bracelet, air conditioning (window units) and thermostats for heating & cooling. Towels and linens if residents chooses. Private bathrooms with call bells, grab bars, tubs and showers with non-slip surfaces and shower curtain. In-suite cable TV provided by residence (residence charges extra). Can have own phone number provided by residence (residence charges extra). Unfurnished suites, furnished suites available for short stays. *Restrictions on electrical appliances*: no toasters or toaster ovens allowed; items must be CSA approved. Suites can be shared (by couples only), roommate picked by resident. Pets allowed (with assessment).
DINING SERVICE: All meals included in fee and served in dining room daily. *Sittings per meal:* Breakfast: 1, Lunch: 1, Dinner: 1. *Menu choices available:* Breakfast: 2, Lunch: 2, Dinner: 2. *Guest Meals*: Available. *Special Diets*: Vegetarian, Low Salt, Diabetic, Minced, Pureed and Thickened. Tray service to room if ill (no charge for a maximum time of 4 days). 3 snacks/day. Party facilities. 24-hour Bistro serving hot and cold beverages.
AMENITIES AND ACTIVITIES: Parking available (outdoor, for visitors and residents). *5 lounges with:* TV (1) and piano (1). Guest suites available. *Residence has a:* library, visiting library, chapel, barber/beauty shop, laundry room(s) (no cost) and tuck/gift shop (open daily; 9:00 a.m. - 5:00 p.m.). Residence provides newspaper delivery to individual suite (extra cost). Mail delivered to resident. *Recreation Facilities*: exercise room, craft room, card room and outdoor patio for socializing. Posted schedule of activities. Internal newsletter for residents. *Recreational Programs*: exercise, shopping, parties, entertainment, art classes, pet visiting, day trips, bingo, interactive games, Happy Hour, Nintendo Wii and X-Box Kinect.
OTHER SERVICES: *Housekeeping*: daily and weekly (included in fee; weekly deep clean). *Laundry*: linen (included in fee if using the homes linens) & towel (included in fee); personal (extra cost) & dry cleaning (resident sends out if they wish). Transportation to medical appointments (resident/family responsible for cost) and for group social activities (minimum fee for selected outings). 24-hour security. Nightly security checks. Telephone & Cable TV (extra cost). Utilities (included in fee).
RENTAL INFORMATION: Rates may vary. Extra cost for 2nd person sharing suite ($550.00/month). Rent paid monthly. *Payment Options*: pre-authorized payments. Rent increases as per Provincial Tenancy Legislation, annual for resident with 3 months' notice given. Will help resident move into residence (extra cost). Short-term respite and trial stays available.

Did you know?

June is Seniors' Month in Ontario. Visit **www.seniors.gov.on.ca/en/seniorsmonth/index.php** to find out about events in your area.

REVERA - MAPLE VIEW TERRACE

279 Horton Street, London, ON N6B 1L3
Tel: (855) 573-8372 • Toll Free: (855) 573-8372
Email: **mapleviewterrace@reveraliving.com**
Website: **www.reveraliving.com/mapleviewterrace**
Contact: **Executive Director or Lifestyle Consultant**
Capacity: **98 residents •** Subsidies: **none**
Price: **$2,055.00/month and up**

Keep living your life, your way, at Maple View Terrace. You'll find the range of services, amenities and choices that fit your lifestyle and requirements – all in a warm and safe environment. With retirement living at Maple View Terrace, you change your address, not your life. Everything is designed to enable you to maintain your independence and privacy, enjoy a full social life, and participate in the activities that you love. Our caring and friendly staff, along with appealing accommodations, support who you are and how you want to live. We're also conveniently located close to shopping, churches, restaurants, a seniors' centre, medical services, an art gallery, public transportation, and more. Explore what we have to offer, to keep you living in freedom and comfort. *Maple View Terrace is part of the Revera family, one of North America's leading and most trusted providers of seniors' accommodation, care and services since 1961.*

RESIDENCE INFORMATION: 48 years in operation. *Near:* Wellington Road and Horton Street. Decorated in 2010. Handrails in hallways. 6 floors, 2 elevators. Wheelchair accessible. Central PA system. *Funding Base:* Corporate/for profit. *Owned and managed by:* Revera Inc. 92 units. *Average Waiting Period*: none. *Average Age*: 84. Can accommodate cognitively impaired people (offer higher level of care if required). Can accommodate physically challenged people (assessment is required). Smoking allowed (designated area outdoors). Alcohol allowed. *Procedures to leave the premises on a temporary basis...* notify reception/nursing - sign in/out book in lobby. *Languages:* English & others. Will accept Public Guardian and Trustee clients. Main doors of residence secured at all times. *Close to:* Public Transit, Shopping, Churches, Synagogues, Seniors' Centre, Library, Major Highway and Local Hospitals (London Health Sciences Centre - University & Victoria Sites , St. Joseph's Health Care & Parkwood Site). Member of ORCA & Better Business Bureau Licensed under the Retirement Homes Act.
STAFFING: *Available Staff/Services*: Pharmacy, Social Work (CCAC), Recreation Therapy, Occupational Therapy (CCAC), Visiting Dentist, Physiotherapy (CCAC), Denturist, Dietitian (CCAC), Companions, Podiatry (CCAC), Speech Pathology (CCAC), Chiropody, Audiology/Hearing Clinic, Hairdressing, Manicures and Pedicures. *External services arranged by:* residence and/or family/resident. Staff trained *re*: visually, hearing and cognitively impaired. 24-hour nursing staff. RPNs, HCAs, PSWs and UCPs on staff. Visiting MD (every other Wednesday). Can retain own MD. Police Check or Vulnerable Person Screening is done for all new staff.
HEALTH SERVICES: Medication administration and/or supervision. Vitals monitored if required. Will accept and provide special assistance for residents who require oxygen, catheters and ostomies. Specialized suites available for post-operative. Assistance with dressing available. Assistance with bathing available as needed (cost). Care plans done. Different levels of care available. Private Duty/Extra Care available. Assisted Living Area. Lab service (visiting). Residents can purchase outside resources and use agency of their choice. Clinic area for medical visits. Will help locate higher level of care if needed (CCAC).
ACCOMMODATION: *Choice of suites available*: studio private suite, deluxe studio private suite, deluxe private suite &1-bedroom suite. *In all suites*: locks, window coverings, light fixtures, linens, smoke detector, sprinkler, call bell system at bedside & in bathroom, emergency response system with wearable pendant/bracelet, air conditioning (central) and thermostats for heating & cooling. Private bathrooms with call bells, grab bars and showers with non-slip surfaces. In-suite cable TV provided by residence (residence charges extra). Can have own phone number provided by residence. Furnished & unfurnished suites available. *Restrictions on electrical appliances:* no stoves; all electrical appliances need to be

approved. Suites can be shared (by couples only), roommate picked by resident. Pets allowed (adherence to Pet Policy).

DINING SERVICE: All meals included in fee and served in dining room daily. *Sittings per meal:* Breakfast: 1, Lunch: 2, Dinner: 2. *Menu choices available:* Breakfast: 2, Lunch: 2, Dinner: 2. *Guest Meals*: Available. *Special Diets*: Vegetarian, Low Salt, Diabetic, Renal, Lactose Free, Low Fat and Cardiac. Tray service to room if ill (no charge for a maximum time of 4 days). Unlimited snacks available at any time. Party facilities. Choice of mealtimes available.

AMENITIES AND ACTIVITIES: Parking available (outdoor, for visitors and residents). *7 lounges with:* TVs (4) and pianos (2). Guest suites available. *Residence has a:* library, visiting library, barber/beauty shop, visiting hairdresser, laundry room(s) (no cost) and tuck/gift shop (hours vary). Residence provides newspaper delivery to individual suite. Mail delivered to individual suite. *Recreation Facilities*: shuffleboard, exercise room, craft room, card room and bar/theatre room. Posted schedule of activities. Internal newsletter for residents. *Recreational Programs*: exercise, shopping, theatre, parties, entertainment, art classes, pet visiting and day trips.

OTHER SERVICES: *Housekeeping*: weekly (included in fee). *Laundry*: linen & towel (included in fee); personal & dry cleaning (extra cost). Either staff or resident label clothing. Transportation for group social activities. Nightly security checks. Telephone & Cable TV (extra cost). Utilities (included in fee). Foot Care.

RENTAL INFORMATION: Rates may vary. Extra cost for 2nd person sharing suite ($550.00/month). Rent paid monthly. *Payment Options*: pre-authorized payments. Rent increases as per Provincial Tenancy Legislation, annual for resident with 3 months' notice given. Will help resident move into residence. Short-term respite and trial stays available.

REVERA - WINDERMERE ON THE MOUNT RETIREMENT RESIDENCE

1486 Richmond Street, London, ON N6G 2M3
Tel: (855) 573-8372 • Toll Free: (855) 573-8372
Email: **windermereonthemount@reveraliving.com**
Website: **www.reveraliving.com/windermere**
Contact: **Executive Director or Lifestyle Consultant**
Capacity: **170 residents** • Subsidies: **none**
Price: **$2,333.00/month and up**

Keep living your life, your way, at Windermere On The Mount. You'll find the range of services, features and choices that fit your lifestyle and requirements – all in a warm and safe environment. Windermere On The Mount offers both independent apartments and full service retirement suites. Located in a prime area of North London, a variety of amenities can be found onsite and close by, from shopping to theatres to golf. Situated on 19 acres of landscaped grounds, seated atop "The Mount" on the Thames River, this residence offers a spectacular view of the Forest City. Everything here is designed to enable you to maintain your independence and privacy, enjoy a full social life, and participate in the activities you love. With retirement living at Windermere on the Mount, you change your address, not your life. *Windermere On The Mount is part of the Revera family, one of North America's leading and most trusted providers of seniors' accommodation, care and services since 1961.*

RESIDENCE INFORMATION: 8 years in operation. *Near:* Richmond Street and Windermere Road. Decorated in 2013. Handrails in hallways. 5 floors, 4 elevators. Wheelchair accessible. *Funding Base:* Corporate/for profit. *Owned and managed by:* Revera Inc. 136 units. *Average Waiting Period*: varies. *Average Age*: 86. Can accommodate cognitively impaired people with some restrictions. Residents have a dress code (dress for dinner). Smoke-free residence. Alcohol allowed (in suites and licenced common areas). *Procedures to leave the premises on a temporary basis...*sign in/out. *Languages:* English. Main doors of residence secured at night only. *Close to:* Public Transit, Shopping, Churches, Synagogues,

Seniors' Centre, Library and Local Hospital (London Health Sciences Centre - University Site). Member of ORCA. Licensed under the Retirement Homes Act.

STAFFING: *Available Staff/Services*: Pharmacy, Social Work (CCAC), Recreation Therapy, Occupational Therapy (CCAC), Physiotherapy (CCAC), Companions and Ministry of Health Flex Clinic. *External services arranged by:* family/resident. Staff trained *re*: visually and hearing impaired. 24-hour nursing and other staff. RPNs and PSWs on staff. Visiting MD (bi-weekly). Can retain own MD. Staff members are bonded. Police Check or Vulnerable Person Screening is done for all new staff.

HEALTH SERVICES: Medication administered if required. Vitals monitored if required. Will accept and provide special assistance for residents who require oxygen. Assistance with dressing available (cost). Weekly assistance with bathing available (cost). Care plans done. Different levels of care available. Private Duty/Extra Care available. Lab service (visiting, $25.00/visit). Residents can purchase outside resources and use agency of their choice. Clinic area for medical visits. Will help locate higher level of care if needed (our Retirement Residence is available to accommodate seniors in need of health services).

ACCOMMODATION: *Choice of suites available*: studios, 1-bedroom, 1-bedroom + den & 2-bedroom suites. *In all suites*: locks, kitchenette, microwave, window coverings, light fixtures, fire alarm, smoke detector, sprinkler, emergency response system with wearable pendant/bracelet, air conditioning (central) and thermostats for heating & cooling. Private bathrooms with grab bars and showers with non-slip surfaces. In-suite cable TV provided by residence. Unfurnished suites. Suites can be shared, roommate picked by resident. Pets allowed (some restrictions).

DINING SERVICE: All meals included in fee and served in dining room daily. *Sittings per meal:* Breakfast: 1, Lunch: 2, Dinner: 2. *Menu choices available:* Breakfast: 3, Lunch: 4, Dinner: 4. *Guest Meals*: Breakfast $5.00, Lunch $9.00, Dinner $14.75. Tray service to room if ill (no charge as long as doctor orders). Party facilities. Fine dining is available through reservation in the Broughdale Dining Room.

AMENITIES AND ACTIVITIES: Parking available (outdoor, for visitors and residents). *4 lounges with:* TVs (2), piano (1), surround sound (1) and fireplace (1). Guest suites available ($95.00/night). *Residence has a:* library, visiting library, chapel, barber/beauty shop, laundry room(s) (no cost) and tuck/gift shop. Mail delivered to main desk. *Recreation Facilities*: pool table, billiards, exercise room, craft room, card room, pub, gourmet kitchen, wellness services, fitness centre, spa and theatre. Posted schedule of activities. Internal newsletter for residents. *Recreational Programs*: exercise, shopping, theatre, parties, entertainment, art classes, day trips, concerts in 400 seat chapel, book clubs, bridge, gardening, billiards and movies.

OTHER SERVICES: *Housekeeping*: daily and weekly. *Laundry*: linen & towel (included in fee); personal & dry cleaning (extra cost). Personal laundry machines on each floor at no additional charge. Transportation for group social activities. 24-hour security. Nightly security checks. Telephone, Cable TV & Utilities (included in fee). Unlimited long distance in North America.

RENTAL INFORMATION: Rates may vary. Extra cost for 2nd person sharing suite ($650.00/month). Rent paid monthly. *Payment Options*: cheques, post-dated cheques, direct deposit and pre-authorized payments. Rent increases as per Provincial Tenancy Legislation, annual for resident with 3 months' notice given. Will help resident move into residence. Short-term respite and trial stays available.

REVERA - WINDERMERE ON THE MOUNT SENIORS APARTMENTS

1486 Richmond Street, London, ON N6G 2M3
Tel: (855) 573-8372 • Toll Free: (855) 573-8372
Email: **windermereonthemount@reveraliving.com**
Website: **www.reveraliving.com/windermere**
Contact: **Executive Director or Lifestyle Consultant**
Capacity: **170 residents** • Subsidies: **none**
Price: **$1,407.00/month and up**

Keep living your life, your way, at Windermere On The Mount Seniors Apartments. You'll find the range of services, features and choices that fit your lifestyle and requirements – all in a warm and safe

environment. Windermere On The Mount Seniors Apartments offers 1-bedroom or 2-bedroom apartments and is situated on 19 acres of landscaped grounds, seated atop "The Mount" on the Thames River, with a spectacular view of the Forest City. Everything here is designed to enable you to maintain your independence and privacy, enjoy a full social life, and participate in the activities that you love. With retirement living at Windermere on the Mount Seniors Apartments, you change your address, not your life. *Windermere On The Mount Seniors Apartments is part of the Revera family, one of North America's leading and most trusted providers of seniors' accommodation, care and services since 1961.*

RESIDENCE INFORMATION: 8 years in operation. *Near:* Richmond Street and Windermere Road. Decorated in 2013. Handrails in hallways. 5 floors, 4 elevators. Wheelchair accessible. *Funding Base:* Corporate/for profit. *Owned and managed by:* Revera Inc. 136 units. *Average Waiting Period*: varies. *Average Age*: 86. Can sometimes accommodate cognitively impaired & physically challenged people (assessed individually). Residents have a dress code (dress for dinner). Smoke-free residence. Alcohol allowed (licenced areas & Independent Apartments & Suites). *Procedures to leave the premises on a temporary basis*...sign in/out. *Languages:* English. Main doors of residence secured at night only. *Close to:* Public Transit, Shopping, Churches, Synagogues, Seniors' Centre, Library and Local Hospital. Member of ORCA.
STAFFING: *Available Staff/Services*: Recreation Therapy. *External services arranged by:* residence and/or family/resident. Staff trained *re*: visually and hearing impaired. 24-hour nursing and other staff. RPNs and PSWs on staff. Staff members are bonded. Police Check or Vulnerable Person Screening is done for all new staff.
HEALTH SERVICES: Lab service (visiting). Residents can purchase outside resources and use agency of their choice. Will help locate higher level of care if needed.
ACCOMMODATION: *Choice of suites available*: 1- bedroom & 2-bedroom apartments. *In all suites*: locks, storage, window coverings, light fixtures, stove, fire alarm, smoke detector, sprinkler, thermostats for heating & cooling, washer/dryer, full kitchens with fridge/freezer and a dishwasher. Private bathrooms with grab bars, tubs and showers with non-slip surfaces. In-suite cable TV provided by residence. Can have own phone number provided by residence. Unfurnished suites. Suites can be shared (by couples only), roommate picked by resident. Pets allowed (as per our Pet Policy).
DINING SERVICE: *Sittings per meal:* Breakfast: 1, Lunch: 1, Dinner: 1. *Menu choices available:* Breakfast: 2, Lunch: 2, Dinner: 2. *Guest Meals*: Breakfast $5.00, Lunch $9.00, Dinner $14.75. *Special Diets*: Low Salt and Diabetic. Party facilities. Full service dining. 24-hour coffee/tea bistro with snacks & fresh fruit daily. Fireside pub. Private dining room.
AMENITIES AND ACTIVITIES: Parking available (outdoor, for visitors and residents). *4 lounges with:* TV (1), piano (1), surround sound theatre (1) and fireplace (1). Guest suites available. *Residence has a:* library, visiting library, chapel, barber/beauty shop and tuck/gift shop. Resident can arrange newspaper delivery to main desk. Mail delivered to main desk. *Recreation Facilities*: billiards, exercise room, craft room, card room, gourmet kitchen, hair salon, spa and theatre. Posted schedule of activities. Internal newsletter for residents. *Recreational Programs*: exercise, shopping, theatre, parties, entertainment, art classes, day trips, concerts in 400 seat chapel, book clubs, bridge, gardening, billiards and movies.
OTHER SERVICES: *Housekeeping*: weekly (as requested and scheduled in advance). Transportation for group social activities. 24-hour security. Nightly security checks. Telephone, Cable TV & Utilities (included in fee). Reservations available in dining room. Rent includes: Concierge & Valet Services, high speed internet and free long distance calls in North America. Membership purchase: adjacent Centre for Activity & Aging.
RENTAL INFORMATION: Rates may vary. No cost for sharing suite. Rent paid monthly. *Payment Options*: cheques and direct deposit. Rent increases as per Provincial Tenancy Legislation, annual for resident with 3 months' notice given.

THE MANOR VILLAGE AT HISTORIC LONDON

230 Victoria Street, London, ON N6A 2C2
Tel: (519) 850-4646 • Fax: (403) 256-6100
Toll Free: (888) 706-2667
Email: **katherineg@statesmanmedical.com**
Website: **www.themanorvillage.com**
Contact: **Katherine Gigante Burnett**
Capacity: **264 residents •** Subsidies: **none**

The newest advancement in The Manor Village concept. The Manor Village at Historic London's amenities and services are designed to provide a myriad of choices in entertainment, activities and social opportunities to our Memory Care and Enhanced Care residents. Our advanced medical services on the main and mezzanine floors are on hand to provide additional care and support to enable our residents to live with dignity. *We are truly the Community with Heart!*

RESIDENCE INFORMATION: *Near:* Victoria Street and Richmond Avenue. Decorated in 2013. Handrails in hallways. 4 floors, 2 elevators. Wheelchair accessible. Central PA system. *Funding Base:* Corporate/for profit. *Owned and managed by:* Manor Village Life Centers. 132 units. *Average Waiting Period*: none. Can accommodate physically challenged people (24-hour care available). Smoke-free residence. Alcohol allowed (individual choice in suite). *Procedures to leave the premises on a temporary basis...*we ask that residents advise us of extended absence or holidays. *Languages:* English. Main doors of residence secured at all times. *Close to:* Public Transit, Shopping, Churches and Local Hospital (St. Joseph's Health Care, London).
STAFFING: *Available Staff/Services*: Pharmacy, Social Work, Recreation Therapy, Occupational Therapy, Visiting Dentist, Physiotherapy, Denturist, Dietitian, Podiatry, Chiropody and Audiology/Hearing Clinic. Additional services to be determined (still in process of securing services). *External services arranged by:* residence and/or family/resident. Staff trained *re*: visually, hearing and cognitively impaired. 24-hour nursing and other staff. RNs, RPNs and HCAs on staff. Visiting MD. Can retain own MD. Police Check or Vulnerable Person Screening is done for all new staff.
HEALTH SERVICES: Medication administration and/or supervision. Assistance with dressing available. Weekly assistance with bathing available. Care plans done. Different levels of care available. Private Duty/Extra Care available. Assisted Living Area. Separate unit for residents with dementia. Lab service (visiting). Residents can purchase outside resources. Clinic area for medical visits.
ACCOMMODATION: *Choice of suites available*: Villas, 1-bedroom & 2-bedroom suites. *In all suites*: locks, window coverings, light fixtures, stove, fire alarm, smoke detector, sprinkler, air conditioning (central) and thermostats for heating & cooling. Private bathrooms with call bells, grab bars, non-slip surfaces and elevated toilet seats. In-suite cable TV provided by residence. Can have own phone number if resident arranges with phone company. Unfurnished suites. Suites can be shared, roommate picked by resident. Pets allowed.
DINING SERVICE: All meals included in fee and served in dining room daily. Tray service to room if ill. Dining services to be determined.
AMENITIES AND ACTIVITIES: Parking available (outdoor, for visitors and indoor & outdoor for residents). 8 lounges. Guest suites available. *Residence has a:* library, chapel, barber/beauty shop, laundry room(s) (no cost) and tuck/gift shop. Banking services on premises (TBA). Resident can arrange newspaper delivery to individual suite (extra cost). Mail delivered to private mailbox with key. *Recreation Facilities*: pool table, billiards, shuffleboard, exercise room, craft room, card room and theatre. Posted schedule of activities. Internal newsletter for residents. *Recreational Programs*: exercise, shopping, theatre, parties, entertainment, art classes and day trips.
OTHER SERVICES: *Housekeeping*: bi-weekly (included in fee). Cable TV & Utilities (included in fee).

RENTAL INFORMATION: Extra cost for 2nd person sharing suite. Option to purchase unit available Rent paid monthly. *Payment Options*: post-dated cheques and pre-authorized payments. 3 months' notice given for rent increases.

THE WAVERLEY RETIREMENT RESIDENCE

10 Grand Avenue, London, ON N6C 1K9
Tel: (519) 667-1381 • Fax: (519) 667-9601
Email: **info.waverley@diversicare.com**
Website: **www.diversicare.ca**
Contact: **Marketing Manager**
Capacity: **65 residents** • Subsidies: **none**
Price: **$1,800.00 - $3,255.00/month**

Built in 1882, The Waverley is one of the mansions that made London's Grand Avenue a showplace during the late nineteenth century. It later gained fame as the home of the renowned Shute Institute, which pioneered the medical application of Vitamin E. Today, The Waverley proudly stands as one of London's finest retirement residences. Designated a Heritage Home by the City of London, The Waverley provides a gracious, relaxed and home-like setting for seniors seeking an independent, enriched, and affordable retirement lifestyle. **The Waverley is owned/managed by Diversicare, who is the proud recipient of the 2003, 2006, 2009 and 2012 Order of Excellence Award given by Excellence Canada.** This award was received for the exceptional quality and customer service we provide to our residents every day.

RESIDENCE INFORMATION: 32 years in operation. *Near:* Wellington Street and Grand Avenue. Decorated in 2008. Handrails in hallways. 4 floors, 2 elevators. Wheelchair accessible. Central PA system. *Funding Base:* Corporate/for profit. *Owned and managed by:* Diversicare Canada Management Services Co., Inc. 65 units. *Average Waiting Period*: less than 2 weeks. *Average Age*: 80. Can accommodate cognitively impaired people with restrictions (individuals with low level cognitive impairments will be accepted). Can sometimes accommodate physically challenged people. Smoking allowed (outdoor patio). Alcohol allowed (for private consumption in their suites). *Procedures to leave the premises on a temporary basis*...resident to sign out. *Languages:* English. Main doors of residence secured at night only. *Close to:* Public Transit, Shopping, Churches, Seniors' Centre, Library, Major Highway and Local Hospital (London Health Sciences Centre). Member of ORCA & Wortley Village Business Association. Licensed under the Retirement Homes Act.
STAFFING: *Available Staff/Services*: Social Work (CCAC), Recreation Therapy, Occupational Therapy (CCAC), Physiotherapy (CCAC), Dietitian, Companions, Podiatry, Chaplaincy, Speech Pathology (CCAC), Hair Salon, Brain Gym® & More and Massage. *External services arranged by:* residence and/or family/resident. Staff trained *re*: visually, hearing and cognitively impaired. 24-hour nursing and other staff. RPNs, HCAs and PSWs on staff. Can retain own MD. Police Check or Vulnerable Person Screening is done for all new staff.
HEALTH SERVICES: Medication administration and/or supervision. Vitals monitored if required. Will accept and provide special assistance for residents who require oxygen, catheters and ostomies. Assistance with dressing available ($215.00/month). Weekly assistance with bathing available. *Extra baths:* $14.00/half hour. Care plans done. Different levels of care available. Private Duty/Extra Care available. Lab service (visiting, $25.00/visit). Residents can purchase outside resources and use agency of their choice. MD visits residents in their rooms/suites. Will help locate higher level of care if needed (with the assistance of CCAC).
ACCOMMODATION: *Choice of suites available*: Lodge: small private (37), large private (4) & turret (13); Mansion: small private (3), large private (5) & 1-bedroom (3) suites. *In all suites*: locks, storage, window coverings, light fixtures, linens, fire alarm, smoke detector, sprinkler, call bell and thermostats for heating.

Private bathrooms with call bells, grab bars, tubs and showers with non-slip surfaces. In-suite cable TV if resident arranges with cable company. Can have own phone number if resident arranges with phone company. Furnished & unfurnished suites available. *Restrictions on electrical appliances*: upon approval. Suites can be shared (2 per room in larger suites), roommate picked by resident. Pets allowed (cats, small dogs - in accordance with Pet Policy).

DINING SERVICE: All meals included in fee and served in dining room daily. *Sittings per meal:* Breakfast: 1, Lunch: 1, Dinner: 1. *Menu choices available:* Breakfast: 2, Lunch: 2, Dinner: 2. *Guest Meals*: Breakfast $6.00, Lunch $6.00, Dinner $10.00. *Special Diets*: Vegetarian, Low Salt, Diabetic, Gluten Free and Celiac. Tray service to room if ill (no charge or restrictions). 3 snacks/day and unlimited snacks available at any time. Party facilities. Open pantry. Air-conditioned dining room with beautiful woodwork.

AMENITIES AND ACTIVITIES: Parking available (outdoor, for visitors and residents). *4 lounges with:* TV (1), piano (1) and computers (1). Guest suites available ($65.00/night). *Residence has a:* library, visiting library, barber/beauty shop and tuck/gift shop (open Friday afternoon). Resident can arrange newspaper delivery to individual suite (extra cost). Mail delivered to dining room. *Recreation Facilities*: shuffleboard, exercise room, greenhouse, craft room, card room and horseshoe pit. Posted schedule of activities. Internal newsletter for residents. *Recreational Programs*: exercise, shopping, theatre, parties, entertainment, pet visiting, day trips (field trips & shopping trips), comedy & music, Brain Gym® & More, physiotherapy, fall prevention program, games, bingo and cards.

OTHER SERVICES: *Housekeeping*: daily and weekly (included in fee). *Laundry*: linen, towel & personal (included in fee). Transportation to medical appointments (extra charge for cab fare & escort service if required) and for group social activities (no cost). Nightly security checks (no cost). Telephone & Cable TV (extra cost). Utilities (included in fee). Hairdressing. Foot Care.

RENTAL INFORMATION: Rates may vary. Small private suites - $1,800.00/month & up; large private suites - $2,050.00/month; turret suites - $2,520.00/month; spacious Mansion suites - $1,850.00/month & up. All suites have their own private ensuite bathroom. Extra cost for 2nd person sharing suite ($550.00/month). Rent paid monthly. *Payment Options*: cheques, post-dated cheques, direct deposit and pre-authorized payments. Rent increases indexed to inflation as per Provincial Tenancy Legislation, annual for resident with 3 months' notice given. Short-term respite and trial stays available (both $100.00/day).

◆ LONDON (DORCHESTER) ◆

LIFESTYLE OASIS RESIDENCE DORCHESTER

143 Byron Avenue, Dorchester, ON N0L 1G3
Tel: (519) 667-1700 • Fax: (519) 667-1703
Email: **info@oasisresidences.com**
Website: **www.oasisresidences.com**
Contact: **Craig Gauld**
Capacity: **146 residents**
Subsidies: **yes, a compassionate subsidy based on income & need is available**
Price: **$2,450.00 - $3,550.00/month**

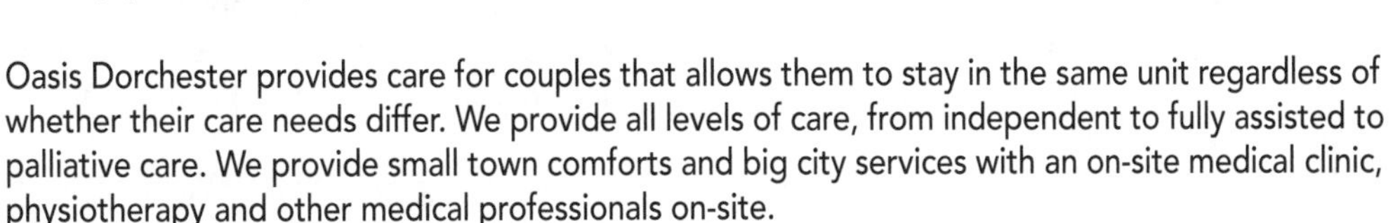
Oasis Dorchester provides care for couples that allows them to stay in the same unit regardless of whether their care needs differ. We provide all levels of care, from independent to fully assisted to palliative care. We provide small town comforts and big city services with an on-site medical clinic, physiotherapy and other medical professionals on-site.

RESIDENCE INFORMATION: New residence. *Near:* Hamilton Road and Dorchester Road. Decorated in 2014. 4 floors, 2 elevators. Wheelchair accessible. *Funding Base:* Corporate/for profit. *Owned by:*

Lifestyle Oasis Dorchester Inc. 92 units. *Average Waiting Period*: none. Can accommodate cognitively impaired people (all levels of impairment can be accommodated). Can accommodate physically challenged people (all levels of physical challenge can be accommodated). Residents have a dress code (appropriate dress for meals and in common areas). Smoking allowed (designated area outside of building). Alcohol allowed (in personal suites). *Procedures to leave the premises on a temporary basis*...with notification to staff. *Languages:* English. Will accept Public Guardian and Trustee clients. Main doors of residence secured at all times. *Close to:* Shopping, Churches, Seniors' Centre, Library and Major Highway. Member of ORCA.

STAFFING: *Available Staff/Services*: Pharmacy, Social Work, Recreation Therapy, Occupational Therapy, Physiotherapy (CCAC), Denturist, Dietitian, Companions, Podiatry, Chaplaincy, Speech Pathology, Chiropody, Audiology/Hearing Clinic and Family Physician (on-site; office hours and by appointment). *External services arranged by:* family/resident. Staff trained *re*: visually, hearing and cognitively impaired. 24-hour staff. RNs, RPNs and PSWs on staff. Can retain own MD. Police Check or Vulnerable Person Screening is done for all new staff.

HEALTH SERVICES: Medication administration and/or supervision. Vitals monitored if required. Will accept and provide special assistance for residents who require oxygen, catheters, ostomies and feeding tubes. Assistance with dressing available (cost). Weekly assistance with bathing available. Care plans done. Different levels of care available. Private Duty/Extra Care available ($400.00 to $1,000.00/month). Assisted Living Area is secured to accommodate residents with dementia. Lab service (visiting). Residents can purchase outside resources and use agency of their choice. MD visits residents in their rooms/suites. Clinic area for medical visits. We provide all levels of care including full and palliative (cost is $400.00 to $1,000.00/month).

ACCOMMODATION: *Choice of suites available*: 92 private suites with studio & 1-bedroom units. *In all suites*: locks, kitchenette, bar fridge, bar sink, microwave, storage, armoire, window coverings, light fixtures, fire alarm, smoke detector, sprinkler, emergency response system with wearable pendant/ bracelet, air conditioning (central) and thermostats for heating & cooling. Private bathrooms with grab bars and showers with non-slip surfaces. In-suite cable TV if resident arranges with cable company. Can have own phone number if resident arranges with phone company. Furnished & unfurnished suites available. *Restrictions on electrical appliances*: no hot plates. Suites can be shared. Pets allowed (small dogs, cats and birds).

DINING SERVICE: All meals included in fee and served in dining room daily. *Sittings per meal:* Breakfast: 2, Lunch: 2, Dinner: 2. *Menu choices available:* Breakfast: 5, Lunch: 2, Dinner: 2. *Guest Meals*: Breakfast $5.00, Lunch $8.00, Dinner $10.00. *Special Diets*: Vegetarian, Low Salt and Diabetic. We accommodate individual dietary needs. Tray service to room if ill (no charge as long as doctor orders). 2 snacks/day. Party facilities. Open pantry. Our chefs prepare delicious and nutritious meals with input from the Residents' Food Council.

AMENITIES AND ACTIVITIES: Parking available (outdoor, for visitors and residents). *5 lounges with:* TVs (5), piano (1) and pool table (1). *Residence has a:* library, chapel, barber/beauty shop and tuck/gift shop. Mail delivered to private mailbox with key. *Recreation Facilities*: pool table, craft room and card room. Posted schedule of activities. *Recreational Programs*: exercise, shopping, theatre, parties, art classes, entertainment, pet visiting and day trips.

OTHER SERVICES: *Housekeeping*: weekly (included in fee; additional services are available). *Laundry*: linen, towel & personal (included in fee); dry cleaning (extra cost). Personal laundry is done separately for each resident. 24-hour security. Nightly security checks. Telephone & Cable TV (external provider sets fee). Utilities (included in fee).

RENTAL INFORMATION: Rates may vary. Extra cost for 2nd person sharing suite ($500.00/month). Rent paid monthly. *Payment Options*: cheques and post-dated cheques. Rent increases as per Provincial Tenancy Legislation, annual with 3 months' notice given. Respite and trial stays start at $125.00/day.

♦ LONDON (LUCAN) ♦

PRINCE GEORGE RETIREMENT RESIDENCE

139 Main Street, Lucan, ON N0M 2J0
Tel: (519) 227-1268 • Fax: (519) 227-4832
Email: **admin@princegeorgerr.com**
Website: **www.princegeorgerr.com**
Contact: **General Manager**
Capacity: **62 residents** • Subsidies: **none**
Price: **$2,950.00 - $4,250.00/month**

Prince George Retirement Residence in Lucan offers a special secure floor for Memory Care, Convalescent Care, Respite, Palliative Care and Retirement Residence. Prince George Retirement Residence's facilities are designed to offer comfortable accommodations and amenities in conjunction with quality health care options. With all levels of care from independent to fully assisted, Prince George offers comprehensive healthcare and wellness services. Services include chef-prepared meals in our full service dining room, housekeeping, laundry, one assisted bath/week, regular health checks and medication administration. Our all-inclusive fees cover accommodations, all meals and 2 snacks each day, laundry, housekeeping, health checks and medication administration as well as a busy calendar of activities.

RESIDENCE INFORMATION: New residence. *On:* Main Street. Decorated in 2012. 3 floors, 1 elevator. Wheelchair accessible. Central PA system. *Funding Base:* Corporate/for profit. *Owned by:* 2301402 Ontario Ltd. 55 units. *Average Waiting Period*: varies by floor. *Average Age*: 82. Residents have a dress code (appropriate dress for meals and in common areas). Smoking allowed (common smoking area is located outside the building). Alcohol allowed (in personal suites). *Procedures to leave the premises on a temporary basis...*with notification to staff. *Languages:* English. Will accept Public Guardian and Trustee clients. Main doors of residence secured at night only. *Close to:* Shopping, Churches, Library, Major Highway and Local Hospitals (London Area). Member of ORCA. Licensed under the Retirement Homes Act.
STAFFING: *Available Staff/Services*: Pharmacy, Recreation Therapy, Physiotherapy, Companions, Podiatry, Chaplaincy, Chiropody, Audiology/Hearing Clinic, Professional Licensed Nurses and Family Physician (in-house). *External services arranged by:* residence and/or family/resident. Staff trained *re*: visually, hearing and cognitively impaired. RPNs, UCPs and PSWs on staff. Visiting MD (weekly & as needed to resident suites). Can retain own MD. Staff members are bonded. Police Check or Vulnerable Person Screening is done for all new staff.
HEALTH SERVICES: Medication administration and/or supervision. Vitals monitored if required. Will accept and provide special assistance for residents who require oxygen, catheters, ostomies and feeding tubes. Assistance with dressing available. Weekly assistance with bathing available. Individual plans of care reflect each resident's personal needs. Will accept residents who have concerns. Each resident assessed individually. Different levels of care available. Special Memory Care Area is secured to accommodate residents with dementia. Residents can purchase outside resources and use agency of their choice. MD visits residents in their rooms/suites. Will help locate higher level of care if needed (we provide all levels of care including full and palliative).
ACCOMMODATION: *Choice of suites available*: all private; studio, deluxe studio & 1-bedroom suites. *In all suites*: kitchenette, bar fridge, microwave, storage, window blinds, towel service, fire alarm, smoke detector, sprinkler, emergency response system with wearable pendant/bracelet, air conditioning (central) and thermostats for heating & cooling. Private bathrooms with grab bars and showers with non-slip surfaces. In-suite cable TV provided by residence. Can have own phone number if resident arranges with phone company. Furnished & unfurnished suites available. *Restrictions on electrical appliances*: no hot plates. Suites can be shared (by couples only). Pets allowed (upon Management approval).

DINING SERVICE: All meals included in fee and served in dining room daily. *Sittings per meal:* Breakfast: 2, Lunch: 2, Dinner: 2. *Menu choices available:* Breakfast: 2, Lunch: 2, Dinner: 2. *Special Diets*: Vegetarian, Low Salt and Diabetic. We accommodate individual dietary needs. Tray service to room if ill (no charge if approved by Charge Nurse). 2 snacks/day in main lounge.
AMENITIES AND ACTIVITIES: Parking available (outdoor, for visitors and residents). *3 lounges with:* TVs (3), pool table (1) and Wii Fit (1). *Residence has a:* barber/beauty shop. Mail delivered to private mailbox with key. *Recreation Facilities*: pool table and card room. Posted schedule of activities. Internal newsletter for residents. *Recreational Programs*: exercise, shopping, parties, entertainment, art classes, church services, pet visiting and day trips.
OTHER SERVICES: *Housekeeping*: daily and weekly (included in fee). *Laundry*: linen, towel & personal (included in fee). Transportation for group social activities. Nightly security checks. Telephone (resident has private contract with telephone provider). Cable TV & Utilities (included in fee).
RENTAL INFORMATION: Rates may vary. Rent & services for Memory Care - $4,000.00/month. Extra cost for 2nd person sharing suite ($600.00/month). Rent paid monthly. *Payment Options*: post-dated cheques and direct withdrawal. Rent increases as per Provincial Tenancy Legislation with 3 months' notice given. Short-term respite and trial stays available.

MAPLE **RICHVIEW MANOR**

Please see VAUGHAN for information on this residence.

♦ MIDLAND ♦

BAYBRIDGE - TIFFIN HOUSE

105 Pillsbury Drive, Midland, ON L4R 0E7
Tel: (705) 527-5522
Email: **jbarry@tiffinhouse.ca**
Website: **www.tiffinhouse.ca**
Contact: **Jen Barry**
Capacity: **164 residents** • Subsidies: **none**

Tiffin House, a BayBridge Senior Living Community is scheduled to open in the Spring of 2014. Our community will have many amenities for the independent senior including bistro areas, large dining room, theatre, fitness/pool, workshop and so much more. Tiffin House will offer independent living in addition to separate areas designed especially for seniors with more specific care needs. In our presentation centre, we offer tours of our studio, 1-bedroom and 2-bedroom model suites; as well as more specific information and pricing. We look forward to meeting you!

RESIDENCE INFORMATION: New residence. *Near:* Highway 12 and William Street. Decorated in 2014. 4 floors, 2 elevators. Wheelchair accessible. *Funding Base:* Corporate/for profit. *Owned by:* BayBridge Midland Inc. *Managed by:* BayBridge Senior Living. 110 units. *Average Waiting Period*: none. Smoke-free residence. *Languages:* English.
ACCOMMODATION: *Choice of suites available*: studio (50), 1-bedroom (43) & 2-bedroom (17) suites. *In all suites*: kitchenette, storage, fire alarm, smoke detector, sprinkler, call bell, emergency response system with wearable pendant/bracelet, air conditioning (individually controlled) and thermostats for heating & cooling. Private bathrooms with grab bars and showers. Suites can be shared, roommate picked by resident. Pets allowed (restrictions to be determined).

DINING SERVICE: All meals included in fee and served in dining room daily.
AMENITIES AND ACTIVITIES: Parking available (outdoor, for visitors and residents). *Residence has a:* library, chapel and barber/beauty shop. Mail delivered to private mailbox with key. *Recreation Facilities*: pool table, exercise room, craft room, card room, swimming pool and Trans Canada Trail adjacent. Posted schedule of activities. Internal newsletter for residents. *Recreational Programs*: exercise, shopping, theatre, parties, entertainment, art classes, pet visiting and day trips.
OTHER SERVICES: *Housekeeping*: weekly (included in fee).
RENTAL INFORMATION: Rent paid monthly. 3 months' notice given for rent increases.

REVERA - KING PLACE

750 King Street, Midland, ON L4R 0B8
Tel: (855) 573-8372 • Toll Free: (855) 573-8372
Email: **kingplace@reveraliving.com**
Website: **www.reveraliving.com/kingplace**
Contact: **Executive Director or Lifestyle Consultant**
Capacity: **70 residents •** Subsidies: **none**
Price: **$1,712.00/month and up**

Keep living your life, your way, at King Place. You'll find the range of services, amenities and choices that fit your lifestyle and requirements – all in a warm and safe environment. Located in picturesque Midland in the heart of cottage country, King Place features a beautifully landscaped garden and expansive green space. Convenient bungalow style, and close to the shores of Georgian Bay, shopping, restaurants and Little Lake Park, with public transit just steps away. Everything is designed for you to maintain your independence and privacy, enjoy a full social life, and participate in the activities that you love. Our caring and friendly staff and appealing accommodations support who you are and how you want to live in freedom and comfort. With retirement living at King Place, you change your address, not your life. *King Place is part of the Revera family, one of North America's leading and most trusted providers of seniors' accommodation, care and services since 1961.*

RESIDENCE INFORMATION: 27 years in operation. *On:* King Street and Highway 12. Decorated in 2010. Handrails in hallways. 1 floor, no elevators. Wheelchair accessible. Central PA system. *Funding Base:* Corporate/for profit. *Owned and managed by:* Revera Inc. 68 units. *Average Waiting Period*: none. *Average Age*: 84. Can accommodate cognitively impaired people with restrictions (upon assessment of level of support required). Can accommodate physically challenged people with restrictions. Residents have a dress code (no sleepwear in common areas). Smoking allowed (designated outdoor area). Alcohol allowed (in resident rooms and dining room). *Procedures to leave the premises on a temporary basis...* sign out at Front Desk and inform Nurse. *Languages:* English & French. Will accept Public Guardian and Trustee clients. Main doors of residence secured at all times. *Close to:* Public Transit, Shopping, Churches, Seniors' Centre, Library, Major Highway and Local Hospital (Georgian Bay General Hospital-Midland Site). Member of ORCA. Licensed under the Retirement Homes Act.
STAFFING: *Available Staff/Services*: Pharmacy, Social Work (CCAC), Recreation Therapy, Occupational Therapy (CCAC), Visiting Dentist, Physiotherapy (CCAC), Dietitian (CCAC), Companions, Podiatry, Chaplaincy, Speech Pathology (CCAC), Audiology/Hearing Clinic and Foot Care Nurse. *External services arranged by:* residence and/or family/resident. Staff trained *re*: visually, hearing and cognitively impaired. 24-hour nursing and other staff. RNs, RPNs, PSWs and UCPs on staff. Can retain own MD. Police Check or Vulnerable Person Screening is done for all new staff.
HEALTH SERVICES: Medication administration and/or supervision. Vitals monitored if required. Will accept and provide special assistance for residents who require oxygen, catheters and ostomies. Assistance with dressing available (cost). Weekly assistance with bathing available (cost). Care plans

done. Different levels of care available. Assisted Living details available. Lab service (visiting). Residents can purchase outside resources and use agency of their choice. MD visits residents in their rooms/suites. Clinic area for medical visits. Will help locate higher level of care if needed (via CCAC).
ACCOMMODATION: *Choice of suites available*: studios, shared suites & 1-bedroom units. *In all suites*: locks, storage, window coverings, light fixtures, linens, fire alarm, smoke detector, sprinkler, call bell and thermostats for heating. Air conditioning in common areas. Private bathrooms with call bells, grab bars, tubs and showers with non-slip surfaces. In-suite cable TV provided by residence (residence charges extra). Can have own phone number provided by residence (residence charges extra). Furnished & unfurnished suites available. *Restrictions on electrical appliances*: no cooking equipment. Suites can be shared. Small pets allowed (in private suites only as per Pet Policy in Tenancy Agreement).
DINING SERVICE: All meals included in fee and served in dining room daily. *Sittings per meal:* Breakfast: 1, Lunch: 1, Dinner: 1. *Menu choices available:* Breakfast: 2, Lunch: 2, Dinner: 2. *Guest Meals*: Available. *Special Diets*: Vegetarian, Low Salt and Diabetic. Tray service to room if ill (no charge for a maximum time of 4 days). 3 snacks/day. Party facilities. Private dining table available for entertaining family & friends.
AMENITIES AND ACTIVITIES: Parking available (outdoor, for visitors and residents). *3 lounges with:* TV (1), piano (1) and fireplaces (2). Guest suites available. *Residence has a:* library, chapel, barber/beauty shop, laundry room(s) (no cost) and tuck/gift shop (open Monday to Friday). Resident can arrange newspaper delivery to individual suite (extra cost). Mail delivered to dining room. *Recreation Facilities*: shuffleboard, craft room, card room, resident bus and computer station. Posted schedule of activities. Internal newsletter for residents. *Recreational Programs*: exercise, shopping, theatre, parties, entertainment, art classes, pet visiting, day trips and local church services.
OTHER SERVICES: *Housekeeping*: weekly (included in fee). *Laundry*: linen, towel & personal (included in fee); dry cleaning (extra cost - pick up and drop off at residence). Either staff or resident label clothing (included in fee). Self-serve laundry area available (soap powder & fabric softener provided complimentary). 24-hour security. Nightly security checks. Telephone & Cable TV (extra cost). Utilities (included in fee).
RENTAL INFORMATION: Rates may vary. Extra cost for 2nd person sharing suite. Rent paid monthly. *Payment Options*: post-dated cheques and pre-authorized payments. Rent increases as per Provincial Tenancy Legislation, annual for resident with 3 months' notice given. Will help resident move into residence. Short-term respite and trial stays available.

♦ MILTON ♦

BAYBRIDGE - MARTINDALE GARDENS RETIREMENT RESIDENCE

45 Martin Street, Milton, ON L9T 2R1
Tel: (905) 693-8592 • Fax: (905) 693-9362
Email: **dbrown@martindalegardens.com**
Website: **www.martindalegardens.com**
Contact: **Dale Brown**
Capacity: **85 residents** • Subsidies: **none**
Price: **$2,600.00 - $5,100.00/month**

Martindale Gardens is located across from the Mill Pond, one short block from shops, restaurants, banks, pharmacy, churches and the Main Street Farmer's Market in downtown Milton.

RESIDENCE INFORMATION: 10 years in operation. *Near:* Martin Street and Main Street. Decorated in 2009. Handrails in hallways. 4 floors, 2 elevators. Wheelchair accessible. Central PA system. *Funding Base:* Corporate/for profit. *Owned and managed by:* BayBridge Senior Living. 75 units. *Average Waiting Period*: varies. *Average Age*: 85. Can accommodate cognitively impaired people with restrictions (no secured floor; exit seekers not accepted). Can sometimes accommodate physically challenged people

(2-person transfers not accepted). Residents have a dress code (no housecoats in dining room; comfortable, casual dress). Smoke-free residence. Alcohol allowed (in residents private suites). *Procedures to leave the premises on a temporary basis*...Short-term: sign in\out at Reception. Overnight & Holidays: sign in\out at Reception notify Director of Care. *Languages:* English. Will accept Public Guardian and Trustee clients. Main doors of residence secured at night only. *Close to:* Public Transit, Shopping, Churches, Seniors' Centre, Library, Major Highway and Local Hospital (Halton Healthcare Services Corporation – Milton District Site). Licensed under the Retirement Homes Act.

STAFFING: *Available Staff/Services*: Pharmacy, Social Work (CCAC), Recreation Therapy, Occupational Therapy (CCAC), Physiotherapy, Denturist, Dietitian (CCAC), Companions, Podiatry (CCAC), Chaplaincy, Speech Pathology (CCAC), Chiropody and Audiology/Hearing Clinic. *External services arranged by:* family/resident. Staff trained *re*: visually, hearing and cognitively impaired. 24-hour nursing and other staff. RNs, RPNs, HCAs and PSWs on staff. Can retain own MD. Police Check or Vulnerable Person Screening is done for all new staff.

HEALTH SERVICES: Medication administration and/or supervision (extra fees apply if not included in a Wellness Package). Vitals monitored if required. Will accept and provide special assistance for residents who require oxygen. Assistance with dressing available (cost). Weekly assistance with bathing available. *Extra baths:* $15.00/bath. Different levels of care available. Private Duty/Extra Care available ($500.00 to $2,500.00/month). Assisted Living Area ($500.00 to $2,500.00/month). Lab service (visiting). Residents can purchase outside resources and use agency of their choice. MD visits residents in their rooms/suites. Will help locate higher level of care if needed (team meeting with families & Director of Care re: CCAC assessment).

ACCOMMODATION: *Choice of suites available*: private studios, 1-bedroom & 2-bedroom suites. *In all suites*: locks, kitchenette, bar fridge, window coverings, light fixtures, linens, fire alarm, smoke detector, sprinkler, emergency response system with wearable pendant/bracelet, air conditioning (central) and thermostats for heating & cooling. Private bathrooms with grab bars, showers with non-slip surfaces and elevated toilet seats. In-suite cable TV if resident arranges with cable company. Can have own phone number provided by residence. Unfurnished suites, furnished suites available for short stays. *Restrictions on electrical appliances*: must have auto shut-off; no toaster ovens, no toasters & no irons. Suites can be shared (by couples only), roommate picked by resident. No pets allowed.

DINING SERVICE: All meals included in fee and served in dining room daily. Residents may dine at their own choice of time from 7:00 a.m. - 7:00 p.m. *Menu choices available:* Breakfast: 2, Lunch: 3, Dinner: 3. *Guest Meals*: Breakfast $5.00, Lunch $8.00, Dinner $14.00. *Special Diets*: Vegetarian, Low Salt, Diabetic and Others (by special request). Tray service to room if ill. 2 snacks/day. Party facilities.

AMENITIES AND ACTIVITIES: Parking available (outdoor, for visitors and residents). *4 lounges with:* TV (1), piano (1), library (1) and theatre - big screen (1). Guest suites available ($79.00/night). *Residence has a:* library, chapel, barber/beauty shop, laundry room(s) (no cost) and tuck/gift shop (open 8:00 a.m. - 8:00 p.m.). Banking services on premises (twice/month). Resident can arrange newspaper delivery to main desk. Mail delivered to private mailbox with key. *Recreation Facilities*: pool table, billiards, shuffleboard, exercise room, craft room and card room. Posted schedule of activities. Internal newsletter for residents. *Recreational Programs*: exercise, shopping, theatre, parties, entertainment, art classes, pet visiting and day trips.

OTHER SERVICES: *Housekeeping*: weekly (included in fee). *Laundry*: linen & towel (included in fee); personal (available at an additional fee) & dry cleaning (resident arranges pick up\delivery). Transportation for group social activities. 24-hour security. Nightly security checks. Telephone (extra cost for long distance only; otherwise included). Cable TV (pay to Cogeco). Utilities (included in fee).

RENTAL INFORMATION: Rates may vary. Extra cost for 2nd person sharing suite ($625.00/month). Rent paid monthly. *Payment Options*: cheques, post-dated cheques, direct deposit, pre-authorized payments and EFT (electronic funds transfer) preferred method. Rent increases as per Provincial Tenancy Legislation, annual for resident with 3 months' notice given. Short-term respite and trial stays available (both $79.00/day, not including Assisted Care if needed).

♦ MISSISSAUGA ♦

CARMEL HEIGHTS SENIORS' RESIDENCE (CATHOLIC)

1720 Sherwood Forrest Circle, Mississauga, ON L5K 1R1
Tel: (905) 822-5298 • Fax: (905) 822-7386
Email: **carmelheights@rogers.com**
Website: **www.carmelheights.ca**
Contact: **Sister M. Veronica Dobson**
Capacity: **48 residents** • Subsidies: **none**
Price: **$1,910.00 - $3,110.00/month**

We are located on an attractive 9 ½ acres. A Roman Catholic residence, Chaplain, daily Holy Mass, Rosary daily, chapel open all day. Located near Erin Mills Parkway and Dundas Street. We accept all faiths. We provide meals, light assisted care, housekeeping, RNs, RPNs and PSWs, etc. Family-style environment, physiotherapy bi-weekly, 24-hour call pendant.

RESIDENCE INFORMATION: 62 years in operation. *Near:* Dundas Street West and Mississauga Road. Decorated in 2002. Handrails in hallways. 4 floors, 1 elevator. Wheelchair accessible. Central PA system. *Funding Base:* Not-for-profit. *Owned and managed by:* Carmelite Sisters of Canada. 48 units. *Average Waiting Period*: none. *Average Age*: 85. Can sometimes accommodate cognitively impaired people (early stages of dementia). Can sometimes accommodate physically challenged people (walkers, canes). Residents have a dress code (clean, neat and appropriate). Smoke-free residence. Alcohol allowed. *Procedures to leave the premises on a temporary basis...*Short-term & Overnight: notify Office, Nursing Station. Holidays: notify Office, Nursing Station. *Languages:* English, German, Filipino, Polish, East Indian Languages, French, Portuguese & Spanish. Will accept Public Guardian and Trustee clients. Main doors of residence secured at night only. *Close to:* Public Transit, Shopping, Churches, Seniors' Centre, Library, Major Highway and Local Hospital (Trillium Health Partners - Credit Valley Hospital Site). *Predominant Cultural Group:* mixed group. Member of ORCA. Licensed under the Retirement Homes Act.
STAFFING: *Available Staff/Services*: Pharmacy, Social Work (CCAC), Recreation Therapy, Physiotherapy (CCAC), Podiatry, Chaplaincy, Hair Salon and Lab Testing (on-site). *External services arranged by:* family/resident. 24-hour staff. RNs, RPNs and PSWs on staff. Visiting MD (weekly). Can retain own MD. Police Check or Vulnerable Person Screening is done for all new staff.
HEALTH SERVICES: Medication administration and/or supervision. Vitals monitored if required. Weekly assistance with bathing available. Care plans done. Lab service. Residents can purchase outside resources and use agency of their choice. MD visits residents in their rooms/suites. Clinic area for medical visits. Will help locate higher level of care if needed (families go through CCAC).
ACCOMMODATION: *Choice of suites available*: shared washroom with private rooms (23) & private room and washroom (24). *In all suites*: locks, storage, window coverings, light fixtures, linens, fire alarm, smoke detector and emergency response system with wearable pendant/bracelet. Air conditioning in chapel, dining room, activity room and halls. Bathrooms (some private rooms share a bathroom with one other person) with grab bars, tubs and showers with non-slip surfaces and elevated toilet seats. In-suite cable TV provided by residence. Can have own phone number if resident arranges with phone company. Furnished suites available on request. *Restrictions on electrical appliances*: no irons, microwave ovens or fridges in rooms. Suites can be shared (by couples only). No pets allowed.
DINING SERVICE: All meals included in fee and served in dining room daily. *Sittings per meal:* Breakfast: 1, Lunch: 1, Dinner: 1. *Menu choices available:* Lunch: 2, Dinner: 2. *Guest Meals*: Breakfast $5.00, Lunch $8.00, Dinner $8.00. *Special Diets*: Low Salt and Diabetic. Tray service to room if ill (no charge or restrictions). 2 snacks/day. Party facilities.

AMENITIES AND ACTIVITIES: Parking available (outdoor, for visitors and indoor & outdoor for residents). *4 lounges with:* TVs (4) and piano (1). Guest suites available ($75.00/night). *Residence has a:* library, chapel, visiting hairdresser, laundry room(s) ($1.50/washer load, $1.00/dryer load) and tuck/gift shop (open Monday to Friday). Residence provides newspaper delivery to individual suite (extra cost). Mail delivered to individual suite. *Recreation Facilities*: craft room, card room and entertainment room. Posted schedule of activities. Internal newsletter for residents. *Recreational Programs*: exercise, shopping, theatre, parties, entertainment and art classes.
OTHER SERVICES: *Housekeeping*: weekly. *Laundry*: linen & towel (included in fee). 24-hour security. Nightly security checks (no cost). Cable TV & Utilities (included in fee). Bathing (no cost).
RENTAL INFORMATION: Rates may vary. Extra cost for 2nd person sharing suite (depends on the size location of room). Rent paid monthly. *Payment Options*: cheques and post-dated cheques. Rent increases indexed to inflation as per Provincial Tenancy Legislation, when necessary with 3 months' notice given. Short-term respite and trial stays available (both $75.00/day; price of rooms is determined by location and size).

EVERGREEN RETIREMENT COMMUNITY

820 Scollard Court, Mississauga, ON L5V 0A1
Tel: (905) 502-8882 • Fax: (905) 502-9994
Email: **mktg2.evergreen@diversicare.ca**
Website: **www.evergreenretirement.ca**
Contact: **Marketing Manager**
Capacity: **160 residents** • Subsidies: **none**
Price: **$2,950.00 - $4,900.00/month**

Located in the heart of Mississauga at Mavis & Eglinton, easily accessible & near all essential neighbourhood conveniences & services. Our retirement community consists of a thirteen-storey condominium residence, a unique three level Garden Flats & a ten-storey full service Retirement Residence offering Independent & Assisted Living lifestyles. Enjoy chef-prepared meals in our beautifully appointed dining room. Amenities include a saltwater pool, spa & fitness centre, bowling alley, art studio & more. Elegant suites, luxurious finishes plus our exemplary services suit all seniors needs for *Aging in Place*. Affordable rates with first class services makes Evergreen an incredible value! **Evergreen Retirement Community is managed by Diversicare the proud recipient of the 2003, 2006, 2009 & 2012 Order of Excellence Award given by Excellence Canada**. This award was received for the exceptional quality and customer service we provide to our residents every day.

RESIDENCE INFORMATION: 6 years in operation. *Near:* Mavis Road and Eglinton Avenue. Decorated in 2008. Handrails in hallways. 10 floors, 3 elevators. Wheelchair accessible. Central PA system. *Funding Base:* Corporate/for profit. *Owned by:* Daniels Capital Group/bcIMC Realty Corporation. *Managed by:* Diversicare Canada Management Services Co., Inc. 140 units. *Average Waiting Period*: varies. *Average Age*: 82. Can accommodate cognitively impaired & physically challenged people (assessment required by RN). Smoke-free residence. Alcohol allowed. *Restrictions around Visitors/Visiting Hours:* all visitors are requested to sign in at Reception. *Procedures to leave the premises on a temporary basis...*sign in/out at Reception. *Languages:* English. Will accept Public Guardian and Trustee clients. Main doors of residence secured at all times. *Close to:* Public Transit, Shopping, Churches, Seniors' Centre, Library, Major Highway and Local Hospital (Trillium Health Partners - Credit Valley Hospital Site). Licensed under the Retirement Homes Act.
STAFFING: *Available Staff/Services*: Pharmacy, Social Work, Recreation Therapy, Occupational Therapy (CCAC), Visiting Dentist, Physiotherapy, Denturist, Dietitian, Companions, Podiatry, Chaplaincy, Speech Pathology, Chiropody, Audiology/Hearing Clinic and Spa Service (facials, manicures & pedicures). *External services arranged by:* residence and/or family/resident. Staff trained *re*: visually, hearing and cognitively

impaired. 24-hour staff. RNs, RPNs, PSWs and UCPs on staff. Visiting MD (twice monthly). Can retain own MD. Staff members are bonded. Police Check or Vulnerable Person Screening is done for all new staff.
HEALTH SERVICES: Medication administration and/or supervision. Vitals monitored if required. Will accept (but not provide special assistance for) residents who require oxygen, catheters, ostomies and feeding tubes. Assistance with dressing available (cost). Assistance with bathing available as needed (cost). Care plans done. Different levels of care available. Assisted Living Area (less than 2 week waiting period) is secured to accommodate residents with dementia. Lab service (visiting). Residents can purchase outside resources and use agency of their choice. Clinic area for medical visits. Will help locate higher level of care if needed (CCAC application assistance).
ACCOMMODATION: *Choice of suites available*: studio, alcove, 1-bedroom, 1-bedroom + den, 2-bedroom (14) & Assisted Living (20). *In all suites*: locks, kitchenette, bar fridge, microwave, granite countertops, patio/balcony (French balconies, single & double balconies), window coverings, light fixtures, fire alarm, smoke detector, carbon monoxide detector, sprinkler, call bell, emergency response system with wearable pendant/bracelet, air conditioning (central), thermostats for heating & cooling, Berber carpeting and laminate flooring. Private bathrooms with call bells, grab bars, showers with non-slip surfaces and elevated toilet seats. In-suite cable TV if resident arranges with cable company. Can have own phone number if resident arranges with phone company. Unfurnished suites, furnished suites available for short stays. Suites can be shared (couples or family), roommate picked by resident. Small pets allowed (resident must take care of them).
DINING SERVICE: All meals included in fee and served in dining room daily. *Sittings per meal:* Breakfast: 1, Lunch: 1, Dinner: 1. *Menu choices available:* Lunch: 2, Dinner: 2. *Guest Meals*: Breakfast $8.00, Lunch $12.00, Dinner $15.00. *Special Diets*: Vegetarian, Low Salt, Diabetic and Healthy Choice Options. Tray service to room if ill (no charge as long as doctor orders). 3 snacks/day. Party facilities. Open pantry. The majority of meals are chef-prepared from scratch. We also feature an à la carte menu.
AMENITIES AND ACTIVITIES: Parking available (outdoor, for visitors: free and indoor for residents: $50.00/month). *9 lounges with:* TV (1) and piano (1). Guest suites available ($99.00/night). *Residence has a:* library, chapel, barber/beauty shop, laundry room(s) (no cost) and tuck/gift shop (open 11:00 a.m. - 3:00 p.m.). Residence provides newspaper delivery to individual suite. Mail delivered to private mailbox with key. *Recreation Facilities*: pool table, billiards, shuffleboard, exercise room, greenhouse, craft room, card room, swimming pool, spa, sauna, recreation area, 6 dining venues, theatre room and 5 pin bowling alley. Posted schedule of activities. Internal newsletter for residents. *Recreational Programs*: exercise, shopping, theatre, parties, art classes, entertainment, pet visiting, day trips, strength-training, dances and cooking classes.
OTHER SERVICES: *Housekeeping*: weekly (included in fee). *Laundry*: linen & towel (weekly, included in fee); personal & dry cleaning (extra cost). Transportation to medical appointments and for group social activities. 24-hour security. Nightly security checks. Telephone (extra cost). Cable TV (extra cost - basic cable). Utilities (included in fee).
RENTAL INFORMATION: Rates may vary based on suite size. Extra cost for 2nd person sharing suite ($600.00/month). Option to purchase unit available (Seniors Condominium or Garden Flat). Rent paid monthly. *Payment Options*: cheques, post-dated cheques, direct deposit and pre-authorized payments. Rent increases as per Provincial Tenancy Legislation, annual for resident with 3 months' notice given. Will help resident move into residence. Short-term respite ($135.00/day) and trial stays ($99.00/day) available.

Did you know?

Funding for home and vehicle modification for disabled persons in Ontario might be available through the March of Dimes Canada. For information please visit: **www.marchofdimes.ca/EN/programs/hvmp/Pages/HomeandVehicle.aspx.**

PALISADES ON THE GLEN

1665 The Collegeway, Mississauga, ON L5L 0A9
Tel: (905) 820-8210 • Fax: (905) 820-8260
Email: **sales@palisadesontheglen.com**
Website: **www.palisadesontheglen.com**
Contact: **Grace Miksa**
Capacity: **194 units** • Subsidies: **none**
Price: **$1,899.00 - $4,831.00/month**

Located in one of Mississauga's most prestigious neighbourhoods, Palisades on the Glen sits alongside the historical and distinguished Glenerin Inn. The opulent design of this luxury retirement residence is set amongst the lush greenery of the Sawmill Valley Ravine and the well-preserved Credit Valley Conservation Area. Lavish studio, 1- bedroom, 2-bedroom or 2-bedroom + den suites are for rent or for sale as condominiums in this very unique retirement residence. Flexible service packages and bankable meals are just one of the many perks that distinguish us from others. ***In 2012 and 2013 Palisades on the Glen was awarded Readers' Choice Platinum for 'Best Retirement Residence in Mississauga!'***

RESIDENCE INFORMATION: 4 years in operation. *Near:* Mississauga Road and Dundas Street. Decorated in 2010. Handrails in hallways. 21 floors, 3 elevators. Wheelchair accessible. Central PA system. *Funding Base:* Corporate/for profit. *Owned by:* Retirement Life Communities/Brookfield. *Managed by:* Retirement Life Communities. *Average Waiting Period*: none. *Average Age*: 81. Can accommodate cognitively impaired people with restrictions (depends on severity of impairment). Can accommodate physically challenged people (wheelchair). Smoking allowed (in residents' suites). Alcohol allowed. *Procedures to leave the premises on a temporary basis...*residents sign in/out. *Languages:* English, French, Croatian, Ukrainian, Tagalog, Greek, Farsi, & Hindi. Main doors of residence secured at all times. *Close to:* Public Transit, Shopping, Churches, Synagogues, Seniors' Centre, Library, Major Highway and Local Hospital (Trillium Health Partners - Credit Valley Hospital Site & Mississauga Hospital Site). *Predominant Cultural Group:* Canadian. Licensed under the Retirement Homes Act.
STAFFING: *Available Staff/Services*: Pharmacy, Social Work (CCAC), Recreation Therapy, Occupational Therapy (CCAC), Visiting Dentist, Physiotherapy, Dietitian (CCAC), Podiatry (CCAC), Chaplaincy, Speech Pathology (CCAC), Chiropody, Audiology/Hearing Clinic, Massage Therapy and Reflexology. *External services arranged by:* residence and/or family/resident. Staff trained *re*: visually, hearing and cognitively impaired. 24-hour staff. RPNs, PSWs and UCPs on staff. Visiting MD (every 2 weeks). Can retain own MD. TB tests, Police Check or Vulnerable Person Screening is done for all new staff.
HEALTH SERVICES: Medication administration (not via IV) and/or supervision. Vitals monitored if required. Will accept and provide special assistance for residents who require oxygen and catheters. Assistance with dressing available (cost). Assistance with bathing available as needed (cost). Care plans done. Different levels of care available. Private Duty/Extra Care available. Lab service (visiting, $25.00/visit). Pharmacy Services. Residents can purchase outside resources and use agency of their choice. MD visits residents in their rooms/suites. Clinic area for medical visits. Will help locate higher level of care if needed (Director of Care will assist).
ACCOMMODATION: *Choice of suites available*: studio, 1-bedroom, 1-bedroom + den, 2-bedroom, 2-bedroom + den condominium suites & rentals apartments. *In all suites*: locks, kitchenette, microwave, stove, patio/balcony, storage, light fixtures, fire alarm, smoke detector, emergency response system with wearable pendant/bracelet, air conditioning (individually controlled heating and cooling HVAC) and thermostats for heating & cooling. Window coverings are provided in rental suites. Private bathrooms with grab bars, tubs and showers with non-slip surfaces and elevated toilet seats. In-suite basic cable TV provided by residence (extra cost for additional channels). Can have own phone number if resident arranges with phone company (residence charges extra). Unfurnished suites, furnished suites available for

short stays. *Restrictions on electrical appliances*: if special outlets required. Suites can be shared (by couples only). Pets allowed (one dog or cat per suite).
DINING SERVICE: Meal/service packages available. *Menu choices available:* Breakfast: 1, Lunch: 5, Dinner: 5. *Guest Meals*: Available. *Special Diets*: Vegetarian, Low Salt, Diabetic and Gluten Free. Tray service to room if ill (no charge for a maximum time of 5 days). Unlimited snacks available at any time. Party facilities. Private dining room. No defined seating or sitting times - breakfast 7:30 a.m. -11:00 a.m., lunch in bistro or dining room 11:30 a.m. - 1:30 p.m., dinner from 4:30 p.m. - 7:00 p.m.
AMENITIES AND ACTIVITIES: Parking available (indoor & outdoor, for visitors and indoor for residents). *5 lounges with:* TVs (2), piano (1), bar (1) and games (1). Guest suites available. *Residence has a:* library, chapel, barber/beauty shop, visiting hairdresser and laundry room(s) (no cost). Residence provides newspaper delivery to individual suite. Mail delivered to private mailbox with key. *Recreation Facilities*: pool table, billiards, shuffleboard, exercise room, craft room, card room, swimming pool, putting green, patio garden, theatre/chapel, wellness centre, hydrotherapy and private family lounge. Posted schedule of activities. Internal newsletter for residents. *Recreational Programs*: exercise, shopping, theatre, parties, entertainment, art classes, pet visiting, day trips, travelogues, lectures, line dancing, bridge, computer training, book club, Posit Science and Zumba.
OTHER SERVICES: *Housekeeping*: weekly (included in fee; daily and monthly also available). *Laundry*: linen, towel (included in fee); personal (extra cost) & dry cleaning (outside service). Personal laundry cost depends on service package; private laundry in condominium suites. Transportation to medical appointments (included in rental packages, extra cost for condominium) and for group social activities (included in fee, except for outside events). 24-hour security. Nightly security checks. Telephone (extra cost). Cable TV (basic cable is included; resident is responsible for ultimate cable package & digital box). Utilities (all utilities included for renters, electricity extra for condominium owners). Amenities vary based on service package purchased.
RENTAL INFORMATION: Rates may vary. Monthly rental rates – call for information. Condominium purchase prices from the low $290,000 range. Extra cost for 2nd person sharing suite (varies on suite size). Option to purchase unit available (floors 12-21). Rent paid monthly. *Payment Options*: cheques and post-dated cheques. Rent increases as per Provincial Tenancy Legislation, annual for resident with 3 months' notice given. Will help resident move into residence. Short-term respite and trial stays available.

PORT CREDIT RESIDENCES

33 Hurontario Street, Mississauga, ON L5G 3G8
Tel: (905) 274-6864 • Fax: (905) 274-6365
Email: **mktg2.pc@diversicare.ca**
Website: **www.portcreditresidences.ca**
Contact: **Marketing Manager**
Capacity: **180 residents** • Subsidies: **none**
Price: **$3,300.00 - $5,600.00/month**

Port Credit Retirement Residence is a spectacular new home that opened in the fall of 2011. Located in the lakeside community of Port Credit at Hurontario Street and Lakeshore Road East, this lovely residence has 150 suites ranging from studios to large 2-bedrooms with balconies and terraces. We offer Independent and Full Service Lifestyle Packages with extra care services available. A large indoor pool and fitness centre featuring our Brain Gym® & More program compliments our ground floor amenities. Lake, marina and shops are all within strolling distance. **Port Credit Residences is owned & managed by Diversicare who is the proud recipient of the 2003, 2006, 2009 and 2012 Order of Excellence Award given by Excellence Canada.** This award was received for the exceptional quality and customer service we provide to our residents every day.

RESIDENCE INFORMATION: 3 years in operation. *Near:* Hurontario Street and Lakeshore Road. Decorated in 2011. Handrails in hallways. 6 floors, 3 elevators. Wheelchair accessible. Central PA system. *Funding Base:* Corporate/for profit. *Owned by:* Diversicare Canada Management Services Co., Inc. 150 units. *Average Waiting Period*: none. Can sometimes accommodate cognitively impaired people (assessment required by RN). Can accommodate physically challenged people. Residents have a dress code. Smoking allowed (in private suite only). Alcohol allowed. *Languages:* English. Will accept Public Guardian and Trustee clients. Main doors of residence secured at night only. *Close to:* Public Transit, Shopping, Churches, Seniors' Centre, Library, Major Highway and Local Hospital (Trillium Health Partners). Member of ORCA. Licensed under the Retirement Homes Act.
STAFFING: *Available Staff/Services*: Pharmacy, Social Work, Recreation Therapy, Occupational Therapy, Physiotherapy, Dietitian, Companions, Podiatry, Speech Pathology and Nurse Practitioner (available 24/7). *External services arranged by:* family/resident. Staff trained *re*: visually, hearing and cognitively impaired. 24-hour nursing and other staff. RNs, RPNs, PSWs and UCPs on staff. Visiting MD (as needed by resident). Can retain own MD. Staff members are bonded. Police Check or Vulnerable Person Screening is done for all new staff.
HEALTH SERVICES: Medication administration and/or supervision. Vitals monitored if required. Will accept (but not provide special assistance for) residents who require oxygen, catheters, ostomies and feeding tubes. Assistance with dressing available (cost). Weekly assistance with bathing available (cost). Care plans done. Different levels of care available. Assisted Living Area. Lab service (visiting). Residents can purchase outside resources and use agency of their choice. Clinic area for medical visits. Will help locate higher level of care if needed (Nurse Practitioner available 24/7).
ACCOMMODATION: *Choice of suites available*: studios, 1-bedroom, 1-bedroom + den & 2-bedroom units. *In all suites*: locks, kitchenette, bar fridge, patio/balcony, storage, window coverings, light fixtures, fire alarm, smoke detector, sprinkler, call bell, emergency response system with wearable pendant/ bracelet, air conditioning (central) and thermostats for heating & cooling. Private bathrooms with call bells, grab bars, showers with non-slip surfaces and elevated toilet seats. In-suite cable TV if resident arranges with cable company (residence charges extra). Can have own phone number if resident arranges with phone company (residence charges extra). Furnished & unfurnished suites available. Suites can be shared, roommate picked by resident. Small pets allowed (resident must take care of them).
DINING SERVICE: All meals included in fee and served in dining room daily. *Guest Meals*: Available. *Special Diets*: Vegetarian, Low Salt, Diabetic and Gluten Free. Tray service to room if ill (no charge as long as doctor orders). 2 snacks/day. Open seating for all meals. Party facilities.
AMENITIES AND ACTIVITIES: Parking available (indoor, for visitors and residents). *4 lounges with:* piano (1) and fireplace (1). Guest suites available. *Residence has a:* library, visiting library, chapel, barber/ beauty shop, visiting hairdresser, laundry room(s) (no cost) and tuck/gift shop. Mail delivered to private mailbox with key. *Recreation Facilities*: billiards, exercise room, craft room, card room, swimming pool, chapel/media room and spa. Posted schedule of activities. Internal newsletter for residents. *Recreational Programs*: exercise, shopping, theatre, parties, entertainment, art classes, pet visiting and day trips.
OTHER SERVICES: *Housekeeping*: weekly (included in fee). *Laundry*: linen & towel (included in fee); personal (extra cost). Complimentary laundry on each floor. Transportation for group social activities. 24-hour security. Nightly security checks. Telephone & Cable TV (extra cost). Utilities (included in fee).
RENTAL INFORMATION: Rates may vary. Extra cost for 2nd person sharing suite ($700.00/month). Rent paid monthly. *Payment Options*: cheques, post-dated cheques and pre-authorized payments. Rent increases as per Provincial Tenancy Legislation, annual for resident with 3 months' notice given. Will help resident move into residence. Short-term respite and trial stays available.

Pricing information for homes listed in *The Guide* may vary slightly.
Please verify rates with the residences you are interested in directly.

REVERA - BOUGH BEECHES PLACE

1130 Bough Beeches Boulevard, Mississauga, ON L4W 4G3
Tel: (855) 573-8372 • Toll Free: (855) 573-8372
Email: **boughbeeches@reveraliving.com**
Website: **www.reveraliving.com/boughbeeches**
Contact: **Executive Director or Lifestyle Consultant**
Capacity: **104 residents •** Subsidies: **none**
Price: **$3,423.00/month and up**

Keep living your life, your way, at Bough Beeches. Here, you'll find the range of services, amenities and choices that fit your lifestyle and requirements – all in a warm and safe environment. Bough Beeches is a one-storey residence nestled within a beautiful, mature neighbourhood, conveniently located close to parkland, shopping, churches, community/senior centres, community services, and public transit. Explore what we have to offer, to keep you living in freedom and comfort. Everything is designed to enable you to maintain your independence and privacy, enjoy a full social life, and participate in the activities you love. Our caring and friendly staff, along with appealing accommodations, support who you are and how you want to live. With retirement living at Bough Beeches, you change your address, not your life. *Bough Beeches is part of the Revera family, one of North America's leading and most trusted providers of seniors' accommodation, care and services since 1961.*

RESIDENCE INFORMATION: 29 years in operation. *Near:* Dixie Road and Burnhamthorpe Road. Decorated in 2011. Handrails in hallways. 1 floor, no elevator. Wheelchair accessible. Central PA system. *Funding Base:* Corporate/for profit. *Owned and managed by:* Revera Inc. 98 units. *Average Waiting Period*: less than 2 weeks. *Average Age*: 81. Can accommodate cognitively impaired people (Secure Living Area within the building). Can accommodate physically challenged people (i.e. walkers, canes, wheelchairs, scooters). Smoking allowed (outside residence). Alcohol allowed. *Restrictions around Visitors/Visiting Hours:* after 9:00 p.m., please ring the doorbell for access. *Procedures to leave the premises on a temporary basis...*Short-term & Overnight: inform Office and Nursing & sign in/out. Holidays: inform Office and Nursing. *Languages:* English, Polish, Italian, Filipino, Ukrainian, Iranian, Japanese, Portuguese and Others. Will accept Public Guardian and Trustee clients. Main doors of residence secured at all times. *Close to:* Public Transit, Shopping, Churches, Seniors' Centre, Library, Major Highway and Local Hospitals (Trillium Health Partners - Mississauga Hospital Site & Credit Valley Hospital Site). Member of ORCA. Licensed under the Retirement Homes Act.
STAFFING: *Available Staff/Services*: Pharmacy, Social Work (CCAC), Recreation Therapy, Occupational Therapy (CCAC), Visiting Dentist, Physiotherapy (CCAC), Denturist, Dietitian (CCAC), Companions, Podiatry, Chaplaincy, Speech Pathology (CCAC), Chiropody and Audiology/Hearing Clinic. *External services arranged by:* residence and/or family/resident. Staff trained *re*: visually, hearing and cognitively impaired. 24-hour nursing and other staff. RNs, RPNs, HCAs, PSWs and UCPs on staff. Visiting MD (weekly and on call). Can retain own MD. Staff members are bonded. Police Check or Vulnerable Person Screening is done for all new staff.
HEALTH SERVICES: Medication administration and/or supervision. Vitals monitored if required. Will accept and provide special assistance for residents who require oxygen, catheters and ostomies. Assistance with dressing available. Weekly assistance with bathing available. Care plans done. Different levels of care available. Assistance with all aspects of personal care. Optional services available. Private Duty/Extra Care available. Separate unit for residents with dementia. Lab service (visiting). Residents can purchase outside resources and use agency of their choice. MD visits residents in their rooms/suites. Clinic area for medical visits. Will help locate higher level of care if needed (through Doctor, Director of Care, Executive Director and CCAC).
ACCOMMODATION: *Choice of suites available*: private suites. *In all suites*: locks, window coverings, light fixtures, linens, fire alarm, smoke detector, carbon monoxide detectors, sprinkler, nursing call bell

system, air conditioning (central) and thermostats for heating & cooling. Optional kitchen pantry and some with kitchenettes. Private bathrooms with call bells, grab bars, tubs and showers with non-slip surfaces. In-suite cable TV provided by residence (residence charges extra). Can have own phone number if resident arranges with phone company (residence charges extra). Furnished & unfurnished suites available. *Restrictions on electrical appliances*: no stoves or hot plates; all appliances require a safety check prior to entering suite. Suites can be shared (pending availability of beds), roommate picked by residence staff. Pets allowed (as per Pet Policy).
DINING SERVICE: All meals included in fee and served in dining room daily. *Sittings per meal:* Breakfast: 1, Lunch: 1, Dinner: 1. *Menu choices available:* Breakfast: 1, Lunch: 2, Dinner: 2. *Guest Meals*: Available. *Special Diets*: Vegetarian, Low Salt, Diabetic, Low Sodium, Pureed, Minced and Others. Tray service to room if ill (no charge for a maximum time of 4 days). Assistance with feeding is part of a care package. 3 snacks/day. Party facilities.
AMENITIES AND ACTIVITIES: Parking available (outdoor, for visitors and residents). *2 lounges with:* TV (1) and piano (1). Guest suites available. *Residence has a:* library, visiting library, barber/beauty shop, visiting hairdresser and tuck/gift shop (schedule in monthly calendar). Resident can arrange newspaper delivery to individual suite (extra cost). Mail delivered to resident. *Recreation Facilities*: craft room, card room and 2 secure outdoor gardens. Posted schedule of activities. Internal newsletter for residents. *Recreational Programs*: exercise, shopping, theatre, parties, entertainment, art classes, pet visiting, day trips, daily activities, socials, community groups, museum visits, visiting programs, etc.
OTHER SERVICES: *Housekeeping*: daily (included in fee). *Laundry*: linen, towel & personal (included in fee); dry cleaning (extra cost - Office Manager can assist). Pen or labels provided to family (no cost). Transportation to medical appointments (extra cost) and for group social activities (extra cost - occasional specific events). 24-hour security. Nightly security checks. Telephone & Cable TV (extra cost). Utilities (included in fee). Private duty, additional shower, tray service and other miscellaneous costs outlined in CHIP (Care Home Information Package).
RENTAL INFORMATION: Rates vary depending on care services. Extra cost for 2nd person sharing suite. Rent paid monthly. *Payment Options*: cheques and pre-authorized payments. Rent increases as per Provincial Tenancy Legislation, annual for resident with 3 months' notice given. Will help resident move into residence. Short-term respite and trial stays available.

REVERA - CONSTITUTION PLACE

3051 Constitution Boulevard, Mississauga, ON L4Y 2Z1
Tel: (855) 573-8372 • Toll Free: (855) 573-8372
Email: **constitution@reveraliving.com**
Website: **www.reveraliving.com/constitution**
Contact: **Executive Director or Lifestyle Consultant**
Capacity: **65 residents** • Subsidies: **none**
Price: **$2,174.00/month and up**

Keep living your life, your way, at Constitution Place. You'll find the range of services, amenities and choices that fit your lifestyle and requirements – all in a warm and safe environment. Constitution Place is an intimate single-storey residence located in a well-established residential neighbourhood in Mississauga, close to shopping, health centres, churches and seniors' centres. Everything is designed to enable you to maintain your independence and privacy, enjoy a full social life, and participate in the activities that you love. Our caring, friendly and multilingual staff, along with appealing accommodations, support who you are and how you want to live in freedom and comfort. With retirement living at Revera, you change your address, not your life. *Constitution Place is part of the Revera family, one of North America's leading and most trusted providers of seniors' accommodation, care and services since 1961.*

RESIDENCE INFORMATION: 36 years in operation. *Near:* Dixie Road and Dundas Street. Decorated in 2012. Handrails in hallways. 1 floor, no elevators. Wheelchair accessible. Central PA system. *Funding Base:* Corporate/for profit. *Owned and managed by:* Revera Inc. 53 units. *Average Waiting Period*: varies. *Average Age*: 82. Can accommodate cognitively impaired people (mild to moderate dementia). Can accommodate physically challenged people (walker, wheelchair bound). Residents have a dress code (casual). Smoke-free residence. Alcohol allowed. *Restrictions around Visitors/Visiting Hours:* doors are locked at 8:00 p.m. but visitors can ring doorbell for access. *Procedures to leave the premises on a temporary basis...*Short-term: sign in/out book. Overnight & Holidays: notify Management. *Languages:* English, Spanish, Polish, Croatian, Russian, French, Ukrainian, Tagalog, Italian & Portuguese. Will accept Public Guardian and Trustee clients. Main doors of residence secured at all times. *Close to:* Public Transit, Shopping, Churches, Seniors' Centre, Major Highway and Local Hospital (Trillium Health Partners). *Predominant Cultural Group:* English & Portuguese. Member of ORCA. Licensed under the Retirement Homes Act.
STAFFING: *Available Staff/Services*: Pharmacy, Social Work (CCAC), Recreation Therapy, Occupational Therapy (CCAC), Visiting Dentist, Physiotherapy (CCAC), Companions, Podiatry, Chaplaincy, Speech Pathology (CCAC), Audiology/Hearing Clinic and Visiting Lab Technicians. *External services arranged by:* residence and/or family/resident. Staff trained *re*: visually, hearing and cognitively impaired. 24-hour nursing and other staff. RNs, RPNs, PSWs and UCPs on staff. Visiting MD (once/week, on call 24/7). Can retain own MD. Police Check or Vulnerable Person Screening is done for all new staff.
HEALTH SERVICES: Medication administration and/or supervision. Vitals monitored if required. Will accept and provide special assistance for residents who require oxygen, catheters and ostomies. Assistance with dressing available (cost). Weekly assistance with bathing available (cost). Care plans done. Different levels of care available. Private Duty/Extra Care available. Lab service (visiting). Residents can purchase outside resources and use agency of their choice. MD visits residents in their rooms/suites. Will help locate higher level of care if needed (with help with alternative level of care/contact CCAC).
ACCOMMODATION: *Choice of suites available*: private studio (40) or semi-private suites (12). *In all suites*: locks, storage, window coverings, light fixtures, smoke detector, carbon monoxide detectors. sprinkler, emergency call bell system, air conditioning (central), thermostats for heating & cooling and wall to wall carpet. Private bathrooms with call bells, grab bars and showers with non-slip surfaces. In-suite cable TV provided by residence (residence charges extra). Can have own phone number if resident arranges with phone company. Furnished & unfurnished suites available. *Restrictions on electrical appliances*: no stoves, microwaves or heaters. Suites can be shared (pending availability of beds), roommate picked by resident & residence staff. Pets allowed (cats, birds and small dogs welcome with assessment).
DINING SERVICE: All meals included in fee and served in dining room daily. *Sittings per meal:* Breakfast: 1, Lunch: 1, Dinner: 1. *Menu choices available:* Breakfast: 2, Lunch: 2, Dinner: 2. *Guest Meals*: Available. *Special Diets*: Vegetarian, Low Salt, Diabetic and Therapeutic. Tray service to room if ill (no charge for a maximum time of 3 days). 3 snacks/day. All meals are home-made and freshly prepared on-site.
AMENITIES AND ACTIVITIES: Parking available (outdoor, for visitors and residents). *2 lounges with:* TV (1) and piano (1). Guest suites available. *Residence has a:* library, visiting library, barber/beauty shop, visiting hairdresser and tuck/gift shop (open Monday to Friday). Banking services on premises (Trust Account). Residence provides newspaper delivery to individual suite. Mail delivered to resident. *Recreation Facilities*: craft room, card room, bowling and shuffleboard. Posted schedule of activities. Internal newsletter for residents. *Recreational Programs*: exercise, shopping, parties, entertainment, art classes, pet visiting, day trips, festivals and theme nights.
OTHER SERVICES: *Housekeeping*: daily and weekly (extra cost). *Laundry*: linen & towel (included in fee); personal (extra cost) & dry cleaning (extra cost to resident or family). Transportation to medical appointments (extra cost - Transhelp, outside agency) and for group social activities (included). 24-hour security. Telephone (extra cost - resident must arrange for installation). Cable TV (extra cost - part of the CHIP agreement). Utilities (included in fee). Internet access.

RENTAL INFORMATION: Rate varies depending on size and services. Extra cost for 2nd person sharing suite. Rent paid monthly. *Payment Options*: pre-authorized payments. Rent increases as per Provincial Tenancy Legislation, annual for resident with 3 months' notice given. Will help resident move into residence. Short-term respite and trial stays (depends on level of care required) subject to availability.

REVERA - KING GARDENS

85 King Street East, Mississauga, ON L5A 4G6
Tel: (855) 573-8372 • Toll Free: (855) 573-8372
Email: **kinggardens@reveraliving.com**
Website: **www.reveraliving.com/kinggardens**
Contact: **Executive Director or Lifestyle Consultant**
Capacity: **175 residents** • Subsidies: **none**
Price: **$1,920.00/month and up**

Keep living your life, your way, at King Gardens. Here, you'll find the range of services, amenities and choices that fit your lifestyle and requirements – all in a warm and safe environment. With retirement living at King Gardens, you change your address, not your life. Located in the heart of Cooksville, just steps from Cooksville Park, 2 shopping malls, public transit, and medical offices. Close to Port Credit Harbour, and Square One Shopping Centre, churches, community services and recreation, Trillium Hospital, the highway, and more. Everything is designed to enable you to maintain your independence and privacy, enjoy a full social life, and participate in the activities that you love. Our caring and friendly staff, along with appealing accommodations, support who you are and how you want to live in freedom and comfort. *King Gardens is part of the Revera family, one of North America's leading and most trusted providers of seniors' accommodation, care and services since 1961.*

RESIDENCE INFORMATION: 23 years in operation. *Near:* Dundas Street and Hurontario Street. Decorated in 2010. Handrails in hallways. 10 floors, 3 elevators. Wheelchair accessible. Central PA system. *Funding Base:* Corporate/for profit. *Owned and managed by:* Revera Inc. 148 units. *Average Waiting Period*: less than 2 weeks. *Average Age*: 84. Can accommodate cognitively impaired people (Alzheimer's/dementia). Can accommodate physically challenged people (wheelchair accessible). Residents have a dress code (proper dress code in effect in all common areas). Smoking allowed (outside only). Alcohol allowed (Kings Pub and licensed dining room also available). *Restrictions around Visitors/Visiting Hours:* access to property after 9:00 p.m. via front door bell. *Procedures to leave the premises on a temporary basis...*resident sign in/out book. *Languages:* English. Staff & residents speak various languages; all cultures welcome. Will accept Public Guardian and Trustee clients. Main doors of residence secured at all times. *Close to:* Public Transit, Shopping, Churches, Seniors' Centre, Library, Major Highway and Local Hospitals (Trillium Health Partners – Mississauga Hospital Site & Credit Valley Hospital Site). Member of ORCA. Licensed under the Retirement Homes Act.
STAFFING: *Available Staff/Services*: Social Work (CCAC), Recreation Therapy, Occupational Therapy (CCAC), Visiting Dentist, Physiotherapy (CCAC), Denturist, Dietitian (CCAC), Companions, Podiatry (CCAC), Chaplaincy, Speech Pathology (CCAC), Chiropody, Audiology/Hearing Clinic and Pet Therapy Visits. *External services arranged by:* residence and/or family/resident. Staff trained *re*: visually, hearing and cognitively impaired. 24-hour nursing and other staff. RPNs, HCAs and PSWs on staff. Visiting MD (once weekly & on call 24/7). Can retain own MD. Staff members are bonded. Police Check or Vulnerable Person Screening is done for all new staff.
HEALTH SERVICES: Medication administered if required (medication administration usually centralized - additional cost). Vitals monitored if required. Will accept and provide special assistance for residents who require oxygen, catheters and ostomies. Assistance with dressing available (cost). Weekly assistance with bathing available (cost). Care plans done. Different levels of care available. Assisted Living Area (less than 2 week waiting period). Separate unit for residents with dementia. Costs for care items and Assisted

Living vary according to needs. Lab service (visiting). Residents can purchase outside resources and use agency of their choice. MD visits residents in their rooms/suites. Clinic area for medical visits. Will help locate higher level of care if needed (family conference arranged to determine future care needs).
ACCOMMODATION: *Choice of suites available*: studio, 1-bedroom, 2-bedroom & a few shared semi-private suites. *In all suites*: locks, kitchenette, bar fridge, patio/balcony, storage, light fixtures, linens, fire alarm, smoke detector, sprinkler, call bell, emergency response system with wearable pendant/bracelet, air conditioning (central) and thermostats for heating & cooling. Bathrooms (most private; semi-private suites are shared with one other resident) with call bells, grab bars, showers with non-slip surfaces and elevated toilet seats. In-suite cable TV provided by residence (residence charges extra). Can have own phone number provided by residence (residence charges extra). Unfurnished suites, furnished suites available for short stays. *Restrictions on electrical appliances*: hot plates not permitted; electric kettles must have automatic shut-off switches. Suites can be shared (by couples only), roommate picked by resident & residence staff. Pets allowed (cats, birds and small dogs with assessment).
DINING SERVICE: All meals included in fee and served in dining room daily. *Sittings per meal:* Breakfast: 2, Lunch: 2, Dinner: 2. *Menu choices available:* Breakfast: 2, Lunch: 2, Dinner: 2. *Guest Meals*: Available. *Special Diets*: Vegetarian, Low Salt, Diabetic and Therapeutic. Tray service to room if ill (no charge for a maximum time of 4 days). 2 snacks/day. Party facilities.
AMENITIES AND ACTIVITIES: Parking available (outdoor, for visitors and indoor for residents). *12 lounges with:* TVs (3), pianos (2), solarium (1) and balconies (9). Guest suites available. *Residence has a:* library, visiting library, chapel, barber/beauty shop, visiting hairdresser, laundry room(s) (no cost) and tuck/gift shop (open 1 hour/week). Banking services on premises (bi-weekly). Resident can arrange newspaper delivery to individual suite (extra cost). Mail delivered to private mailbox with key. *Recreation Facilities*: pool table, billiards, shuffleboard, exercise room, craft room, card room, swimming pool, potting shed and resident garden. Posted schedule of activities. Internal newsletter for residents. *Recreational Programs*: exercise, shopping, theatre, parties, entertainment, art classes, pet visiting, day trips, horticulture program and baking/cooking demonstrations.
OTHER SERVICES: *Housekeeping*: weekly (included in fee; options available for more or less, daily can be arranged). *Laundry*: linen & towel (included in fee), personal (extra cost - for Independent residents; included for Assisted Floor). Transportation for group social activities (most included; some are user pay). 24-hour security. Nightly security checks. Telephone (mandatory add-on to fee). Cable TV (optional add-on to fee with Rogers Cable). Utilities (included in fee). Private dining room.
RENTAL INFORMATION: Rates vary depending on suite type and services chosen. Extra cost for 2nd person sharing suite (fee varies depending on service). Rent paid monthly. *Payment Options*: cheques, post-dated cheques and pre-authorized payments. Rent increases as per Provincial Tenancy Legislation, annual for resident with 3 months' notice given. Will help resident move into residence (extra cost). Short-term respite and trial stays available (cost variable). Hotel suites available.

REVERA - THE BEECHWOOD

1500 Rathburn Road East, Mississauga, ON L4W 4L7
Tel: (855) 573-8372 • Toll Free: (855) 573-8372
Email: **beechwood@reveraliving.com**
Website: **www.reveraliving.com/beechwood**
Contact: **Executive Director or Lifestyle Consultant**
Capacity: **202 units** • Subsidies: **none**
Price: **$2,099.00/month and up**

Keep living your life, your way, at The Beechwood. You'll find a full range of options to choose from, you can select the lifestyle that suits you best. The Beechwood exudes classic elegance. Located in the heart of Rockwood Village, Mississauga; you're steps away from Rockwood Mall, groceries, banks, public transit & picturesque Beechwood Park. With the sophisticated décor of a fine hotel, The Beechwood

caters to independent active seniors, while also offering Assisted Living options. Everything here is designed to enable you to maintain your independence and privacy, enjoy a full social life, and participate in the activities that you love. With retirement living at The Beechwood, you change your address, not your life. *The Beechwood is part of the Revera family, one of North America's leading and most trusted providers of seniors' accommodation, care and services since 1961.*

RESIDENCE INFORMATION: 27 years in operation. *Near:* Dixie Road and Rathburn Road. Decorated in 2010. Handrails in hallways. 4 floors, 2 elevators. Wheelchair accessible. Central PA system. *Funding Base:* Corporate/for profit. *Owned and managed by:* Revera Inc. *Average Waiting Period*: none. *Average Age*: 84. Can accommodate cognitively impaired people (mild to moderate dementia). Can accommodate physically challenged people (wheelchair accessible). Residents have a dress code (casual). Smoke-free residence. Alcohol allowed. *Procedures to leave the premises on a temporary basis*...inform staff. *Languages:* English. Staff speak various languages. Will accept Public Guardian and Trustee clients. Main doors of residence secured at all times. *Close to:* Public Transit, Shopping, Churches, Seniors' Centre, Library, Major Highway and Local Hospitals (Trillium Health Partners – Mississauga Hospital Site & Credit Valley Hospital Site). *Predominant Cultural Group:* English speaking. Member of ORCA. Licensed under the Retirement Homes Act.
STAFFING: *Available Staff/Services*: Pharmacy, Social Work, Recreation Therapy, Occupational Therapy, Visiting Dentist, Physiotherapy (CCAC), Dietitian, Companions, Podiatry, Speech Pathology (CCAC), Audiology/Hearing Clinic and 24-hour Emergency Response. *External services arranged by:* residence and/or family/resident. Staff trained *re*: visually, hearing and cognitively impaired. 24-hour nursing and other staff. RNs, RPNs, HCAs, PSWs and UCPs on staff. Visiting MD (weekly). Can retain own MD. Police Check or Vulnerable Person Screening is done for all new staff.
HEALTH SERVICES: Medication administered if required. Vitals monitored if required. Will accept and provide special assistance for residents who require oxygen, catheters and ostomies. Assistance with dressing available (cost). Assistance with bathing available as needed (cost). Care plans done. Different levels of care available. Assisted Living Area. Lab service (visiting). Residents can purchase outside resources and use agency of their choice. MD visits residents in their rooms/suites. Clinic area for medical visits. Will help locate higher level of care if needed (family conference arranged to determine future care needs).
ACCOMMODATION: *Choice of suites available*: studio, 1-bedroom & 2-bedroom suites. *In all suites*: locks, storage, window coverings, light fixtures, fire alarm, smoke detector, sprinkler, call bell, emergency response system with wearable pendant/bracelet, air conditioning (central) and thermostats for heating & cooling. Carbon monoxide detector - main floor of Independent Residence. Private bathrooms with call bells, grab bars, tubs and showers with non-slip surfaces and elevated toilet seats. Can have own phone number provided by residence (residence charges extra). Unfurnished suites, furnished suites available for short stays. *Restrictions on electrical appliances*: no cooking appliances in Assisted Living suites. Suites can be shared (by couples only). Pets allowed (case-by-case basis with assessment).
DINING SERVICE: All meals included in fee and served in dining room daily. *Sittings per meal:* Breakfast: 1, Lunch: 4, Dinner: 4. *Menu choices available:* Breakfast: 3, Lunch: 4, Dinner: 4. *Special Diets*: Vegetarian, Low Salt, Diabetic, Therapeutic and Minced. Tray service to room if ill (no charge for a maximum time of 4 days). 2 snacks/day. Party facilities. Private parties can be arranged/catered. Private dining room available.
AMENITIES AND ACTIVITIES: Parking available (outdoor, for visitors and residents). *7 lounges with:* TVs (7), pianos (3) and pool table (1). Guest suites available. *Residence has a:* library, barber/beauty shop, laundry room(s) (no cost) and tuck/gift shop (open 2 hours/week). Banking services on premises (once every 2 weeks). Resident can arrange newspaper delivery to individual suite. Mail delivered to private mailbox with key. *Recreation Facilities*: pool table, billiards, exercise room, craft room, card room, van for day trips, culinary kitchen and physiotherapy room. Posted schedule of activities. Internal newsletter for residents. *Recreational Programs*: exercise, shopping, theatre, parties, entertainment, art classes, pet visiting, day trips, daily tea social, card games and in-house movie nights.

OTHER SERVICES: *Housekeeping*: daily and weekly (included in fee). *Laundry*: linen & towel (included in fee - Independent Living (&) Assisted Living); personal (extra cost; included ONLY in Assisted Living) & dry cleaning (arranged by resident). Transportation for group social activities. 24-hour security. Telephone & Cable TV (monthly cost to resident). Utilities (included in fee).
RENTAL INFORMATION: Suite rate varies depending on size and care/service package requested. Extra cost for 2nd person sharing suite. Rent paid monthly. *Payment Options*: cheques, post-dated cheques and pre-authorized payments. Rent increases as per Provincial Tenancy Legislation, annual for resident with 3 months' notice given. Short-term respite and trial stays available.

TYNDALL SENIORS VILLAGE

1044 Eglinton Avenue East, Mississauga, ON L4W 3A5
Tel: (905) 624-5027 • Fax: (905) 629-9346
Email: **awilliams@tyndallestates.com**
Website: **www.svch.ca**
Contact: **Andrea Williams**
Capacity: **58 residents** • Subsidies: **none**
Price: **$1,542.00 - $3,077.00/month**

There are many reasons why our residents have chosen to live in a Sharon Village Care Home. For some, it's the benefit of living together in a safe caring environment. For others, it's access to discrete Assisted Living Services in a continuum of care model. Whatever the reason, Sharon Village Care Homes is committed to enriching the mental and physical welfare of our residents through the comforts of home. Tyndall Seniors Village offers affordable retirement for seniors & is set on 2.5 acres landscaped grounds with a brook. Tyndall Seniors Village is just the right size - large enough to offer residents the right range of services and small enough for personalized attention and care. Residents can choose from attractively designed apartments, studios and bedsitting rooms. Attractive landscaping with trees and relaxing garden terraces create warm home-like ambience.

RESIDENCE INFORMATION: 34 years in operation. *Near:* Tomken Road and Dixie Road. Decorated in 2011. Handrails in hallways. 4 floors, 1 elevator. Wheelchair accessible. Central PA system. *Funding Base:* Corporate/for profit. *Managed by:* Sharon Village Care Homes. 49 units. *Average Waiting Period*: none. *Average Age*: 83. Can accommodate cognitively impaired people (early cognitive impairment with ability to be independent in most areas of ADL). Can accommodate physically challenged people. Smoke-free residence. Alcohol allowed (restrictions: as per doctor's orders). *Restrictions around Visitors/Visiting Hours:* 8:00 a.m. to 9:00 p.m. *Procedures to leave the premises on a temporary basis...*sign out at Front Entrance and check with Nurse for medication. *Languages:* English, Italian & Portuguese. Will accept Public Guardian and Trustee clients. Main doors of residence secured at all times. *Close to:* Public Transit, Shopping, Churches, Synagogues, Seniors' Centre, Library, Major Highway and Local Hospitals (Trillium Health Partners – Mississauga Hospital Site & Credit Valley Hospital Site). Member of ORCA & OLTCA. Licensed under the Retirement Homes Act.
STAFFING: *Available Staff/Services*: Pharmacy, Social Work (CCAC), Recreation Therapy, Occupational Therapy (CCAC), Visiting Dentist, Physiotherapy, Dietitian, Companions, Podiatry, Chaplaincy, Speech Pathology, Chiropody, Audiology/Hearing Clinic and Lab Services. *External services arranged by:* residence and/or family/resident. Staff trained *re*: visually, hearing and cognitively impaired. 24-hour nursing staff. RPNs, HCAs and PSWs on staff. Visiting MD (2 times/month & on call 24/7). Can retain own MD. Police Check or Vulnerable Person Screening is done for all new staff.
HEALTH SERVICES: Medication administration and/or supervision. Vitals monitored if required. Will accept and provide special assistance for residents who require oxygen and catheters. Assistance with dressing available. Weekly assistance with bathing available. Care plans done. Different levels of care available. Lab service (visiting, $25.00/visit). Residents can purchase outside resources and use agency of

their choice. MD visits residents in their rooms/suites. Clinic area for medical visits. Will help locate higher level of care if needed (long-term care home adjacent, CCAC visits).

ACCOMMODATION: *Choice of suites available*: bedsitting room (24), studio (14) & 1-bedroom apartments (11). *In all suites*: locks, window coverings, light fixtures, linens, smoke detector, air conditioning (in apartments only; individual air conditioning permitted) and thermostats for heating. Private bathrooms with grab bars, tubs and showers with non-slip surfaces. In-suite cable TV if resident arranges with cable company. Can have own phone number if resident arranges with phone company. Furnished suites for short-term stays & unfurnished suites available. *Restrictions on electrical appliances*: no stoves. Suites can be shared (pending availability of beds), roommate picked by resident & residence staff. Pets allowed (birds only; no cats or dogs).

DINING SERVICE: All meals included in fee and served in dining room daily. *Sittings per meal:* Breakfast: 1, Lunch: 1, Dinner: 1. *Menu choices available:* Breakfast: 1, Lunch: 2, Dinner: 2. *Guest Meals*: Breakfast $2.00, Lunch $7.00, Dinner $10.00. *Special Diets*: Vegetarian, Low Salt, Diabetic and Renal. Tray service to room if ill (no charge as long as doctor orders). 3 snacks/day. Open pantry. Residents have input for special holidays and suggestions given in Resident's Council Meetings.

AMENITIES AND ACTIVITIES: Parking available (outdoor, for visitors: free and residents: $60.00/ month). *6 lounges with:* TVs (3). *Residence has a:* visiting library, chapel, barber/beauty shop, visiting hairdresser, laundry room(s) (cost), tuck/gift shop (open Monday to Friday; 9:00 a.m. - 5:00 p.m.). Mail delivered to resident. *Recreation Facilities*: exercise room and craft room. Posted schedule of activities. Internal newsletter for residents. *Recreational Programs*: exercise, shopping, theatre, parties, entertainment, art classes, pet visiting, day trips, bingo, crafts, Jeopardy, carpet bowling, walking club & more....

OTHER SERVICES: *Housekeeping*: weekly (included in fee). *Laundry*: linen & towel (included in fee); personal ($50.00/month). There are facilities for residents to do their own laundry. Transportation for group social activities (cost depends on outing). 24-hour security. Nightly security checks (signed consent required). Telephone & Cable TV (resident arranged). Utilities (included in fee).

RENTAL INFORMATION: Rates may vary. Extra cost for 2nd person sharing suite ($500.00/month). Rent paid monthly. *Payment Options*: cheques, post-dated cheques, direct deposit and cash. Rent increases as per Provincial Tenancy Legislation, annual for resident with 3 months' notice given. Short-term respite and trial stays available (both $75.00/day).

V!VA MISSISSAUGA RETIREMENT COMMUNITY

5575 Bonnie Street, Mississauga, ON L5M 0N8
Tel: (905) 566-4500
Email: **mississauga@vivalife.ca**
Website: **www.vivalife.ca**
Capacity: **124 units**
Subsidies: **none**

Located next to a plaza and medical centre, V!VA Mississauga is just minutes from Streetsville, and Erin Mills Town Centre. Amenities abound with an indoor saltwater pool, pub, movie theatre, concierge services and more. Spacious suites range in size from studio to 2-bedroom with options for Independent and Assisted Living. Three healthy and delicious meals are prepared fresh daily.

RESIDENCE INFORMATION: 3 years in operation. *On:* Thomas Street near Winston Churchill Boulevard. Decorated in 2011. Handrails in some of the hallways. 6 floors, 3 elevators. Wheelchair accessible. Central PA system. *Funding Base:* Corporate/for profit. *Owned and managed by:* V!VA Retirement Communities. *Average Waiting Period*: none. Can accommodate cognitively impaired people (early stage Alzheimer's and dementia). Can accommodate physically challenged people. Smoke-free residence. Alcohol allowed. *Procedures to leave the premises on a temporary basis...*advise Concierge. *Languages:* English. Will

accept Public Guardian and Trustee clients. Main doors of residence secured at night only. *Close to:* Public Transit, Shopping, Churches, Seniors' Centre, Library, Major Highway and Local Hospital (Trillium Health Partners - Credit Valley Hospital Site). Member of ORCA. Licensed under the Retirement Homes Act.
STAFFING: *Available Staff/Services*: Pharmacy, Social Work (CCAC), Recreation Therapy, Occupational Therapy (CCAC), Visiting Dentist, Physiotherapy (CCAC), Denturist, Dietitian (CCAC), Companions, Podiatry (CCAC), Chaplaincy, Speech Pathology (CCAC), Chiropody and Audiology/Hearing Clinic. *External services arranged by:* residence and/or family/resident. Staff trained *re*: visually, hearing and cognitively impaired. 24-hour nursing and other staff. RNs, RPNs, HCAs and PSWs on staff. Visiting MD (weekly and as needed). Can retain own MD. Police Check or Vulnerable Person Screening is done for all new staff.
HEALTH SERVICES: Medication administration and/or supervision. Vitals monitored if required. Will accept and provide special assistance for residents who require oxygen, catheters and ostomies. Assistance with dressing available. Weekly assistance with bathing available. Care plans done. Different levels of care available. Private Duty/Extra Care available. Assisted Living Area. Lab service (visiting). Residents can purchase outside resources and use agency of their choice. Clinic area for medical visits. Will help locate higher level of care if needed.
ACCOMMODATION: *Choice of suites available*: studio, 1-bedroom, 1-bedroom + den & 2-bedroom suites. *In all suites*: locks, kitchenette, microwave, storage, window coverings, light fixtures, fire alarm, smoke detector, sprinkler, call bell, emergency response system with wearable pendant/bracelet, air conditioning (central) and thermostats for heating & cooling. Kitchenettes with full-size fridge and microwave provided in Independent Living suites only. Private bathrooms with call bells, grab bars, showers with non-slip surfaces and elevated toilet seats. In-suite cable TV provided by residence. Can have own phone number if resident arranges with phone company. Furnished & unfurnished suites available. *Restrictions on electrical appliances*: CSA approved and inspection by our Environmental Coordinator. Suites can be shared, roommate picked by resident. Pets allowed.
DINING SERVICE: All meals included in fee and served in dining room daily. *Guest Meals*: Available. Tray service to room if ill (no charge as long as doctor orders). Unlimited snacks available at any time. Party facilities. Open pantry. Children's menu available.
AMENITIES AND ACTIVITIES: Parking available (outdoor, for visitors and residents). *10 lounges with:* TVs (7) and piano (1). Guest suites available. *Residence has a:* library, chapel, barber/beauty shop and laundry room(s) (no cost). Banking services on premises (bi-weekly). Residence provides newspaper delivery to individual suite (extra cost). Mail delivered to private mailbox with key. *Recreation Facilities*: pool table, billiards, shuffleboard, exercise room, greenhouse, craft room, card room, swimming pool, pub, Brain Gym, movie theatre, spa, massage room, strength & stretch studio and raised garden beds. Posted schedule of activities. Internal newsletter for residents. *Recreational Programs*: exercise, art classes, shopping, theatre, parties, entertainment, pet visiting, day trips and V!VAfit program focused on cardio, strength, balance & flexibility.
OTHER SERVICES: *Housekeeping*: weekly (included in fee). *Laundry*: linen & towel (included in fee); personal (extra cost). Washer/dryers located on each floor. Transportation for group social activities (aboard V!VA shuttle bus). 24-hour security. Nightly security checks. Cable TV & Utilities (included in fee).
RENTAL INFORMATION: Extra cost for 2nd person sharing suite. Rent paid monthly. *Payment Options*: cheques, post-dated cheques, direct deposit and pre-authorized payments. Rent increases as per Provincial Tenancy Legislation, annual for resident with 3 months' notice given. Will help resident move into residence (extra cost). Short-term respite and trial stays available.

Have you found our Guide helpful?

Please let the residences you contact know that you found them here!!!

WALDEN CIRCLE RETIREMENT COMMUNITY

1907 Lakeshore Road West, Mississauga, ON L5J 1J6
Tel: (905) 403-8660
Email: **info@waldencircleretirement.com**
Website: **www.waldencircleretirement.com**
Contact: **Executive Director or Marketing Manager**
Capacity: **150 residents** • Subsidies: **none**
Price: **$3,600.00 - $6,070.00/month**

Looking for more energy every day? Ready to step out with a new sense of positive vitality? Then come to life at Walden Circle, a community devoted to helping you bring positive energy to everything you do, with a comprehensive program of activities and services designed to help make every day fantastic! Located in the heart of Clarkson Village. Independent Living, personal on-site care, Assisted Living. Trial stays and respite stays. Full service dining room. Spectacular views. Movie theatre. Saltwater swimming pool and wellness care.

RESIDENCE INFORMATION: New residence. *Near:* Lakeshore Road and Southdown Road. Decorated in 2013. Handrails in some of the hallways. 8 floors, 3 elevators. Wheelchair accessible. Central PA system. *Owned and managed by:* Signature Retirement Living. 120 units. *Average Waiting Period*: none. Smoke-free residence. Alcohol allowed. *Procedures to leave the premises on a temporary basis...*check in with Concierge. *Languages:* English. Main doors of residence secured at all times. *Close to:* Public Transit, Shopping, Churches, Synagogues, Seniors' Centre, Library, Major Highway and Local Hospital (Trillium Health Partners - Credit Valley Hospital Site). Member of ORCA. Licensed under the Retirement Homes Act. More information to be provided upon community opening.
STAFFING: *Available Staff/Services*: Pharmacy, Recreation Therapy and Companions. RNs and PSWs on staff. Visiting MD. Can retain own MD. Police Check or Vulnerable Person Screening is done for all new staff. More information to be provided upon community opening.
HEALTH SERVICES: Medication administration and/or supervision (if required; the care plan for medication administration will be discussed with our Director of Care). Vitals monitored if required. Will accept and provide special assistance for residents who require oxygen and catheters. Assistance with dressing available. Assistance with bathing available as needed. Care plans done. Different levels of care available. Private Duty/Extra Care available. Assisted Living Area. Lab service (visiting). Residents can purchase outside resources and use agency of their choice. Clinic area for medical visits. Please call us today for more information/personal tours.
ACCOMMODATION: *In all suites*: locks, kitchenette, bar fridge, microwave, patio/balcony, storage, window coverings, light fixtures, fire alarm, smoke detector, sprinkler, emergency response system with wearable pendant/bracelet, air conditioning (central) and thermostats for heating & cooling. Private bathrooms with call bells, grab bars, tubs and showers and elevated toilet seats. In suite cable TV provided by residence (extra). Can have own phone number if resident arranges with phone company (extra). Furnished & unfurnished suites available. Pets allowed (with approval of Management). More information to be provided upon community opening.
DINING SERVICE: All meals included in fee and served in dining room daily. *Menu choices available:* Breakfast: 10, Lunch: 6, Dinner: 6. *Guest Meals*: Available. *Special Diets*: Vegetarian, Low Salt and Diabetic. Tray service to room if ill (no charge as long as doctor orders). Unlimited snacks available at any time. Party facilities. Open pantry. More information to be provided upon community opening.
AMENITIES AND ACTIVITIES: Parking available (indoor & outdoor, for visitors: free and indoor for residents: $50.00/month). Guest suites available. *Residence has a:* library, visiting library, chapel, barber/beauty shop, visiting hairdresser and laundry room(s) (no cost). Residence provides newspaper delivery to individual suite. Mail delivered to resident. *Recreation Facilities*: pool table, billiards,

shuffleboard, exercise room, greenhouse, craft room, card room and swimming pool. Posted schedule of activities. Internal newsletter for residents. *Recreational Programs*: exercise, shopping, theatre, parties, entertainment, art classes and day trips. More information to be provided upon community.

OTHER SERVICES: *Housekeeping*: weekly. *Laundry*: linen & towel (included in fee). 24-hour security. Nightly security checks. Telephone & Cable TV (extra). Utilities (included in fee). More information to be provided upon community opening.

RENTAL INFORMATION: Rates may vary. Extra cost for 2nd person sharing suite ($700.00/month). Rent paid monthly. *Payment Options*: cheques, direct deposit and pre-authorized payments. Rent increases as per Provincial Tenancy Legislation with 3 months' notice given. Will help resident move into residence. Short-term respite ($120.00/day) and trial stays ($85.00/day) available.

WAWEL VILLA SENIORS RESIDENCE

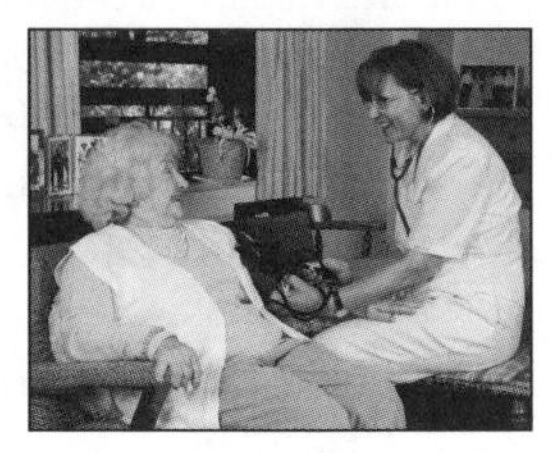

880 Clarkson Road South, Mississauga, ON L5J 4N4
Tel: (905) 823-3650 • Fax: (905) 823-5462
Email: **enquires@wawel.org**
Website: **www.wawel.org**
Contact: **Ted Syposz**
Capacity: **90 residents**
Subsidies: **yes, subject to income**
Price: **$2,520.00 - $3,368.00/month**

European retirement residence with a European heart and light 24-hour nursing care.

RESIDENCE INFORMATION: 33 years in operation. *Near:* Lakeshore Road and Southdown Road. Decorated in 2013. Handrails in hallways. 3 floors, 2 elevators. Wheelchair accessible. Central PA system. *Funding Base:* Not-for-profit. *Owned and managed by:* Wawel Villa Inc. 88 units. *Average Waiting Period*: varies. *Average Age*: 89. Can accommodate cognitively impaired people. Can accommodate physically challenged people (upon approval of Director of Care and Administrator). Smoke-free residence. *Procedures to leave the premises on a temporary basis...*inform Nursing Station and Office. *Languages:* English, Polish & Ukrainian. Will accept Public Guardian and Trustee clients. Main doors of residence secured at all times. *Close to:* Public Transit, Shopping, Churches, Major Highway and Local Hospitals (Trillium Health Partners – Mississauga Hospital Site & Credit Valley Hospital Site & Halton Healthcare Services Corporation – Oakville Site). *Predominant Cultural Group:* 72% Polish. Member of ORCA & Ontario Non Profit Housing Association (ONPHA). Accredited through Accreditation Canada. Licensed under the Retirement Homes Act.

STAFFING: *Available Staff/Services*: Pharmacy, Social Work (CCAC), Recreation Therapy, Occupational Therapy (CCAC), Visiting Dentist, Physiotherapy, Dietitian (CCAC), Podiatry, Chaplaincy and Chiropody. *External services arranged by:* residence and/or family/resident. Staff trained *re*: visually, hearing and cognitively impaired. 24-hour nursing and other staff. RNs, RPNs and PSWs on staff. Visiting MD (twice/week). Can retain own MD. Staff members are bonded. Police Check or Vulnerable Person Screening is done for all new staff.

HEALTH SERVICES: Medication administration (Wawel administers the medication at all times) and/or supervision. Vitals monitored if required. Will accept and provide special assistance for residents who require oxygen, catheters and ostomies. Assistance with dressing available. Weekly assistance with bathing available. *Extra baths:* $10.00/half hour. Care plans done. Different levels of care available. Assisted Living Area is secured to accommodate residents with dementia (2 – 3 weeks waiting period). Lab service (visiting, $7.50/visit). Residents can purchase outside resources and use agency of their choice. MD visits residents in their rooms/suites. Clinic area for medical visits. Will help locate higher level of care if needed (Director of Care & CCAC).

ACCOMMODATION: *Choice of suites available*: private (88) units. *In all suites*: locks, window coverings, light fixtures, linens, fire alarm, smoke detector, sprinkler, call bell, air conditioning (window units) and thermostats for heating & cooling. Private bathrooms with call bells, grab bars, tubs and showers with non-slip surfaces. In-suite cable & satellite TV provided by residence. Can have own phone number if resident arranges with phone company. Furnished suites available on request. *Restrictions on electrical appliances*: no stoves. Suites can be shared (by couples only). Pets allowed (each case considered separately).
DINING SERVICE: All meals included in fee and served in dining room daily. *Sittings per meal:* Breakfast: 1, Lunch: 1, Dinner: 1. *Menu choices available:* Breakfast: 4, Lunch: 2, Dinner: 2. *Guest Meals*: Breakfast $3.00, Lunch $5.00, Dinner $6.00. *Special Diets*: Vegetarian, Low Salt, Diabetic and any other Special Needs. Tray service to room if ill (no charge as long as doctor orders). 2 snacks/day and unlimited snacks available at any time. Party facilities. All meals prepared on-site with European flair.
AMENITIES AND ACTIVITIES: Parking available (outdoor, for visitors and residents). *3 lounges with:* TVs (3) and pianos (2). Guest suites available ($80.00/night). *Residence has a:* library, visiting library, chapel, barber/beauty shop, visiting hairdresser, laundry room(s) (no cost) and tuck/gift shop (open 3:30 p.m. - 4:00 p.m.). Residence provides newspaper delivery to main desk. Mail delivered to dining room. *Recreation Facilities*: shuffleboard, exercise room, greenhouse, craft room and card room. Posted schedule of activities. Internal newsletter for residents. *Recreational Programs*: exercise, shopping, parties, entertainment, pet visiting, day trips and in-house movie afternoons.
OTHER SERVICES: *Housekeeping*: daily (included in fee). *Laundry*: linen & towel (included in fee); personal ($9.00/load). Either staff or resident label clothing (included in fee). Transportation to medical appointments (minimum $6.25 one way) and for group social activities. 24-hour security. Nightly security checks. Telephone (cost depends on plan with provider). Cable TV & Utilities (included in fee). Basic Satellite TV (TV Polonia - included in fee).
RENTAL INFORMATION: Rates may vary. Small room - $2,520.00/month; medium room - $2,700.00/month; large room - $3,368.00/month. Extra cost for 2nd person sharing suite ($1,895.00/month). Rent paid monthly. *Payment Options*: cheques and post-dated cheques. Rent increases are a set percentage indexed to inflation as per Provincial Tenancy Legislation, annual for resident with 3 months' notice given. Will help resident move into residence. Short-term respite and trial stays available (both $80.00/day).

♦ MOUNT FOREST ♦

BIRMINGHAM RETIREMENT COMMUNITY

356A Birmingham Street East, Mount Forest, ON N0G 2L2
Tel: (519) 323-4019 • Fax: (519) 323-3005
Email: **brcmarketing@wightman.ca**
Website: **www.birminghamretirement.ca**
Contact: **Roslyn Fortier**
Capacity: **87 units**
Subsidies: **yes, Through County of Wellington, Social Services Dept.**
Price: **$1,610.00 - $2,810.00/month**

Birmingham Retirement Community is nestled in the heart of Mount Forest. Boasting spacious private rooms, large lounges, and a formal dining room. Homey atmosphere with a small-town feeling. Delicious home-cooked meals with your choice of 2 entrees. Elevator, stairs and ramp access to 3 floors. Free parking is available. Residence van for outings. Live entertainment weekly. Private gardens with walking paths, 2 block walk to downtown with all of the amenities: Tim Horton's, parks, clothing stores, cafés, Home Hardware, dollar store and more. Respite stays available in our fully furnished suites.

RESIDENCE INFORMATION: 22 years in operation. *Near:* Highway 6 and Birmingham Street. Decorated in 2010. Handrails in hallways. 3 floors, 2 elevators. Wheelchair accessible. *Funding Base:* Corporate/for profit. *Owned by:* BayBridge Senior Living. *Managed by:* International Care Management Services. *Average Waiting Period*: varies. *Average Age*: 85. Can sometimes accommodate cognitively impaired people (based on assessment). Can accommodate physically challenged people (wheelchair accessible; scooters outside). Residents have a dress code (no pyjamas or housecoats except in own suite). Smoking allowed (designated smoking area). Alcohol allowed (within resident's rooms). *Restrictions around Visitors/Visiting Hours:* guests must sign in/out. *Procedures to leave the premises on a temporary basis...*Short-term: sign out at Front Desk. Overnight & Holidays: sign out at Front Desk, and notify staff. *Languages:* English. Will accept Public Guardian and Trustee clients. Main doors of residence secured at night only. *Close to:* Shopping, Churches, Seniors' Centre, Library, Major Highway and Local Hospital (North Wellington Health Care Corporation - Louise Marshall Hospital). *Predominant Cultural Group:* Farming Community. Member of Chamber of Commerce. Licensed under the Retirement Homes Act.
STAFFING: *Available Staff/Services*: Pharmacy, Social Work (CCAC), Recreation Therapy, Occupational Therapy (CCAC), Physiotherapy (CCAC), Dietitian (CCAC), Companions, Podiatry (CCAC), Chaplaincy, Speech Pathology (CCAC), Chiropody, Audiology/Hearing Clinic and Hair Salon. *External services arranged by:* residence and/or family/resident. Staff trained *re*: visually, hearing and cognitively impaired. 24-hour staff. RPNs, HCAs and PSWs on staff. Visiting MD (monthly for his patients). Can retain own MD. Police Check or Vulnerable Person Screening is done for all new staff and volunteers.
HEALTH SERVICES: Medication administration and/or supervision. Vitals monitored if required. Will accept and provide special assistance for residents who require oxygen, catheters and ostomies. Assistance with dressing available (cost). Weekly assistance with bathing available. *Extra baths:* $15.00/half hour. Care plans done. Different levels of care available. Private Duty/Extra Care available. Assisted Living Area (1 - 2 months waiting period). Lab service (visiting, $25.00/visit). Residents can purchase outside resources. MD visits residents in their rooms/suites. Will help locate higher level of care if needed (via CCAC).
ACCOMMODATION: Choice of suites available. *In all suites*: locks, storage, window coverings, light fixtures, linens, fire alarm, smoke detector, emergency response system with wearable pendant/bracelet and air conditioning (option of window units in suites at resident cost). Some suites have kitchenettes. Central air conditioning in common rooms. Bathrooms (subsidized rooms share bathroom amongst 2 same gender residents) with grab bars, tubs and showers. In-suite cable TV if resident arranges with cable company (residence charges extra). Can have own phone number if resident arranges with phone company. Unfurnished suites, furnished suites available for short stays. *Restrictions on electrical appliances*: approval required upon move in; no toaster or toaster ovens. Suites can be shared (by couples only). No pets allowed (residence has pet therapy dogs that visit).
DINING SERVICE: All meals included in fee and served in dining room daily. *Sittings per meal:* Breakfast: 2, Lunch: 2, Dinner: 2. *Menu choices available:* Breakfast: 2, Lunch: 2, Dinner: 2. *Guest Meals*: Lunch $7.00, Dinner $11.00. *Special Diets*: Vegetarian, Low Salt, Diabetic and Others (discuss upon assessment). Tray service to room if ill. 3 snacks/day. Party facilities. Catering available. No charge booking for room rental for resident parties.
AMENITIES AND ACTIVITIES: Parking available (outdoor, for visitors and residents). *4 lounges with:* TVs (2), piano (1) and games tables (1). *Residence has a:* library, barber/beauty shop and tuck/gift shop (upon request). Resident can arrange newspaper delivery to individual suite (extra cost). Mail delivered to main desk. *Recreation Facilities*: exercise room, craft room and card room. Most activities in multipurpose room. Posted schedule of activities. Internal newsletter for residents. *Recreational Programs*: exercise, shopping, theatre, parties, entertainment, pet visiting, day trips, baking, gardening and game nights.
OTHER SERVICES: *Housekeeping*: daily and weekly (extra cost if more frequent than weekly). *Laundry*: linen & towel (included in fee); personal (extra cost if excessive amounts) & dry cleaning (resident required to arrange). Transportation to medical appointments (extra fee per VON) and for group social activities (for some activities). 24-hour security. Nightly security checks (extra cost). Telephone & Cable TV (extra cost per supplier). Utilities (included in fee).

RENTAL INFORMATION: Rates may vary - prices subject to change. Extra cost for 2nd person sharing suite ($500.00/month). Rent paid monthly. *Payment Options*: cheques, post-dated cheques and pre-authorized payments. Rent increases as per Provincial Tenancy Legislation, annual for resident with 3 months' notice given. Short-term respite and trial stays available (both $74.00/day).

NEPEAN

CRYSTAL VIEW LODGE
LYNWOOD PARK LODGE RETIREMENT RESIDENCE
THE COURT AT BARRHAVEN

Please see OTTAWA REGION (NEPEAN) for information on these residences.

◆ NEWMARKET ◆

THE ROXBOROUGH

1 Roxborough Road, Newmarket, ON L3Y 2P8
Tel: (905) 853-4573 • Fax: (905) 853-4928
Email: **mktg1.rox@diversicare.ca**
Website: **www.theroxborough.ca**
Contact: **Marketing Manager**
Capacity: **160 residents** • Subsidies: **none**
Price: **$2,795.17 - $5,330.17/month**

The Roxborough Retirement Residence is located in Newmarket across from Southlake Regional Health Centre. This seven-storey building has 148 suites ranging from studio to 2-bedrooms. We offer Independent and Full Service Lifestyle Packages. Extra care services are available. **The Roxborough is owned/managed by Diversicare, who is the proud recipient of the 2003, 2006, 2009 and 2012 Order of Excellence Award given by Excellence Canada.** This award was received for the exceptional quality and customer service we provide to our residents every day.

RESIDENCE INFORMATION: *On:* Roxborough Road and Davis Drive. Decorated in 2010. Handrails in hallways. 7 floors, 3 elevators. Wheelchair accessible. *Funding Base:* Corporate/for profit. *Owned by:* Diversicare Canada Management Services Co., Inc. 148 units. *Average Waiting Period*: none. *Average Age*: 83. Can accommodate cognitively impaired & physically challenged people (assessment required by RN). Smoke-free residence. Alcohol allowed. *Languages:* English. Will accept Public Guardian and Trustee clients. Main doors of residence secured at night only. *Close to:* Public Transit, Shopping, Churches, Synagogues, Seniors' Centre, Library, Major Highway and Local Hospital (Southlake Regional Health Centre). Member of ORCA. Licensed under the Retirement Homes Act.
STAFFING: *Available Staff/Services*: Pharmacy, Social Work, Recreation Therapy, Occupational Therapy, Physiotherapy, Dietitian, Podiatry, Chaplaincy, Speech Pathology and Audiology/Hearing Clinic. *External services arranged by:* residence and/or family/resident. Staff trained *re*: visually, hearing and cognitively impaired. 24-hour staff. RNs, RPNs, PSWs and UCPs on staff. Visiting MD (weekly). Can retain own MD. Staff members are bonded. Police Check or Vulnerable Person Screening is done for all new staff.
HEALTH SERVICES: Medication administration and/or supervision. Vitals monitored if required. Will accept (but not provide special assistance for) residents who require oxygen, catheters, ostomies and feeding tubes. Assistance with dressing available (cost). Assistance with bathing available as needed (cost). Care plans done. Different levels of care available. Lab service (visiting). Residents can purchase outside resources and use agency of their choice. MD visits residents in their rooms/suites. Clinic area for

medical visits. Will help locate higher level of care if needed (nursing staff will work with physician and CCAC to help find an appropriate care facility).

ACCOMMODATION: *Choice of suites available*: studio, 1-bedroom, 1-bedroom + den, 2-bedroom & 2-bedroom + den suites. *In all suites*: locks, kitchenette, bar fridge, patio/balcony, window coverings, light fixtures, fire alarm, smoke detector, sprinkler, call bell, emergency response system with wearable pendant/bracelet, air conditioning (central) and thermostats for heating & cooling. Private bathrooms with call bells, grab bars, showers with non-slip surfaces and elevated toilet seats. In-suite satellite TV provided by residence, cable if resident arranges with cable company. Can have own phone number if resident arranges with phone company. Unfurnished suites, furnished suites available for short stays. Suites can be shared (by couples only). Small pets allowed.

DINING SERVICE: All meals included in fee and served in dining room daily. *Menu choices available:* Lunch: 2, Dinner: 2. *Guest Meals*: Lunch $8.00, Dinner $15.00. *Special Diets*: Vegetarian, Low Salt and Diabetic. Tray service to room if ill (no charge as long as doctor orders). Unlimited snacks available at any time. Party facilities. Open seating.

AMENITIES AND ACTIVITIES: Parking available (indoor, for visitors: free and residents: $50.00/month). *3 lounges with:* TVs (2) and piano (1). Guest suites available. *Residence has a:* library, chapel, barber/beauty shop, visiting hairdresser, laundry room(s) (no cost) and tuck/gift shop. Resident can arrange newspaper delivery to individual suite. Mail delivered to private mailbox with key. *Recreation Facilities*: pool table, billiards, shuffleboard, exercise room, craft room, card room, courtyard for gardening and a walking path. Posted schedule of activities. Internal newsletter for residents. *Recreational Programs*: exercise, shopping, theatre, parties, entertainment, art classes, pet visiting, day trips and Brain Gym® & More Program.

OTHER SERVICES: *Housekeeping*: weekly. *Laundry*: linen & towel (included in fee); personal ($20.00/load). Transportation for group social activities. 24-hour security. Nightly security checks. Telephone & Cable TV (extra cost). Utilities (included in fee).

RENTAL INFORMATION: Rates may vary. Studio - $2,795.17 to $3,120.17/month; 1-bedroom - $3,310.17 to $4,355.17/month; 1-bedroom + den - $3,925.17 to $4,440.17/month; 2-bedroom - $4,665.17 to $4,715.17/month; 2-bedroom + den - $5,280.17 to $5,330.17/month. Extra cost for 2nd person sharing suite ($700.00/month). Rent paid monthly. *Payment Options*: cheques, post-dated cheques and pre-authorized payments. Rent increases as per Provincial Tenancy Legislation, annual for resident with 3 months' notice given. Will help resident move into residence. Short-term respite and trial stays available (both $125.00/day; double occupancy is $150.00/day).

♦ NIAGARA FALLS ♦

CAVENDISH MANOR RETIREMENT RESIDENCE

5781 Dunn Street, Niagara Falls, ON L2G 2N9
Tel: (905) 354-2733 • Fax: (905) 354-4164
Email: **info.cavendish@diversicare.ca**
Website: **www.diversicare.ca**
Contact: **Marketing Manager**
Capacity: **89 residents** • Subsidies: **none**
Price: **$1,713.00 - $2,693.00/month**

At Cavendish Manor the bus stops right at our front door. Shopping, churches and community activities are nearby. Outside you can relax in the courtyard, and indoors are a variety of amenities to make life enjoyable. We offer a stimulating new program called Brain Gym® & More. Our dining room features a tasty nutritious menu each day. With weekly or daily housekeeping, a visiting physician, and visiting lab service to support your independence, living at Cavendish Manor means living with peace of mind.

Cavendish Manor is the recipient of the 2009 Award of Excellence from the Ontario Retirement Communities Association ORCA. **Cavendish Manor is owned by Diversicare, who is the proud recipient of the 2003, 2006, 2009 and 2012 Order of Excellence Award given by Excellence Canada.** This award was received for the exceptional quality and customer service we provide to our residents every day.

RESIDENCE INFORMATION: 27 years in operation. *Near:* Drummond Street and Dunn Street. Decorated in 2008. Handrails in hallways. 3 floors, 1 elevator. Wheelchair accessible. Central PA system. *Funding Base:* Corporate/for profit. *Owned by:* Diversicare Canada Management Services Co., Inc. 69 units. *Average Waiting Period*: none. *Average Age*: 82. Can accommodate cognitively impaired people with restrictions (assessment required). Can accommodate physically challenged people (assessment required). Residents have a dress code (must dress for all meals). Smoking allowed (outdoors). Alcohol allowed. *Procedures to leave the premises on a temporary basis*...notify staff & sign out. *Languages:* English. Will accept Public Guardian and Trustee clients. Main doors of residence secured at night only. *Close to:* Public Transit, Shopping, Churches, Seniors' Centre, Library, Major Highway and Local Hospital (Niagara Health System - Greater Niagara General Hospital Site). Member of ORCA & Chamber of Commerce. Licensed under the Retirement Homes Act.
STAFFING: *Available Staff/Services*: Pharmacy, Social Work, Recreation Therapy, Occupational Therapy, Physiotherapy, Dietitian, Podiatry, Chaplaincy, Speech Pathology and Chiropody. *External services arranged by:* family/resident. Staff trained *re*: visually, hearing and cognitively impaired. 24-hour nursing staff. RNs, RPNs, HCAs, PSWs and UCPs on staff. Visiting MD (every Tuesday). Can retain own MD. Police Check or Vulnerable Person Screening is done for all new staff.
HEALTH SERVICES: Medication administration and/or supervision. Vitals monitored if required. Will accept (but not provide special assistance for) residents who require catheters and ostomies. Will accept and provide special assistance for residents who require oxygen. Assistance with dressing available (cost). Weekly assistance with bathing available ($80.00/month). *Extra baths:* $20.00/bath. Care plans done. Different levels of care available. Private Duty/Extra Care available ($390.00 to $690.00/month). Lab service (visiting, $20.00/visit). Residents can purchase outside resources and use agency of their choice. MD visits residents in their rooms/suites. Clinic area for medical visits. Will help locate higher level of care if needed (via CCAC).
ACCOMMODATION: *Choice of suites available*: private & semi-private suites. *In all suites*: locks, light fixtures, linens, fire alarm, smoke detector, sprinkler, call bell, air conditioning (central & window units) and thermostats for heating. Private bathrooms with call bells, grab bars, tubs and showers with non-slip surfaces. In-suite cable TV if resident arranges with cable company. Can have own phone number if resident arranges with phone company. Unfurnished suites, furnished suites available for short stays. *Restrictions on electrical appliances*: no toasters, hot plates or microwaves. Suites can be shared, roommate picked by resident & residence staff. Small pets allowed.
DINING SERVICE: All meals included in fee and served in dining room daily. *Sittings per meal:* Breakfast: 2, Lunch: 2, Dinner: 2. *Menu choices available:* Breakfast: 4, Lunch: 2, Dinner: 2. *Guest Meals*: Breakfast $6.00, Lunch $7.50, Dinner $8.50. *Special Diets*: Vegetarian, Low Salt and Diabetic. Tray service to room if ill (no charge as long as doctor orders). 1 snack/day. Party facilities. Specialty dinners served on all special occasions. Outdoor BBQ's during the summer.
AMENITIES AND ACTIVITIES: Parking available (outdoor, for visitors and residents). *2 lounges with:* TVs (2) and piano (1). Guest suites available ($50.00/night). *Residence has a:* library, chapel, barber/beauty shop and tuck/gift shop. Mail delivered to dining room. *Recreation Facilities*: exercise room, craft room and card room. Posted schedule of activities. Internal newsletter for residents. *Recreational Programs*: exercise, shopping, theatre, parties, entertainment, pet visiting, day trips and Brain Gym® & More programs.
OTHER SERVICES: *Housekeeping*: daily (included in fee). *Laundry*: linen, towel & personal (included in fee). Transportation for group social activities. 24-hour security. Nightly security checks. Telephone & Cable TV (extra cost). Utilities (included in fee).

RENTAL INFORMATION: Rates may vary. Cost for sharing suite - fee is per person. Rent paid monthly. *Payment Options*: pre-authorized payments. Rent increases as per Provincial Tenancy Legislation, annual for resident with 3 months' notice given. Short-term respite and trial stays available (both semi-private - $35.00/day; private - $50.00/day).

REVERA - LUNDY MANOR

7860 Lundy's Lane, Niagara Falls, ON L2H 1H1
Tel: (855) 573-8372 • Toll Free: (855) 573-8372
Email: **lundy@reveraliving.com**
Website: **www.reveraliving.com/lundy**
Contact: **Executive Director or Lifestyle Consultant**
Capacity: **96 residents** • Subsidies: **none**
Price: **$2,295.00/month and up**

Keep living your life, your way, at Lundy Manor. Here, you'll find the range of services, amenities and choices that fit your lifestyle and requirements – all in a warm and safe environment. With retirement living at Lundy Manor, you change your address, not your life. Located in Niagara Falls our residence truly reflects our community – elegant yet informal, energetic yet relaxed. Everything is designed to enable you to maintain your independence and privacy, enjoy a full social life, and participate in the activities that you love. Our caring and friendly staff, as well as appealing accommodations support who you are and how you want to live. We are conveniently close to shopping, restaurants, medical services, public transportation, and more. Explore what we have to offer, to keep you living in freedom and comfort. *Lundy Manor is part of the Revera family, one of North America's leading and most trusted providers of seniors' accommodation, care and services since 1961.*

RESIDENCE INFORMATION: 22 years in operation. *Near:* Montrose Road and Kalar Road. Decorated in 2010. Handrails in hallways. 3 floors, 1 elevator. Wheelchair accessible. *Funding Base:* Corporate/for profit. *Owned and managed by:* Revera Inc. 96 units. *Average Waiting Period*: varies. *Average Age*: 84. Can accommodate cognitively impaired & physically challenged people (assessment required). Smoke-free residence. Alcohol allowed. *Procedures to leave the premises on a temporary basis...*Short-term: sign out. Overnight & Holidays: check with nursing staff regarding medication requirements. *Languages:* English. Will accept Public Guardian and Trustee clients. Main doors of residence secured at night only. *Close to:* Public Transit, Shopping, Major Highway and Local Hospital (Niagara Health System - Greater Niagara General Hospital Site). Member of ORCA. Licensed under the Retirement Homes Act.
STAFFING: *Available Staff/Services*: Pharmacy, Social Work, Recreation Therapy, Occupational Therapy, Physiotherapy (CCAC), Dietitian, Companions, Podiatry, Speech Pathology, Chiropody and Audiology/Hearing Clinic. *External services arranged by:* family/resident. Staff trained *re*: visually, hearing and cognitively impaired. 24-hour nursing staff. RPNs, HCAs, PSWs and UCPs on staff. Visiting MD (house physician - as required). Can retain own MD. Police Check or Vulnerable Person Screening is done for all new staff.
HEALTH SERVICES: Medication administration and/or supervision. Vitals monitored if required. Will accept and provide special assistance for residents who require oxygen, catheters and ostomies. Assistance with dressing available (cost). Assistance with bathing available as needed (cost). Care plans done. Different levels of care available. Lab service (visiting). Residents can purchase outside resources and use agency of their choice. MD visits residents in their rooms/suites. Will help locate higher level of care if needed (family conference arranged to determine future care needs).
ACCOMMODATION: *Choice of suites available*: private studios & suites. *In all suites*: locks, window coverings, light fixtures, linens, fire alarm, smoke detector, sprinkler, call bell, emergency response system with wearable pendant/bracelet, air conditioning (incremental units) and thermostats for heating

& cooling. Private bathrooms with call bells, grab bars, showers with non-slip surfaces and elevated toilet seats. In-suite cable TV provided by residence (residence charges extra). Can have own phone number provided by residence (residence charges extra). Unfurnished suites, furnished suites available for short stays. *Restrictions on electrical appliances*: toasters. Suites can be shared, roommate picked by resident. Pets allowed (pending assessment).
DINING SERVICE: All meals included in fee and served in dining room daily. *Sittings per meal:* Breakfast: 3, Lunch: 3, Dinner: 3. *Menu choices available:* Breakfast: 3, Lunch: 2, Dinner: 4. *Guest Meals*: Available. *Special Diets*: Vegetarian, Low Salt, Diabetic and Theme Meals. Tray service to room if ill (no charge as long as doctor orders). 3 snacks/day. Party facilities.
AMENITIES AND ACTIVITIES: Parking available (outdoor, for visitors and residents). *4 lounges with:* TV (1), piano (1) and theatre surround (1). Guest suites available. *Residence has a:* library, chapel and barber/beauty shop. Resident can arrange newspaper delivery to dining room (extra cost). Mail delivered to main desk. *Recreation Facilities*: card room, craft/games room, recreation/activity area, chapel/theatre room and outside patio. Posted schedule of activities. Internal newsletter for residents. *Recreational Programs*: exercise, shopping, parties, entertainment, art classes, pet visiting, day trips, outings and chapel services.
OTHER SERVICES: *Housekeeping*: weekly. *Laundry*: linen, towel & personal (included in fee). Transportation for group social activities. 24-hour security. Telephone & Cable TV (extra cost). Utilities (included in fee).
RENTAL INFORMATION: Rates may vary. Extra cost for 2nd person sharing suite ($500.00/month). Rent paid monthly. *Payment Options*: pre-authorized payments. Rent increases as per Provincial Tenancy Legislation with 3 months' notice given. Will help resident move into residence (extra cost). Short-term respite (assessment required; additional care cost may apply) and trial stays available.

RIVER ROAD RETIREMENT RESIDENCE

4067 River Road, Niagara Falls, ON L2E 3E5
Tel: (905) 374-2015 • Fax: (905) 374-7746
Email: **info@riverroadretirement.com**
Website: **www.riverroadretirement.com**
Contact: **Linda Upham**
Capacity: **120 residents** • Subsidies: **none**
Price: **$1,695.00 - $3,900.00/month**

Overlooking the beauty of the Niagara River and located close to many amenities and services, the River Road Retirement Residence provides the perfect setting to maintain an independent and secure lifestyle in the Niagara Region.

RESIDENCE INFORMATION: 3 years in operation. *Near:* Bridge Street and River Road. Decorated in 2011. Handrails in some of the hallways. 4 floors, 1 elevator. Wheelchair accessible. Central PA system. *Funding Base:* Corporate/for profit. Privately owned. 96 units. *Average Waiting Period*: none. *Average Age*: 80. Can sometimes accommodate cognitively impaired people (mild dementia). Can accommodate physically challenged people (slow mobility; some assistance). Smoking allowed (outdoors). Alcohol allowed. *Procedures to leave the premises on a temporary basis*...Short-term: resident can choose to inform Concierge. Overnight & Holidays: inform Concierge. *Languages:* English. Will accept Public Guardian and Trustee clients. Main doors of residence secured at night only. *Close to:* Public Transit, Shopping, Churches, Synagogues, Seniors' Centre, Library, Major Highway and Local Hospital (Niagara Health System - Greater Niagara General Hospital Site). Member of Chamber of Commerce. Licensed under the Retirement Homes Act.

STAFFING: *Available Staff/Services*: Pharmacy, Social Work, Recreation Therapy, Occupational Therapy, Visiting Dentist, Physiotherapy, Denturist, Dietitian, Companions, Podiatry, Chaplaincy, Speech Pathology, Audiology/Hearing Clinic and Aqua-physio. *External services arranged by:* residence and/or family/resident. Staff trained *re*: visually and hearing impaired. 24-hour nursing and other staff. RPNs, PSWs and UCPs on staff. Visiting MD (as required). Can retain own MD. Staff members are bonded. Police Check or Vulnerable Person Screening is done for all new staff.
HEALTH SERVICES: Medication administered if required. Vitals monitored if required. Will accept and provide special assistance for residents who require oxygen. Assistance with dressing available ($80.00/month). Assistance with bathing available as needed ($80.00/month). *Extra baths:* $15.00/half hour. Care plans done. Different levels of care available. Private Duty/Extra Care available ($20.00 to $25.00/month). Assisted Living Area. Lab service (visiting). Residents can purchase outside resources and use agency of their choice. MD visits residents in their rooms/suites. Clinic area for medical visits. Will help locate higher level of care if needed.
ACCOMMODATION: *Choice of suites available*: private (86) & semi-private (10) units. *In all suites*: locks, kitchenette, bar fridge, storage, window coverings, light fixtures, linens, fire alarm, smoke detector, sprinkler, call bell, Emergency Response System with wearable pendant/bracelet (Lifeline system), air conditioning (central & window units), thermostats for heating & cooling, electric fireplace and Wi-Fi (included). Private bathrooms with call bells, grab bars, tubs and showers with non-slip surfaces and elevated toilet seats. In-suite cable TV provided by residence. Can have own phone extension number provided by residence (residence charges extra). Furnished & unfurnished suites available. *Restrictions on electrical appliances*: CSA approved. Suites can be shared (by couples only). Small pets only allowed.
DINING SERVICE: All meals included in fee and served in dining room daily. *Sittings per meal:* Breakfast: 1, Lunch: 1, Dinner: 1. *Menu choices available:* Breakfast: 2, Lunch: 3, Dinner: 3. *Guest Meals*: Breakfast $6.00, Lunch $12.00, Dinner $12.00. *Special Diets*: Vegetarian, Low Salt and Diabetic. Tray service to room if ill (no charge as long as doctor orders). 3 snacks/day and unlimited snacks available at any time. Party facilities. Private dining room.
AMENITIES AND ACTIVITIES: Parking available (outdoor, for visitors and residents). *2 lounges with:* TVs (2). Guest suites available ($75.00/night). *Residence has a:* library, visiting library, chapel, barber/beauty shop and laundry room(s) (no cost). Resident can arrange newspaper delivery to individual suite (extra cost). Mail delivered to dining room. *Recreation Facilities*: shuffleboard, exercise room, card room and swimming exercise pool. Posted schedule of activities. Internal newsletter for residents. *Recreational Programs*: exercise, shopping, theatre, parties, entertainment, art classes, pet visiting and day trips.
OTHER SERVICES: *Housekeeping*: weekly (included in fee). *Laundry*: linen & towel (included in fee); personal ($10.00/load) & dry cleaning (extra cost). Transportation to medical appointments and for group social activities. 24-hour security. Nightly security checks. Telephone (extra cost; includes100 minutes Long Distance). Cable, Utilities & Lifeline (included in fee).
RENTAL INFORMATION: Rates may vary. Above price range is for single rear view to double 900 sq. ft. living/bedroom/kitchenette units. Extra cost for 2nd person sharing suite ($600.00/month - extra resident meals). Rent paid monthly. *Payment Options*: cheques, post-dated cheques, direct deposit and pre-authorized payments. Rent increases as per Provincial Tenancy Legislation, annual for resident with 3 months' notice given. Will help resident move into residence. Short-term respite ($69.00/day) and trial stays (fee may be waived) available.

Might we suggest...

Regardless of one's age or medical condition, it is important to have up-to-date Powers of Attorney for both Personal Care and Property. To obtain a free Power of Attorney kit visit: **www.attorneygeneral.jus.gov.on.ca/english/family/pgt/poakit.asp.**

STAMFORD ESTATES

3900 Portage Road, Niagara Falls, ON L2J 4L8
Tel: (905) 357-7857 • Fax: (905) 357-1426
Email: **5267-manager@holidaytouch.com**
Website: **www.stamfordestates.net**
Contact: **Community Managers**
Capacity: **115 units** • Subsidies: **none**
Price: **$1,784.00/month and up (rates may vary)**

Holiday Retirement believes retirement living should be relaxing and carefree, spent doing the things you love. That's why our communities provide a unique independent retirement lifestyle in a warm and welcoming environment. In one affordable, all-inclusive month-to-month rent, residents enjoy 3 delicious chef-prepared meals daily, enriching activities to share with friendly neighbours, housekeeping service, complimentary transportation, and so much more. Each Holiday community also features 2 sets of compassionate, dedicated live-in Managers available 24/7 to ensure safety and security. We do not provide any health care services; however, residents are welcome to receive services from any outside home health care provider of their choice to help them continue enjoying life at our community. Discover the peace-of-mind, happiness and fulfillment you deserve. Contact us today to schedule your personal tour!

RESIDENCE INFORMATION: 10 years in operation. *Near:* Thorold Stone Road and Portage Road. Decorated in 2004. Handrails in hallways. 4 floors, 2 elevators. Wheelchair accessible. Central PA system. *Funding Base:* Corporate/for profit. *Owned and managed by:* Holiday Retirement. *Average Waiting Period*: varies. *Average Age*: 83. Can sometimes accommodate cognitively impaired people (must not be at risk). Can accommodate physically challenged people (mobility aids welcome, CCAC homecare available). Residents have a dress code (casual, no sleepwear in common areas). Smoking allowed (in own apartment). Alcohol allowed (self-governed, in own apartment). *Procedures to leave the premises on a temporary basis...* Overnight & Holidays: let Front Office know. *Languages:* English. Will accept Public Guardian and Trustee clients. Main doors of residence secured at night only. *Close to:* Public Transit, Shopping, Churches, Synagogues, Seniors' Centre, Library, Major Highway and Local Hospital (Niagara Health System).
STAFFING: *Available Staff/Services*: Social Work (CCAC), Recreation Therapy, Occupational Therapy (CCAC), Physiotherapy (CCAC), Dietitian (CCAC), Podiatry (CCAC), Speech Pathology (CCAC) and Audiology/Hearing Clinic. *External services arranged by:* family/resident. 24-hour staff. Can retain own MD. Staff members are bonded. Police Check or Vulnerable Person Screening is done for all new staff.
HEALTH SERVICES: Will accept (but not provide special assistance for) residents who require oxygen, catheters, ostomies and feeding tubes. Residents can purchase outside resources and use agency of their choice.
ACCOMMODATION: *Choice of suites available*: different styles and sizes of studio, 1-bedroom & 2-bedroom suites. *In all suites*: locks, kitchenette, full fridge with freezer, window coverings, light fixtures, linens, fire alarm, smoke detector, sprinkler, call bell, Emergency Response System with wearable pendant/bracelet, air conditioning (wall unit) and thermostats for heating & cooling. Most apartments have balconies. Private bathrooms with call bells and showers with non-slip surfaces. In-suite cable TV provided by residence. Can have own phone number if resident arranges with phone company. Furnished & unfurnished suites available. *Restrictions on electrical appliances*: no stoves or hot plates. Suites can be shared, roommate picked by resident. Pets allowed.
DINING SERVICE: All meals included in fee and served in dining room daily. *Sittings per meal:* Breakfast: 1, Lunch: 1, Dinner: 1. *Menu choices available:* Breakfast: 6, Lunch: 6, Dinner: 6. *Guest Meals*: Breakfast $8.00, Lunch $10.00, Dinner $8.00. *Special Diets*: Vegetarian, Low Salt and Diabetic. Tray service to room if ill (no charge or restrictions). 2 snacks/day. Party facilities. Fresh fruit, coffee, tea & goodies available all day.

AMENITIES AND ACTIVITIES: Parking available (outdoor, for visitors and indoor & outdoor for residents). *7 lounges with:* TVs (2), pianos (3), computer kiosks (1) and billiards room (1). Guest suites available ($75.00/night). *Residence has a:* library, chapel, barber/beauty shop and laundry room(s) (no cost). Resident can arrange newspaper delivery to individual suite. Mail delivered to private mailbox with key. *Recreation Facilities*: pool table, billiards, shuffleboard, exercise room, craft room, card room and private dining room for entertaining. Posted schedule of activities. Internal newsletter for residents. *Recreational Programs*: exercise, shopping, theatre, parties, entertainment, art classes, pet visiting, day trips and resident suggestions.
OTHER SERVICES: *Housekeeping*: weekly (included in fee). *Laundry*: linen & towel (included in fee). Free laundry rooms for personal use. Transportation to medical appointments and for group social activities. 24-hour security. Telephone (resident obtains own phone number). Cable TV & Utilities (included in fee). Parking (charge for indoor only).
RENTAL INFORMATION: Rates may vary. Rate listed above is based on single occupancy. Extra cost for 2nd person sharing suite ($660.00/month; please call for specifics). Rent paid monthly. *Payment Options*: cheques and pre-authorized payments. Rent increases indexed to inflation as per Provincial Tenancy Legislation, annual for resident with 3 months' notice given. Will help resident move into residence. Trial stays available (see Managers).

◆ NORTH BAY ◆

MARINA POINT

225 Oak Street, North Bay, ON P1B 0A9
Tel: (705) 474-9494 • Fax: (705) 474-9467
Email: **bbosselle@autumnwood.ca**
Website: **www.autumnwood.ca**
Contact: **Becky Bosselle**
Capacity: **123 units** • Subsidies: **none**
Price: **$1,975.00 - $4,450.00/month**

Marina Point Village has the spectacular view of Lake Nipissing and is in walking distance to the downtown core. It is close to public transportation, banking, shopping, restaurants, churches and other community amenities. With this in mind, many seniors are choosing to seek a new and different lifestyle; a lifestyle that allows them to remain independent and still enjoy all the things they love while living in a supportive community.

RESIDENCE INFORMATION: 7 years in operation. *Near:* Oak Street and Cassells Avenue. 3 floors, 3 elevators. Wheelchair accessible. Central PA system. *Funding Base:* Corporate/for profit. *Owned and managed by:* Autumnwood Mature Lifestyle Communities. *Average Waiting Period*: none. *Average Age*: 82. Can accommodate cognitively impaired people with restrictions. Can accommodate physically challenged people. Smoking allowed (outside). Alcohol allowed. *Procedures to leave the premises on a temporary basis...*give notification to the Front Desk. *Languages:* English & French. Main doors of residence secured at all times. *Close to:* Public Transit, Shopping, Churches, Seniors' Centre, Major Highway and Local Hospital. Licensed under the Retirement Homes Act.
STAFFING: *Available Staff/Services*: Pharmacy, Social Work (CCAC), Recreation Therapy, Occupational Therapy (CCAC), Physiotherapy (CCAC), Podiatry (CCAC), Chaplaincy, Speech Pathology (CCAC), Chiropody and Audiology/Hearing Clinic. *External services arranged by:* family/resident. Staff trained *re*: visually, hearing and cognitively impaired. 24-hour nursing and other staff. RNs, RPNs and PSWs on staff. Can retain own MD. Police Check or Vulnerable Person Screening is done for all new staff.

HEALTH SERVICES: Medication administration and/or supervision. Vitals monitored if required. Will accept (but not provide special assistance for) residents who require oxygen, catheters, ostomies and feeding tubes. Assistance with dressing available. Weekly assistance with bathing available. *Extra baths:* $15.00/bath. Care plans done. Private Duty/Extra Care available ($20.00 to $25.00/hour). Assisted Living Area. Lab service (visiting). Residents can purchase outside resources and use agency of their choice. Clinic area for medical visits. Will help locate higher level of care if needed (work with CCAC and refer to long-term care).
ACCOMMODATION: Choice of suites available. *In all suites*: storage, window coverings, light fixtures, fire alarm, smoke detector, sprinkler, air conditioning (window units) and thermostats for heating & cooling. Private bathrooms with call bells, grab bars, tubs and showers with non-slip surfaces. Unfurnished suites. No pets allowed.
DINING SERVICE: All meals included in fee and served in dining room daily. *Sittings per meal:* Breakfast: 1, Lunch: 1, Dinner: 1. *Menu choices available:* Lunch: 2, Dinner: 2. *Guest Meals*: Breakfast $8.00, Lunch $10.00, Dinner $15.00. *Special Diets*: Vegetarian, Low Salt, Diabetic, Lactose Free and Gluten Free. Tray service to room if ill (no charge or restrictions). Unlimited snacks available at any time. The servery/pantry is self-serve daily. Party facilities. Continental breakfast in the morning.
AMENITIES AND ACTIVITIES: Parking available (outdoor, for visitors and residents). *4 lounges with:* TV (1) and piano (1). Guest suites available ($85.00/night). *Residence has a:* library, barber/beauty shop and laundry room(s) (no cost). Resident can arrange newspaper delivery to individual suite. Mail delivered to private mailbox with key. *Recreation Facilities*: pool table, craft room and card room. Posted schedule of activities. *Recreational Programs*: exercise, shopping, theatre, parties, entertainment, art classes, pet visiting and day trips.
OTHER SERVICES: *Housekeeping*: weekly (included in fee). *Laundry*: linen & towel (included in fee); personal (purchase service). Transportation for group social activities. 24-hour security. Nightly security checks. Telephone & Cable TV (extra cost). Utilities (included in fee).
RENTAL INFORMATION: Rates may vary. There is a large variety of styles, sizes and amenities available that influence price. Extra cost for 2nd person sharing suite ($650.00/month). Rent paid monthly. *Payment Options*: pre-authorized payments. 3 months' notice given for rent increases. Short-term respite and trial stays available (both $75.00/day; the cost depends on the size of suite selected & if there is a second person).

THE EMPIRE

425 Fraser Street, North Bay, ON P1B 3X1
Tel: (705) 474-9555 • Fax: (705) 474-9827
Email: **asavard@theempire.ca**
Website: **www.theempire.ca**
Contact: **Ariane Savard**
Capacity: **158 residents**
Subsidies: **for Veterans only**

The Empire is an historical North Bay Landmark that offers health and wellness options required to maintain an independent lifestyle in your home. We emphasize delicious meals, full activity and social schedules as well as entertainment, exercise and health monitoring programs.

RESIDENCE INFORMATION: 16 years in operation. *Near:* Main Street and McIntyre Street. Decorated in 2013. Handrails in hallways. 5 floors, 3 elevators. Wheelchair accessible. Central PA system. *Funding Base:* Corporate/for profit. *Owned by:* Retirement Living Centres. 158 units. *Average Waiting Period*: none. *Average Age*: 80. Can accommodate cognitively impaired & physically challenged people. Smoking allowed (designated outdoors). Alcohol allowed. *Procedures to leave the premises on a temporary basis*...notify staff. *Languages:* English & French. Will accept Public Guardian and Trustee clients. Main

doors of residence secured at night only. *Close to:* Public Transit, Shopping, Churches, Synagogues, Seniors' Centre, Library, Major Highway and Local Hospital (North Bay Regional Health Centre). Member of ORCA. Licensed under the Retirement Homes Act.

STAFFING: *Available Staff/Services*: Pharmacy, Social Work (CCAC), Recreation Therapy, Occupational Therapy (CCAC), Physiotherapy (CCAC), Dietitian (CCAC), Companions, Podiatry (CCAC), Chaplaincy, Speech Pathology (CCAC) and 24-hour Health Care Aides. Staff trained *re*: visually, hearing and cognitively impaired. 24-hour nursing staff. RPNs and PSWs on staff. Visiting MD (every 2 weeks). Can retain own MD.

HEALTH SERVICES: Medication administration and/or supervision. Vitals monitored if required. Will accept (but not provide special assistance for) residents who require ostomies. Will accept and provide special assistance for residents who require oxygen and catheters. Assistance with dressing available ($25.00/hour). Assistance with bathing available as needed ($25.00/hour). Residents can purchase outside resources and use agency of their choice. Clinic area for medical visits. Will help locate higher level of care if needed (via CCAC).

ACCOMMODATION: *Choice of suites available*: bedsitting, 1-bedroom & 2-bedroom units. *In all suites*: locks, kitchenette, bar fridge (limited quantity), storage, window coverings, light fixtures, smoke detector, sprinkler, call bell, air conditioning (window units) and thermostats for heating & cooling. Private bathrooms with call bells, grab bars, tubs and showers with non-slip surfaces and elevated toilet seats. In-suite cable TV if resident arranges with cable company (residence charges extra). Can have own phone extension number provided by residence (residence charges extra $20.00/month). Unfurnished suites, furnished suites available for short stays. *Restrictions on electrical appliances*: toasters, kettles and microwaves only. Suites can be shared (by couples only). Pets allowed (quiet animals only).

DINING SERVICE: All meals included in fee and served in dining room daily. *Sittings per meal:* Breakfast: 3, Lunch: 3, Dinner: 3. *Menu choices available:* Breakfast: 2, Lunch: 2, Dinner: 2. *Guest Meals*: Breakfast $6.00, Lunch $8.00, Dinner $12.00. *Special Diets*: Vegetarian, Low Salt, Diabetic and Doctor Ordered. Tray service to room if ill. 3 snacks/day. Open pantry. Party facilities. For private dining, chef will make food as per residents' recipes if desired.

AMENITIES AND ACTIVITIES: Parking available (outdoor for residents: $20.00/month). *4 lounges with:* TV (1), piano (1), ball room (1) and games room (1). Guest suites available ($100.00/night). *Residence has a:* library, chapel, barber/beauty shop, visiting hairdresser, laundry room(s) (no cost) and tuck/gift shop (open daily, 1:00 p.m. – 4:00 p.m.). Resident can arrange newspaper delivery to individual suite (extra cost). Mail delivered to private mailbox with key. *Recreation Facilities*: pool table, billiards, shuffleboard, exercise room, card room and backyard gazebo. Posted schedule of activities. Internal newsletter for residents. *Recreational Programs*: exercise, shopping, theatre, parties, entertainment, art classes, pet visiting and day trips.

OTHER SERVICES: *Housekeeping*: weekly. *Laundry*: personal ($50.00/month). Transportation for group social activities. 24-hour security. Nightly security checks. Utilities (included in fee).

RENTAL INFORMATION: Prices are available by contacting the Relationship Manager. Extra cost for 2nd person sharing suite. Rent paid monthly. *Payment Options*: direct deposit and pre-authorized payments. Rent increases as per Provincial Tenancy Legislation, annual for resident with 3 months' notice given. Short-term respite and trial stays available (cost depends on size available).

Did you know?

You can find out about upcoming Seniors Events including seminars for seniors in your area by visiting **www.seniors.gov.on.ca/en/events/index.php.**

NORTH YORK

BAYBRIDGE – KENSINGTON PLACE RETIREMENT RESIDENCE
CANTERBURY PLACE RETIREMENT RESIDENCE
DELMANOR NORTHTOWN
DELMANOR WYNFORD
GREENVIEW LODGE SENIOR CARE RESIDENCE
L'CHAIM RETIREMENT HOMES INC.
REVERA – DON MILLS SENIORS' APARTMENTS
REVERA – DONWAY PLACE
REVERA – RAYOAK PLACE
REVERA – TERRACE GARDENS

Please see TORONTO (NORTH YORK) for information on these residences.

◆ OAKVILLE ◆

DELMANOR GLEN ABBEY

1459 Nottinghill Gate, Oakville, ON L6M 4W1
Tel: (905) 469-3232 • Fax: (905) 469-7495
Email: **KBristow@delmanor.com**
Website: **www.delmanor.com**
Contact: **Kelley Bristow**
Capacity: **135 residents** • Subsidies: **none**
Price: **$3,295.00 - $6,345.00/month**

Award-winning Tridel-inspired retirement community located near the prestigious Glen Abbey golf course. Attentive, caring staff support an active and independent lifestyle. Delmanor Glen Abbey's low-rise, intimate, manor-style building offers superior dining with white linens, fine china and a private dining room for entertaining family and friends. Living***Well*** personal coaching program is individualized just for you. Registered nursing staff available 24/7 with Assisted Living Regal Services. In-suite safety and personal security monitoring. Lush, manicured grounds, a putting green, private courtyards, spa, home theatre/chapel, conservatory, library, internet and fireplace lounges for your enjoyment. You'll also enjoy many planned excursions in our exclusive Delmanor bus.

RESIDENCE INFORMATION: 10 years in operation. *Near:* Upper Middle Road and Nottinghill Gate. Decorated in 2013. Handrails in hallways. 3 floors, 2 elevators. Wheelchair accessible. Central PA system. *Funding Base:* Corporate/for profit. *Owned by:* Tridel Corporation. *Managed by:* Delmanor Seniors Communities Inc. 112 units. *Average Waiting Period*: varies. *Average Age*: 84. Can sometimes accommodate cognitively impaired people (we are not staffed for residents who wander). Can accommodate physically challenged people (we do accept walkers, scooter parking). Residents have a dress code (appropriate attire in common areas). Smoke-free residence. Alcohol allowed (licensed residence). *Procedures to leave the premises on a temporary basis...*advise Concierge/Nurse. *Languages:* English, Polish, Hungarian, Spanish & German. Will accept Public Guardian and Trustee clients. Main doors of residence secured at night only. *Close to:* Public Transit, Shopping, Churches, Seniors' Centre, Library, Major Highway and Local Hospital (Halton Healthcare Services Corporation – Oakville Site). Member of ORCA & Oakville Chamber of Commerce. Licensed under the Retirement Homes Act.
STAFFING: *Available Staff/Services*: Pharmacy, Recreation Therapy, Occupational Therapy, Visiting Dentist, Physiotherapy, Dietitian, Chaplaincy, Chiropody, Audiology/Hearing Clinic and Registered Massage Therapist. *External services arranged by:* residence and/or family/resident. Staff trained *re*:

visually and hearing impaired. 24-hour nursing and other staff. RPNs and PSWs on staff. Visiting MD (bi-weekly). Can retain own MD. Police Check (required for all staff) or Vulnerable Person Screening is done for all new staff.
HEALTH SERVICES: Medication administration and/or supervision (no sliding scales for Diabetics). Vitals monitored if required. Will accept and provide special assistance for residents who require oxygen. Assistance with dressing available (cost). Assistance with bathing available as needed (cost). Care plans done. Different levels of care available. Private Duty/Extra Care available. Assisted Living Area ($775.00/month). Lab service (visiting). Residents can purchase outside resources and use agency of their choice. MD visits residents in their rooms/suites. Clinic area for medical visits. Will help locate higher level of care if needed (staff members are familiar with local long-term care residences).
ACCOMMODATION: *Choice of suites available*: studio, 1-bedroom & 2-bedroom suites. *In all suites*: locks, kitchenette, fridges with separate freezer, microwave, window coverings, light fixtures, fire alarm, smoke detector, sprinkler, call bell, Emergency Response System with wearable pendant/bracelet, air conditioning (central air & in-suite unit) and thermostats for heating & cooling. Private bathrooms with call bells, grab bars, showers and elevated toilet seats. In-suite cable TV provided by residence. Can have own phone number provided by residence. Unfurnished suites, furnished suites available for short stays. *Restrictions on electrical appliances*: no stoves, electric grills/fry pans or hot plates. Suites can be shared (by couples only). Pets allowed (maximum 20 lbs.; residents must sign Pet Waiver).
DINING SERVICE: All meals included in fee and served in dining room daily. *Sittings per meal:* Breakfast: 1, Lunch: 2, Dinner: 2. *Menu choices available:* Lunch: 3, Dinner: 3. *Guest Meals*: Breakfast $5.50, Lunch $11.00, Dinner $17.00. *Special Diets*: Vegetarian, Low Salt and Diabetic. Alternative menu selections & 5 week seasonal menu. Tray service to room if ill (no charge as long as doctor orders). 3 snacks/day. Party facilities. Continental breakfast provided in café which is open from 8:00 a.m. Fairway Dining Room offers a full hot breakfast.
AMENITIES AND ACTIVITIES: Parking available (outdoor, for visitors: free and residents: $30.00/month). *5 lounges with:* TVs (4) and piano (1). Guest suites available. *Residence has a:* library, chapel, barber/beauty shop, visiting hairdresser, laundry room(s) (no cost) and tuck/gift shop (open Tuesday; 3:00 p.m. - 4:00 p.m.). Banking services on premises (bi-weekly). Resident can arrange newspaper delivery to individual suite. Mail delivered to Concierge. *Recreation Facilities*: pool table, billiards, shuffleboard, exercise room, greenhouse, craft room, card room, theatre, chapel and putting green. Posted schedule of activities. Internal newsletter for residents. *Recreational Programs*: exercise, shopping, theatre, parties, entertainment, art classes, pet visiting, day trips and guest speakers.
OTHER SERVICES: *Housekeeping*: weekly (included in fee). *Laundry*: linen & towel (included in fee); personal ($88.00/month/person) & dry cleaning (weekly pick and return service by outside company). Transportation for group social activities. 24-hour security. Nightly security checks. Telephone, Cable TV & Utilities (included in fee).
RENTAL INFORMATION: Rates may vary. Starting from: Studio - $3,445.00/month; 1-bedroom - $4,275.00/month; 2-bedroom - $5,195.00/month. Extra cost for 2nd person sharing suite ($775.00/month). Rent paid monthly. *Payment Options*: post-dated cheques and pre-authorized payments. Rent increases as per Provincial Tenancy Legislation, annual for resident with 3 months' notice given. Will help resident move into residence. Short-term respite and trial stays available (both $110.00/day for a maximum of 30 days).

Downsizing Tip

Get a floor plan of the apartment or suite you will be moving into with the exact square footage of the rooms. This will allow you to determine what large items will fit in the space you have.

OAKVILLE SENIOR CITIZENS RESIDENCE

2220-2222 Lakeshore Road West, Oakville, ON L6L 5G5
Tel: (905) 827-4139 • Fax: (905) 827-8047
Email: **oscr@oakvilleseniors.com**
Website: **www.oakvilleseniors.com**
Contact: **Angela Katunas**
Capacity: **172 residents** • Subsidies: **rent is geared to income; subsidies for rent portion available for qualified individuals**
Price: **$445.00 - $1,085.00/month**

Situated by Lake Ontario in Bronte close to attractive shops, restaurants and lakeside walks, OSCR promotes independence, self-determination and choice, both in the apartments and in the residence where seniors remain active and engaged in the community receiving supports for daily living.

RESIDENCE INFORMATION: 42 years in operation. *Near:* Highway 25 and Lakeshore Road. Decorated in 2012. Handrails in hallways. 9 floors, 3 elevators. Central PA system. *Funding Base:* Not-for-profit. *Owned by:* Region of Halton. *Managed by:* Oakville Senior Citizens Residence. 172 units. *Average Waiting Period*: 1 - 2 years. *Average Age*: 86. Can sometimes accommodate cognitively impaired & physically challenged people (will be assessed). Residents have a dress code (must dress for meals). Smoke-free residence. Alcohol allowed (available at Kozy Korner bar hours). *Restrictions around Visitors/Visiting Hours:* main doors of residence are locked 9:00 p.m. to 7:00 a.m., but clients can admit guests. *Procedures to leave the premises on a temporary basis...*Short-term: advise staff only if away at mealtimes. Overnight & Holidays: inform staff. *Languages:* English. Will accept Public Guardian and Trustee clients. Main doors of residence secured at night only. *Close to:* Public Transit, Shopping, Churches, Seniors' Centre, Library, Major Highway and Local Hospital (Halton Healthcare Services Corporation - Oakville Trafalgar Memorial Hospital). *Predominant Cultural Group:* Canadian. Member of OANHSS.
STAFFING: *Available Staff/Services*: Pharmacy, Social Work (CCAC), Recreation Therapy, Occupational Therapy (CCAC), Physiotherapy (CCAC), Dietitian, Podiatry (CCAC), Chaplaincy and Chiropody. PSWs on staff and on-site 24-hours/day. Nursing agency staff on-site. *External services arranged by:* residence and/or family/resident. Staff trained *re*: visually, hearing and cognitively impaired. 24-hour staff. Can retain own MD. Police Check or Vulnerable Person Screening is done for all new staff.
HEALTH SERVICES: Medication administration supervised. Vitals monitored if required. Will accept (but not provide special assistance for) residents who require oxygen, catheters and ostomies. Assistance with dressing available. Weekly assistance with bathing available. Care plans done. Different levels of care available. Assisted Living Area (1 - 2 year waiting period). Lab service (visiting). Residents can purchase outside resources. Clinic area for medical visits. Will help locate higher level of care if needed (on-site CCAC Care Coordinator).
ACCOMMODATION: *Choice of suites available*: all 172 units are private bedsitting rooms with a full private bath and no kitchen. *In all suites*: locks, storage, window coverings, light fixtures, linens, fire alarm, smoke detector and thermostats for heating. Private bathrooms with grab bars, tubs and showers. In-suite cable TV if resident arranges with cable company. Can have own phone number if resident arranges with phone company. Unfurnished suites. *Restrictions on electrical appliances*: kettle must be auto shut-off. No pets allowed.
DINING SERVICE: All meals included in fee and served in dining room daily. *Sittings per meal:* Breakfast: 2, Lunch: 2, Dinner: 2. *Menu choices available:* Breakfast: 1, Lunch: 2, Dinner: 2. *Guest Meals*: Lunch $6.00, Dinner $8.00. *Special Diets*: Vegetarian, Low Salt and Diabetic. Tray service to room if ill. 2 snacks/day. Party facilities.
AMENITIES AND ACTIVITIES: Parking available (outdoor, for visitors: free and indoor & outdoor for residents: $30.00/month). 8 lounges. Guest suites available ($75.00/night). *Residence has a:* library, visiting library, chapel, barber/beauty shop and tuck/gift shop (open 10:00 a.m. - 6:00 p.m.). Banking

services on premises (monthly). Resident can arrange newspaper delivery to individual suite. Mail delivered to private mailbox with key. *Recreation Facilities*: shuffleboard, exercise room, craft room, card room, gardens, patios, bar, gazebo and spiritual centre. Posted schedule of activities. Internal newsletter for residents. *Recreational Programs*: exercise, shopping, theatre, parties, entertainment, art classes, pet visiting and day trips.

OTHER SERVICES: *Housekeeping*: weekly (included in fee). *Laundry*: linen, towel & personal (included in fee). Transportation for group social activities (extra cost varies according to trip). Nightly security checks. Telephone (resident /family arranges with phone company). Cable TV (resident/family arranges with cable company). Utilities (included in fee). Accommodation fee includes meal service, linen service & recreation program.

RENTAL INFORMATION: Rates may vary. Rent is geared to income: 30% of gross income to a maximum rent is $445.00/month + accommodation fee of $640.00/month to a maximum of $1,085.00/month. Rent paid monthly. *Payment Options*: pre-authorized payments. Rent increases: rent geared to income, annual for resident with 3 months' notice given.

REVERA - CHURCHILL PLACE

345 Church Street, Oakville, ON L6J 7G4
Tel: (855) 573-8372 • Toll Free: (855) 573-8372
Email: **churchillplace@reveraliving.com**
Website: **www.reveraliving.com/churchillplace**
Contact: **Executive Director or Lifestyle Consultant**
Capacity: **75 residents** • Subsidies: **none**
Price: **$2,900.00/month and up**

At Churchill Place you'll find the range of services, features and choices that fit your lifestyle and requirements – all in a warm and safe environment. Located in downtown Oakville near Lake Ontario, mature parks and historic homes, Churchill Place has a long standing reputation for exceptional service and is on par with some of the finest boutique hotels. It is also conveniently located near shopping, dining, places of worship, recreation, medical services, the Oakville Centre for the Performing Arts, public library, public transportation, and more. Everything is designed for you to maintain your independence and privacy, enjoy a full social life, and participate in the activities you love. Our caring and friendly staff, along with appealing accommodations, support who you are and how you want to live. *Churchill Place is part of the Revera family, one of North America's leading and most trusted providers of seniors' accommodation, care and services since 1961.*

RESIDENCE INFORMATION: 26 years in operation. *On:* Church Street and Allen Street. Decorated in 2010. Handrails in hallways. 4 floors, 2 elevators. Wheelchair accessible. Central PA system. *Funding Base:* Corporate/for profit. *Owned and managed by:* Revera Inc. 70 units. *Average Waiting Period*: none. *Average Age*: 88. Can accommodate cognitively impaired people (mild dementia). Can accommodate physically challenged people (assessed by Director of Health & Wellness). Smoke-free residence. Alcohol allowed (Cocktail Hour and licensed dining room also available). *Restrictions around Visitors/Visiting Hours:* front door is locked from 8:00 p.m. to 8:00 a.m. & visitors access building by buzzing in to Nurse. *Procedures to leave the premises on a temporary basis...*inform Reception. *Languages:* English. Will accept Public Guardian and Trustee clients. Main doors of residence secured at night only. *Close to:* Public Transit, Shopping, Churches, Synagogues, Seniors' Centre, Library, Major Highway and Local Hospital (Halton Healthcare Services Corporation - Oakville Site). Member of ORCA. Licensed under the Retirement Homes Act.

STAFFING: *Available Staff/Services*: Pharmacy, Social Work (CCAC), Recreation Therapy, Occupational Therapy, Visiting Dentist, Physiotherapy (CCAC), Denturist, Dietitian, Companions, Podiatry, Chaplaincy, Speech Pathology, Chiropody, Audiology/Hearing Clinic, Foot Clinic, Massage Therapist and Chiropractic.

External services arranged by: residence and/or family/resident. Staff trained *re*: visually, hearing and cognitively impaired. 24-hour nursing and other staff. RPNs, HCAs, PSWs and UCPs on staff. Visiting MD (weekly clinic/on-call). Can retain own MD. Police Check or Vulnerable Person Screening is done for all new staff.

HEALTH SERVICES: Medication administration and/or supervision. Vitals monitored if required. Will accept and provide special assistance for residents who require oxygen, catheters and ostomies. Assistance with dressing available (cost). Weekly assistance with bathing available (cost). Care plans done. Different levels of care available. Private Duty/Extra Care available. Lab service (visiting). Residents can purchase outside resources and use agency of their choice. MD visits residents in their rooms/suites. Clinic area for medical visits. Will help locate higher level of care if needed (family conference arranged to determine future care needs).

ACCOMMODATION: *Choice of suites available*: 1-bedroom & studio suites. *In all suites*: locks, kitchenette, bar fridge, storage, window coverings, light fixtures, fire alarm, smoke detector, sprinkler, emergency call bells, air conditioning (central) and thermostats for heating & cooling. Private bathrooms with call bells, grab bars and showers with shower curtain and non-slip surfaces. In-suite cable TV provided by residence (residence charges extra). Can have own phone number provided by residence (residence charges extra). Furnished & unfurnished suites available. *Restrictions on electrical appliances*: no hot plates; auto-shut-off kettles only. Suites can be shared. Pets allowed (cats, birds and small dogs with assessment).

DINING SERVICE: All meals included in fee and served in dining room daily. *Sittings per meal:* Breakfast: 2, Lunch: 2, Dinner: 2. *Menu choices available:* Breakfast: 3, Lunch: 2, Dinner: 2. *Guest Meals*: Available. *Special Diets*: Vegetarian, Low Salt, Diabetic, Low Fat, Lactose Free, Gluten Free and Heart Smart. Tray service to room if ill (no charge for a maximum time of 4 days). 3 snacks/day and unlimited snacks available at any time. Party facilities. Open pantry. Flexible dining and open seating. Breakfast - 8:00 a.m. to 9:30 a.m.; Lunch - 12:00 noon to 1:30 p.m.; 2 seatings for Dinner - 5:00 p.m. & 6:15 p.m.

AMENITIES AND ACTIVITIES: Parking available (outdoor, for visitors and indoor for residents). *4 lounges with:* TVs (2), piano (1) and double-sided fireplace (1). Guest suites available. *Residence has a:* library, barber/beauty shop, visiting hairdresser and laundry room(s) (no cost). Banking services on premises (once/week). Resident can arrange newspaper delivery to individual suite (extra cost). Mail delivered to private mailbox with key. *Recreation Facilities*: exercise room, craft room, card room, computer with internet access, bakery and company van. Posted schedule of activities. Internal newsletter for residents. *Recreational Programs*: exercise, shopping, theatre, parties, entertainment, art classes, pet visiting, special events and day & overnight trips.

OTHER SERVICES: *Housekeeping*: weekly (included in fee). *Laundry*: linen & towel (included in fee); personal (extra cost). Resident laundry room available. Transportation for group social activities. 24-hour security. Nightly security checks. Telephone & Cable TV (extra cost). Utilities (included in fee). Private dining room & catering available.

RENTAL INFORMATION: Rates vary depending on suite size, location and services. Suites - $2,900.00/ month & up. Extra cost for 2nd person sharing suite. Rent paid monthly. *Payment Options*: cheques, post-dated cheques and pre-authorized payments. Rent increases as per Provincial Tenancy Legislation, annual for resident with 90 days' notice given. Will help resident move into residence (extra cost). Short-term respite and trial stays available (price of vacation/short stay varies depending on level of care and services; minimum stay is 1 month).

Did you know?

There are several 'Safety Tips' that can prevent falls in the winter. For a detailed information sheet visit **www.seniors.gov.on.ca/en/seminars/docs/WinterSafetyTips.pdf.**

REVERA - THE KENSINGTON

25 Lakeshore Road West, Oakville, ON L6K 1C6
Tel: (855) 573-8372 • Toll Free: (855) 573-8372
Email: **kensington-oakville@reveraliving.com**
Website: **www.reveraliving.com/kensington-oakville**
Contact: **Executive Director or Lifestyle Consultant**
Capacity: **117 units** • Subsidies: **none**
Price: **$2,995.00/month and up**

At The Kensington you'll find the range of services, features and choices that fit your lifestyle and requirements – all in a warm and safe environment. Located a block from Lake Ontario, The Kensington is a gracious residence with the amenities of a 5-star hotel. The harbour location, magnificent rooftop garden and stellar reputation for customer service set us apart. Conveniently located close to shopping, dining, places of worship, recreation, medical services, the Oakville Centre for the Performing Arts, public library, public transportation, and more. Everything is designed for you to maintain your independence and privacy, enjoy a full social life, and participate in the activities that you love. Our caring and friendly staff, along with appealing accommodations, support who you are and how you want to live. *The Kensington is part of the Revera family, one of North America's leading and most trusted providers of seniors' accommodation, care and services since 1961.*

RESIDENCE INFORMATION: 20 years in operation. *Near:* Dorval Road and Lakeshore Road. Decorated in 2010. Handrails in hallways. 5 floors, 3 elevators. Wheelchair accessible. Central PA system. *Funding Base:* Corporate/for profit. *Owned and managed by:* Revera Inc. *Average Waiting Period*: varies. *Average Age*: 84. Can sometimes accommodate cognitively impaired & physically challenged people (assessed by Director of Health & Wellness). Residents have a dress code (no shorts in the dining room at dinner). Smoke-free residence. Alcohol allowed (Happy Hour also offered). *Procedures to leave the premises on a temporary basis...*advise the Reception Desk. *Languages:* English, French, Filipino, Romanian & Italian. Main doors of residence secured at night only. *Close to:* Public Transit, Shopping, Churches, Seniors' Centre, Library, Major Highway and Local Hospital (Halton Healthcare Services Corporation - Oakville Site). Member of ORCA. Licensed under the Retirement Homes Act.
STAFFING: *Available Staff/Services*: Pharmacy, Social Work (CCAC), Recreation Therapy, Occupational Therapy (CCAC), Physiotherapy (CCAC), Dietitian (CCAC), Podiatry (CCAC), Chaplaincy, Speech Pathology (CCAC), Foot Clinic and Massage Therapist. *External services arranged by:* residence and/or family/resident. Staff trained *re*: visually, hearing and cognitively impaired. 24-hour nursing and other staff. RNs, RPNs, HCAs and PSWs on staff. Visiting MD (weekly). Can retain own MD. Police Check or Vulnerable Person Screening is done for all new staff.
HEALTH SERVICES: Medication administration and/or supervision. Vitals monitored if required. Will accept and provide special assistance for residents who require oxygen, catheters and ostomies. Assistance with dressing available (cost). Weekly assistance with bathing available (cost). Care plans done. Different levels of care available. Optional services available. Assisted Living Area. Lab service (visiting). Residents can purchase outside resources. MD visits residents in their rooms/suites. Clinic area for medical visits. Will help locate higher level of care if needed (family conference arranged to determine future care needs).
ACCOMMODATION: *Choice of suites available*: unique studio, 1-bedroom & 2-bedroom suites, some with panoramic views of Lake Ontario. *In all suites*: locks, kitchenette, bar fridge, microwave, storage, window coverings, light fixtures, fire alarm, smoke detector, sprinkler, call bell, air conditioning (central) and thermostats for heating & cooling. Private bathrooms with heat lamp, call bells, grab bars and showers with non-slip surfaces. In-suite cable TV provided by residence (residence charges extra). Can have own phone number if resident arranges with phone company. Unfurnished suites, furnished suites

available for short stays. *Restrictions on electrical appliances*: no hot plates. Suites can be shared (by couples, relatives, friends). Pets allowed (small dogs, cats - assessment required).

DINING SERVICE: All meals included in fee and served in dining room daily. *Sittings per meal:* Breakfast: 1, Lunch: 1, Dinner: 2. *Menu choices available:* Breakfast: 2, Lunch: 2, Dinner: 2. *Guest Meals*: Available. *Special Diets*: Vegetarian, Low Salt, Diabetic and Low Fat. Heart Smart Menu available. Tray service to room if ill (no charge for a maximum time of 4 days). 3 snacks/day. Fresh fruit is available throughout the day. Café service offered in a.m./p.m. Party facilities.

AMENITIES AND ACTIVITIES: Parking available (indoor, for visitors and residents). *4 lounges with:* TVs (2), piano (1) and billiard table (1). Guest suites available. *Residence has a:* library, visiting library, barber/beauty shop, laundry room(s) (no cost) and tuck/gift shop (open weekly). Banking services on premises (twice/month). Residence provides newspaper delivery to individual suite (extra cost). Mail delivered to private mailbox with key. *Recreation Facilities*: pool table, billiards, shuffleboard, exercise room, craft room, card room, van for scheduled trips and rooftop garden. Posted schedule of activities. Internal newsletter for residents. *Recreational Programs*: exercise, shopping, theatre, parties, entertainment, art classes, pet visiting, day trips, lectures, concerts, trips to theatre and casino.

OTHER SERVICES: *Housekeeping*: weekly (included in fee). *Laundry*: linen & towel (included in fee); personal (extra cost on Retirement Living Floor) & dry cleaning (extra cost). Transportation for group social activities. 24-hour security. Nightly security checks. Telephone (resident to order). Cable TV (extra cost). Utilities (included in fee).

RENTAL INFORMATION: Prices vary depending on suite size, location and services provided. Extra cost for 2nd person sharing suite. Rent paid monthly. *Payment Options*: post-dated cheques and pre-authorized payments. Rent increases as per Provincial Tenancy Legislation, annual for resident with 90 days' notice given. Trial stays available. Vacation and short-term respite stays subject to availability & assessment.

REVERA - TRAFALGAR LODGE

299 Randall Street, Oakville, ON L6J 6B4
Tel: (855) 573-8372 • Toll Free: (855) 573-8372
Email: **trafalgar@reveraliving.com**
Website: **www.reveraliving.com/trafalgar**
Contact: **Lifestyle Consultant or Executive Director**
Capacity: **74 residents** • Subsidies: **none**
Price: **$2,300.00/month and up**

At Trafalgar Lodge, you'll find the range of services, amenities and choices that fit your lifestyle and requirements – all in a warm, charming and safe environment. Trafalgar Lodge is an intimate two-storey residence, which combines homey comfort with distinguished elegance. Located in the heart of charming old Oakville means that you're steps away from quaint shops, fabulous restaurants, churches, parks, and Lake Ontario. We're also close to medical services, recreation, a seniors' centre, and cultural amenities. Everything here is designed to enable you to maintain your independence and privacy, enjoy a full social life, and participate in the activities that you love. Our caring and friendly staff, along with appealing accommodations, support who you are and how you want to live in freedom and comfort. *Trafalgar Lodge is part of the Revera family, one of North America's leading and most trusted providers of seniors' accommodation, care and services since 1961.*

RESIDENCE INFORMATION: 30 years in operation. *Near:* Trafalgar Road and Lakeshore Road. Decorated in 2010. Handrails in hallways. 3 floors, 2 elevators. Wheelchair accessible. Central PA system. *Funding Base:* Corporate/for profit. *Owned and managed by:* Revera Inc. 69 units. *Average Waiting Period*: varies. *Average Age*: 84. Can sometimes accommodate cognitively impaired people (mild dementia only). Can accommodate physically challenged people (walkers, wheelchairs accepted; no 2-person transfers).

Smoking allowed (outdoor courtyard). Alcohol allowed (Cocktail Hour also offered). *Procedures to leave the premises on a temporary basis...*Short-term: sign in/out at Reception. Overnight & Holidays: sign in/out; inform staff. *Languages:* English, Filipino & Italian. Will accept Public Guardian and Trustee clients. Main doors of residence secured at night only. *Close to:* Public Transit, Shopping, Churches, Seniors' Centre, Library, Major Highway and Local Hospital (Halton Healthcare Services Corporation - Oakville Trafalgar Memorial Hospital). Member of ORCA. Licensed under the Retirement Homes Act.
STAFFING: *Available Staff/Services*: Social Work (CCAC), Recreation Therapy, Occupational Therapy (CCAC), Physiotherapy (CCAC), Dietitian (CCAC), Companions, Chaplaincy, Speech Pathology (CCAC), Audiology/Hearing Clinic, House Physician, Chiropodist and Dental Hygienist. *External services arranged by:* residence and/or family/resident. Staff trained *re*: visually, hearing and cognitively impaired. 24-hour staff. RNs, RPNs, PSWs and UCPs on staff. Visiting MD (weekly/on call 24/7). Can retain own MD. Police Check or Vulnerable Person Screening is done for all new staff.
HEALTH SERVICES: Medication administration and/or supervision. Vitals monitored if required. Will accept and provide special assistance for residents who require oxygen, catheters and ostomies. Assistance with dressing available (cost). Weekly assistance with bathing available (cost). Care plans done. Different levels of care available. Optional services available. Assisted Living Area. Lab service (visiting). Residents can purchase outside resources and use agency of their choice. MD visits residents in their rooms/suites. Clinic area for medical visits. Will help locate higher level of care if needed (family conference arranged to determine future care needs).
ACCOMMODATION: *Choice of suites available*: studio & 1-bedroom suites. *In all suites*: locks, storage, window coverings, light fixtures, fire alarm, smoke detector, sprinkler, call bell, Emergency Response System with wearable pendant/bracelet, air conditioning (window units) and thermostats for heating & cooling. Central air conditioning in common areas. Private bathrooms with call bells, grab bars and showers with non-slip surfaces. In-suite cable TV provided by residence (residence charges extra). Can have own phone number provided by residence (residence charges extra). Unfurnished suites. *Restrictions on electrical appliances*: no hot plates, no electric blankets. Pets allowed (cats, birds and small dogs with assessment).
DINING SERVICE: All meals included in fee and served in dining room daily. *Sittings per meal:* Breakfast: 2, Lunch: 2, Dinner: 2. *Menu choices available:* Breakfast: 2, Lunch: 2, Dinner: 2. *Guest Meals*: Available. *Special Diets*: Vegetarian, Low Salt and Diabetic. Heart Smart Menu available. Tray service to room if ill (no charge for a maximum time of 4 days). 2 snacks/day. Tea, coffee, fruit & snacks available throughout the day. Party facilities.
AMENITIES AND ACTIVITIES: Parking available (outdoor, for visitors and residents). *4 lounges with:* TV (1), piano (1), card tables, exercise equipment (1) and resident computer (1). *Residence has a:* library, barber/beauty shop, laundry room(s) (no cost) and tuck/gift shop. Residence provides newspaper delivery to individual suite (extra cost). Mail delivered to main desk. *Recreation Facilities*: pool table, billiards, exercise room, craft room, card room, piano lounge and tea room. Posted schedule of activities. Internal newsletter for residents. *Recreational Programs*: exercise, shopping, theatre, parties, entertainment, art classes, pet visiting, day trips, lectures, concerts and theme dinners.
OTHER SERVICES: *Housekeeping*: weekly (daily for an extra fee). *Laundry*: towel (included in fee); personal (extra cost). Transportation for group social activities (theatre, casino, etc.). 24-hour security. Nightly security checks. Telephone & Cable TV (extra cost). Utilities (included in fee).
RENTAL INFORMATION: Rent varies depending on suite type and services. Extra cost for 2nd person sharing suite. Rent paid monthly. *Payment Options*: cheques and pre-authorized payments. Rent increases indexed to inflation as per Provincial Tenancy Legislation, annual for resident with 3 months' notice given. Trial stays subject to availability.

Pricing information for homes listed in *The Guide* may vary slightly.
Please verify rates with the residences you are interested in directly.

THE QUEENS AVENUE RETIREMENT RESIDENCE

1056 Queens Avenue, Oakville, ON L6H 6R3
Tel: (905) 815-0862 • Fax: (905) 815-0812
Toll Free: (800) 752-2648
Email: **nicola@queensavenueretirement.com**
Website: **www.queensavenueretirement.com**
Contact: **Nicola Houlihan**
Capacity: **100 residents** • Subsidies: **none**
Price: **$2,550.00 - $4,100.00/month**

24-hour medic alert monitoring bracelet. Call bell in bathroom. Independent living. Outdoor terrace off main dining room. Patios off main common areas. Fully equipped complimentary laundry facilities on each floor. Basic cable included. Complimentary underground parking. TOLL FREE NUMBER: **(800) 752-2648.**

RESIDENCE INFORMATION: 15 years in operation. *Near:* Trafalgar Road and McCraney Street. Decorated in 2007. Handrails in hallways. 8 floors, 2 elevators. Wheelchair accessible. *Funding Base:* Corporate/for profit. Privately owned. 89 units. *Average Waiting Period*: 2 - 4 months. *Average Age*: 80. Can accommodate cognitively impaired people with restrictions (cannot accept anyone who wanders). Can accommodate physically challenged people (wheelchairs, scooters). Smoke-free residence. Alcohol allowed. *Procedures to leave the premises on a temporary basis...*sign out. *Languages:* English, French, Hungarian, Polish, Spanish & Italian. Main doors of residence secured at all times. *Close to:* Public Transit, Shopping, Churches, Seniors' Centre, Library, Major Highway and Local Hospital (Halton Healthcare Services Corporation - Trafalgar Memorial Hospital). *Predominant Cultural Group:* Anglo-Saxon. Licensed under the Retirement Homes Act.
STAFFING: *Available Staff/Services*: Pharmacy, Social Work (CCAC), Recreation Therapy, Occupational Therapy, Physiotherapy, Denturist, Dietitian, Companions, Podiatry, Chaplaincy, Chiropody, Audiology/ Hearing Clinic, 24-hour Staffing, House Doctor, FT/RPN and Medic Alert. *External services arranged by:* residence and/or family/resident. Staff trained *re*: visually, hearing and cognitively impaired. 24-hour nursing and other staff. RPNs, PSWs and UCPs on staff. Visiting MD (on call basis). Can retain own MD. Police Check or Vulnerable Person Screening is done for all new staff.
HEALTH SERVICES: Medication administration (pharmacy pours medications/blister packs) and/or supervision. Vitals monitored if required. Will accept and provide special assistance for residents who require oxygen, catheters and ostomies. Assistance with dressing available ($30.00/hour). Assistance with bathing available as needed ($30.00/hour). Care plans done. Different levels of care available. Enhanced Care Packages available at additional cost. Private Duty/Extra Care available ($500.00 to $4,000.00/month).

Lab service (visiting, $35.00/visit). Residents can purchase outside resources and use agency of their choice. MD visits residents in their rooms/suites. Will help locate higher level of care if needed (Manager of residence; Care Coordinator; CCAC).

ACCOMMODATION: *Choice of suites available*: studio with full-size fridge, stove, counter & sink (17), 1-bedroom (55) & 2-bedroom (17) units. *In all suites*: locks, kitchenette, stove, storage, window coverings, light fixtures, smoke detector, Emergency Response System with wearable pendant/bracelet, air conditioning (central) and thermostats (with individual controls) for heating & cooling. Full kitchen, pantry, cupboards, full-size fridge & stove in 1-bedroom & 2-bedroom units. Private bathrooms with call bells, grab bars and showers with non-slip surfaces. In-suite cable TV provided by residence. Can have own phone number if resident arranges with phone company. Unfurnished suites, furnished suites available for short stays. *Restrictions on electrical appliances*: must be in good condition. Suites can be shared (no more than 2 occupants/suite), roommate picked by resident. Pets allowed (dogs).

DINING SERVICE: Breakfast and Dinner included in fee and served in dining room daily. *Sittings per meal:* Breakfast: 1, Dinner: 1. *Menu choices available:* Breakfast: 1, Dinner: 3. *Guest Meals*: Lunch $5.00, Dinner $15.00. *Special Diets*: Vegetarian, Low Salt and Diabetic. Tray service to room if ill (no charge for a maximum time of 3 days). 2 snacks/day. Party facilities. Continental breakfast, lunch program and 5-course evening meal daily.

AMENITIES AND ACTIVITIES: Parking available (outdoor, for visitors and indoor for residents). *2 lounges with:* TVs (2), pianos (2), fireplaces (2) and piano (1). Guest suites available ($85.00/night). *Residence has a:* library, visiting library, barber/beauty shop, visiting hairdresser and laundry room(s) (no cost). Mail delivered to private mailbox with key. *Recreation Facilities*: shuffleboard, exercise room, craft room, card room, library and 2 large flat screen TVs. Posted schedule of activities. Internal newsletter for residents. *Recreational Programs*: exercise, shopping, theatre, parties, entertainment, art classes, pet visiting and day trips. Recreation Director runs daily programs.

OTHER SERVICES: *Housekeeping*: weekly (included in fee). *Laundry*: linen & towel (included in fee); personal (under Enhanced Care Program $75.00/month) & dry cleaning (residents responsibility). Laundry room on each floor. Transportation for group social activities (weekly shopping bus to grocery store & mall). 24-hour security. Nightly security checks. Telephone (resident to make arrangements). Cable TV & Utilities (included in fee). Continental Breakfast. Afternoon tea. 5-course dinner. Indoor parking. 24-hour medic alert monitoring.

RENTAL INFORMATION: Rates may vary. Studio - $2,550.00/month; 1-bedroom - $3,300.00 to $3,500.00/month; 2-bedroom - $3,500.00 to $4,100.00/month. Extra cost for 2nd person sharing suite ($590.00/month). Rent paid monthly. *Payment Options*: cheques. Rent increases as per Provincial Tenancy Legislation, annual for resident with 3 months' notice given. Will help resident move into residence ($30.00/hour). Short-term respite ($120.00/day - price based on assessment) and trial stays ($85.00/day) subject to availability.

Downsizing Tip

When planning your move, make a list of tasks, target dates and if you are getting assistance with relocation, who will be responsible for each item. Don't forget to send notifications to family, friends, your bank, insurance company, government pension offices, telephone & cable companies, newspapers and anyone else who sends you mail. You may also wish to complete a "mail redirection" through your local post office. Notify your landlord and the utility company as soon as possible. Arrange movers and if necessary, people to assist you with packing.

◆ OSHAWA ◆

CARRIAGE HOUSE RETIREMENT RESIDENCE

60 Bond Street East, Oshawa, ON L1G 8C9
Tel: (905) 725-2599 • Fax: (905) 436-5573
Email: **generalmanager@carriagehouseoshawa.com**
Website: **www.carriagehouseoshawa.com**
Contact: **Sylvia Ward**
Capacity: **94 units** • Subsidies: **none**
Price: **$2,200.00 - $3,250.00/month**

Great location! Close to: hospital, doctors, cancer clinic, shopping, public transit, seniors centre, library, museums. ***5X Diamond Award Winner***. Great food - nutritious home-style meals cooked fresh daily. Variety of activities. 24/7 emergency response. Health services available. Suites: small to large deluxe. Want the best value for your money? Call Now!!!

RESIDENCE INFORMATION: 13 years in operation. *Near:* Mary Street and Bond Street. Decorated in 2011. 6 floors, 2 elevators. Wheelchair accessible. Central PA system. *Average Waiting Period*: varies. *Average Age*: 75. Can accommodate cognitively impaired people with restrictions. Smoking allowed (outdoors). Alcohol allowed. *Restrictions around Visitors/Visiting Hours:* 9:00 a.m. - 10:00 p.m. *Procedures to leave the premises on a temporary basis...*sign out/in book and special form. *Languages:* English. Main doors of residence secured at all times. *Close to:* Public Transit, Shopping, Churches, Synagogues, Seniors' Centre, Library, Major Highway and Local Hospital (only 5 minutes from hospital). Licensed under the Retirement Homes Act.
STAFFING: *Available Staff/Services*: Pharmacy, Social Work (CCAC), Recreation Therapy, Occupational Therapy (CCAC), Physiotherapy (CCAC), Dietitian (CCAC), Podiatry, Chaplaincy and Foot Clinic (once/ month; optional & extra cost). *External services arranged by:* family/resident. 24-hour nursing staff. RNs, RPNs and PSWs on staff. Can retain own MD. Staff members are bonded. Police Check or Vulnerable Person Screening is done for all new staff.
HEALTH SERVICES: Medication administered if required (Medication Management is an available option). Vitals monitored if required. Will accept and provide special assistance for residents who require oxygen. Assistance with dressing available (cost). Weekly assistance with bathing available (cost). Care plans done. Different levels of care available. Residents can purchase outside resources and use agency of their choice. Will help locate higher level of care if needed (CCAC).
ACCOMMODATION: *Choice of suites available*: studios, bedsitting & 1-bedroom units. *In all suites*: locks, storage, light fixtures, fire alarm, smoke detector, sprinkler, venetian blinds, Emergency Response System with wearable pendant (emergency call bell attached to phone), air conditioning (HVAC) and thermostats for heating & cooling. Patios - some on 2nd floor with suites. Kitchenettes in some suites. Private bathrooms (all 3-piece - tub/sit down shower, sink & vanity and toilet) with grab bars. In-suite cable TV if resident arranges with cable company (residence charges extra $35.09/month). Can have own phone number provided by residence (residence charges extra $34.95/month). Unfurnished suites, furnished suites available for short stays. *Restrictions on electrical appliances*: no electric toasters or hot plates allowed. Pets allowed (cats only).
DINING SERVICE: All meals included in fee and served in dining room daily. *Sittings per meal:* Breakfast: 1, Lunch: 1, Dinner: 1. *Menu choices available:* Breakfast: 2, Lunch: 2, Dinner: 2. *Guest Meals*: Breakfast $5.00, Lunch $7.00, Dinner $9.00. *Special Diets*: Vegetarian, Low Salt, Diabetic and Renal (can be arranged with kitchen). Tray service to room when ill (short-term). Unlimited snacks available at any time. Open pantry. Café with juice, coffee, tea, fruit and pastries. Party facilities. Private dining room available for residents and guests.

AMENITIES AND ACTIVITIES: Parking available (outdoor, for visitors: free and residents: $57.00/month). *6 lounges with:* TVs (2), piano (1) and fireplaces (1). Guest suites available ($85.00/night). *Residence has a:* library, visiting library, chapel, barber/beauty shop and laundry room(s) (no cost). Residence provides newspaper delivery to individual suite (extra cost). Mail delivered to individual suite. *Recreation Facilities*: pool table, shuffleboard, exercise room, craft room and card room. Posted schedule of activities. Internal newsletter for residents. *Recreational Programs*: exercise, shopping, theatre, parties, entertainment, art classes, day trips, 4 weekly activity programs, Party Night, shuffleboard and games, etc.
OTHER SERVICES: *Housekeeping*: weekly (included in fee). *Laundry*: linen (included in fee - resident provides own linen), towel (resident provides own towels), dry cleaning (extra cost). Transportation to medical appointments (extra cost) and for group social activities (extra cost). 24-hour security. Nightly security checks. Telephone & Cable TV (extra cost). Utilities (included in fee). Medication Management (optional). 1 personal laundry/week (optional). Bathing assist (optional).
RENTAL INFORMATION: Rates may vary. Monthly lease with 30 day notice. Extra cost for 2nd person sharing suite ($500.00/month). Rent paid monthly. *Payment Options*: cheques and post-dated cheques. Rent increases as per Provincial Tenancy Legislation, annual for resident with 3 months' notice given. Short-term respite (includes 3 meals/day) and trial stays available (both $85.00/day).

HARMONY HILL RETIREMENT COMMUNITY

1335 Benson Street, Oshawa, ON
Tel: (888) 224-2294 • Toll Free: (888) 224-2294
Email: **info@harmony-hill.ca**
Website: **www.harmony-hill.ca**
Contact: **Betty Smith**
Capacity: **400 residents** • Subsidies: **none**
Price: **$2,900.00 - $5,000.00/month**

Independent Living Apartments: 1-bedroom & 2-bedroom with full kitchens, in-suite laundry, and underground parking. Retirement Suites: spacious studios and 1-bedroom suites with kitchenettes and a walk-in closet in each. Plus all the desirable amenities you expect: nutritious gourmet meals in our elegant dining room, a heated indoor pool, fitness centre, 24-hour security and care staff, housekeeping, Activity Coordinator and much more.

RESIDENCE INFORMATION: New residence. *Near:* Taunton Road and Harmony Road. Decorated in 2014. 4 floors, 4 elevators. Wheelchair accessible. *Funding Base:* Corporate/for profit. *Managed by:* Greenwood Retirement Communities. 206 units. *Average Waiting Period*: none. Smoke-free residence. *Languages:* English.
STAFFING: *Available Staff/Services*: Pharmacy. RNs, RPNs and PSWs on staff. Visiting MD. Police Check or Vulnerable Person Screening is done for all new staff.
HEALTH SERVICES: Medication administration supervised. Vitals monitored if required. Will accept and provide special assistance for residents who require oxygen, catheters and ostomies.
ACCOMMODATION: *Choice of suites available*: studio, 1-bedroom & 2-bedroom units. *In all suites*: window coverings, smoke detector, sprinkler, Emergency Response System with wearable pendant/ bracelet, air conditioning (central) and thermostats for heating & cooling. Private bathrooms with call bells, grab bars and showers. Furnished & unfurnished suites available. Pets allowed.
AMENITIES AND ACTIVITIES: Parking available (indoor & outdoor, for visitors and residents). 5 lounges. *Residence has a:* library, chapel, barber/beauty shop, visiting hairdresser, laundry room(s) (no cost) and tuck/gift shop. Mail delivered to resident. *Recreation Facilities*: pool table, exercise room, greenhouse, craft room and swimming pool. Posted schedule of activities. Internal newsletter for residents. *Recreational Programs*: exercise, shopping, theatre, parties, entertainment, art classes, pet visiting and day trips.

OTHER SERVICES: *Housekeeping*: weekly.
RENTAL INFORMATION: Rates may vary. Extra cost for 2nd person sharing suite ($500.00/month). Rent paid monthly. *Payment Options*: cheques, post-dated cheques and pre-authorized payments. 3 months' notice given for rent increases.

REVERA - CEDARCROFT PLACE

649 King Street East, Oshawa, ON L1H 8P9
Tel: (855) 573-8372 • Toll Free: (855) 573-8372
Email: **cedarcroft@reveraliving.com**
Website: **www.reveraliving.com/cedarcroft**
Contact: **Lifestyle Consultant or Executive Director**
Capacity: **76 units** • Subsidies: **none**
Price: **$2,670.00/month and up**

Keep living your life, your way, at Cedarcroft Place. Here, you'll find the range of services, amenities and choices that fit your lifestyle and requirements – all in a warm and safe environment. With retirement living at Cedarcroft Place, you change your address, not your life. Our vibrant residence is within walking distance of shopping, restaurants, banks, and a church. We offer caring and friendly staff, along with appealing accommodations, that support who you are and how you want to live. Everything is designed to enable you to maintain your independence and privacy, enjoy a full social life, and participate in the activities that you love. Explore what we have to offer, to keep you living in freedom and comfort. *Cedarcroft Place is part of the Revera family, one of North America's leading and most trusted providers of seniors' accommodation, care and services since 1961, and is Canadian owned.*

RESIDENCE INFORMATION: 24 years in operation. *Near:* Wilson Road and King Street. Decorated in 2009. Handrails in hallways. 5 floors, 2 elevators. Wheelchair accessible. Central PA system. *Funding Base:* Corporate/for profit. *Owned and managed by:* Revera Inc. *Average Waiting Period*: varies. *Average Age*: 80. Can accommodate cognitively impaired people (with restrictions upon assessment). Can accommodate physically challenged people. Smoking allowed (in a designated smoking area outside). Alcohol allowed (but we are not licensed to sell). *Procedures to leave the premises on a temporary basis...*sign in/out sheet at Reception. *Languages:* English, Polish, Ukrainian, Italian, German & French. Will accept Public Guardian and Trustee clients. Main doors of residence secured at night only. *Close to:* Public Transit, Shopping, Churches, Synagogues, Seniors' Centre, Library, Major Highway and Local Hospital (Lakeridge Health, Oshawa). *Predominant Cultural Group:* many Scottish, Irish & British. Member of ORCA. Licensed under the Retirement Homes Act.
STAFFING: *Available Staff/Services*: Pharmacy, Social Work (CCAC), Recreation Therapy, Occupational Therapy (CCAC), Visiting Dentist, Physiotherapy (CCAC), Denturist, Dietitian (CCAC), Companions, Podiatry, Chaplaincy, Speech Pathology, Chiropody, Audiology/Hearing Clinic, Visiting Physician and Hairdressing. *External services arranged by:* residence and/or family/resident. Staff trained *re*: visually, hearing and cognitively impaired. Staff have been educated in acquired brain injuries. 24-hour nursing and other staff. RPNs and PSWs on staff. Visiting MD (office on-site; weekly visits and on call). Can retain own MD. Staff members are bonded. Police Check or Vulnerable Person Screening is done for all new staff.
HEALTH SERVICES: Medication administration and/or supervision. Vitals monitored if required. Will accept and provide special assistance for residents who require oxygen, catheters and ostomies. Assistance with dressing available (cost). Assistance with bathing available as needed (cost). Care plans done. Different levels of care available. Private Duty/Extra Care available. Lab service (visiting). Residents can purchase outside resources and use agency of their choice. Clinic area for medical visits. Will help locate higher level of care if needed (through community connections, we are able to assist families through the next transition).

ACCOMMODATION: *Choice of suites available*: studio suites, galleries, 1-bedroom & 2-bedroom suites. *In all suites*: locks, kitchenette, bar fridge, storage, window coverings, light fixtures, fire alarm, smoke detector, sprinkler, call bell, 24-hour wireless pendant Emergency Response System, air conditioning (central & window units), thermostats for heating & cooling and large bright bay windows. Private bathrooms with call bells, grab bars, walk–in showers with non-slip surfaces and elevated toilet seats. In-suite cable TV provided by residence (residence charges extra). Can have own phone number if resident arranges with phone company (residence charges extra). Unfurnished suites, furnished suites available for short stays. *Restrictions on electrical appliances*: microwaves and automatic shut-off kettles allowed; no open flames or candles permitted. Suites can be shared (with partner as 2nd occupant) OR can have roommate picked by residence staff. Pets allowed (small animals permitted as per Pet Policy).
DINING SERVICE: All meals included in fee and served in dining room daily. *Sittings per meal:* Breakfast: 2, Lunch: 2, Dinner: 2. *Menu choices available:* Breakfast: 8, Lunch: 6, Dinner: 6. *Guest Meals*: Available. *Special Diets*: Vegetarian, Low Salt and Diabetic. Can accommodate most dietary requests. Tray service to room if ill. 3 snacks/day. Party facilities. On-site catering services available for private functions and events.
AMENITIES AND ACTIVITIES: Parking available (outdoor, for visitors and residents). *7 lounges with:* TV (1), pianos (2), card tables (2) and fireplaces (2). Guest suites available. *Residence has a:* library, visiting library, chapel, barber/beauty shop and visiting hairdresser. Resident can arrange newspaper delivery to main desk. Mail delivered to resident. *Recreation Facilities*: billiards, exercise room, greenhouse, card room, horticulture area, outside patio, craft/games room, recreation/activity area and pool in neighbourhood. Posted schedule of activities. Internal newsletter for residents. *Recreational Programs*: exercise, shopping, theatre, parties, entertainment, art classes, pet visiting, day trips, bible study available, variety of church services scheduled in-house and also a full Catholic mass.
OTHER SERVICES: *Housekeeping*: weekly (included in fee - light housekeeping weekly). *Laundry*: linen (included in fee; bed linens changed weekly bring own linens), towel & personal (included in fee). Transportation to medical appointments and for group social activities. Indoor scooter parking recharging (included). 24-hour security. Nightly security checks (included in fee). Telephone (extra cost - includes unlimited long distance in North America). Cable TV (extra cost - pre-wired with Ultimate Rogers Package). Utilities (included in fee). In-house Spa. Resident raised-garden for planting. Residents involved in many charity fundraisers! Weekly music entertainment. Outings. Spectacular Recreational Program.
RENTAL INFORMATION: Rates may vary. Semi-private suites also available - $1,500.00/month & up. Extra cost for 2nd person sharing suite. Rent paid monthly. *Payment Options*: pre-authorized payments. Rent increases as per Provincial Tenancy Legislation, annual for resident with 3 months' notice given. Will help resident move into residence (extra cost). Short-term respite (includes Level 1 Care Plan) and trial stays available (2 night complimentary trial guest stay).

TRADITIONS OF DURHAM

1255 Bloor Street East, Oshawa, ON L1H 0B3
Tel: (905) 432-0002 • Fax: (905) 432-2228
Email: **eleanor.hastie@specialtyliving.ca**
Website: **www.specialtyliving.ca**
Contact: **Eleanor Hastie**
Capacity: **175 residents** • Subsidies: **none**
Price: **$2,575.00/month and up**

Traditions of Durham has redefined retirement living with a thoughtfully designed home that offers great value and impressive services. Here you can do things your way – while continuing to enjoy things that matter – time with family, connections with friends and being involved in the community. Our innovative *Zest for Life™* signature service promotes the health and well-being of each resident by focusing on the needs of mind, body and spirit. We work with you one-on-one to connect you with activities and services that spark your particular interests. Come and explore Traditions of Durham for yourself. If you are looking for a rewarding place to live and you too have a zest for life – our doors are open!

RESIDENCE INFORMATION: 4 years in operation. *Near:* Grandview Avenue and Bloor Street. Decorated in 2010. Handrails in some of the hallways. 4 floors, 2 elevators. Wheelchair accessible. *Managed by:* Specialty Care. 140 units. *Average Waiting Period*: varies. *Average Age*: 85. Can accommodate cognitively impaired people with restrictions (no risk of elopement or aggressive behaviour). Can accommodate physically challenged people with restrictions (require nursing assessment). Smoke-free residence. Alcohol allowed. *Procedures to leave the premises on a temporary basis...*Short-term & Overnight: sign out sheet with date of return. Holidays: notify Administration. *Languages:* English. Main doors of residence secured at night only. *Close to:* Public Transit, Shopping, Churches, Seniors' Centre, Library, Major Highway and Local Hospital (Lakeridge Health). Member of ORCA, Oshawa Chamber of Commerce & Clarington Board of Trade. Licensed under the Retirement Homes Act.
STAFFING: *Available Staff/Services*: Pharmacy, Social Work (CCAC), Recreation Therapy, Occupational Therapy (CCAC), Physiotherapy, Dietitian, Speech Pathology (CCAC) and Chiropody. *External services arranged by:* residence and/or family/resident. Staff trained *re*: visually, hearing and cognitively impaired. 24-hour staff. RNs, RPNs, PSWs and UCPs on staff. Visiting MD (once/week). Can retain own MD. Police Check or Vulnerable Person Screening is done for all new staff.
HEALTH SERVICES: Medication administration and/or supervision (centralized). Vitals monitored if required. Will accept (but not provide special assistance for) residents who require catheters and ostomies. Will accept and provide special assistance for residents who require oxygen. Assistance with dressing available (cost). Assistance with bathing available as needed (cost). Care plans done. Different levels of care available. Assisted Living Area ($465.00/month). Lab service (visiting). Residents can purchase outside resources and use agency of their choice. Clinic area for medical visits. Will help locate higher level of care if needed (nurse will give CCAC info to resident/family).
ACCOMMODATION: *Choice of suites available*: studios, 1-bedroom & 2-bedrooms suites. *In all suites*: locks, storage, bar fridge, window coverings, light fixtures, smoke detector, sprinkler, Emergency Response System with wearable pendant/bracelet and thermostats for heating & cooling. Private bathrooms with call bells, grab bars and showers with non-slip surfaces. In-suite cable TV provided by residence (residence charges extra). Can have own phone number if resident arranges with phone company (residence charges extra). Unfurnished suites, furnished suites available for short stays. *Restrictions on electrical appliances*: must be approved by Administration. Suites can be shared (couples, friends or family members). Pets allowed (small lap dog, cat, must be approved by Administration).
DINING SERVICE: All meals included in fee and served in dining room daily. *Sittings per meal:* Breakfast: 2, Lunch: 3, Dinner: 3. *Menu choices available:* Breakfast: 8, Lunch: 5, Dinner: 5. *Guest Meals*: Breakfast $8.20, Lunch $10.45, Dinner $15.80. *Special Diets*: Vegetarian, Low Salt, Diabetic and Healthy Choices (options identified on menu). Tray service to room if ill (no charge for a maximum time of 3 days). Unlimited snacks available at any time. Party facilities. Private dining room or wine bar bistro for family meals/birthday parties.
AMENITIES AND ACTIVITIES: Parking available (outdoor, for visitors and residents). *5 lounges with:* TVs (4), piano (1) and fireplaces (2). Guest suites available. *Residence has a:* library, visiting library, barber/beauty shop, laundry room(s) (no cost) and tuck/gift shop. Resident can arrange newspaper delivery to main desk (extra cost). Mail delivered to private mailbox with key. *Recreation Facilities*: exercise room, craft room and card room. Posted schedule of activities. Internal newsletter for residents. *Recreational Programs*: shopping, theatre, parties, entertainment, pet visiting, day trips and *Zest for Life™*.
OTHER SERVICES: *Housekeeping*: weekly (included in fee; weekly on all floors, Service Plus daily tidy up). *Laundry*: linen, towel & personal (extra cost); dry cleaning (use community cleaners). Full laundry service on Service Plus floor. Transportation to medical appointments (weekly) and for group social activities. 24-hour security. Telephone & Cable TV (extra cost - arranged through residence). Utilities (included in fee).
RENTAL INFORMATION: Rates may vary. Extra cost for 2nd person sharing suite ($650.00/month). Rent paid monthly. *Payment Options*: pre-authorized payments. Rent increases as per Provincial Tenancy

Legislation, annual for resident with 3 months' notice given. Short-term respite ($118.00/day - rest & recuperation stays are offered on Service Plus floor which provides additional support and services. This also offered on Independent floor) and trial stays ($75.00/day) available.

◆ OSHAWA (COURTICE) ◆

WHITE CLIFFE TERRACE

1460 Highway #2, Courtice, ON L1E 3C4
Tel: (905) 579-0800 • Fax: (905) 579-1255
Email: **info.wct@diversicare.ca**
Website: **www.diversicare.ca**
Contact: **Marketing Manager**
Capacity: **130 residents** • Subsidies: **none**
Price: **$2,600.00 - $4,800.00/month**

White Cliffe Terrace offers a selection of lovely studio, 1-bedroom & 2-bedroom suites, all individually climate controlled. Dining is always a pleasure with several menu selections for each meal. Our welcoming outdoor garden patio is a wonderful place to relax and the social calendar has many opportunities for outings and activities. We offer an on-site hair salon and easy access to banking, shopping, health care professionals. **White Cliffe Terrace is managed by Diversicare who is the proud recipient of the 2003, 2006, 2009 and 2012 Order of Excellence Award given by Excellence Canada.** This award was received for the exceptional quality and customer service we provide to our residents every day.

RESIDENCE INFORMATION: 15 years in operation. *Near:* Townline Road and Highway # 2. Decorated in 2013. Handrails in hallways. 5 floors, 2 elevators. Wheelchair accessible. Central PA system. *Funding Base:* Corporate/for profit. *Owned and managed by:* Diversicare Canada Management Services Co., Inc. 112 units. *Average Waiting Period*: varies. *Average Age*: 84. Can accommodate cognitively impaired people. Can accommodate physically challenged people (assessment required). Residents have a dress code (Business casual in dining room). Smoking allowed (designated smoking area). Alcohol allowed. *Procedures to leave the premises on a temporary basis...*notify Front Desk of your departure and expected return. *Languages:* English. Will accept Public Guardian and Trustee clients. Main doors of residence secured at night only. *Close to:* Public Transit, Shopping, Churches, Seniors' Centre, Library, Major Highway and Local Hospital (Lakeridge Health - Oshawa General Hospital Site). Member of ORCA. Licensed under the Retirement Homes Act.
STAFFING: *Available Staff/Services*: Social Work (CCAC), Recreation Therapy, Occupational Therapy (CCAC), Dietitian (CCAC), Chaplaincy, Speech Pathology (CCAC), Foot Care and Physiotherapy (via CCAC & in-house service through ACTIVE Health Management - covered by OHIP with MD referral). *External services arranged by:* family/resident. Staff trained *re*: visually and hearing impaired. 24-hour nursing and other staff. RPNs and PSWs on staff. Can retain own MD. Police Check or Vulnerable Person Screening is done for all new staff.
HEALTH SERVICES: Medication administration and/or supervision. Vitals monitored if required. Will accept (but not provide special assistance for) residents who require oxygen, catheters and ostomies. Assistance with dressing available. Assistance with bathing available as needed. Care plans done. Different levels of care available. Assisted Living Area (2 - 3 week waiting period) can accommodate residents that require assistance with care for daily living. Lab service (visiting, $25.00/visit). Residents can purchase outside resources and use agency of their choice. Will help locate higher level of care if needed (through placement coordination at CCAC).

ACCOMMODATION: *Choice of suites available*: studio (24), 1-bedroom (50), 2-bedroom (4) & Assisted Living (36) units. *In all suites*: locks, kitchenette, bar fridge, storage, window coverings, light fixtures, smoke detector, sprinkler, call bell, air conditioning (central) and thermostats for heating & cooling. Private bathrooms with call bells, grab bars, showers with non-slip surfaces and elevated toilet seats. In-suite cable TV if resident arranges with cable company. Can have own phone number if resident arranges with phone company. Unfurnished suites, furnished suites available for short stays. *Restrictions on electrical appliances*: no toaster ovens, electric blankets, humidifiers. Pets allowed (cats, lap dogs and birds).
DINING SERVICE: All meals included in fee and served in dining room daily. *Sittings per meal:* Breakfast: 1, Lunch: 1, Dinner: 1. *Menu choices available:* Lunch: 4, Dinner: 4. *Guest Meals*: Breakfast $5.00, Lunch $7.00, Dinner $10.00. *Special Diets*: Vegetarian, Low Salt and Diabetic. Tray service to room if ill. Unlimited snacks available at any time. Party facilities. Guest tables available for family and visitors.
AMENITIES AND ACTIVITIES: Parking available (outdoor, for visitors and residents). *5 lounges with:* TVs (2), piano (1), library (1) and computer (1). Guest suites available ($100.00/night). *Residence has a:* library, chapel, barber/beauty shop, visiting hairdresser, laundry room(s) (no cost) and tuck/gift shop (open 1 day/week; 3:00 p.m.- 4:00 p.m.). Residence provides newspaper delivery to main desk. Mail delivered to private mailbox with key. *Recreation Facilities*: pool table, billiards, exercise room, greenhouse, craft room, multipurpose room, meeting room and card room. Posted schedule of activities. Internal newsletter for residents. *Recreational Programs*: exercise, shopping, theatre, parties, entertainment, day trips & Brain Gym® & More programs.
OTHER SERVICES: *Housekeeping*: weekly (included in fee). *Laundry*: linen, towel & personal (extra cost for Independent residents; included on Assisted Living Floor only). Complimentary laundry facilities for independent residents. Transportation for group social activities. 24-hour security. Nightly security checks. Telephone & Cable TV (extra cost). Utilities (included in fee).
RENTAL INFORMATION: Rates may vary. Extra cost for 2nd person sharing suite ($550.00/month available for 1-bedroom or 2-bedroom suites). Rent paid monthly. *Payment Options*: cheques and pre-authorized payments. Rent increases as per Provincial Tenancy Legislation, annual for resident with 3 months' notice given. Short-term respite and trial stays available (both $100.00/day, costs vary depending on individual needs).

Did you know?

www.211Ontario.ca is a growing directory of community, social, health and government agencies and services across Ontario. For those who aren't able to access a computer to look up this information, in some regions, dialing 211 from your telephone leads you to a FREE call centre where a 24/7 phone service can give you the same information.

♦ OTTAWA REGION ♦

OTTAWA REGION (pages 228 - 244) - Due to the size of the amalgamated Ottawa area, we have subdivided this section into Central & West Regions – within the West Region we have subdivided the homes alphabetically by the (former) area designations/cities (Carleton Place, Kanata & Nepean). Arnprior is now in its own area and can be found after Alliston earlier in the text.

◆ OTTAWA (CENTRAL) ◆

BLACKBURN LODGE SENIORS RESIDENCE INC.

2412 Cleroux Crescent, Ottawa, ON K1W 1A3
Tel: (613) 837-7467 • Fax: (613) 837-0250
Email: **porterd@blackburnlodge.com**
Website: **www.blackburnlodge.com**
Contact: **David Porter**
Capacity: **62 residents**
Subsidies: **a few residents are approved for internal subsidies; no government subsidies**
Price: **$1,500.00 - $3,500.00/month**

The first thing visitors to Blackburn Lodge notice is the easy-going atmosphere where residents, staff and family members are all on a first name basis, talking, laughing and enjoying life together. The second is the list of comprehensive service packages at truly affordable prices.

RESIDENCE INFORMATION: 28 years in operation. *Near:* Cleroux Crescent and Innes Road. Decorated in 2003. Handrails in hallways. 3 floors, 1 elevator. Wheelchair accessible. Central PA system. *Funding Base:* Corporate/for profit. *Owned by:* Blackburn Lodge Seniors Residence Inc. 54 units. *Average Waiting Period*: 2 - 3 weeks. *Average Age*: 82. Can accommodate cognitively impaired people with restrictions (no wandering or aggressive residents). Can accommodate physically challenged people with restrictions (we cannot accommodate 2-person transfers). Residents have a dress code (no pyjamas or dressing gowns in public areas except en-route to tub room). Smoke-free residence. Alcohol allowed (we believe this a resident decision). *Restrictions around Visitors/Visiting Hours:* overnight guests permitted in resident's room; or, for a fee, in a separate room. *Procedures to leave the premises on a temporary basis...*sign out. *Languages:* English & French. Will accept Public Guardian and Trustee clients. Main doors of residence secured at night only. *Close to:* Public Transit, Shopping, Churches, Library, Major Highway and Local Hospital (The Ottawa Hospital - General Site & Montfort Hospital). *Predominant Cultural Group:* 80% English, 20% French. Licensed under the Retirement Homes Act.
STAFFING: *Available Staff/Services*: Pharmacy, Social Work (CCAC), Recreation Therapy, Occupational Therapy (CCAC), Visiting Dentist, Physiotherapy (CCAC), Dietitian (CCAC), Companions, Podiatry (CCAC), Chaplaincy, Speech Pathology (CCAC), Foot Care and Hairdressing. *External services arranged by:* residence and/or family/resident. Staff trained *re*: visually, hearing and cognitively impaired. 24-hour staff. RPNs, PSWs and UCPs on staff. Visiting MD (every 2 weeks & in emergencies). Can retain own MD. Police Check or Vulnerable Person Screening is done for all new staff.
HEALTH SERVICES: Medication administration (extra charge) and/or supervision. Vitals monitored if required. Will accept and provide special assistance for residents who require oxygen. Assistance with dressing available ($14.00/half hour). Assistance with bathing available twice a week ($72.00/month). *Extra baths:* $15.00/bath. Care plans done. Different levels of care available. Private Duty/Extra Care available ($68.00 to $486.00/month). Lab service (visiting, $25.00/visit). Residents can purchase outside resources and use agency of their choice. MD visits residents in their rooms/suites. Clinic area for medical visits. Will help locate higher level of care if needed (counselling re CCAC and long-term care homes).
ACCOMMODATION: *Choice of suites available*: apartment (8), mini-apartment (6), small private (10) & large private (29) units. *In all suites*: locks, window coverings, linens, fire alarm, smoke detector, call bell, thermostats for heating and 1 or 2 closets. Many have kitchenettes. Private bathrooms (4-piece for most or 2-piece) with call bells and grab bars. In-suite cable TV provided by residence. Can have own phone number if resident arranges with phone company. Furnished & unfurnished suites available. *Restrictions on electrical appliances*: no stoves except in apartments. Suites can be shared (must meet admission criteria), roommate picked by resident & residence staff. Pets allowed (Management approval required).

DINING SERVICE: Meal options available - normal: 3 meals/day & snacks; alternate packages (discounts given) 1 or 2 meals/day. Those in apartments with stoves can opt out of breakfast and 1 other meal. All meals are served in dining room daily. *Sittings per meal:* Breakfast: 1, Lunch: 1, Dinner: 1. *Menu choices available:* Breakfast: 3, Lunch: 3, Dinner: 3. *Guest Meals*: Breakfast $4.00, Lunch $7.00, Dinner $7.00. *Special Diets*: Vegetarian, Low Salt, Diabetic and Pureed. Tray service to room if ill (no charge for a maximum time of 14 days). 2 snacks/day. Party facilities. Open pantry.
AMENITIES AND ACTIVITIES: Parking available (outdoor, for visitors and residents). *5 lounges with:* TVs (2), pianos (2) and fireplace (1). Guest suites available ($34.00/night). *Residence has a:* library, chapel, barber/beauty shop, visiting hairdresser, laundry room(s), shop (open 1 day/week; 3:30 p.m. - 4:00 p.m.). Banking services on premises (once/month). Resident can arrange newspaper delivery to individual suite ($28.00/month). Mail delivered to main desk. *Recreation Facilities*: shuffleboard, craft room, card room and puzzle room. Posted schedule of activities. Internal newsletter for residents. *Recreational Programs*: exercise, shopping, theatre, parties, entertainment, art classes, pet visiting, day trips and many others.
OTHER SERVICES: *Housekeeping*: daily and weekly (included in fee). *Laundry*: linen, towel & personal (included in fee); dry cleaning (sent out at resident cost). Laundry must be machine washable & dryable, no ironing. Carpet cleaning, as needed or for a fee. Transportation for group social activities. 24-hour security. Nightly security checks. Cable TV & Utilities (included in fee). Meals. Activities. Basic level of care.
RENTAL INFORMATION: Rates may vary. Typical costs are: small singles - $1,500.00/month; large singles - $1,750.00/month; mini-apartments - $2,000.00/month; apartments - $2,500.00/month. Extra cost for 2nd person sharing suite ($500.00/month; prices here are averaged or typical, not exact). Rent paid monthly. *Payment Options*: cheques, post-dated cheques, direct deposit and pre-authorized payments. Rent increases as per Provincial Tenancy Legislation, services fee increases relate to inflation, annual for resident with 3 months' notice given. Will help resident move into residence. Short-term respite ($75.00/day; may cost more depending on care level) and trial stays ($40.00/day) available.

GOVERNOR'S WALK

150 Stanley Avenue, Ottawa, ON K1M 2J7
Tel: (613) 564-9255 • Fax: (613) 564-6696
Email: **info@governorswalkresidence.com**
Website: **www.governorswalkresidence.com**
Contact: **Brian Bruni**
Capacity: **84 residents** • Subsidies: **none**
Price: **$2,300.00 - $6,500.00/month**

Governor's Walk is Ottawa's choice for an intimate boutique-style retirement residence, featuring a personal, friendly, gracious retirement living lifestyle. Discretely located near Rockcliffe Park and surrounded by gorgeous pathways on the Rideau River and Governor General's, this residence is in the historical district of New Edinburgh and offers a special intimate option for elegant retirement living.

RESIDENCE INFORMATION: 12 years in operation. *On:* Stanley Avenue near Sussex Drive. Handrails in hallways. 4 floors, 2 elevators. Wheelchair accessible. *Funding Base:* Corporate/for profit. *Owned and managed by:* AgeCare Investments. 74 units. *Average Waiting Period*: varies. *Average Age*: 83. Can accommodate cognitively impaired people (Governor's Lane secured specialized care area for persons with dementia & other cognitive disabilities). Can accommodate physically challenged people (wheelchairs, scooters, walkers, canes, etc.). Residents have a dress code (appropriate dining room attire; no sleepwear, slippers, shorts, tank tops, bare feet, etc.). Smoking allowed (residents can smoke outside). Alcohol allowed. *Restrictions around Visitors/Visiting Hours:* per resident's discretion. *Procedures to leave the premises on a temporary basis...*residents notify Reception/sign out. *Languages:* English & French. Main doors of residence secured at night only. *Close to:* Public Transit, Shopping, Churches, Synagogues, Seniors' Centre, Library, Major Highway and Local Hospital (Monfort Hospital). Member of ORCA. Licensed under the Retirement Homes Act.

STAFFING: *Available Staff/Services*: Pharmacy, Social Work (CCAC), Recreation Therapy, Occupational Therapy (CCAC), Visiting Dentist, Physiotherapy (CCAC), Companions, Podiatry, Chaplaincy, Salon, Housekeeping, Garbage Removal, Handyman Services, Blood Pressure Clinic and Information Sessions. *External services arranged by:* residence and/or family/resident. Staff trained *re*: visually, hearing and cognitively impaired. 24-hour nursing and other staff. RNs, RPNs, HCAs and PSWs on staff. Visiting MD (varies due to demand). Can retain own MD. Police Check or Vulnerable Person Screening is done for all new staff.
HEALTH SERVICES: Medication administration and/or supervision. Will accept (but not provide special assistance for) residents who require ostomies and feeding tubes. Will accept and provide special assistance for residents who require oxygen and catheters. Assistance with dressing available. Assistance with bathing available twice a week. Care plans done. Different levels of care available. Residence has in-house physiotherapy 5 days/week. Private Duty/Extra Care available. Assisted Living Area (less than 2 week waiting period) is secured to accommodate residents with dementia. Lab service (visiting, $25.00/visit). Residents can purchase outside resources and use agency of their choice. MD visits residents in their rooms/suites. Clinic area for medical visits. Will help locate higher level of care if needed (long-term care home search).
ACCOMMODATION: *Choice of suites available*: studio (45), deluxe studio (9), 1-bedroom (16) & 2-bedroom (4) units. *In all suites*: locks, window coverings, light fixtures, linens, fire alarm, smoke detector, sprinkler, emergency call bell system, air conditioning (central), thermostats for heating & cooling and telephone line. Private bathrooms with call bells, grab bars, tubs and showers with non-slip surfaces. In-suite cable TV provided by residence (residence charges extra $49.95/month). Can have own phone number provided by residence (residence charges extra $39.95/month). Unfurnished suites, furnished suites available for short stays. Suites can be shared, roommate picked by resident. Some small pets allowed.
DINING SERVICE: All meals included in fee and served in dining room daily. *Sittings per meal:* Lunch: 2, Dinner: 2. *Menu choices available:* Lunch: 2, Dinner: 2. Meal Choices: Breakfast: resident's choice. Lunch & Dinner: 3 course meal with choice of 2 main courses. *Guest Meals*: Breakfast $7.50, Lunch $14.00, Dinner $14.00. *Special Diets*: Vegetarian, Low Salt, Diabetic, Glucose and Others. À la carte menu is always available, and special meals can be made on request. Tray service to room if ill. Unlimited snacks available at any time. Party facilities. Open pantry. Sunday Buffet.
AMENITIES AND ACTIVITIES: Parking available (outdoor, for visitors and residents). *4 lounges with:* TV (1), piano (1), card room (1) and lounge & patio terrace (1). Guest suites available ($55.00/night). *Residence has a:* library, visiting library, chapel, barber/beauty shop, visiting hairdresser and laundry room(s) (no cost). Resident can arrange newspaper delivery to individual suite (extra cost). Mail delivered to private mailbox with key. *Recreation Facilities*: exercise room, craft room, card room, park, movie room, games and flower arranging. Posted schedule of activities. Internal newsletter for residents. *Recreational Programs*: exercise, shopping, theatre, parties, entertainment, art classes, pet visiting, day trips, Yoga, bingo, park walks, picnics, music & singing, social hour, visiting concerts and dance shows, etc.
OTHER SERVICES: *Housekeeping*: daily and weekly (included in fee). *Laundry*: linen, towel & personal (included in fee); dry cleaning (extra cost - visiting service). Laundry can be done by residents or by staff. Transportation to medical appointments (on Tuesday & Thursday) and for group social activities (on Monday, Wednesday and Friday). 24-hour security. Nightly security checks. Telephone & Cable TV (extra cost). Utilities (included in fee). Optional Long Distance phone plans $19.99/month or standard pay per minute long distance.
RENTAL INFORMATION: Rates may vary. Studio - $2,300.00/month; standard studio - $2,995.00/month; large studio - $3,495.00/month; deluxe studio - $4,200.00/month; 1-bedroom - $4,000.00/month; 2-bedroom - $6,500.00/month - room price depends on square footage. Extra cost for 2nd person sharing suite ($500.00/month). Rent paid monthly. *Payment Options*: cheques, post-dated cheques, direct deposit and pre-authorized payments. Rent increases as per Provincial Tenancy Legislation, annual for resident with 3 months' notice given. Will help resident move into residence. Short-term respite and trial

stays available (both $85.00/day, cost for an additional person in the short-term or trial stay room is an additional $15.00/day. Trial and respite stay costs include all meals and care, phone line and cable TV).

OAKPARK RETIREMENT COMMUNITY

Two Valour Drive, Ottawa, ON K1G 3T5
Tel: (613) 260-7144 • Fax: (613) 260-7185
Email: **tkloppenburg@riverstoneretirement.ca**
Website: **www.oakparkretirement.com**
Contact: **Tom Kloppenburg**
Capacity: **140 residents •** Subsidies: **none**
Price: **$2,775.00 - $8,475.00/month**

Oakpark presents a new dawn in retirement living. Nurture your body and soul with our on-site spa and physiotherapy services, gourmet dining and one of the most innovative and challenging activity and social programs in Canada. Nestled amongst mature trees, this elegant residence offers a broad range of suite styles, a 4-star dining room, inviting library and lounge with grand piano. Take a stroll along one of the adjacent nature trails or simply relax on one of our 2 outdoor patios with mature landscape views. Oakpark is conveniently located in Alta Vista, close to the General Hospital, shopping and all downtown amenities. We offer a full continuum of care catering to your choice of lifestyle options in a safe and carefree environment. Our secure Assisted Living Centre provides a warm and active living environment for residents with dementia.

RESIDENCE INFORMATION: 6 years in operation. *Near:* Alta Vista Drive and Smyth Road. Decorated in 2008. Handrails in hallways. 5 floors, 2 elevators. Wheelchair accessible. Central PA system. *Funding Base:* Corporate/for profit. *Owned by:* Claridge Homes. *Managed by:* Riverstone Retirement Communities. 120 units. *Average Waiting Period*: varies. *Average Age*: 85. Can accommodate cognitively impaired people (secure Assisted Living Area with private patio). Can accommodate physically challenged people (Assisted Living Area). Smoke-free residence. Alcohol allowed. *Procedures to leave the premises on a temporary basis...*notify Reception and nursing dept. *Languages:* English & French. Will accept Public Guardian and Trustee clients. Main doors of residence secured at night only. *Close to:* Public Transit, Shopping, Churches, Synagogues, Seniors' Centre, Library, Major Highway and Local Hospitals (The Ottawa Hospital - General and Riverside Sites). Member of ORCA. Licensed under the Retirement Homes Act.
STAFFING: *Available Staff/Services*: Pharmacy, Social Work (CCAC), Recreation Therapy, Occupational Therapy (CCAC), Visiting Dentist, Physiotherapy, Dietitian (CCAC), Podiatry, Chaplaincy, Speech Pathology (CCAC) and Audiology/Hearing Clinic. *External services arranged by:* residence and/or family/resident. Staff trained *re*: visually, hearing and cognitively impaired. 24-hour nursing staff. RNs, RPNs, PSWs and UCPs on staff. Visiting MD (every week). Can retain own MD. Police Check or Vulnerable Person Screening is done for all new staff.
HEALTH SERVICES: Medication administration and/or supervision. Vitals monitored if required. Will accept (but not provide special assistance for) residents who require catheters and ostomies. Will accept and provide special assistance for residents who require oxygen. Assistance with dressing available. Weekly assistance with bathing available. *Extra baths:* $25.00/half hour. Care plans done. Different levels of care available. Assisted Living Area ($4,300.00 to $8,475.00/month) is secured to accommodate residents with dementia. Lab service (visiting, $25.00/visit). Residents can purchase outside resources and use agency of their choice. Clinic area for medical visits. Will help locate higher level of care if needed (continuum of care with secure Assisted Living Area on 2nd floor).
ACCOMMODATION: *Choice of suites available*: 2-bedroom, 1-bedroom, 1-bedroom + den, studio suites & studios. *In all suites*: locks, kitchenette, bar fridge, microwave, patio/balcony, storage, window coverings, light fixtures, linens, fire alarm, smoke detector, sprinkler, call bell, Emergency Response System with wearable pendant/bracelet, air conditioning (central) and thermostats for heating & cooling.

Private bathrooms with call bells, grab bars, showers with non-slip surfaces and elevated toilet seats. Furnished & unfurnished suites available. Pets allowed.

DINING SERVICE: All meals included in fee and served in dining room daily. *Sittings per meal:* Breakfast: 2, Lunch: 2, Dinner: 2. *Menu choices available:* Breakfast: 4, Lunch: 4, Dinner: 4. *Guest Meals*: Breakfast $8.00, Lunch $15.00, Dinner $17.00. *Special Diets*: Vegetarian, Low Salt, Diabetic and Gluten Free. An alternative menu is available. Tray service to room if ill (no charge as long as doctor orders). 3 snacks/day. Party facilities.

AMENITIES AND ACTIVITIES: Parking available (indoor & outdoor, for visitors: free and indoor for residents: $60.00/month). *3 lounges with:* TVs (3) and pianos (2). Guest suites available ($95.00/night). *Residence has a:* library, visiting library, chapel, barber/beauty shop, visiting hairdresser, laundry room(s) (no cost) and tuck/gift shop. Residence provides newspaper delivery to main desk (extra cost). Mail delivered to private mailbox with key. *Recreation Facilities*: pool table, exercise room, craft room, card room and 2 outdoor patios. Posted schedule of activities. Internal newsletter for residents. *Recreational Programs*: exercise, shopping, theatre, parties, entertainment, art classes, pet visiting, day trips and resident centred.

OTHER SERVICES: *Housekeeping*: daily and weekly (included in fee). *Laundry*: linen, towel & personal (included in fee); dry cleaning (extra cost). Transportation to medical appointments (extra cost) and for group social activities. 24-hour security. Nightly security checks. Telephone ($41.00/month). Cable TV ($41.00/month), Utilities (included in fee). Indoor parking. Lab fees. Foot care. Spa. Esthetician services. In-suite safe rental.

RENTAL INFORMATION: Rates may vary. Extra cost for 2nd person sharing suite ($660.00/month; $685.00/month for Assisted Living). Rent paid monthly. *Payment Options*: cheques, post-dated cheques, direct deposit and pre-authorized payments. Rent increases as per Provincial Tenancy Legislation, annual for resident with 3 months' notice given. Will help resident move into residence. Short-term respite available (both $95.00/day).

SYMPHONY SENIOR LIVING AT THE PALISADES

480 Metcalfe Street, Ottawa, ON K1S 3N6
Tel: (613) 565-5212 • Fax: (613) 565-8902
Email: **crc1palisades@symphonyseniorliving.com**
Website: **www.symphonyseniorliving.com/the-palisades.php**
Contact: **Sales & Marketing**
Capacity: **154 units** • Subsidies: **none**
Price: **$2,875.00 - $7,500.00/month**

Active and assisted retirement living in the heart of the Glebe near the Rideau Canal. Choice of renovated suites, many with views of the Rideau Canal and Pretoria Bridge. Enjoy your free time with Executive Chef prepared meals, busy social program with excursions to cultural and sporting events, exercise classes and wireless internet. Elegant dining rooms and lounges, heated indoor swimming pool, beauty/barber shop with spa, cinema room, ballroom for dances and so much more. Our health and wellness program with nurse available 24/7 if needed, offers peace of mind. Let us take care of the snow shoveling and maintenance so you may enjoy your new friends!

RESIDENCE INFORMATION: 16 years in operation. *On:* Isabella Street and Metcalfe Street. Decorated in 2007. Handrails in hallways. 10 floors, 2 elevators. Wheelchair accessible. *Funding Base:* Corporate/for profit. *Managed by:* Symphony Senior Living. *Average Waiting Period*: none. *Average Age*: 80. Can accommodate cognitively impaired people with restrictions (non-restraint residence therefore low level cognitive impairment only accepted). Can accommodate physically challenged people. Residents have a dress code (our residents dress for dinner). Smoke-free residence. Alcohol allowed (non-licensed residence therefore we do not charge for the alcohol when it is served). *Procedures to leave the premises on a*

temporary basis...notify the Reception Desk. *Languages:* English & French. Will accept Public Guardian and Trustee clients. Main doors of residence secured at night only. *Close to:* Public Transit, Shopping, Churches, Seniors' Centre, Library, Major Highway and Local Hospitals (The Ottawa Hospital - General and Civic Sites). *Predominant Cultural Group:* English. Member of ORCA. Licensed under the Retirement Homes Act.
STAFFING: *Available Staff/Services*: Pharmacy, Social Work, Recreation Therapy, Occupational Therapy (CCAC), Visiting Dentist, Physiotherapy, Denturist, Dietitian, Companions, Podiatry, Chaplaincy, Speech Pathology (CCAC), Audiology/Hearing Clinic, Certified Massage Therapist and Certified Reflexology. In-house full time physician and hairdresser. *External services arranged by:* residence and/or family/resident. Staff trained *re*: visually, hearing and cognitively impaired. 24-hour nursing and other staff. RPNs, HCAs and PSWs on staff. Can retain own MD. Staff members are bonded. Police Check or Vulnerable Person Screening is done for all new staff.
HEALTH SERVICES: Medication administration and/or supervision. Vitals monitored if required. Will accept and provide special assistance for residents who require oxygen, catheters, ostomies and feeding tubes. Assistance with dressing available (cost). Weekly assistance with bathing available (cost). Care plans done. Different levels of care available. Private Duty/Extra Care available. Assisted Living Area. Lab service (visiting). Residents can purchase outside resources and use agency of their choice. MD visits residents in their rooms/suites. Clinic area for medical visits.
ACCOMMODATION: *Choice of suites available*: bachelor, studio, 1-bedroom, 1-bedroom + den & 2-bedroom suites. *In all suites*: window coverings, light fixtures, linens, stove, fire alarm, smoke detector, emergency response system with wearable pendant/bracelet, air conditioning (Incremental Units located under windows) and thermostats for heating & cooling. 90% of suites have full kitchens, 10% kitchenettes, full fridge and convection/microwave. Private bathrooms with grab bars, tubs and showers with non-slip surfaces. Can have own phone number provided by residence. Unfurnished suites, furnished suites available for short stays. *Restrictions on electrical appliances*: must pass safety inspection. Suites can be shared (by couples only). Pets allowed (must receive annual shots; must be leashed in common areas, resident must be able to look after own).
DINING SERVICE: All meals included in fee and served in dining room daily. *Sittings per meal:* Breakfast: 1, Lunch: 2, Dinner: 2. *Menu choices available:* Breakfast: 1, Lunch: 10, Dinner: 15. *Guest Meals*: Available. *Special Diets*: Vegetarian, Low Salt, Diabetic and Gluten Free. Most special diets accommodated. Unlimited snacks available at any time. Party facilities. Executive Chef prepared meals. Breakfast is à la carte.
AMENITIES AND ACTIVITIES: Parking available (outdoor, for visitors: free and indoor & outdoor for residents: $160.00/month). 7 *lounges with:* TVs (2), pianos (2), computers (1), pool table and cards (2). *Residence has a:* library, chapel, barber/beauty shop and laundry room(s) (no cost). Residence provides newspaper delivery to individual suite. Mail delivered to private mailbox with key. *Recreation Facilities*: billiards, exercise room, craft room, card room, swimming pool, movie theatre, ballroom, computer room, pub lounge, spa and outdoor patio. Posted schedule of activities. Internal newsletter for residents. *Recreational Programs*: shopping, theatre, parties, entertainment, art classes, pet visiting, day trips, aquafit, Yoga, Tai Chi, ballroom dancing, line dancing, dinner theatre, computer training and languages.
OTHER SERVICES: *Housekeeping*: weekly for Independent; daily for Assisted Living (included in fee). *Laundry*: linen & towel (included in fee); personal (extra cost; included for Assisted Living) & dry cleaning

(extra cost). Extra cost for laundry services depends on level of care. Transportation for group social activities. 24-hour security. Nightly security checks. Telephone (extra cost). Cable TV & Utilities (included in fee). Emergency Response Pendant.
RENTAL INFORMATION: Rates may vary. Extra cost for 2nd person sharing suite (cost depends on level of care). Rent paid monthly. *Payment Options*: cheques, post-dated cheques, direct deposit and pre-authorized payments. Rent increases as per Provincial Tenancy Legislation, annual with 3 months' notice given. Short-term respite (cost depends on level of care) and trial stays (complimentary) available.

SYMPHONY SENIOR LIVING AT THE REDWOODS

2604 Draper Avenue, Ottawa, ON K2H 9B1
Tel: (613) 828-8540 • Fax: (613) 828-7554
Email: **crcredwoods@symphonyseniorliving.com**
Website: **www.symphonyseniorliving.com/the-redwoods.php**
Contact: **Sales & Marketing**
Capacity: **240 residents** • Subsidies: **none**
Price: **$2,625.00 - $5,100.00/month**

Newly renovated retirement community conveniently located in West Ottawa. Choice of several suite styles in varying price ranges with full kitchens and balconies. Join our friendly and active community for chef-prepared meals and an activities program to meet everyone's interests. Our health and wellness program with nurse available 24/7 if needed, offers assistance in living and peace of mind and services to keep you active and feeling your best! Meet for ice cream (or martinis) in the bistro, swim in our heated pool or join a game of poker in the card room. There is always fun to be had! The service you deserve with care if needed.

RESIDENCE INFORMATION: 16 years in operation. *Near:* Baseline Road and Greenbank Road. Decorated in 2007. Handrails in hallways. 17 floors, 3 elevators. Wheelchair accessible. Central PA system. *Funding Base:* Corporate/for profit. *Managed by:* Symphony Senior Living. 210 units. *Average Waiting Period*: varies. *Average Age*: 82. Can accommodate cognitively impaired people with restrictions (no locked floors). Can accommodate physically challenged people with restrictions (evaluation required). Smoke-free residence. Alcohol allowed. *Procedures to leave the premises on a temporary basis...*advise staff of absence. *Languages:* English & French. Will accept Public Guardian and Trustee clients. Main doors of residence secured at all times. *Close to:* Public Transit, Shopping, Churches, Seniors' Centre, Library, Major Highway and Local Hospital (Queensway-Carleton Hospital). *Predominant Cultural Group:* English speaking. Member of ORCA. Licensed under the Retirement Homes Act.
STAFFING: *Available Staff/Services*: Pharmacy, Social Work (CCAC), Recreation Therapy, Occupational Therapy, Physiotherapy, Companions, Podiatry, Chaplaincy, Speech Pathology, Chiropody, Audiology/Hearing Clinic, Hairdresser, Esthetician, Massage Therapy and Yoga. *External services arranged by:* residence and/or family/resident. Staff trained *re*: visually, hearing and cognitively impaired. 24-hour nursing and other staff. RPNs and PSWs on staff. Visiting MD (weekly appointment and on call). Can retain own MD. Staff members are bonded. Police Check or Vulnerable Person Screening is done for all new staff.
HEALTH SERVICES: Medication administration and/or supervision. Vitals monitored if required. Will accept (but not provide special assistance for) residents who require ostomies and feeding tubes. Will accept and provide special assistance for residents who require oxygen and catheters. Emergency wrist button or pendant to call nursing department in emergency. Assistance with dressing available (cost). Weekly assistance with bathing available (cost). Care plans done. Different levels of care available. Private Duty/Extra Care available. Assisted Living Area. Lab service (visiting). Residents can purchase outside resources and use agency of their choice. MD visits residents in their rooms/suites. Clinic area for medical visits. Will help locate higher level of care if needed.

ACCOMMODATION: *Choice of suites available*: 2-bedroom (90) & 1-bedroom (120) units. *In all suites*: locks, kitchenette, full-size fridge, stove, storage, window coverings, light fixtures, fire alarm, smoke detector, call bell, emergency response system with wearable pendant/bracelet, air conditioning (residents can have air conditioners installed in windows at extra fee) and thermostats for heating. 95% of suites have balconies. Private bathrooms with grab bars, tubs and showers. Can have own phone number provided by residence. Unfurnished suites, furnished suites available for short stays. *Restrictions on electrical appliances*: no dishwashers or portable washing machines. Suites can be shared (by couples only). Pets allowed (must be able to care for own).
DINING SERVICE: All meals included in fee and served in dining room daily. *Sittings per meal:* Breakfast: 1, Lunch: 2, Dinner: 2. *Menu choices available:* Lunch: 2, Dinner: 2. Alternates are always available other than the 2 meal choices. *Guest Meals*: Available. *Special Diets*: Vegetarian, Low Salt, Diabetic and Gluten Free. Most special diets accommodated. Tray service to room if ill (no charge for a maximum time of 21 days). Unlimited snacks available at any time. Party facilities. Breakfast is continental-style. Residents can choose meals included in level of care or add extra.
AMENITIES AND ACTIVITIES: Parking available (outdoor, for visitors and indoor for residents). *5 lounges with:* TVs (2), piano (1), pool table (1) and cocktail bar (1). Guest suites available. *Residence has a:* library, visiting library, chapel, barber/beauty shop, visiting hairdresser and laundry room(s) (no cost). Resident can arrange newspaper delivery to individual suite (extra cost). Mail delivered to private mailbox with key. *Recreation Facilities*: pool table, billiards, shuffleboard, exercise room, craft room, card room, swimming pool and outdoor deck with BBQ. Posted schedule of activities. Internal newsletter for residents. *Recreational Programs*: exercise, shopping, theatre, parties, entertainment, art classes, pet visiting, day trips and varied program with resident input.
OTHER SERVICES: *Housekeeping*: daily and weekly (included in fee; depends on level of care). *Laundry*: linen & towel (included in fee); personal (extra cost; included for Assisted Living) & dry cleaning (extra cost). Extra cost for laundry services depends on level of care. Transportation for group social activities. Nightly security checks. Telephone & Cable TV (extra cost). Utilities (included in fee).
RENTAL INFORMATION: Rates may vary. We offer 9 types of suites. Extra cost for 2nd person sharing suite (cost depends on level of care). Rent paid monthly. *Payment Options*: cheques, post-dated cheques, direct deposit and pre-authorized payments. Rent increases as per Provincial Tenancy Legislation (rent portion per RTA; care portion separate), annual for resident with 3 months' notice given. Short-term respite (cost depends on level of care) and trial stays (complimentary) available.

THE ROCKCLIFFE RETIREMENT RESIDENCE

100 Island Lodge Road, Ottawa, ON K1N 0A2
Tel: (613) 562-3555 • Fax: (613) 562-7891
Email: **info@therockcliffe.com**
Website: **www.therockcliffe.com**
Contact: **Executive Director or Marketing Manager**
Capacity: **140 residents** • Subsidies: **none**
Price: **$4,200.00/month and up**

Surrounded by the beauty of the Rideau River and the tranquil charm of Rockcliffe Park - New Edinburgh neighbourhood, The Rockcliffe Retirement Residence provides the perfect setting and first rate amenities to maintain an independent and secure lifestyle. *The Rockcliffe: beautiful views, premier location and first class Signature Service!* An oasis to be discovered in the heart of the city.

RESIDENCE INFORMATION: 6 years in operation. *Near:* St. Patrick Street and Cobourg Street. Decorated in 2008. Handrails in hallways. 10 floors, 2 elevators. Wheelchair accessible. Central PA system. *Funding Base:* Corporate/for profit. *Managed by:* Signature Retirement Living. 127 units. *Average Waiting Period*: varies. *Average Age*: 82. Can sometimes accommodate cognitively impaired people

(Aging in Place). Can accommodate physically challenged people (Aging in Place). Residents have a dress code (must be dressed in common areas). Smoke-free residence. Alcohol allowed. *Procedures to leave the premises on a temporary basis*...sign out. *Languages:* English & French. Will accept Public Guardian and Trustee clients. Main doors of residence secured at night only. *Close to:* Public Transit, Shopping, Churches, Synagogues, Seniors' Centre, Library, Major Highway and Local Hospital (The Ottawa Hospital - General Site). Licensed under the Retirement Homes Act.

STAFFING: *Available Staff/Services*: Pharmacy, Social Work, Recreation Therapy, Occupational Therapy (CCAC), Physiotherapy, Denturist, Dietitian, Companions, Podiatry, Chaplaincy, Speech Pathology (CCAC), Chiropody and Audiology/Hearing Clinic. *External services arranged by:* residence and/or family/resident. Staff trained *re*: visually, hearing and cognitively impaired. 24-hour nursing and other staff. RNs, RPNs and PSWs on staff. Visiting MD (as needed). Can retain own MD. Police Check or Vulnerable Person Screening is done for all new staff.

HEALTH SERVICES: Medication administration and/or supervision. Vitals monitored if required. Will accept (but not provide special assistance for) residents who require feeding tubes. Will accept and provide special assistance for residents who require oxygen, catheters and ostomies. Assistance with dressing available ($600.00/month). Weekly assistance with bathing available ($85.00/month). *Extra baths:* $25.00/bath. Care plans done. Different levels of care available. Assisted Living Area ($1,700.00/ month; 1 - 2 month waiting period). Lab service (visiting, $25.00/visit). Residents can purchase outside resources and use agency of their choice. MD visits residents in their rooms/suites. Clinic area for medical visits. Will help locate higher level of care if needed.

ACCOMMODATION: *Choice of suites available*: 1-bedroom, 1-bedroom + den & 2-bedroom suites. *In all suites*: kitchenette, storage, bar fridge, window coverings, microwave, light fixtures, linens, fire alarm, smoke detector, sprinkler, call bell, air conditioning (central) and thermostats for heating & cooling. Private bathrooms with call bells, grab bars, showers with non-slip surfaces and elevated toilet seats. In-suite cable TV provided by residence (residence charges extra $43.00/month). Can have own phone number provided by residence (residence charges extra $30.00/month). Furnished & unfurnished suites available. *Restrictions on electrical appliances*: must be approved by Maintenance Manager. Suites can be shared (by couples only). Pets allowed (with approval of Management).

DINING SERVICE: All meals included in fee and served in dining room daily. *Guest Meals*: Breakfast $6.00, Lunch $10.00, Dinner $15.00. *Special Diets*: Vegetarian, Low Salt and Diabetic. Tray service to room if ill (no charge for a maximum time of 4 days). Unlimited snacks available at any time. Party facilities.

AMENITIES AND ACTIVITIES: Parking available (outdoor, for visitors and residents). *4 lounges with:* TVs (3), piano (1), computer (1) and library (1). Guest suites available ($100.00/night). *Residence has a:* library, visiting library, chapel, barber/beauty shop, visiting hairdresser and laundry room(s) (no cost). Residence provides newspaper delivery to individual suite. Mail delivered to private mailbox with key. *Recreation Facilities*: exercise room, greenhouse, craft room, card room, therapeutic spa and whirlpool. Posted schedule of activities. Internal newsletter for residents. *Recreational Programs*: exercise, art classes, shopping, theatre, parties, entertainment, pet visiting, day trips, book club, Yoga, bridge and cooking classes.

OTHER SERVICES: *Housekeeping*: weekly (included in fee; daily tidy with bed making). *Laundry*: linen & towel (included in fee); personal ($85.00/single; $100.00/couple/month) & dry cleaning (extra cost). Transportation to medical appointments (free shuttle services) and for group social activities (free shuttle service, occasional cost). 24-hour security. Nightly security checks. Telephone ($30.00/month). Cable TV ($43.00/month). Utilities (included in fee).

RENTAL INFORMATION: Rates may vary. Prices are subject to change. Extra cost for 2nd person sharing suite ($725.00/month). Rent paid monthly. *Payment Options*: cheques, post-dated cheques, direct deposit and pre-authorized payments. Rent increases as per Provincial Tenancy Legislation with 3 months' notice given. Will help resident move into residence (extra cost). Short-term respite and trial stays available (both $100.00/day).

◆ OTTAWA WEST (CARLETON PLACE) ◆

WATERSIDE - A V!VA RETIREMENT COMMUNITY

105 McNeely Avenue, Carleton Place, ON K7C OB6
Tel: (613) 253-2010
Email: **info@thewaterside.ca**
Website: **www.thewaterside.ca**
Capacity: **88 units**
Subsidies: **none**

Situated on the banks of the Mississippi River, Waterside features a heated indoor saltwater pool, stretch and strength studios, pub, movie theatre, beauty salon, concierge services and more. Our spacious suites range in size from studio to 2-bedroom. Three healthy and delicious meals are prepared fresh daily featuring a rotating menu of incredible options to satisfy every palette.

RESIDENCE INFORMATION: 6 years in operation. *On:* McNeely Avenue near Townline Road. Decorated in 2008. 4 floors, 3 elevators. Wheelchair accessible. Central PA system. *Funding Base:* Corporate/for profit. *Owned and managed by:* V!VA Retirement Communities. *Average Waiting Period*: varies. Can accommodate physically challenged people. Smoke-free residence. Alcohol allowed. *Procedures to leave the premises on a temporary basis...*verbal notice to Concierge. *Languages:* English. Will accept Public Guardian and Trustee clients. Main doors of residence secured at night only. *Close to:* Public Transit, Shopping, Churches, Major Highway and Local Hospital (Carleton Place and District Memorial Hospital). Member of ORCA. Licensed under the Retirement Homes Act.
STAFFING: *Available Staff/Services*: Pharmacy, Social Work (CCAC), Recreation Therapy, Occupational Therapy (CCAC), Physiotherapy, Denturist, Dietitian (CCAC), Companions, Podiatry (CCAC), Chaplaincy, Speech Pathology (CCAC), Chiropody and Audiology/Hearing Clinic. *External services arranged by:* residence and/or family/resident. Staff trained *re*: visually and hearing impaired. 24-hour nursing and other staff. RNs, RPNs, HCAs, PSWs and UCPs on staff. Visiting MD (weekly). Can retain own MD. Police Check or Vulnerable Person Screening is done for all new staff.
HEALTH SERVICES: Medication administration and/or supervision. Vitals monitored if required. Will accept and provide special assistance for residents who require oxygen. Assistance with dressing available (cost). Weekly assistance with bathing available (cost). Care plans done. Different levels of care available. Residents can purchase outside resources and use agency of their choice. Clinic area for medical visits. Will help locate higher level of care if needed.
ACCOMMODATION: *Choice of suites available*: studio, 1-bedroom, 1-bedroom + den & 2-bedroom units. *In all suites*: locks, kitchenette, full-size fridge, microwave, storage, walk-in closet, window coverings, light fixtures, fire alarm, smoke detector, sprinkler, call bell, air conditioning (central) and thermostats for heating & cooling. Private bathrooms with call bells, grab bars and showers with non-slip surfaces. In-suite cable TV provided by residence. Can have own phone number if resident arranges with phone company. Furnished & unfurnished suites available. *Restrictions on electrical appliances*: CSA approval and inspection by our Environmental Coordinator. Suites can be shared, roommate picked by resident. Pets allowed.
DINING SERVICE: All meals included in fee and served in dining room daily. *Guest Meals*: Available. *Special Diets*: Vegetarian, Low Salt and Diabetic. Tray service to room if ill (no charge as long as doctor orders). Unlimited snacks available at any time. Party facilities. Open pantry.
AMENITIES AND ACTIVITIES: Parking available (outdoor, for visitors and residents). *6 lounges with:* TVs (4) and piano (1). Guest suites available. *Residence has a:* library, chapel, barber/beauty shop, visiting hairdresser and laundry room(s) (no cost). Resident can arrange newspaper delivery to individual suite. Mail delivered to private mailbox with key. *Recreation Facilities*: pool table, shuffleboard, exercise room,

craft room, card room, swimming pool, theatre, pub, bistro, garden and proximity to walking trail. Posted schedule of activities. Internal newsletter for residents. *Recreational Programs*: exercise, shopping, theatre, parties, entertainment, art classes, pet visiting, day trips, Yoga, aquafit, massage and other interest classes as directed by residents.
OTHER SERVICES: *Housekeeping*: weekly (included in fee; if required more often, additional charges apply). *Laundry*: linen, towel & personal (included in fee); dry cleaning (as per local dry cleaner). Transportation for group social activities. 24-hour security. Telephone (as per telephone provider). Cable TV & Utilities (included in fee). Internet (as per internet provider).
RENTAL INFORMATION: Extra cost for 2nd person sharing suite. Rent paid monthly. *Payment Options*: cheques, post-dated cheques, direct deposit and pre-authorized payments. Rent increases as per Provincial Tenancy Legislation, annual for resident with 3 months' notice given. Will help resident move into residence (extra cost). Short-term respite and trial stays available.

♦ OTTAWA WEST (KANATA) ♦

THE ROYALE - KANATA

3501 Campeau Drive, Ottawa, ON K2K 0C1
Tel: (613) 592-6426
Email: **Kanata@theroyale.ca**
Website: **www.theroyale.ca**
Contact: **Community Relations Manager**
Capacity: **158 units** • Subsidies: **none**
Price: **$3,500.00 - $6,900.00/month**

This new state-of-the-art residence offers amenities, features and benefits that are unsurpassed. With the largest selection of 1-bedroom & 2-bedroom retirement suite/apartments in Ottawa, these suites boast complete kitchens with stainless steel fridge and stove, hardwood flooring and spacious bathrooms that will allow you to feel refreshed and relaxed from the moment you step in the door. Offering both Independent and Assisted Living lifestyles, this is truly '*Aging in Place*'. With a saltwater pool, on-site theatre, demonstration kitchen, greenhouse, woodworking workshop, wine bar and wine cellar, this is living life to its fullest.

RESIDENCE INFORMATION: *Near:* March Road and Campeau Drive. Decorated in 2009. Handrails in some of the hallways. 5 floors, 4 elevators. Wheelchair accessible. *Funding Base:* Corporate/for profit. *Owned by:* Leisureworld Senior Care Corporation. *Average Waiting Period*: none. *Average Age*: 82. Can accommodate cognitively impaired people (based on assessment with our Director of Wellness). Can accommodate physically challenged people (based on assessment with our Director of Wellness). Smoke-free residence. Alcohol allowed. We welcome visitors anytime. *Languages:* English, French & some Spanish. Will accept Public Guardian and Trustee clients. Main doors of residence secured at all times. *Close to:* Public Transit, Shopping, Churches, Seniors' Centre, Library, Major Highway and Local Hospital (Queensway-Carleton Hospital). Member of ORCA. Licensed under the Retirement Homes Act.
STAFFING: *Available Staff/Services*: Pharmacy, Social Work (CCAC), Occupational Therapy (CCAC), Visiting Dentist, Physiotherapy, Denturist, Dietitian (CCAC), Companions, Podiatry (CCAC), Speech Pathology (CCAC) and Physician (in-house). *External services arranged by:* residence and/or family/ resident. Staff trained *re*: visually, hearing and cognitively impaired. 24-hour nursing and other staff. RNs, RPNs and PSWs on staff. Visiting MD. Can retain own MD. Police Check or Vulnerable Person Screening is done for all new staff.
HEALTH SERVICES: Medication administered if required. Vitals monitored if required. Will accept (but not provide special assistance for) residents who require catheters and feeding tubes. Will accept and

provide special assistance for residents who require oxygen and ostomies. Assistance with dressing available (cost). Weekly assistance with bathing available (cost). Care plans done (our Director of Wellness will create a personalized plan of care). Different levels of care available. Private Duty/Extra Care available. Assisted Living Area is secured to accommodate residents with dementia. Residents can purchase outside resources and use agency of their choice. MD visits residents in their rooms/suites. Clinic area for medical visits. Will help locate higher level of care if needed.

ACCOMMODATION: *Choice of suites available*: 1-bedroom & 2-bedroom suites; studios only available on Assisted Living Floor. *In all suites*: locks, kitchenette, microwave, patio/balcony, light fixtures, smoke detector, sprinkler, call bell, emergency response system with wearable pendant/bracelet, air conditioning (central) and thermostats for heating & cooling. Full-size stainless steel fridge & stove in all suites; Assisted Living has kitchenettes with stainless steel bar fridge. Private bathrooms with call bells, tubs and showers with non-slip surfaces. In-suite cable TV provided by residence. Can have own phone number provided by residence (residence charges extra $40.00/month). Unfurnished suites, furnished suites available for short stays. Suites can be shared (by couples only). Small pets welcome (dog walking service available).

DINING SERVICE: All meals included in fee and served in dining room daily. *Menu choices available:* Breakfast: 5, Lunch: 6, Dinner: 6. *Guest Meals*: Available. *Special Diets*: Vegetarian, Low Salt and Diabetic. Tray service to room if ill (no charge as long as doctor orders). 2 snacks/day and unlimited snacks available at any time. Party facilities.

AMENITIES AND ACTIVITIES: Parking available (outdoor, for visitors and indoor & outdoor for residents). 12 lounges. *Residence has a:* library, visiting library, chapel, barber/beauty shop, visiting hairdresser, laundry room(s) (no cost) and tuck/gift shop (open 8:00 a.m. -10:00 p.m.). Resident can arrange newspaper delivery to individual suite (extra cost). Mail delivered to private mailbox with key. *Recreation Facilities*: pool table, exercise room, greenhouse, craft room, card room, swimming pool, theatre, demonstration kitchen, Bocce Ball Court, woodworking workshop, wine cellar and computer lounge. Posted schedule of activities. Internal newsletter for residents. *Recreational Programs*: shopping, theatre, parties, entertainment, art classes, pet visiting, day trips, Yoga, Tai Chi, cooking classes, Men's breakfast, adult education, etc....

OTHER SERVICES: *Housekeeping*: weekly (included in fee, daily bed making is available). *Laundry*: linen & towel (extra cost); personal (available for an extra cost) & dry cleaning (Hillary's Dry Cleaning is available). Transportation to medical appointments and for group social activities (extra cost). 24-hour security. Nightly security checks (available for a fee). Telephone & Cable TV (extra cost). Utilities (included in fee).

RENTAL INFORMATION: Rates may vary. 1-bedroom to 2-bedroom suites size ranging from 420 sq. ft. to 1,184 sq. ft. Extra cost for 2nd person sharing suite ($600.00/month). Rent paid monthly. *Payment Options*: cheques, post-dated cheques, direct deposit and pre-authorized payments. Rent increases are a set percentage indexed to inflation as per Provincial Tenancy Legislation, annual for resident with 3 months' notice given. Short-term respite and trial stays available (both $99.00/day).

♦ OTTAWA WEST (NEPEAN) ♦

CRYSTAL VIEW LODGE

6 Meridian Place, Ottawa, ON K2G 6L9
Tel: (613) 225-4560 • Fax: (613) 225-6960
Email: **5075-manager@holidaytouch.com**
Website: **www.crystalviewlodge.com**
Contact: **Community Managers**
Capacity: **119 units** • Subsidies: **none**
Price: **$2,495.00/month and up (rates may vary)**

Holiday Retirement believes retirement living should be relaxing and carefree, spent doing the things you love. That's why our communities provide a unique independent retirement lifestyle in a warm and welcoming environment. In one affordable, all-inclusive month-to-month rent, residents enjoy 3 delicious chef-prepared meals daily, enriching activities to share with friendly neighbours, housekeeping service, complimentary transportation, and so much more. Each Holiday community also features 2 sets of compassionate, dedicated live-in Managers available 24/7 to ensure safety and security. We do not provide any health care services; however, residents are welcome to receive services from any outside home health care provider of their choice to help them continue enjoying life at our community. Discover the peace-of-mind, happiness and fulfillment you deserve. Contact us today to schedule your personal tour!

RESIDENCE INFORMATION: 15 years in operation. *Near:* Centrepointe Crescent and Tallwood Avenue. Handrails in hallways. 3 floors, 1 elevator. Wheelchair accessible. Central PA system. *Funding Base:* Corporate/for profit. *Owned and managed by:* Holiday Retirement. *Average Waiting Period*: none. *Average Age*: 82. Can sometimes accommodate cognitively impaired people. Can accommodate physically challenged people (must be independent, wheelchair, walkers, scooters are welcome). Residents have a dress code (casual, no sleepwear in common areas). Smoking allowed (in own apartment). Alcohol allowed (in own apartment). *Procedures to leave the premises on a temporary basis...*Overnight & Holidays: let Front Office know. *Languages:* English. Will accept Public Guardian and Trustee clients. Main doors of residence secured at night only. *Close to:* Public Transit, Shopping, Churches, Synagogues, Seniors' Centre, Library, Major Highway and Local Hospital (Queensway-Carleton Hospital).
STAFFING: *External services arranged by:* family/resident. 24-hour staff. Can retain own MD. Staff members are bonded.
HEALTH SERVICES: Will accept (but not provide special assistance for) residents who require oxygen, catheters, ostomies and feeding tubes. Residents can purchase outside resources and use agency of their choice. Will help locate higher level of care if needed (information available from Front Office and local government health agencies).
ACCOMMODATION: *Choice of suites available*: studio, 1-bedroom, 2-bedroom & Cottages. *In all suites*: locks, kitchenette, storage, window coverings, light fixtures, linens, smoke detector, sprinkler, call bell, air conditioning (through the wall) and thermostats for heating. Most have patios or balconies. Private bathrooms with call bells, grab bars, tubs and showers with non-slip surfaces. In-suite cable TV provided by residence. Can have own phone number if resident arranges with phone company. Furnished & unfurnished suites available. *Restrictions on electrical appliances*: no hot plates or stoves. Suites can be shared, roommate picked by resident. Pets allowed.
DINING SERVICE: All meals included in fee and served in dining room daily. *Sittings per meal:* Breakfast: 1, Lunch: 1, Dinner: 1. *Menu choices available:* Breakfast: 2, Lunch: 4, Dinner: 4. *Guest Meals*: Breakfast $8.00, Lunch $10.00, Dinner $8.00. *Special Diets*: Vegetarian, Low Salt and Diabetic. Tray service to room if ill. 1 snack/day. Party facilities. Private Dining Area. Large meal of day served at noon-time. Fresh fruit, coffee, tea & goodies available all day.

AMENITIES AND ACTIVITIES: Parking available (outdoor, for visitors and residents). *4 lounges with:* TV (1), piano (1), exercise room (1) and pool table & shuffleboard (1). Guest suites available ($75.00/ night). *Residence has a:* library, chapel, barber/beauty shop and laundry room(s) (no cost). Resident can arrange newspaper delivery to individual suite. Mail delivered to private mailbox with key. *Recreation Facilities*: pool table, billiards, shuffleboard, exercise room, craft room and card room. Posted schedule of activities. Internal newsletter for residents. *Recreational Programs*: exercise, shopping, theatre, parties, entertainment, art classes, pet visiting, day trips and resident suggestions.
OTHER SERVICES: *Housekeeping*: weekly (included in fee). *Laundry*: linen & towel (included in fee). Free laundry rooms for personal use. Transportation to medical appointments and for group social activities. 24-hour security. Cable TV & Utilities (included in fee). Garages (extra cost).
RENTAL INFORMATION: Rates may vary. Rate listed above is based on single occupancy. Extra cost for 2nd person sharing suite (please call for specifics). Rent paid monthly. *Payment Options*: cheques, post-dated cheques and pre-authorized payments. Rent increases indexed to inflation as per Provincial Tenancy Legislation, annual for resident with 3 months' notice given. Will help resident move into residence. Trial stays available (see Managers).

LYNWOOD PARK LODGE RETIREMENT RESIDENCE

1 Eaton Street, Ottawa, ON K2H 9P1
Tel: (613) 596-6969 • Fax: (613) 596-5688
Email: **amatcheskie@regallc.com**
Website: **www.regallc.com**
Contact: **Amy Matcheskie, Community Relations Manager**
Capacity: **155 residents •** Subsidies: **none**
Price: **$2,010.00 - $4,430.00/month**

Lynwood Park Lodge one of Ottawa's premier residences, offers the perfect environment to enjoy an active lifestyle, customized to reflect your unique individuality. Our stunning front entrance, complete with solarium and floor-to-ceiling windows, inviting the beautiful morning sunshine in for all to enjoy. Our gorgeous mezzanine level offers an ideal space for either quiet reflective reading by our fireplaces or a private place to visit with for friends and family.

RESIDENCE INFORMATION: 25 years in operation. *Near:* Richmond Road and Lynhar Avenue. Decorated in 2013. Handrails in hallways. 6 floors, 2 elevators. Wheelchair accessible. Central PA system. *Funding Base:* Corporate/for profit. 142 units. *Average Waiting Period*: 2 - 4 months. *Average Age*: 82. Can accommodate cognitively impaired people with restrictions. Residents have a dress code. Smoke-free residence. Alcohol allowed. *Restrictions around Visitors/Visiting Hours:* for security, outside doors are locked at 8:00 p.m., access available. *Procedures to leave the premises on a temporary basis...*sign out at Front Desk. *Languages:* English & some French. *Close to:* Public Transit, Shopping, Churches, Seniors' Centre, Library, Major Highway and Local Hospital (Queensway-Carleton Hospital). Licensed under the Retirement Homes Act.
STAFFING: *Available Staff/Services*: Pharmacy, Social Work (CCAC), Recreation Therapy, Occupational Therapy (CCAC), Visiting Dentist, Physiotherapy (CCAC), Denturist, Dietitian, Companions, Podiatry, Chaplaincy, Speech Pathology (CCAC), Chiropody, Audiology/Hearing Clinic and Massage Therapy. *External services arranged by:* residence and/or family/resident. Staff trained *re*: visually, hearing and cognitively impaired. 24-hour nursing staff. RNs, RPNs, HCAs, PSWs and UCPs on staff. Can retain own MD. Police Check or Vulnerable Person Screening is done for all new staff.
HEALTH SERVICES: Medication administration and/or supervision. Vitals monitored if required. Will accept (but not provide special assistance for) residents who require oxygen. Weekly assistance with bathing available ($77.00/month). Care plans done. Different levels of care available. Assisted Living

Services ($895.00/month). Private Duty/Extra Care available. Lab service (visiting, $30.00/visit). Residents can purchase outside resources and use agency of their choice. Clinic area for medical visits. Will help locate higher level of care if needed (we help liaise with CCAC).

ACCOMMODATION: *Choice of suites available*: studio (100) & 1-bedroom (42) suites. *In all suites*: locks, window coverings, smoke detector, call bell, emergency response system with wearable pendant/bracelet, air conditioning (window units), thermostats for heating & cooling and security lock box. Private bathrooms with call bells and grab bars. In-suite cable TV provided by residence. Can have own phone number provided by residence (residence charges extra). Unfurnished suites, furnished suites available for short stays. *Restrictions on electrical appliances*: only auto shut-off appliances allowed. Suites can be shared (by couples only). Pets allowed (Pet Policy Agreement must be signed).

DINING SERVICE: All meals included in fee and served in dining room daily. *Sittings per meal:* Breakfast: 1, Lunch: 2, Dinner: 2. Breakfast is served from 7:30 a.m. to 9:00 a.m., Lunch is served either at 11:30 a.m. or 1:00 p.m., Dinner is served at either 4:45 p.m. or 6:00 p.m. *Menu choices available:* Breakfast: 2, Lunch: 2, Dinner: 2. *Guest Meals*: Breakfast $3.00, Lunch $10.00, Dinner $12.00. *Special Diets*: Vegetarian, Low Salt, Diabetic, Celiac, Pureed and Lactose Free. Tray service to room if ill (no charge for a maximum time of 7 days). 3 snacks/day. Party facilities.

AMENITIES AND ACTIVITIES: Parking available (outdoor, for visitors and residents). *2 lounges with:* TV (1), with solarium (1) and mezzanine level (1). Guest suites available ($67.00/night). *Residence has a:* library, visiting library, barber/beauty shop, laundry room(s) (no cost) and tuck/gift shop (open 10:00 a.m. - 11:15 a.m.). Banking services on premises (monthly). Resident can arrange newspaper delivery to individual suite (extra cost). Mail delivered to resident. *Recreation Facilities*: exercise room, craft room, card room, horticulture area, café, outdoor gardens and patio. Posted schedule of activities. Internal newsletter for residents. *Recreational Programs*: exercise, shopping, parties, entertainment, art classes, pet visiting, day trips, horticulture group and creative writing group.

OTHER SERVICES: *Housekeeping*: weekly. *Laundry*: linen & towel (included in fee); personal (extra cost). Transportation for group social activities. 24-hour security. Nightly security checks. Cable TV (extra cost - basic and combination package with Rogers). Utilities (included in fee). À la carte services individually priced.

RENTAL INFORMATION: Rates may vary. Cost varies by room size. Extra cost for 2nd person sharing suite ($695.00/month). Rent paid monthly. *Payment Options*: cheques and pre-authorized payments. Rent increases as per Provincial Tenancy Legislation, annual for resident with 3 months' notice given. Short-term respite ($98.00/day) and trial stays ($67.00/day) available.

Did you know?

Senioropolis Inc. has created some very unique Apps for our users. Our **Retirement Home Cost Calculator App** allows users to determine the difference in cost between living in their own home vs. living in a retirement setting. This App is available in the Apple store for IPhones. Our *Free* **GPS App** allows users to search our database of homes for contact information and will map them from their current location to the home of their choice. This works across Canada and contains information on all retirement residences and long-term care homes that are active on our site. This GPS App is available for IPhones and Androids. Go to the store of your device and enter *Senioropolis* into the search bar.

THE COURT AT BARRHAVEN

1111 Longfields Drive, Ottawa, ON K2J 5A9
Tel: (613) 823-2763 • Fax: (613) 823-2712
Email: **5251-manager@holidaytouch.com**
Website: **www.courtatbarrhaven.com**
Contact: **Community Managers**
Capacity: **135 residents** • Subsidies: **none**
Price: **$2,495.00/month and up (rates may vary)**

Holiday Retirement believes retirement living should be relaxing and carefree, spent doing the things you love. That's why our communities provide a unique independent retirement lifestyle in a warm and welcoming environment. In one affordable, all-inclusive month-to-month rent, residents enjoy 3 delicious chef-prepared meals daily, enriching activities to share with friendly neighbours, housekeeping service, complimentary transportation, and so much more. Each Holiday community also features 2 sets of compassionate, dedicated live-in Managers available 24/7 to ensure safety and security. We do not provide any health care services; however, residents are welcome to receive services from any outside home health care provider of their choice to help them continue enjoying life at our community. Discover the peace-of-mind, happiness and fulfillment you deserve. Contact us today to schedule your personal tour!

RESIDENCE INFORMATION: 11 years in operation. *Near:* Stranherd Street and Longfields Drive. Decorated in 2003. Handrails in hallways. 3 floors, 1 elevator. Wheelchair accessible. Central PA system. *Funding Base:* Corporate/for profit. *Owned and managed by:* Holiday Retirement. 114 units. *Average Waiting Period*: none. *Average Age*: 82. Can sometimes accommodate cognitively impaired people. Can accommodate physically challenged people (mobility aids welcome, CCAC home care available). Residents have a dress code (casual, no sleepwear in common areas). Smoking allowed (in apartments). Alcohol allowed (in apartments). *Procedures to leave the premises on a temporary basis...*Overnight & Holidays: let Front Office know. *Languages:* English & French. Will accept Public Guardian and Trustee clients. Main doors of residence secured at night only. *Close to:* Public Transit, Shopping, Churches, Seniors' Centre, Library, Major Highway and Local Hospital (Queensway-Carleton Hospital).
STAFFING: *External services arranged by:* family/resident. 24-hour staff. Can retain own MD. Staff members are bonded. Police Check or Vulnerable Person Screening is done for all new staff.
HEALTH SERVICES: Will accept (but not provide special assistance for) residents who require oxygen, catheters, ostomies and feeding tubes. Residents can purchase outside resources and use agency of their choice. Will help locate higher level of care if needed (information is available from the office and CCAC).
ACCOMMODATION: *Choice of suites available*: studio, 1-bedroom & 2-bedroom suites. *In all suites*: locks, kitchenette, storage, window coverings, light fixtures, linens, fire alarm, smoke detector, sprinkler, call bell, air conditioning (wall unit) and thermostats for heating & cooling. All apartments have fridges with freezers. Most units have patios/balconies. Private bathrooms with call bells and showers with non-slip surfaces. In-suite cable TV provided by residence. Can have own phone number if resident arranges with phone company. Unfurnished suites. *Restrictions on electrical appliances*: no hot plates or stoves. Suites can be shared, roommate picked by resident. Pets allowed.
DINING SERVICE: All meals included in fee and served in dining room daily. *Sittings per meal:* Breakfast: 1, Lunch: 1, Dinner: 1. *Menu choices available:* Breakfast: 4, Lunch: 6, Dinner: 6. *Guest Meals*: Breakfast $9.00, Lunch $11.00, Dinner $9.00. *Special Diets*: Vegetarian, Low Salt and Diabetic. Tray service to room if ill. 2 snacks/day. Party facilities. Fresh Fruit, coffee, tea & goodies available all day.
AMENITIES AND ACTIVITIES: Parking available (outdoor, for visitors and indoor & outdoor for residents). *4 lounges with:* TV (1), piano (1), computer kiosks (1) and pool table (1). Guest suites available ($89.00/night). *Residence has a:* library, chapel, barber/beauty shop, laundry room(s) (no cost) and tuck/gift shop (open once/week for 2 hours). Banking services on premises (once/month). Resident can arrange newspaper delivery to individual suite. Mail delivered to private mailbox with key. *Recreation Facilities*: pool table,

billiards, exercise room, craft room, card room, screened gazebo and outside deck. Posted schedule of activities. Internal newsletter for residents. *Recreational Programs*: exercise, shopping, theatre, parties, entertainment, art classes, pet visiting, day trips and resident suggestions.
OTHER SERVICES: *Housekeeping*: weekly (included in fee). *Laundry*: linen & towel (included in fee). Free laundry facilities for personal use on each floor. Transportation to medical appointments and for group social activities. 24-hour security. Telephone (resident pays own phone). Cable TV & Utilities (included in fee). Free outdoor parking; extra cost for garages.
RENTAL INFORMATION: Rates may vary. Rate listed above is based on single occupancy. Extra cost for 2nd person sharing suite ($710.00/month; Please call for specifics). Rent paid monthly. *Payment Options*: cheques, post-dated cheques and pre-authorized payments. Rent increases indexed to inflation as per Provincial Tenancy Legislation, annual for resident with 3 months' notice given. Short-term respite and trial stays available (see Managers).

♦ PERTH ♦

BAYBRIDGE - CAROLINA RETIREMENT SUITES

105 North Street, Perth, ON K7H 3R1
Tel: (613) 267-7000 • Fax: (613) 267-7975
Email: **CLeBreton@carolinasuites.ca**
Website: **www.carolinasuites.ca**
Contact: **Chantale LeBreton**
Capacity: **120 residents** • Subsidies: **none**
Price: **$2,577.00 - $3,999.00/month**

Carolina Retirement Suites is located on the banks of the Tay River in the beautiful town of Perth. We feature 2-bedroom, 1-bedroom and studio suites with many services included while at the same time encouraging an independent lifestyle.

RESIDENCE INFORMATION: 14 years in operation. *On:* Wilson Street and North Street. Decorated in 2006. 4 floors, 2 elevators. Wheelchair accessible. *Funding Base:* Corporate/for profit. *Owned and managed by:* BayBridge Senior Living. 84 units. *Average Waiting Period*: 6 - 12 months. *Average Age*: 85. Can accommodate cognitively impaired people with restrictions. Can accommodate physically challenged people. Residents have a dress code (full dress; appropriate dress for dining room). Smoking allowed (designated smoking area 9-metres from building). Alcohol allowed (in suite or in common areas while served by staff). *Procedures to leave the premises on a temporary basis...*Short-term: sign out book at Front Door. Overnight: please mention it to the staff. Holidays: please inform the General Manager as a courtesy discount may apply. *Languages:* English. Main doors of residence secured at night only. *Close to:* Shopping, Churches, Seniors' Centre, Library, Major Highway and Local Hospital (Perth and Smiths Falls District Hospital). Member of ORCA & Perth Chamber of Commerce. Licensed under the Retirement Homes Act.
STAFFING: *Available Staff/Services*: Pharmacy, Social Work (CCAC), Recreation Therapy, Occupational Therapy (CCAC), Physiotherapy (CCAC), Dietitian (CCAC), Podiatry, Speech Pathology (CCAC) and Audiology/Hearing Clinic. *External services arranged by:* residence and/or family/resident. Staff trained *re*: visually, hearing and cognitively impaired. 24-hour staff. RPNs, HCAs and PSWs on staff. Can retain own MD. Police Check or Vulnerable Person Screening is done for all new staff.
HEALTH SERVICES: Medication administration (required to use our pharmacy - no extra charge) and/or supervision. Vitals monitored if required. Will accept (but not provide special assistance for) residents who require oxygen, catheters, ostomies and feeding tubes. Assistance with dressing available ($179.00/month).

Weekly assistance with bathing available ($74.00/month). Care plans done. Lab service (visiting). Residents can purchase outside resources and use agency of their choice. MD visits residents in their rooms/suites. Will help locate higher level of care if needed (can provide additional care for an extra cost).
ACCOMMODATION: *Choice of suites available*: 2-bedroom (6), 1-bedroom (44) & studio (34) units. *In all suites*: locks, kitchenette, bar fridge, window coverings, light fixtures, fire alarm, smoke detector, sprinkler, emergency response system with wearable pendant/bracelet, air conditioning (wall unit) and thermostats for heating & cooling. Private bathrooms with tubs and showers with non-slip surfaces. Can have own phone number if resident arranges with phone company (residence charges extra). Unfurnished suites, furnished suites available for short stays. *Restrictions on electrical appliances*: must be CSA approved and require an automatic shut-off. Suites can be shared (by couples only), roommate picked by resident. Small pets are welcome (fish, birds, cats, small friendly dogs).
DINING SERVICE: All meals included in fee and served in dining room daily. *Sittings per meal:* Breakfast: 1, Lunch: 2, Dinner: 2. *Menu choices available:* Breakfast: 2, Lunch: 2, Dinner: 2. *Guest Meals*: Breakfast $4.00, Lunch $6.00, Dinner $8.00. *Special Diets*: Vegetarian, Low Salt, Diabetic, Celiac and Most Therapeutic Diets. Tray service to room if ill (no charge for a maximum time of 7 days). 2 snacks/day. Party facilities.
AMENITIES AND ACTIVITIES: Parking available (outdoor, for visitors and residents). *5 lounges with:* TV (1), piano (1) and sitting room (1). Guest suites available ($89.50/night). *Residence has a:* library, visiting library, barber/beauty shop, visiting hairdresser, laundry room(s) (no cost) and tuck/gift shop (hours will vary). Resident can arrange newspaper delivery to individual suite. Mail delivered to individual suite. *Recreation Facilities*: shuffleboard and activity room. Posted schedule of activities. Internal newsletter for residents. *Recreational Programs*: exercise, shopping, parties, entertainment and day trips.
OTHER SERVICES: *Housekeeping*: weekly (daily tidy available at an extra cost). *Laundry*: linen & towel (Linen & Towel Service is $86.00/month); personal ($150.00/ month). Complimentary laundry soap. Transportation to medical appointments and for group social activities (cost determined by length of trip). 24-hour security. Nightly security checks. Telephone (available through local suppliers). Cable TV (extra cost). Utilities (included in fee). Emergency call system.
RENTAL INFORMATION: Rates may vary. Studios - $2,577.00/month & up; 2-bedrooms - $3,999.00/ month. Extra cost for 2nd person sharing suite ($650.00/month). Rent paid monthly. *Payment Options*: pre-authorized payments. Rent increases as per Provincial Tenancy Legislation, annual for resident with 3 months' notice given. Short-term respite ($92.50/day) and trial stays ($100.00/week) available.

◆ PETERBOROUGH ◆

APPLEWOOD RETIREMENT RESIDENCE

1500 Lansdowne Street West, Peterborough, ON K9J 2A2
Tel: (705) 749-1500 • Fax: (705) 749-1991
Email: **betty@applewoodrr.com**
Website: **www.applewoodrr.com**
Contact: **Betty Smith**
Capacity: **136 residents** • Subsidies: **none**
Price: **$2,667.00 - $3,308.00/month**

Applewood Retirement Residence is a well-established, warm retirement community nestled on 2 acres of beautifully landscaped gardens in picturesque Peterborough. Every suite has a balcony or patio. We offer short-term trial, convalescent, respite, or winter stays as well as permanent residency. Join us for a few weeks, a few months, or make Applewood your home.

RESIDENCE INFORMATION: 26 years in operation. *Near:* Kawartha Heights Boulevard on Lansdowne Street. Decorated in 2012. Handrails in hallways. 3 floors, 3 elevators. Wheelchair accessible. Central PA system. *Funding Base:* Corporate/for profit. *Owned by:* Private Investors. *Managed by:* Greenwood Retirement Communities. 125 units. *Average Waiting Period*: varies. *Average Age*: 87. Can accommodate cognitively impaired people (must be safe in their room on their own). Can accommodate physically challenged people with restrictions (3 barrier-free suites - must be safe in room by themselves). Residents have a dress code (no night wear in the dining room). Smoke-free residence. Alcohol allowed. *Procedures to leave the premises on a temporary basis...*sign out/notify Front Desk. *Languages:* English. Main doors of residence secured at night only. *Close to:* Public Transit, Shopping, Churches, Seniors' Centre, Major Highway and Local Hospital (Peterborough Regional Health Centre). Member of ORCA. Licensed under the Retirement Homes Act.
STAFFING: *Available Staff/Services*: Pharmacy, Social Work (CCAC), Recreation Therapy, Occupational Therapy (CCAC), Physiotherapy, Dietitian (CCAC), Podiatry (CCAC), Chaplaincy, Speech Pathology (CCAC) and Audiology/Hearing Clinic. *External services arranged by:* residence and/or family/resident. Staff trained *re*: visually, hearing and cognitively impaired. 24-hour nursing and other staff. RPNs, HCAs and PSWs on staff. Visiting MD (once monthly on-site - more often at his office). Can retain own MD. Police Check or Vulnerable Person Screening is done for all new staff.
HEALTH SERVICES: Medication administration and/or supervision. Vitals monitored if required. Will accept and provide special assistance for residents who require oxygen, catheters, ostomies and feeding tubes. Assistance with dressing available ($212.00/month). Weekly assistance with bathing available. *Extra baths:* $20.00/half hour. Care plans done. Different levels of care available. Lab service (visiting, $25.00/visit). Residents can purchase outside resources and use agency of their choice. Clinic area for medical visits. Will help locate higher level of care if needed (CCAC involvement; long-term care wait list).
ACCOMMODATION: *Choice of suites available*: private studio (97) or private 1-bedroom (28) suites. *In all suites*: locks, kitchenette, bar fridge, microwave, patio/balcony, window coverings, light fixtures, linens, smoke detector, call bell, emergency response system with wearable pendant/bracelet, air conditioning (in wall unit) and thermostats for heating & cooling. Private bathrooms with call bells, grab bars, tubs or walk-in showers with non-slip surfaces. In-suite cable TV provided by residence, satellite TV if resident arranges with satellite company (residence charges extra $40.00/month). Can have own phone number if resident arranges with phone company (residence charges extra $40.00/month). Unfurnished suites, furnished suites available for short stays. *Restrictions on electrical appliances*: no hot plates or frying pans. Suites can be shared (by couples only), roommate picked by resident. Pets allowed (no dogs; cats & birds allowed).
DINING SERVICE: All meals included in fee and served in dining room daily. *Sittings per meal:* Breakfast: 1, Lunch: 1, Dinner: 1. *Menu choices available:* Breakfast: 2, Lunch: 2, Dinner: 2. *Guest Meals*: Breakfast $4.00, Lunch $6.00, Dinner $8.00. *Special Diets*: Vegetarian, Low Salt, Diabetic, Celiac and Renal. Alternate menu available. Tray service to room if ill (no charge for a maximum time of 3 days). Unlimited snacks available at any time. Open pantry. Party facilities. Private dining room for family/guests.
AMENITIES AND ACTIVITIES: Parking available (outdoor, for visitors and indoor & outdoor for residents). *3 lounges with:* TVs (2) and pianos (2). Guest suites available ($50.00/night). *Residence has a:* library, chapel, barber/beauty shop, laundry room(s) (no cost) and tuck/gift shop (open Thursday; 3:00 p.m. – 4:00 p.m.). Residence provides newspaper delivery to individual suite. Mail delivered to individual suite. *Recreation Facilities*: shuffleboard, exercise room, craft room, card room, plant room, raised garden beds and horseshoes. Posted schedule of activities. Internal newsletter for residents. *Recreational Programs*: exercise, shopping, theatre, parties, entertainment, art classes, pet visiting, day trips, lunch club, book club, craft classes and dementia program.
OTHER SERVICES: *Housekeeping*: daily and weekly (included in fee). *Laundry*: linen & towel (included in fee); personal (extra cost; included in Supportive & Assisted Programs) & dry cleaning (extra cost - pick up & delivery on-site). Residents may do own laundry in our free laundry room. Transportation to medical

appointments ($10.00/round trip). 24-hour security. Nightly security checks. Telephone ($40.00/month - local & long distance). Cable TV ($40.00/month). Utilities (included in fee). Covered parking ($40.00/month).
RENTAL INFORMATION: Rates may vary. Studio: $2,667.00 to $3,306.00/month; 1-bedroom suites: $3,500.00 to $4,382.00/month. Extra cost for 2nd person sharing suite ($450.00/month; $900.00/person on Supportive Program). Rent paid monthly. *Payment Options*: cheques and pre-authorized payments. Rent increases: as per regulation, annual with 3 months' notice given. Short-term respite and trial stays available (both $50.00/day, for 7- 30 days).

RUBIDGE RETIREMENT RESIDENCE

246-270 Rubidge Street, Peterborough, ON K9J 3P2
Tel: (705) 748-4000 • Fax: (705) 749-3335
Email: **outreach@rubidge.ca**
Website: **www.rubidge.ca**
Contact: **Barb Overwijk**
Capacity: **115 residents** • Subsidies: **none**
Price: **$2,358.00 - $4,268.00/month**

Large variety of suite types and prices from a cozy studio to a large 2-bedroom penthouse suite. We offer the largest selection of room styles at prices less than you might expect. All meals and snacks are included and prepared by experienced chefs. We have an on-site Medical Director Dr. Susan Tainsh to meet any medical concerns right in your own home. We are close to downtown with plenty of parking for visitors and residents.

RESIDENCE INFORMATION: 27 years in operation. *On:* Rubidge Street and Sherbrooke Street. Decorated in 2013. Handrails in hallways. 4 floors, 2 elevators. Wheelchair accessible. Central PA system. *Funding Base:* Corporate/for profit. *Owned by:* Retirement Living Centres. 101 units. *Average Waiting Period*: varies. *Average Age*: 80. Can sometimes accommodate cognitively impaired people (beginning stages only). Can accommodate physically challenged people (wheelchair equipped). Smoking allowed (on back porch or in room). Alcohol allowed (within licensed areas, and in personal suite). *Procedures to leave the premises on a temporary basis...*sign out and alert Nurse in charge. *Languages:* English. Will accept Public Guardian and Trustee clients. Main doors of residence secured at night only. *Close to:* Public Transit, Shopping, Churches, Seniors' Centre, Library and Local Hospital (Peterborough Regional Health Centre). Member of ORCA. Licensed under the Retirement Homes Act.
STAFFING: *Available Staff/Services*: Pharmacy, Social Work (CCAC), Recreation Therapy, Occupational Therapy (CCAC), Physiotherapy (CCAC), Dietitian (CCAC), Companions, Podiatry, Chaplaincy, Speech Pathology (CCAC), Chiropody and Massage Therapy. *External services arranged by:* family/resident. Staff trained *re*: visually, hearing and cognitively impaired. 24-hour nursing and other staff. RNs, RPNs and PSWs on staff. Visiting MD (bi-weekly). Can retain own MD. Police Check or Vulnerable Person Screening is done for all new staff.
HEALTH SERVICES: Medication administration and/or supervision. Vitals monitored if required. Will accept and provide special assistance for residents who require oxygen, catheters, ostomies and feeding tubes. Assistance with dressing available (cost). Weekly assistance with bathing available ($50.00/month). *Extra baths:* $12.50/half hour. Care plans done. Different levels of care available. Private Duty/Extra Care available ($25.00/hour). Lab service ($30.00/visit). Residents can purchase outside resources and use agency of their choice. Clinic area for medical visits. Will help locate higher level of care if needed (via CCAC).
ACCOMMODATION: *Choice of suites available*: all are private suites. *In all suites*: locks, storage, window coverings, light fixtures, linens, smoke detector, call bell, air conditioning (central & window units) and thermostats for heating & cooling. Private bathrooms with grab bars, tubs and showers with non-slip surfaces. In-suite cable TV provided by residence. Can have own phone number if resident

arranges with phone company. Furnished & unfurnished suites available. Suites can be shared (by couples only). Pets allowed (cats, birds, fish and small dogs).
DINING SERVICE: All meals included in fee and served in dining room daily. *Sittings per meal:* Breakfast: 1, Lunch: 1, Dinner: 1. *Menu choices available:* Breakfast: 2, Lunch: 2, Dinner: 2. *Guest Meals*: Breakfast $5.00, Lunch $7.00, Dinner $10.00. *Special Diets*: Vegetarian, Low Salt, Diabetic, Puree/Minced and Low Fat. Tray service to room if ill (no charge or restrictions). Unlimited snacks available at any time. Open pantry. Party facilities. Private family dining room.
AMENITIES AND ACTIVITIES: Parking available (outdoor, for visitors and residents). *5 lounges with:* TVs (4), piano (1) and pool table (1). Guest suites available ($50.00/night). *Residence has a:* library, visiting library, chapel, barber/beauty shop, visiting hairdresser and laundry room(s) (no cost). Residence provides newspaper delivery to individual suite. Mail delivered to main desk. *Recreation Facilities*: greenhouse, card room, spa room, movie theatre and hair salon. Posted schedule of activities. Internal newsletter for residents. *Recreational Programs*: exercise, shopping, theatre, parties, entertainment, art classes, pet visiting and day trips.
OTHER SERVICES: *Housekeeping*: weekly. *Laundry*: linen & towel (included in fee). Transportation for group social activities. 24-hour security. Nightly security checks. Telephone, Cable TV & Utilities (included in fee).
RENTAL INFORMATION: Rates may vary. Extra cost for 2nd person sharing suite ($650.00/month). Rent paid monthly. *Payment Options*: cheques, post-dated cheques, direct deposit and pre-authorized payments. Rent increases as per Provincial Tenancy Legislation, annual for resident with 3 months' notice given. Short-term respite and trial stays available (both $80.00/day).

SHERBROOKE HEIGHTS

1434 Sherbrooke Street, Peterborough, ON K9K 2L7
Tel: (705) 750-1020 • Fax: (705) 750-1135
Email: **5407-manager@holidaytouch.com**
Website: **www.sherbrookeheights.com**
Contact: **Community Managers**
Capacity: **114 units** • Subsidies: **none**
Price: **$2,546.00/month and up (rates may vary)**

Holiday Retirement believes retirement living should be relaxing and carefree, spent doing the things you love. That's why our communities provide a unique independent retirement lifestyle in a warm and welcoming environment. In one affordable, all-inclusive month-to-month rent, residents enjoy 3 delicious chef-prepared meals daily, enriching activities to share with friendly neighbours, housekeeping service, complimentary transportation, and so much more. Each Holiday community also features 2 sets of compassionate, dedicated live-in Managers available 24/7 to ensure safety and security. We do not provide any health care services; however, residents are welcome to receive services from any outside home health care provider of their choice to help them continue enjoying life at our community. Discover the peace-of-mind, happiness and fulfillment you deserve. Contact us today to schedule your personal tour!

RESIDENCE INFORMATION: 14 years in operation. *Near:* Sherbrooke Street and Braeley Avenue. Handrails in hallways. 3 floors, 1 elevator. Wheelchair accessible. Central PA system. *Funding Base:* Corporate/for profit. *Owned and managed by:* Holiday Retirement. *Average Waiting Period*: varies. *Average Age*: 83. Can sometimes accommodate cognitively impaired people. Can accommodate physically challenged people (must be independent; wheelchair, walkers, scooters are welcome). Residents have a dress code (casual, no sleepwear in common areas). Smoking allowed (in own apartment). Alcohol allowed (in own apartment). *Procedures to leave the premises on a temporary basis...*Overnight & Holidays: please inform Front Office. *Languages:* English. Will accept Public

Guardian and Trustee clients. Main doors of residence secured at night only. *Close to:* Public Transit, Shopping, Churches, Seniors' Centre, Library, Major Highway and Local Hospital.
STAFFING: *External services arranged by:* family/resident. 24-hour staff. Can retain own MD. Staff members are bonded.
HEALTH SERVICES: Will accept (but not provide special assistance for) residents who require oxygen, catheters, ostomies and feeding tubes. Residents can purchase outside resources and use agency of their choice. Will help locate higher level of care if needed (information).
ACCOMMODATION: *Choice of suites available*: studio, 1-bedroom & 2-bedroom/2-bath suites. *In all suites*: locks, kitchenette, bar fridge, storage, window coverings, light fixtures, linens, smoke detector, sprinkler, call bell, air conditioning (wall unit) and thermostats for heating & cooling. Most with balconies. Private bathrooms with call bells, grab bars, tubs and showers with non-slip surfaces. In-suite cable TV provided by residence. Furnished & unfurnished suites available. *Restrictions on electrical appliances*: no hot plates/stoves. Suites can be shared, roommate picked by resident. Pets allowed.
DINING SERVICE: All meals included in fee and served in dining room daily. *Sittings per meal:* Breakfast: 1, Lunch: 1, Dinner: 1. *Menu choices available:* Breakfast: 5, Lunch: 6, Dinner: 5. *Guest Meals*: Breakfast $8.00, Lunch $10.00, Dinner $8.00. *Special Diets*: Vegetarian, Low Salt and Diabetic. Tray service to room if ill. 2 snacks/day. Party facilities. Private Dining Area. Large meal served at noon-time. Fresh fruit, tea, coffee & goodies available all day.
AMENITIES AND ACTIVITIES: Parking available (outdoor, for visitors and indoor & outdoor for residents). *4 lounges with:* TV (1), pianos (2), computer kiosks (1) and pool table (1). Guest suites available ($75.00/night). *Residence has a:* library, chapel, barber/beauty shop and laundry room(s) (no cost). Resident can arrange newspaper delivery to individual suite. Mail delivered to private mailbox with key. *Recreation Facilities*: pool table, billiards, shuffleboard, exercise room, craft room and card room. Posted schedule of activities. Internal newsletter for residents. *Recreational Programs*: exercise, shopping, theatre, parties, entertainment, art classes, pet visiting and day trips.
OTHER SERVICES: *Housekeeping*: weekly (included in fee). *Laundry*: linen & towel (included in fee). Free laundry rooms for personal use. Transportation to medical appointments and for group social activities. 24-hour security. Cable TV & Utilities (included in fee).
RENTAL INFORMATION: Rates may vary. Rate listed above is based on single occupancy. Extra cost for 2nd person sharing suite (please call for specifics). Rent paid monthly. *Payment Options*: cheques, post-dated cheques and pre-authorized payments. Rent increases indexed to inflation as per Provincial Tenancy Legislation, annual for resident with 3 months' notice given. Trial stays available (see Managers).

◆ PICKERING ◆

ABBEYLAWN MANOR RETIREMENT HOME

534 Rodd Avenue, Pickering, ON L1W 2B2
Tel: (905) 509-2582 • Fax: (905) 509-5467
Toll Free: (888) 999-5668
Email: **dof@abbeylawnmanor.com**
Website: **www.abbeylawnmanor.com**
Contact: **Lorianne Muir**
Capacity: **60 residents** • Subsidies: **none**
Price: **$2,640.00 - $4,890.00/month**

Picturesque setting by Lake Ontario surrounded by the Petticoat Creek Conservation Area. A Country Inn setting in the city.

RESIDENCE INFORMATION: 7 years in operation. *Near:* Whites Road and Highway 401. Decorated in 2007. Handrails in hallways. 4 floors, 1 elevator. Wheelchair accessible. Central PA system. *Funding Base:* Corporate/for profit. *Owned by:* Abbeylawn Manor Inc. 57 units. *Average Waiting Period*: none. *Average Age*: 83. Can accommodate cognitively impaired people (Enhanced Living with secure indoor/outdoor area). Smoking allowed (designated outdoor areas). *Procedures to leave the premises on a temporary basis...*Short-term: sign out/in. Overnight & Holidays: advise the Nurse and sign out/in. *Languages:* English. Will accept Public Guardian and Trustee clients. Main doors of residence secured at night only. *Close to:* Public Transit, Shopping, Churches, Seniors' Centre, Library, Major Highway and Local Hospital (Rouge Valley Health System). *Predominant Cultural Group:* Canadian / English speaking. Member of ORCA & Board of Trade Pickering/Ajax. Licensed under the Retirement Homes Act.
STAFFING: *Available Staff/Services*: Pharmacy, Social Work (CCAC), Recreation Therapy, Occupational Therapy (CCAC), Physiotherapy (CCAC), Dietitian (CCAC), Companions, Podiatry, Chaplaincy, Speech Pathology (CCAC) and Physiotherapy Assistant (3 days/week). *External services arranged by:* residence and/or family/resident. Staff trained *re*: visually, hearing and cognitively impaired. 24-hour nursing and other staff. RNs, RPNs, PSWs and UCPs on staff. Visiting MD (weekly/phone consult 24/7). Can retain own MD. Police Check or Vulnerable Person Screening is done for all new staff.
HEALTH SERVICES: Medication administration and/or supervision. Vitals monitored if required. Will accept and provide special assistance for residents who require oxygen, catheters and ostomies. Assistance with dressing available ($34.00/hour). Weekly assistance with bathing available. *Extra baths:* $17.00/bath. Care plans done. Different levels of care available. Private Duty/Extra Care available ($34.00/hour). Assisted Living Area ($1,035.00/month). Separate unit for residents with dementia. Lab service (visiting, $25.00/visit). Residents can purchase outside resources and use agency of their choice. MD visits residents in their rooms/suites. Will help locate higher level of care if needed (contact with CCAC Care Coordinator to initiate placement papers).
ACCOMMODATION: *Choice of suites available*: small, medium, large, studio apartment with kitchenette; penthouse. *In all suites*: locks, storage, window coverings, light fixtures, linens, smoke detector, air conditioning (window units if desired) and call bell. Studio has kitchenette with bar fridge & microwave. All common areas have air conditioning. Private bathrooms with call bells, grab bars, tubs and showers. In-suite cable TV if resident arranges with cable company. Can have own phone number if resident arranges with phone company. Unfurnished suites, furnished suites available for short stays. *Restrictions on electrical appliances*: must be CSA approved. Suites can be shared (by couples only). Pets allowed (Pet Policy Agreement is required).
DINING SERVICE: All meals included in fee and served in dining room daily. *Sittings per meal:* Breakfast: 1, Lunch: 1, Dinner: 1. *Menu choices available:* Breakfast: 4, Lunch: 2, Dinner: 2. *Special Diets*: Vegetarian, Low Salt, Diabetic and Therapeutic. Tray service to room if ill (no charge for a maximum time of 3 days). 3 snacks/day and unlimited snacks available at any time. Open pantry. Cost varies on assistance needed - all based on $34.00/hour. Party facilities.
AMENITIES AND ACTIVITIES: Parking available (outdoor, for visitors and residents). *4 lounges with:* TVs (3) and pianos (2). *Residence has a:* library, visiting library, chapel, barber/beauty shop and Tuck Cart (door to door, twice/month). Residence provides newspaper delivery to main desk. Mail delivered to individual suite. *Recreation Facilities*: exercise room, craft room and card room. Posted schedule of activities. Internal newsletter for residents. *Recreational Programs*: exercise, shopping, theatre, parties, entertainment, art classes, pet visiting and day trips.
OTHER SERVICES: *Housekeeping*: weekly (included in fee). *Laundry*: linen, towel & personal (included in fee); dry cleaning (extra cost). Transportation for group social activities. 24-hour security. Nightly security checks. Telephone & Cable TV (resident orders both services). Utilities (included in fee).
RENTAL INFORMATION: Rates may vary. Small - $2,640.00/month; medium - $2,845.00/month; large - $3,415.00/month; studio apartment with kitchenette - 3,855.00/month; Assisted & Secured Living: small - $3,675.00/month; medium - $3,880.00/month; large - $4,450.00/month; studio apartment with kitchenette - $4,890.00/month; penthouse - $4,890.00/month. Extra cost for 2nd person sharing suite ($780.00/month

or $1,815.00/month in Assisted Living). Rent paid monthly. *Payment Options*: cheques, post-dated cheques and pre-authorized payments. Rent increases as per Provincial Tenancy Legislation (Tenant Protection Act), annual for resident with 90 days' notice given. Will help resident move into residence. Short-term respite and trial stays available (both $97.50/day).

ORCHARD VILLA RETIREMENT RESIDENCE

1955 Valley Farm Road, Pickering, ON L1V 3R6
Tel: (905) 831-2641 • Fax: (905) 831-5033
Toll Free: (866) 471-9039
Email: **mgaudet@clmi.ca**
Website: **www.orchardvilla.ca**
Contact: **Meghan Gaudet**
Capacity: **74 residents** • Subsidies: **none**
Price: **$2,950.00 - $4,125.00/month (rates may vary)**

Orchard Villa is nestled in a residential area in the community of Pickering, just minutes away from the Pickering Town Centre, City Hall, Pickering Public Library and a variety of shopping centres. Orchard Villa boasts a home-like environment. Our beautiful Victoria Courtyard has a wonderful array of perennials and annuals and our atrium is a tropical oasis complete with a waterfall and a koi sanctuary. That is just the surroundings. Our residents choose Orchard Villa because of the home like atmosphere created by all who live and work here. *Orchard Villa Retirement Residence: Where everyone is family!*

RESIDENCE INFORMATION: 34 years in operation. *Near:* Highway 2 and Brock Road. Decorated in 2006. Handrails in hallways. 2 floors, 1 elevator. Wheelchair accessible. Central PA system. *Funding Base:* Corporate/for profit. *Owned and managed by:* Community Lifecare Inc. 61 units. *Average Waiting Period*: 2 - 4 months. *Average Age*: 84. Can accommodate cognitively impaired & physically challenged people with restrictions. Residents have a dress code (casual attire at lunch & supper). Smoking allowed (at main entrance). Alcohol allowed (and served). *Procedures to leave the premises on a temporary basis*...inform staff. *Languages:* English. Will accept Public Guardian and Trustee clients. Main doors of residence secured at all times. *Close to:* Public Transit, Shopping, Churches, Seniors' Centre, Library, Major Highway and Local Hospital (Rouge Valley Health System - Ajax and Pickering Health Centre Site). Licensed under the Retirement Homes Act.
STAFFING: *Available Staff/Services*: Pharmacy, Social Work (CCAC), Recreation Therapy, Occupational Therapy (CCAC), Physiotherapy (CCAC), Dietitian (CCAC), Companions, Podiatry (CCAC), Chaplaincy, Hair Salon and Walker Repair. *External services arranged by:* family/resident. Staff trained *re*: visually, hearing and cognitively impaired. 24-hour nursing and other staff. RPNs, HCAs, PSWs and UCPs on staff. Visiting MD (24-hours/day based upon on call). Can retain own MD. Police Check or Vulnerable Person Screening is done for all new staff.
HEALTH SERVICES: Medication administration (some restrictions may apply) and/or supervision. Vitals monitored if required. Will accept (but not provide special assistance for) residents who require oxygen and catheters. Weekly assistance with bathing available. *Extra baths:* $105.00/month. Care plans done. Different levels of care available. Lab service (visiting, $25.00/visit). Residents can purchase outside resources and use agency of their choice. MD visits residents in their rooms/suites. Will help locate higher level of care if needed (CCAC is contacted to determine the level of care the resident needs).
ACCOMMODATION: *Choice of suites available*: private (46) & 1-bedroom (15) apartments. *In all suites*: locks, storage, window coverings, light fixtures, linens, fire alarm, smoke detector, emergency response system with wearable pendant/bracelet, air conditioning (available only in the 1-bedroom apartments). Sprinkler system in designated areas. Private bathrooms with grab bars, tubs and showers with non-slip surfaces. In-suite cable TV provided by residence. Can have own phone number provided by residence (residence charges extra $30.00/month). Unfurnished suites, furnished suites available for short stays.

Restrictions on electrical appliances: must be CSA approved; no hot plates. Suites can be shared (by couples only). Pets allowed (must be approved by General Manager and a contract signed).

DINING SERVICE: All meals included in fee and served in dining room daily. *Sittings per meal:* Breakfast: 1, Lunch: 1, Dinner: 1. *Menu choices available:* Breakfast: 2, Lunch: 2, Dinner: 2. *Guest Meals*: Breakfast $4.00, Lunch $5.00, Dinner $7.00. *Special Diets*: Vegetarian, Low Salt and Diabetic. Tray service to room if ill (no charge as long as doctor orders). 3 snacks/day. Party facilities. Open pantry. Wine served at dinner every Sunday evening.

AMENITIES AND ACTIVITIES: Parking available (outdoor, for visitors and residents). *3 lounges with:* TVs (2). *Residence has a:* library, visiting library, chapel, barber/beauty shop, visiting hairdresser, laundry room(s) (no cost) and tuck/gift shop (open Monday, Wednesday, Friday; 10:00 a.m.- 11:00 a.m.). Resident can arrange newspaper delivery to main desk (extra cost). Mail delivered to individual mailbox. *Recreation Facilities*: pool table, billiards, shuffleboard, exercise room, craft room and card room. Full-time program director on staff. Posted schedule of activities. Internal newsletter for residents. *Recreational Programs*: exercise, shopping, theatre, parties, entertainment, art classes, pet visiting and day trips.

OTHER SERVICES: *Housekeeping*: weekly (included in fee). *Laundry*: linen, towel & personal (included in fee). Personal laundry is ironed for residents. Transportation for group social activities. 24-hour security. Nightly security checks. Telephone (extra cost). Cable TV & Utilities (included in fee). Meals. RPN Supervision. Medication administration. Programs & activities.

RENTAL INFORMATION: Rates may vary. Studio - $2,950.00/month & up; 1-bedroom suite - $4,000.00/ month & up. Extra cost for 2nd person sharing suite ($650.00/month). Rent paid monthly. *Payment Options*: pre-authorized payments. Rent increases are a set percentage as per Provincial Tenancy Legislation, annual for resident with 3 months' notice given. Short-term respite ($79.00/day) and trial stays available (based on availability).

V!VA PICKERING RETIREMENT COMMUNITY

1880 Glengrove Road (at Kingston Road), Pickering, ON L1V 0C6
Tel: (905) 831-2088
Email: **pickering@vivalife.ca**
Website: **www.vivalife.ca**
Capacity: **137 units**
Subsidies: **none**

Located across from the Pickering Town Centre and near the Pickering Recreation Centre, V!VA Pickering features a wellness spa with an indoor saltwater pool, movie theatre, concierge services and more. Spacious suites range in size from studio to 2-bedroom with options for Independent and Assisted Living. Three healthy and delicious meals are prepared fresh daily.

RESIDENCE INFORMATION: New residence. *On:* Kingston Road and Glengrove Road. Decorated in 2012. Handrails in some of the hallways. 7 floors, 3 elevators. Wheelchair accessible. Central PA system. *Funding Base:* Corporate/for profit. *Owned and managed by:* V!VA Retirement Communities. *Average Waiting Period*: none. Can accommodate cognitively impaired people (early stage Alzheimer's and dementia). Can accommodate physically challenged people. Smoke-free residence. Alcohol allowed. *Procedures to leave the premises on a temporary basis...*advise Concierge. *Languages:* English. Will accept Public Guardian and Trustee clients. Main doors of residence secured at night only. *Close to:* Public Transit, Shopping, Churches, Seniors' Centre, Library, Major Highway and Local Hospital. Member of ORCA. Licensed under the Retirement Homes Act.

STAFFING: *Available Staff/Services*: Pharmacy, Social Work (CCAC), Recreation Therapy, Occupational Therapy (CCAC), Visiting Dentist, Physiotherapy (CCAC), Denturist, Dietitian (CCAC), Companions, Podiatry (CCAC), Chaplaincy, Speech Pathology (CCAC), Chiropody and Audiology/Hearing Clinic.

External services arranged by: residence and/or family/resident. Staff trained *re*: visually, hearing and cognitively impaired. 24-hour nursing and other staff. RNs, RPNs, HCAs and PSWs on staff. Visiting MD (weekly or as needed). Can retain own MD. Police Check or Vulnerable Person Screening is done for all new staff.
HEALTH SERVICES: Medication administration and/or supervision. Vitals monitored if required. Will accept and provide special assistance for residents who require oxygen, catheters and ostomies. Assistance with dressing available (cost). Weekly assistance with bathing available (cost). Care plans done. Different levels of care available. Private Duty/Extra Care available. Assisted Living Area. Lab service (visiting). Residents can purchase outside resources and use agency of their choice. MD visits residents in their rooms/suites. Clinic area for medical visits. Will help locate higher level of care if needed.
ACCOMMODATION: *Choice of suites available*: studio, junior 1-bedroom, 1-bedroom, 1-bedroom + den & 2-bedroom units. *In all suites*: locks, storage, bar fridge, microwave, window coverings, light fixtures, fire alarm, smoke detector, sprinkler, emergency response system with wearable pendant/bracelet, air conditioning (central) and thermostats for heating & cooling. Kitchenettes with full-size fridge and microwave provided in Independent Living Suites only. Private bathrooms with call bells, grab bars, showers with non-slip surfaces and elevated toilet seats. In-suite cable TV provided by residence. Can have own phone number if resident arranges with phone company. Furnished & unfurnished suites available. *Restrictions on electrical appliances*: CSA approval and inspection by our Environmental Coordinator. Suites can be shared, roommate picked by resident. Pets allowed (size restrictions).
DINING SERVICE: All meals included in fee and served in dining room daily. *Guest Meals*: Available. *Special Diets*: Vegetarian, Low Salt and Diabetic. Tray service to room if ill (no charge as long as doctor orders). Unlimited snacks available at any time. Party facilities. Open pantry. Children's menu available.
AMENITIES AND ACTIVITIES: Parking available (outdoor, for visitors and residents). *10 lounges with:* TVs (7) and piano (1). Guest suites available. *Residence has a:* library, chapel, barber/beauty shop and laundry room(s) (no cost). Banking services on premises. Mail delivered to private mailbox with key. *Recreation Facilities*: pool table, billiards, shuffleboard, exercise room, greenhouse, craft room, card room, swimming pool, pub, movie theatre, spa, massage room, stretch & strength studios and raised garden beds. Posted schedule of activities. Internal newsletter for residents. *Recreational Programs*: exercise, shopping, theatre, parties, entertainment, art classes, pet visiting, day trips and V!VAfit program for cardio, strength, balance & flexibility.
OTHER SERVICES: *Housekeeping*: weekly (included in fee). *Laundry*: linen & towel (included in fee): personal & dry cleaning (extra cost). Transportation for group social activities (aboard shuttle bus). Nightly security checks. Telephone (extra cost). Cable TV & Utilities (included in fee).
RENTAL INFORMATION: Extra cost for 2nd person sharing suite. Rent paid monthly. *Payment Options*: cheques, post-dated cheques, direct deposit and pre-authorized payments. Rent increases as per Provincial Tenancy Legislation, annual for resident with 3 months' notice given. Will help resident move into residence (extra cost). Short-term respite and trial stays available.

♦ PORT PERRY ♦

PORT PERRY VILLA

15987 Simcoe Street, Port Perry, ON L9L 1N5
Tel: (905) 985-3312 • Fax: (905) 985-8797
Toll Free: (866) 778-4552
Email: **darmstrong@regallc.com**
Website: **www.regallc.com**
Contact: **Debbie Armstrong**
Capacity: **138 residents** • Subsidies: **none**
Price: **$2,990.00 - $4,850.00/month**

With a reputation of welcoming warmth and small town charm Port Perry Villa offers a friendly and supportive atmosphere in a picturesque community. Newly opened in Fall 2009: a brand new 100 suite retirement community offering a wide variety of accommodations and amenities, from studios to 1-bedroom & 2-bedroom suites with or without balconies. Enjoy an independent and carefree lifestyle with the added pleasure of rewarding activities, superior amenities and the friendship of wonderful neighbours. *Affordable luxury awaits!*

RESIDENCE INFORMATION: 35 years in operation. *Near:* Highway 7A and Simcoe Street. Decorated in 2009. 4 floors, 2 elevators. Wheelchair accessible. *Funding Base:* Corporate/for profit. 100 units. *Average Waiting Period*: 4 - 6 months. *Average Age*: 85. Can accommodate cognitively impaired people with restrictions (no secure area available). Can accommodate physically challenged people (medical assessment required). Smoking allowed (exterior smoking area). Alcohol allowed. *Procedures to leave the premises on a temporary basis...*Short-term: sign out. Overnight & Holidays: inform Management and sign out. *Languages:* English. Main doors of residence secured at night only. *Close to:* Public Transit, Shopping, Churches, Seniors' Centre, Library, Major Highway and Local Hospital (Lakeridge Health - Port Perry Site). *Predominant Cultural Group:* Canadian. Licensed under the Retirement Homes Act.
STAFFING: *Available Staff/Services*: Pharmacy, Recreation Therapy, Occupational Therapy, Physiotherapy, Dietitian, Podiatry (CCAC), Chaplaincy and Audiology/Hearing Clinic. *External services arranged by:* family/resident. Staff trained *re*: visually and hearing impaired. 24-hour nursing and other staff. RPNs and PSWs on staff. Can retain own MD. Police Check or Vulnerable Person Screening is done for all new staff.
HEALTH SERVICES: Medication administration (some restrictions based on assessed needs) and/or supervision. Vitals monitored if required. Will accept (but not provide special assistance for) residents who require oxygen, catheters and ostomies. Assistance with dressing available ($260.00/month). Weekly assistance with bathing available ($70.00/month). *Extra baths:* $35.00/bath. Care plans done. Different levels of care available. Private Duty/Extra Care available ($30.00 to $45.00/hour). Lab service (visiting, $20.00/visit). Residents can purchase outside resources and use agency of their choice. Clinic area for medical visits. Will help locate higher level of care if needed (will direct resident/family to CCAC and give information and a tour of Port Perry Nursing Home).
ACCOMMODATION: *Choice of suites available*: studios (10), 1-bedroom (69) & 2-bedroom (21) units. *In all suites*: locks, kitchenette with standard sink, fridge & space for microwave, window coverings, light fixtures, fire alarm, smoke detector, sprinkler, call bell, emergency response system with wearable pendant/bracelet (living room & bathroom), air conditioning (central) and thermostats for heating & cooling. Private ensuite bathrooms with grab bars, shower or traditional tub/shower unit with non-slip surfaces and elevated toilet seats. In-suite cable TV provided by residence. Can have own phone number provided by residence (residence charges extra). Unfurnished suites, furnished suites available for short stays. *Restrictions on electrical appliances*: appliances with auto shut-off, i.e. microwave, toaster, kettle, coffee maker. Suites can be shared, roommate picked by resident. Pets allowed (fish, bird, dog or cat under 20 lbs.; those with pets must upgrade to weekly housekeeping service).

DINING SERVICE: All meals included in fee and served in dining room daily. *Sittings per meal:* Breakfast: 1, Lunch: 1, Dinner: 1. *Menu choices available:* Breakfast: 2, Lunch: 2, Dinner: 2. *Guest Meals*: Breakfast $4.00, Lunch $6.00, Dinner $10.00. *Special Diets*: Vegetarian, Low Salt, Diabetic and Others (to be arranged). Tray service to room if ill (no charge for a maximum time of 14 days). Unlimited snacks available at any time. Party facilities. Open pantry. Two choices of main entree and dessert at dinner & supper.
AMENITIES AND ACTIVITIES: Parking available (outdoor, for visitors and residents). *3 lounges with:* TVs (2), pianos (2), Nintendo Wii (1) and books & birds (1). Guest suites available ($80.00/night). *Residence has a:* library, visiting library, chapel, barber/beauty shop, laundry room(s) (no cost) and tuck/gift shop (TBD). Banking services on premises (once/month). Resident can arrange newspaper delivery to individual suite. Mail delivered to private mailbox with key. *Recreation Facilities*: pool table, billiards, shuffleboard, exercise room, craft room, card room, large auditorium, chapel/theatre, pub-style café, games room, library with fireplace and TV lounge. Posted schedule of activities. Internal newsletter for residents. *Recreational Programs*: exercise, shopping, theatre, parties, entertainment, art classes, pet visiting, day and overnight trips.
OTHER SERVICES: *Housekeeping*: bi-weekly (included in fee). *Laundry*: personal ($125.00/month). Complimentary laundry facilities provided on each floor. Transportation for group social activities (Port Perry Villa van is used for group activities). 24-hour security. Nightly security checks. Telephone (extra cost). Cable TV & Utilities (included in fee).
RENTAL INFORMATION: Rates may vary. Studios - $2,990.00/month; 1-bedroom - $3,561.00/month; 1-bedroom with balcony - $3,570.00/month; 2-bedroom - $4,528.00/month; 2-bedroom with balcony - $4,850.00/month. Extra cost for 2nd person sharing suite ($750.00/month). Rent paid monthly. *Payment Options*: direct deposit and pre-authorized payments. Rent increases as per Provincial Tenancy Legislation, annual for resident with 3 months' notice given. Short-term respite ($95.00/day) and trial stays ($2,450.00/month) available.

◆ RICHMOND HILL ◆

DELMANOR ELGIN MILLS

80 Elgin Mills Road East, Richmond Hill, ON L4C 0L3
Tel: (905) 770-7963 • Fax: (905) 737-7446
Email: **sapplebaum@delmanor.com**
Website: **www.delmanor.com**
Contact: **Susan Applebaum**
Capacity: **145 residents** • Subsidies: **none**
Price: **$3,195.00 - $5,595.00/month**

Award winning Delmanor Elgin Mills offers both Independent and Assisted Living with attentive hotel-style service. Crisp linens and fine dining with menu choices and table service at each meal, with snacks all day in the café. There is a full Recreation & Living***Well*** personal coaching program. Enjoy the theatre, chapel, fitness room, private dining room, conservatory, lush private gardens as well as an exclusive Delmanor Bus for excursions. Proud member of ORCA.

RESIDENCE INFORMATION: 12 years in operation. *Near:* Yonge Street on Elgin Mills Road. Decorated in 2011. Handrails in hallways. 3 floors, 2 elevators. Wheelchair accessible. Central PA system. *Funding Base:* Corporate/for profit. *Owned by:* Tridel. *Managed by:* Delmanor Seniors Communities Inc. 126 units. *Average Waiting Period*: varies. *Average Age*: 84. Can accommodate cognitively impaired people with restrictions (must not wander/exit seek). Can accommodate physically challenged people (1-person transfer only). Residents have a dress code (appropriate attire in common areas). Smoke-free residence.

Alcohol allowed. *Procedures to leave the premises on a temporary basis*...sign in/out at Concierge. *Languages:* English. Will accept Public Guardian and Trustee clients. Main doors of residence secured at night only. *Close to:* Public Transit, Shopping, Churches, Synagogues, Seniors' Centre, Library, Major Highway and Local Hospital (MacKenzie Health formerly York Central Hospital). Member of ORCA & Richmond Hill Chamber of Commerce. Licensed under the Retirement Homes Act.

STAFFING: *Available Staff/Services*: Pharmacy, Social Work, Recreation Therapy, Occupational Therapy (CCAC), Visiting Dentist, Physiotherapy, Dietitian, Companions, Podiatry, Chaplaincy, Chiropody, Audiology/Hearing Clinic, Massage Therapist and Optician. *External services arranged by:* residence and/or family/resident. Staff trained *re*: visually, hearing and cognitively impaired. 24-hour nursing and other staff. RNs, RPNs and PSWs on staff. Visiting MD (every 2 weeks). Can retain own MD. Police Check or Vulnerable Person Screening is done for all new staff.

HEALTH SERVICES: Medication administration and/or supervision. Vitals monitored if required. Will accept and provide special assistance for residents who require oxygen, catheters, ostomies and feeding tubes. Assistance with dressing available (cost). Assistance with bathing available as needed (cost). Care plans done. Different levels of care available. Private Duty/Extra Care available ($26.00 to $33.40/hour). Lab service (visiting). Residents can purchase outside resources and use agency of their choice. Clinic area for medical visits. Will help locate higher level of care if needed.

ACCOMMODATION: *Choice of suites available*: studios, 1-bedroom & 2-bedroom suites. *In all suites*: locks, bar fridge, microwave, window coverings, light fixtures, linens, fire alarm, smoke detector, sprinkler, call bell, emergency response system with wearable pendant/bracelet, air conditioning (central) and thermostats for heating & cooling. Private bathrooms with grab bars, showers with non-slip surfaces and elevated toilet seats. In-suite cable TV provided by residence. Can have own phone extension number provided by residence. Furnished & unfurnished suites available. *Restrictions on electrical appliances*: no hot plates or stoves. Suites can be shared (by couples only), roommate picked by resident. Small pets allowed (maximum 20 lbs.; must sign a Pet Waiver).

DINING SERVICE: 3 meals/day included for Regal service; Presidential includes 2 meals/day. All meals served in dining room daily. *Sittings per meal:* Breakfast: 1, Lunch: 2, Dinner: 2. *Menu choices available:* Breakfast: 6, Lunch: 2, Dinner: 2. *Guest Meals*: Breakfast $6.50, Lunch $11.00, Dinner $17.00. *Special Diets*: Vegetarian, Low Salt and Diabetic. Alternative menu choices & 5 week seasonal menus. Tray service to room if ill (no charge as long as doctor orders). Unlimited snacks available at any time. Snacks all day in the café from 8:00 a.m. Open pantry. Party facilities.

AMENITIES AND ACTIVITIES: Parking available (outdoor, for visitors: free and residents: $25.00/month). *10 lounges with:* TVs (6), piano (1), billiards (1) and fitness equipment (1). Guest suites available ($110.00/ night). *Residence has a:* library, chapel, barber/beauty shop, visiting hairdresser, laundry room(s) (no cost) and tuck/gift shop (open 5 morning/week). Residence provides newspaper delivery to individual suite (extra cost). Mail delivered to main desk. *Recreation Facilities*: pool table, billiards, exercise room, greenhouse, craft room, card room, potting room, private courtyards and lush gardens. Posted schedule of activities. Internal newsletter for residents. *Recreational Programs*: exercise, shopping, theatre, parties, entertainment, art classes, pet visiting, day trips and Living***Well*** personal coaching program.

OTHER SERVICES: *Housekeeping*: daily and weekly (included in Regal Service). *Laundry*: linen & towel (included in fee); personal (extra cost on Presidential Plan; included for Regal Service). Dry cleaning (extra cost - cleaners will pick up and return items). Transportation for group social activities (extra cost for trips to theatre, restaurants). 24-hour security. Nightly security checks. Telephone, Cable TV & Utilities (included in fee).

RENTAL INFORMATION: Rates may vary. Extra cost for 2nd person sharing suite ($775.00/month). Rent paid monthly. *Payment Options*: post-dated cheques and pre-authorized payments. Rent increases as per Provincial Tenancy Legislation, annual for resident with 3 months' notice given. Will help resident move into residence. Short-term respite and trial stays available (both $95.00/day).

OAK RIDGES RETIREMENT COMMUNITY

12925 Yonge Street, Richmond Hill, ON L4E 0T7
Tel: (905) 773-4220 • Fax: (905) 313-2394
Email: **info@oakridgesretirement.com**
Website: **www.oakridgesretirement.com**
Contact: **Executive Director or Marketing Manager**
Capacity: **150 residents** • Subsidies: **none**
Price: **$3,190.00 - $5,758.00/month**

Welcome to Signature Living's newest retirement community in Richmond Hill - Oak Ridges Retirement Community. We're committed to helping you bring positive energy to everything you do, with a comprehensive program of activities and services designed to make every day vibrant and joyous! Developed and co-owned by award winning Builder Armour Heights. Timeless architecture featuring; spacious balconies, elegant stone and brick exterior, soaring vaulted ceilings, crown moldings, coffered ceilings and rich cream wood details and traditional wainscoting surrounds you. *It is retirement living refined ~ Signature Style.*

RESIDENCE INFORMATION: New residence. *Near:* King Side Road and Yonge Street. Decorated in 2012. Handrails in some of the hallways. 6 floors, 3 elevators. Wheelchair accessible. Central PA system. *Funding Base:* Corporate/for profit. *Managed by:* Signature Retirement Living. 129 units. *Average Waiting Period*: none. *Average Age*: 80. Can sometimes accommodate cognitively impaired people (Aging in Place; assessment with our nurse is necessary). Can accommodate physically challenged people (Aging in Place). Residents have a dress code (must be dressed in common areas). Smoke-free residence. Alcohol allowed (liquor licensed). *Procedures to leave the premises on a temporary basis...*Short-term: sign in/out. *Languages:* English. Main doors of residence secured at night only. *Close to:* Public Transit, Shopping, Churches, Synagogues, Seniors' Centre, Library, Major Highway and Local Hospital (MacKenzie Health formerly York Central Hospital & 2 minutes from local critical care medical centre). Member of ORCA. Licensed under the Retirement Homes Act.
STAFFING: *Available Staff/Services*: Pharmacy, Social Work, Recreation Therapy, Occupational Therapy, Visiting Dentist, Physiotherapy, Denturist, Dietitian, Companions, Podiatry, Chaplaincy, Speech Pathology, Chiropody and Audiology/Hearing Clinic. *External services arranged by:* residence and/or family/resident. Staff trained *re*: visually, hearing and cognitively impaired. 24-hour nursing and other staff. RNs, RPNs, HCAs and PSWs on staff. Visiting MD (as needed). Can retain own MD. Police Check or Vulnerable Person Screening is done for all new staff.
HEALTH SERVICES: Medication administered if required. Will accept and provide special assistance for residents who require oxygen, catheters, ostomies and feeding tubes. Assistance with dressing available. Assistance with bathing available as needed ($85.00/month). Care plans done. Different levels of care available. Assisted Living Area ($1,300.00/month) is secured to accommodate residents with dementia. Lab service (visiting). Residents can purchase outside resources and use agency of their choice. Clinic area for medical visits. Will help locate higher level of care if needed.
ACCOMMODATION: *Choice of suites available*: suite, alcove,1-bedroom, 1-bedroom + den & 2-bedroom suites. *In all suites*: locks, kitchenette, stainless steel fridge/freezer, microwave, granite counters, patio/ balcony, storage, window coverings, light fixtures, fire alarm, smoke detector, sprinkler, call bell, emergency response system with wearable pendant/bracelet, air conditioning (central), thermostats for heating & cooling and porcelain flooring. All 1-bedrooms & up have washer & dryer. Private bathrooms with call bells, grab bars, showers with shower seat, non-slip surfaces and elevated toilet seats. In-suite cable TV provided by residence (residence charges extra $40.00/month). Can have own phone number if resident arranges with phone company (residence charges extra $35.00/month). Unfurnished suites, furnished suites available for short stays. *Restrictions on electrical appliances*: must be approved by Maintenance Director. Suites can be shared (by couples only). Pets allowed (with approval of Management).

DINING SERVICE: Lunch and Dinner included in fee and served in dining room daily. *Sittings per meal:* Lunch: 1, Dinner: 1. *Menu choices available:* Lunch: 2, Dinner: 2. *Guest Meals*: Available. *Special Diets*: Vegetarian, Low Salt and Diabetic. Tray service to room if ill. Unlimited snacks available at any time. Party facilities. Open pantry. Continental breakfast in our Winham Café; lunch and dinner served in our Elegant Bellagio Dining Room; snacks served in our Sunset Pub.
AMENITIES AND ACTIVITIES: Parking available (indoor & outdoor, for visitors: free and indoor for residents: $50.00/month). *11 lounges with:* TVs (6), pianos (2) and garden patios (3). Guest suites available ($95.00/night). *Residence has a:* library, chapel, barber/beauty shop and laundry room(s) (no cost). Residence provides newspaper delivery to individual suite. Mail delivered to resident. *Recreation Facilities*: greenhouse, craft room, card room, saltwater swimming pool, theatre, salon, craft kitchen, fitness centre, 3 rooftop terraces and greenhouse. TV monitor listing events and birthdays, etc. Posted schedule of activities. Internal newsletter for residents. *Recreational Programs*: exercise, shopping, theatre, parties, entertainment, art classes, pet visiting, day trips and spa.
OTHER SERVICES: *Housekeeping*: weekly (included in fee). *Laundry*: linen & towel (included in fee); personal (extra cost or resident can do own) & dry cleaning (extra cost). Three laundry rooms; most suites have own washer and dryer. Transportation for group social activities. Nightly security checks. Telephone & Cable TV (extra cost). Utilities (included in fee).
RENTAL INFORMATION: Rates may vary. Price depends on size of suite. Extra cost for 2nd person sharing suite ($700.00/month). Rent paid monthly. *Payment Options*: cheques, direct deposit and pre-authorized payments. Rent increases as per Provincial Tenancy Legislation, annual with 3 months' notice given. Will help resident move into residence. Short-term respite and trial stays available (both $95.00/day; Assisted Living $140.00/day).

REVERA - BROOKSIDE COURT

980 Elgin Mills Road East, Richmond Hill, ON L4S 1M4
Tel: (855) 573-8372 • Toll Free: (855) 573-8372
Email: **brookside@reveraliving.com**
Website: **www.reveraliving.com/brookside**
Contact: **Executive Director or Lifestyle Consultant**
Capacity: **43 units** • Subsidies: **none**
Price: **$2,921.00/month and up**

Keep living your life, your way, at Brookside Court. You'll find the range of services, amenities and choices that fit your lifestyle and requirements – all in a warm and safe environment. Brookside Court, a one-storey residence located next to Hilltop Place, situated on beautiful, expansive grounds, boasts the tranquility of a country oasis. Conveniently located close to an array of shops, community services, places of worship, parks, public transit and major highways. Everything is designed to enable you to maintain your independence and privacy, enjoy a full social life, and participate in the activities you love. Our caring and friendly staff and appealing accommodations support who you are and how you want to live in freedom and comfort. At Brookside Court, you change your address, not your life. *Brookside Court is part of the Revera family, one of North America's leading and most trusted providers of seniors' accommodation, care and services since 1961.*

RESIDENCE INFORMATION: 40 years in operation. *On:* Bayview Avenue near Elgin Mills Road. Decorated in 2010. Handrails in hallways. 2 floors, 1 elevator. Wheelchair accessible. Central PA system. *Funding Base:* Corporate/for profit. *Owned and managed by:* Revera Inc. *Average Waiting Period*: varies. *Average Age*: 84. Can accommodate cognitively impaired people (2nd floor). Can accommodate physically challenged people (wheelchair - provide hoyer lift service). Residents have a dress code (casual dress for dining). Smoke-free environment (smoking is permitted outdoors). Alcohol allowed (only in residents own suite; we also provide Happy Hour). *Restrictions around Visitors/Visiting Hours:* we ask

that you sign in at Reception. *Procedures to leave the premises on a temporary basis...*Short-term: sign in/out system. Overnight & Holidays: sign in/out system, no restrictions on overnight outings. *Languages:* English, Italian, Portuguese, Spanish, Tagalog/Filipino, Russian, Persian & Others. Will accept Public Guardian and Trustee clients. Main doors of residence secured at night only. *Close to:* Public Transit, Shopping, Churches, Synagogues, Seniors' Centre, Library, Major Highway and Local Hospital (MacKenzie Health formerly York Central Hospital). Member of ORCA. Licensed under the Retirement Homes Act.
STAFFING: *Available Staff/Services*: Pharmacy, Social Work (CCAC), Recreation Therapy, Visiting Dentist, Physiotherapy (CCAC), Denturist, Dietitian, Companions, Podiatry, Chaplaincy, Audiology/Hearing Clinic, Hairdresser, Foot Care Nurse, Medical Lab Work and Director of Care. *External services arranged by:* residence and/or family/resident. Staff trained *re*: visually, hearing and cognitively impaired. 24-hour nursing and other staff. RNs, RPNs, HCAs and PSWs on staff. Visiting MD (twice/week and on call). Can retain own MD. Staff members are bonded. Police Check or Vulnerable Person Screening is done for all new staff.
HEALTH SERVICES: Medication administration and/or supervision. Vitals monitored if required. Will accept (but not provide special assistance for) residents who require catheters. Will accept and provide special assistance for residents who require oxygen. Assistance with dressing available (cost). Weekly assistance with bathing available (cost). Care plans done. Different levels of care available. Assisted Living Area is secured to accommodate residents with dementia. Lab service (visiting). Residents can purchase outside resources and use agency of their choice. MD visits residents in their rooms/suites. Will help locate higher level of care if needed (referral to Revera residence; assistance coordinating services through CCAC).
ACCOMMODATION: *Choice of suites available*: semi-private, private, 1-bedroom, studio & suites. *In all suites*: locks, window coverings, light fixtures, smoke detector/alarm, heat detector, sprinkler, call bell, air conditioning (option for window air conditioner in units) and thermostats for heating. Air conditioning in common areas. Private bathrooms with call bells and grab bars. In-suite cable TV if resident arranges with cable company (residence charges extra). Can have own phone number if resident arranges with phone company (residence charges extra). Furnished & unfurnished suites available. Restrictions on electrical appliances. Pets allowed (as per Pet Policy within the Tenancy Agreement).
DINING SERVICE: All meals included in fee and served in dining room daily. *Sittings per meal:* Breakfast: 1, Lunch: 1, Dinner: 1. *Menu choices available:* Breakfast: 2, Lunch: 2, Dinner: 2. *Guest Meals*: Available. *Special Diets*: Vegetarian, Low Salt, Diabetic and Various Dietary Restrictions & Food Textures. Tray service to room if ill (no charge for a maximum time of 4 days). 3 snacks/day. Coffee, tea & light refreshments available at all times. Party facilities.
AMENITIES AND ACTIVITIES: Parking available (outdoor, for visitors and residents). *5 lounges with:* TVs (2) and piano (1). Guest suites available. *Residence has a:* library, visiting library, chapel, barber/beauty shop, visiting hairdresser, laundry room(s) (no cost) and tuck/gift shop. Resident can arrange newspaper delivery to main desk (extra cost). Mail delivered to main desk. *Recreation Facilities*: craft room, card room and garden. Posted schedule of activities. Internal newsletter for residents. *Recreational Programs*: exercise, shopping, theatre, parties, entertainment, art classes, pet visiting and day trips.
OTHER SERVICES: *Housekeeping*: weekly (or more often if requested at an extra cost). *Laundry*: linen, towel & personal (weekly included in fee); dry cleaning (extra cost). Transportation for group social activities. 24-hour security. Nightly security checks (if requested). Telephone & Cable TV (extra cost). Utilities (included in fee). Medication administration. Assistance with bathing. Additional housekeeping.
RENTAL INFORMATION: Rates may vary. Extra cost for 2nd person sharing suite. Rent paid monthly. *Payment Options*: pre-authorized payments. Credit card payment available for short-term stays. Rent increases as per Provincial Tenancy Legislation, annual for resident with 3 months' notice given. Will help resident move into residence (extra cost). Short-term respite and trial stays available (individually priced based on needs, space permitting).

REVERA - HILLTOP PLACE

1000 Elgin Mills Road East, Richmond Hill, ON L4S 1M4
Tel: (855) 573-8372 • Toll Free: (855) 573-8372
Email: **Hilltop@reveraliving.com**
Website: **www.reveraliving.com/hilltop**
Contact: **Executive Director or Lifestyle Consultant**
Capacity: **45 units** • Subsidies: **none**
Price: **$2,724.00/month and up**

Keep living your life, your way, at Hilltop Place. You'll find the range of services, amenities and choices that fit your lifestyle and requirements – all in a warm and safe environment. Hilltop Place, a one-storey residence located next to Brookside Court, is situated on beautiful, expansive grounds with the tranquility of a country oasis. Conveniently located close to an array of shops, community services, places of worship, parks, public transit, and major highways. Everything is designed to enable you to maintain your independence and privacy, enjoy a full social life, and participate in the activities that you love. Our caring and friendly staff and appealing accommodations support who you are and how you want to live in freedom and comfort. At Hilltop Place, you change your address, not your life. *Hilltop Place is part of the Revera family, one of North America's leading and most trusted providers of seniors' accommodation, care and services since 1961.*

RESIDENCE INFORMATION: Handrails in hallways. 1 floor, no elevators. Wheelchair accessible. Central PA system. *Owned and managed by:* Revera Inc. *Average Waiting Period*: varies. Can accommodate cognitively impaired people (can transition to Brookside Court). Can sometimes accommodate physically challenged people (wheelchair). Smoking allowed (outdoors only). Alcohol allowed. *Procedures to leave the premises on a temporary basis...*Short-term: sign out. Overnight & Holidays: sign out and inform staff. *Languages:* English, Italian & Persian. Main doors of residence secured at night only. *Close to:* Public Transit, Shopping, Churches, Seniors' Centre, Library, Major Highway and Local Hospital (Mackenzie Health). Member of ORCA. Licensed under the Retirement Homes Act.
STAFFING: *Available Staff/Services*: Recreation Therapy, Visiting Dentist, Physiotherapy (CCAC) and Foot Care Nurse. *External services arranged by:* family/resident. 24-hour staff. RPNs, PSWs and UCPs on staff. Visiting MD (on call, visits once/week). Can retain own MD. Staff members are bonded. Police Check or Vulnerable Person Screening is done for all new staff.
HEALTH SERVICES: Medication administration and/or supervision. Vitals monitored if required. Assistance with dressing available (cost). Weekly assistance with bathing available (cost). Care plans done. Different levels of care available. Lab service (visiting). Residents can purchase outside resources and use agency of their choice. MD visits residents in their rooms/suites. Will help locate higher level of care if needed (Transition to Brookside Court).
ACCOMMODATION: Choice of suites available. *In all suites*: locks, window coverings, light fixtures, smoke detector, sprinkler, call bell, thermostats for heating and some have kitchenettes. Private bathrooms with call bells, grab bars and showers with non-slip surfaces. Unfurnished suites, furnished suites available for short stays. Pets allowed.
DINING SERVICE: All meals included in fee and served in dining room daily. *Sittings per meal:* Breakfast: 1, Lunch: 1, Dinner: 1. *Menu choices available:* Breakfast: 2, Lunch: 2, Dinner: 2. *Guest Meals*: Available. *Special Diets*: Vegetarian, Low Salt, Diabetic and Halal. Tray service to room if ill (no charge for a maximum time of 4 days). 3 snacks/day. Party facilities.
AMENITIES AND ACTIVITIES: Parking available (indoor & outdoor, for visitors and residents). *2 lounges with:* TV (1) and piano (1). Guest suites available. *Residence has a:* library, barber/beauty shop, visiting hairdresser and laundry room(s) (no cost). Mail delivered to individual suite. *Recreation Facilities*: exercise room, craft room and bistro. Posted schedule of activities. Internal newsletter for residents. *Recreational Programs*: exercise, shopping, entertainment, art classes and day trips.

OTHER SERVICES: *Housekeeping*: weekly. *Laundry*: linen & towel (included in fee). Transportation for group social activities (outings). Telephone & Cable TV (extra cost). Utilities (included in fee).
RENTAL INFORMATION: Rates may vary. Extra cost for 2nd person sharing suite ($515.00/month). Rent paid monthly. *Payment Options*: pre-authorized payments. Rent increases as per Provincial Tenancy Legislation, annual for resident with 3 months' notice given. Will help resident move into residence. Short-term respite and trial stays available.

RICHMOND HILL RETIREMENT RESIDENCE

70 Bernard Avenue, Richmond Hill, ON L4C 0W7
Tel: (905) 770-4704 • Fax: (905) 770-0253
Email: **mktg2.richmondhill@diversicare.ca**
Website: **www.richmondhillretirement.ca**
Contact: **Marketing Manager**
Capacity: **145 residents** • Subsidies: **none**
Price: **$3,300.00 - $5,600.00/month**

Richmond Hill Retirement Residence is a fabulous new home conveniently located at 70 Bernard Avenue, just east of Yonge Street and one light north of Elgin Mills Road. It is close to all amenities including shopping, restaurants, entertainment and public transit. This five-storey residence consists of 130 suites ranging from studios to 2-bedrooms, some with dens and balconies. Richmond Hill Retirement Residence offers its residents a comfortable, luxurious home environment with the choice of an Independent or Full Service Lifestyle. Extra care services available. **Owned by Diversicare, who is the proud recipient of the 2003, 2006 2009 and 2012 Order of Excellence Award given by Excellence Canada.** The award was received for the exceptional quality and customer service we provide to our residents every day.

RESIDENCE INFORMATION: New residence. *Near:* Yonge Street and Elgin Mills Road East. Decorated in 2012. Handrails in hallways. 5 floors, 3 elevators. Wheelchair accessible. Central PA system. *Funding Base:* Corporate/for profit. *Owned by:* Diversicare Canada Management Services Co., Inc. 130 units. *Average Waiting Period*: none. *Average Age*: 80. Can accommodate cognitively impaired people with restrictions (consultation with our Nurse is required). Can accommodate physically challenged people. Smoking allowed (private terrace). Alcohol allowed. *Languages:* English. Richmond Hill is very diverse, as are our residents. Will accept Public Guardian and Trustee clients. Main doors of residence secured at night only. *Close to:* Public Transit, Shopping, Churches, Synagogues, Seniors' Centre, Library, Major Highway and Local Hospital (MacKenzie Health & Southlake Regional Health Centre). Member of ORCA. Licensed under the Retirement Homes Act.
STAFFING: *Available Staff/Services*: Pharmacy, Social Work, Recreation Therapy, Occupational Therapy, Physiotherapy, Dietitian, Podiatry, Chaplaincy, Speech Pathology, Chiropody, Audiology/Hearing Clinic and Nurse Practitioner (available 24/7). *External services arranged by:* residence and/or family/resident. Staff trained *re*: visually, hearing and cognitively impaired. 24-hour nursing and other staff. RNs, RPNs, PSWs and UCPs on staff. Visiting MD (as per resident requirements). Can retain own MD. Police Check or Vulnerable Person Screening is done for all new staff.
HEALTH SERVICES: Medication administration and/or supervision. Vitals monitored if required. Will accept (but not provide special assistance for) residents who require oxygen, catheters, ostomies and feeding tubes. Assistance with dressing available. Weekly assistance with bathing available (cost). Care plans done. Different levels of care available. Nurse Practitioner is available 24/7. Lab service (visiting). Residents can purchase outside resources and use agency of their choice. Clinic area for medical visits. Will help locate higher level of care if needed.
ACCOMMODATION: *Choice of suites available*: 130 private studio, 1-bedroom & 2-bedroom suites; some with dens and balconies. *In all suites*: locks, kitchenette, bar fridge, patio/balcony, storage, window coverings, light fixtures, fire alarm, smoke detector, sprinkler, call bell, emergency response system with

wearable pendant/bracelet, air conditioning (central) and thermostats for heating & cooling. Private bathrooms with call bells, grab bars, showers with non-slip surfaces and elevated toilet seats. In-suite cable TV if resident arranges with cable company. Can have own phone number if resident arranges with phone company. Unfurnished suites, furnished suites available for short stays. *Restrictions on electrical appliances*: no stoves or hot plates. Suites can be shared (by couples only). Pets allowed (weight restrictions).
DINING SERVICE: All meals included in fee and served in dining room daily. *Menu choices available:* Lunch: 2, Dinner: 2. *Guest Meals*: Lunch $8.50, Dinner $15.00. *Special Diets*: Vegetarian, Low Salt, Diabetic and Food Allergies. Tray service to room if ill (no charge as long as doctor orders). Unlimited snacks available at any time. Party facilities. Open pantry. Open seating.
AMENITIES AND ACTIVITIES: Parking available (outdoor, for visitors and residents). *4 lounges with:* TVs (2), piano (1), pool table (1) and 2 computers (1). Guest suites available ($125.00/night). *Residence has a:* library, chapel, barber/beauty shop, visiting hairdresser, laundry room(s) (no cost) and tuck/gift shop (open 7:00 a.m. – 8:00 p.m.). Residence provides newspaper delivery to main desk. Mail delivered to private mailbox with key. *Recreation Facilities*: billiards, exercise room, craft room and card room. Posted schedule of activities. Internal newsletter for residents. *Recreational Programs*: exercise, shopping, theatre, parties, entertainment, pet visiting, day trips and Brain Gym® & More program.
OTHER SERVICES: *Housekeeping*: weekly (included in fee). *Laundry*: linen & towel (included in fee); personal (extra cost; washers and dryers no charge for residents). Transportation for group social activities. 24-hour security. Nightly security checks. Telephone & Cable TV (resident to arrange with their provider). Utilities (included in fee).
RENTAL INFORMATION: Rates may vary. Extra cost for 2nd person sharing suite ($700.00/month). Rent paid monthly. *Payment Options*: cheques, post-dated cheques, direct deposit and pre-authorized payments. Rent increases as per Provincial Tenancy Legislation, annual for resident with 3 months' notice given. Will help resident move into residence (extra cost). Short-term respite ($99.00/day) and trial stays ($85.00/day) available.

See VAUGHAN & THORNHILL for additional homes in this region.

◆ SARNIA ◆

BAYBRIDGE - FAIRWINDS LODGE

1218 Michigan Avenue, Sarnia, ON N7S 6L1
Tel: (519) 542-8814 • Fax: (519) 542-8838
Email: **kerry.belliveau@fairwindslodge.com**
Website: **www.fairwindslodge.com**
Contact: **Kerry Belliveau**
Capacity: **120 residents** • Subsidies: **none**
Price: **$2,182.00/month and up**

At Fairwinds Lodge we believe retirement living should be relaxing and carefree, spent doing the things you love. That's why our community provides a unique independent retirement lifestyle in a warm and welcoming environment. In one affordable, all-inclusive month-to-month rent, residents enjoy 3 delicious chef-prepared meals daily, enriching activities to share with friendly neighbours, housekeeping service, complimentary transportation, and so much more. We do not provide any health care services; however, residents are welcome to receive services from any outside home health care provider of their choice to help them continue enjoying life independently at our community. Discover the peace-of-mind, happiness and fulfillment you deserve. Contact us today to schedule your personal tour!

RESIDENCE INFORMATION: 13 years in operation. *Near:* Murphy Road and Michigan Avenue. Decorated in 2001. Handrails in hallways. 3 floors, 1 elevator. Wheelchair accessible. Central PA system. *Funding Base:* Corporate/for profit. *Owned and managed by:* BayBridge Senior Living. 111 units. *Average Waiting Period*: varies. *Average Age*: 83. Can sometimes accommodate cognitively impaired people. Can accommodate physically challenged people (must be independent). Residents have a dress code (casual, no sleepwear in common areas). Smoking allowed (on balcony or patio only). Alcohol allowed (self-managed). *Procedures to leave the premises on a temporary basis...*notify the Office. *Languages:* English. Will accept Public Guardian and Trustee clients. Main doors of residence secured at night only. *Close to:* Public Transit, Shopping, Churches, Seniors' Centre, Library, Major Highway and Local Hospital (Bluewater Health).
STAFFING: *Available Staff/Services*: Social Work (CCAC), Recreation Therapy, Occupational Therapy (CCAC), Physiotherapy (CCAC), Dietitian (CCAC), Companions, Podiatry (CCAC), Chaplaincy and Speech Pathology (CCAC). *External services arranged by:* family/resident. Can retain own MD. Staff members are bonded. Police Check or Vulnerable Person Screening is done for all new staff.
HEALTH SERVICES: Will accept (but not provide special assistance for) residents who require oxygen, catheters, ostomies and feeding tubes. Residents can purchase outside resources and use agency of their choice. Will help locate higher level of care if needed (can provide names and numbers).
ACCOMMODATION: *Choice of suites available*: studio, 1-bedroom & 2-bedroom units. *In all suites*: locks, kitchenette, apartment-size fridge, window coverings, light fixtures, linens, fire alarm, smoke detector, sprinkler, call bell, air conditioning (wall-mounted) and thermostats for heating & cooling. Most have patios/balconies. Private bathrooms with call bells, grab bars, showers with non-slip surfaces and elevated toilet seats. In-suite cable TV provided by residence. Can have own phone number if resident arranges with phone company (residence charges extra). Unfurnished suites, furnished suites available for short stays. *Restrictions on electrical appliances*: no stoves. Suites can be shared, roommate picked by resident. Pets allowed (small dogs only).
DINING SERVICE: All meals included in fee and served in dining room daily. *Sittings per meal:* Breakfast: 1, Lunch: 1, Dinner: 1. *Menu choices available:* Breakfast: 5, Lunch: 6, Dinner: 5. *Guest Meals*: Breakfast $10.00, Lunch $12.00, Dinner $10.00. *Special Diets*: Vegetarian, Low Salt and Diabetic. Unlimited snacks available at any time. Fresh fruit, goodies, coffee & tea available all day. Party facilities.
AMENITIES AND ACTIVITIES: Parking available (outdoor, for visitors and residents). *4 lounges with:* TVs (2), piano (1), library (1) and chapel (1). *Residence has a:* library, chapel, barber/beauty shop and laundry room(s) (no cost). Resident can arrange newspaper delivery to individual suite. Mail delivered to private mailbox with key. *Recreation Facilities*: pool table, billiards, shuffleboard, exercise room, craft room, card room, chapel and beauty salon. Posted schedule of activities. Internal newsletter for residents. *Recreational Programs*: exercise, shopping, theatre, parties, entertainment, art classes, pet visiting, day trips and many programs to suit the interests of the residents.
OTHER SERVICES: *Housekeeping*: weekly (included in fee). *Laundry*: linen & towel (included in fee). Free laundry rooms for personal use. Transportation to medical appointments (no cost for our shuttle service) and for group social activities (no cost for bus). 24-hour security. Telephone (resident pays for own phone service). Cable TV & Utilities (included in fee). Garages (extra cost).
RENTAL INFORMATION: Rates may vary. Rate listed above is based on single occupancy. Extra cost for 2nd person sharing suite (please call for specifics). Rent paid monthly. *Payment Options*: cheques, post-dated cheques, direct deposit and pre-authorized payments. Rent increases indexed to inflation as per Provincial Tenancy Legislation, annual for resident with 3 months' notice given. Will help resident move into residence. Short-term respite and trial stays available.

Pricing information for homes listed in *The Guide* may vary slightly.
Please verify rates with the residences you are interested in directly.

SCARBOROUGH

ALEXIS LODGE RETIREMENT RESIDENCE
MCCOWAN RETIREMENT RESIDENCE
RETIREMENT SUITES BY THE LAKE
SCARBOROUGH RETIREMENT RESIDENCE
SHEPHERD TERRACE RETIREMENT RESIDENCE
STS. PETER AND PAUL RESIDENCE
VILLA PUGLIESE ASSISTED LIVING FACILITY

Please see TORONTO (SCARBOROUGH) for information on these residences.

◆ ST. CATHARINES ◆

ANCHOR POINTE

540 Ontario Street, St. Catharines, ON L2N 7S2
Tel: (905) 938-7070 • Fax: (905) 938-3684
Email: **5002-manager@holidaytouch.com**
Website: **www.anchorpointe.com**
Contact: **Community Managers**
Capacity: **125 units** • Subsidies: **none**
Price: **$2,200.00/month and up (rates may vary)**

Holiday Retirement believes retirement living should be relaxing and carefree, spent doing the things you love. That's why our communities provide a unique independent retirement lifestyle in a warm and welcoming environment. In one affordable, all-inclusive month-to-month rent, residents enjoy 3 delicious chef-prepared meals daily, enriching activities to share with friendly neighbours, housekeeping service, complimentary transportation, and so much more. Each Holiday community also features 2 sets of compassionate, dedicated live-in Managers available 24/7 to ensure safety and security. We do not provide any health care services; however, residents are welcome to receive services from any outside home health care provider of their choice to help them continue enjoying life at our community. Discover the peace-of-mind, happiness and fulfillment you deserve. Contact us today to schedule your personal tour!

RESIDENCE INFORMATION: 15 years in operation. *Near:* Ontario Street and Linwell Road. Decorated in 2012. Handrails in hallways. 3 floors, 1 elevator. Wheelchair accessible. Central PA system. *Funding Base:* Corporate/for profit. *Owned and managed by:* Holiday Retirement. *Average Waiting Period*: varies. *Average Age*: 83. Can sometimes accommodate cognitively impaired people. Can accommodate physically challenged people (must be independent; wheelchairs, walkers, scooters are welcome). Residents have a dress code (casual, no sleepwear in common areas). Smoking allowed (in own apartment). Alcohol allowed (in own apartment, and residents may bring to their dining room meals). *Procedures to leave the premises on a temporary basis...*Overnight & Holidays: inform Front Office. *Languages:* English. Will accept Public Guardian and Trustee clients. Main doors of residence secured at night only. *Close to:* Public Transit, Shopping, Churches, Synagogues, Seniors' Centre, Library, Major Highway and Local Hospital.
STAFFING: *Available Staff/Services*: Social Work (CCAC), Recreation Therapy, Occupational Therapy (CCAC), Physiotherapy (CCAC), Speech Pathology (CCAC) and Audiology/Hearing Clinic. *External services arranged by:* family/resident. 24-hour staff. Visiting MD (contact personally for appointments). Can retain own MD. Police Check or Vulnerable Person Screening is done for all new staff.
HEALTH SERVICES: Will accept (but not provide special assistance for) residents who require oxygen, catheters, ostomies and feeding tubes. CCAC provides free assistance with Activities of Daily Living

(including bathing, dressing). Residents can purchase outside resources and use agency of their choice. MD visits residents in their rooms/suites. Will help locate higher level of care if needed (information available from Front Office and local government health agencies).
ACCOMMODATION: *Choice of suites available*: studio, 1-bedroom, 2-bedroom/2-bath & Garden Cottages. *In all suites*: locks, kitchenette, window coverings, light fixtures, linens, smoke detector, sprinkler, call bell, air conditioning (wall unit) and thermostats for heating & cooling. Most have balconies. Windows fully open. Private bathrooms with call bells, grab bars and showers with non-slip surfaces. In-suite cable TV provided by residence. Can have own phone number if resident arranges with phone company. Unfurnished suites, furnished suites available for short stays. *Restrictions on electrical appliances*: no hot plates or stoves. Suites can be shared, roommate picked by resident. Well-behaved pets are more than welcome.
DINING SERVICE: All meals included in fee and served in dining room daily. *Sittings per meal:* Breakfast: 1, Lunch: 1, Dinner: 1. *Menu choices available:* Breakfast: 2, Lunch: 6, Dinner: 5. *Guest Meals*: Breakfast $8.00, Lunch $10.00, Dinner $8.00. *Special Diets*: Vegetarian, Low Salt and Diabetic. Many options to choose from and depending on needs. Tray service to room if ill. 2 snacks/day. Fresh fruit, coffee, tea & fresh baked homemade treats available all day. Party facilities. Private Dining Area. Large meal served at noon-time.
AMENITIES AND ACTIVITIES: Parking available (outdoor, for visitors and residents). *4 lounges with:* TVs (2), piano (1), computer kiosks (1) and pool table (1). Guest suites available ($75.00/night). *Residence has a:* library, chapel, barber/beauty shop and laundry room(s) (no cost). Resident can arrange newspaper delivery to individual suite. Mail delivered to private mailbox with key. *Recreation Facilities*: pool table, billiards, shuffleboard, exercise room, chapel, craft room and card room. Pre-paid pool card provided for new city pool visits on Wednesdays. Posted schedule of activities. Internal newsletter for residents. *Recreational Programs*: exercise, shopping, theatre, parties, entertainment, art classes, pet visiting, day trips, Tai Chi, Yoga for seniors, lawn bowling and poker nights.
OTHER SERVICES: *Housekeeping*: weekly (included in fee). *Laundry*: linen & towel (included in fee); personal (extra cost; each resident takes care of their own). Free laundry rooms for personal use. Transportation to medical appointments (bus will take you door to door on medical appointment days) and for group social activities. 24-hour security. Nightly security checks (nightly walk through at closing). Cable TV & Utilities (included in fee). Physiotherapy (see Office for details on this great program).
RENTAL INFORMATION: Rates may vary. Rate listed above is based on single occupancy. Extra cost for 2nd person sharing suite ($710.00/month; please call for specifics). Rent paid monthly. *Payment Options*: cheques, post-dated cheques and pre-authorized payments. Rent increases indexed to inflation as per Provincial Tenancy Legislation, annual for resident with 3 months' notice given. Will help resident move into residence. Trial stays available (see Managers).

BAYBRIDGE - ST. CATHARINES PLACE RETIREMENT RESIDENCE

113 Scott Street, St. Catharines, ON L2N 7L2
Tel: (905) 646-1311 • Fax: (905) 646-0055
Email: **denise.chambers@primetimeliving.ca**
Website: **www.primetimeliving.ca/residences/st-catharines-place**
Contact: **Denise Chambers**
Capacity: **100 residents** • Subsidies: **none**
Price: **$2,944.00 - $5,700.00/month**

In the heart of Niagara, unique one level living offering safety, comfort and security. Experience the art of living well with exciting activities and events. Enjoy our park-like setting and new garden courtyard. Bay windows, efficiency kitchens and fireplaces complete this picturesque residence.

RESIDENCE INFORMATION: 26 years in operation. *Near:* Lake Street and Scott Street. Decorated in 2009. Handrails in hallways. 1 floor, no elevators. Wheelchair accessible. Central PA system. *Funding Base:* Corporate/for profit. *Owned and managed by:* BayBridge Senior Living. 87 units. *Average Waiting Period*: 1 - 2 months. *Average Age*: 90. Can accommodate cognitively impaired & physically challenged people with restrictions. Residents have a dress code (casual dress for mealtime). Smoking allowed (outside only). Alcohol allowed. *Procedures to leave the premises on a temporary basis...*notify the Nurse on duty. *Languages:* English. Main doors of residence secured at night only. *Close to:* Public Transit, Shopping, Churches, Seniors' Centre, Library, Major Highway and Local Hospitals (Hotel Dieu Hospital, St. Catharines & Niagara Health System - St. Catharines Site). Member of ORCA & Niagara Senior Services Network. Licensed under the Retirement Homes Act.

STAFFING: *Available Staff/Services*: Pharmacy, Social Work (CCAC), Recreation Therapy, Occupational Therapy (CCAC), Visiting Dentist, Physiotherapy (CCAC), Denturist, Dietitian (CCAC), Companions, Podiatry (CCAC), Chaplaincy, Speech Pathology (CCAC), Chiropody, Audiology/Hearing Clinic and Massage Therapy. *External services arranged by:* residence and/or family/resident. Staff trained *re*: visually, hearing and cognitively impaired. 24-hour nursing staff. RPNs, HCAs, PSWs and UCPs on staff. Visiting MD (on call). Can retain own MD. Staff members are bonded. Police Check or Vulnerable Person Screening is done for all new staff.

HEALTH SERVICES: Medication administration and/or supervision. Vitals monitored if required. Will accept and provide special assistance for residents who require oxygen, catheters, ostomies and feeding tubes. Assistance with dressing available. Weekly assistance with bathing available. Care plans done. Lab service (visiting). Residents can purchase outside resources and use agency of their choice. MD visits residents in their rooms/suites. Clinic area for medical visits. Will help locate higher level of care if needed (through Niagara CCAC).

ACCOMMODATION: *Choice of suites available*: private suite, private with efficiency & 1-bedroom suites (suites range in size from 227 sq. ft. to 562 sq. ft.). *In all suites*: locks, storage, window coverings, light fixtures, linens, fire alarm, smoke detector, sprinkler, call bell, emergency response system with wearable pendant/bracelet, air conditioning (central) and thermostats for heating & cooling. Private bathrooms with call bells, grab bars, tubs and showers with non-slip surfaces. In-suite cable TV if resident arranges with cable company (residence charges extra). Can have own phone number if resident arranges with phone company (residence charges extra $26.00/month). Unfurnished suites. *Restrictions on electrical appliances*: no toaster or toaster oven. Suites can be shared, roommate picked by resident. Pets allowed (only dogs under 30 lbs.; resident must be able to care for animals).

DINING SERVICE: All meals included in fee and served in dining room daily. *Sittings per meal:* Breakfast: 1, Lunch: 1, Dinner: 1. *Menu choices available:* Breakfast: 2, Lunch: 2, Dinner: 2. *Guest Meals*: Breakfast $5.00, Lunch $10.00, Dinner $8.00. *Special Diets*: Vegetarian, Low Salt and Diabetic. Tray service to room if ill (no charge for a maximum time of 21 days). Unlimited snacks available at any time. Party facilities. Open pantry.

AMENITIES AND ACTIVITIES: Parking available (outdoor, for visitors and residents). *4 lounges with:* TVs (2) and piano (1). Guest suites available ($75.00/night). *Residence has a:* library, visiting library, chapel, barber/beauty shop, visiting hairdresser, laundry room(s) (no cost) and tuck/gift shop. Banking services on premises (varies). Mail delivered to main desk. *Recreation Facilities*: exercise room, craft room and card room. Posted schedule of activities. Internal newsletter for residents. *Recreational Programs*: exercise, shopping, theatre, parties, entertainment, art classes, pet visiting and day trips.

OTHER SERVICES: *Housekeeping*: daily. *Laundry*: linen, towel & personal (included in fee). Transportation for group social activities. 24-hour security. Nightly security checks. Utilities (included in fee).

RENTAL INFORMATION: Rates may vary. Extra cost for 2nd person sharing suite ($695.00/month). Rent paid monthly. *Payment Options*: cheques, post-dated cheques and pre-authorized payments. Rent increases indexed to inflation as per Provincial Tenancy Legislation, annual for resident with 3 months' notice given. Short-term respite available.

BAYBRIDGE - THE HEATHERWOOD RETIREMENT RESIDENCE

115 Scott Street, St. Catharines, ON L2N 0A1
Tel: (905) 646-0000 • Fax: (905) 646-0300
Email: **denise.chambers@primetimeliving.ca**
Website: **www.primetimeliving.ca/residences/heatherwood**
Contact: **Denise Chambers**
Capacity: **100 residents** • Subsidies: **none**
Price: **$2,944.00 - $6,000.00/month**

Nestled in the heart of Canada's Niagara Region close to parks, shopping malls and less than 30 minutes from Niagara Falls, The Heatherwood is a luxury retirement community designed for the active retiree. Offering premium services, accommodations and amenities, our community provides you with the retirement lifestyle you've always dreamed of. The Heatherwood is committed to providing seniors with the very best lifestyle for their retirement years. We hand pick a select team of experienced and well-trained residential staff and health care personnel to ensure our residents receive only the finest in customer service.

RESIDENCE INFORMATION: 6 years in operation. *Near:* Lake Street and Scott Street. Decorated in 2010. Handrails in hallways. 4 floors, 2 elevators. Wheelchair accessible. Central PA system. *Funding Base:* Corporate/for profit. *Owned and managed by:* BayBridge Senior Living. 80 units. *Average Waiting Period*: 2 - 4 months. *Average Age*: 85. Can accommodate physically challenged people with restrictions. Residents have a dress code (casual dress for mealtime). Smoking allowed (outside only). Alcohol allowed. *Procedures to leave the premises on a temporary basis...*Front Desk. *Languages:* English. *Close to:* Public Transit, Shopping, Churches, Seniors' Centre, Library, Major Highway and Local Hospital (Niagara Health System - St. Catharines Site). Member of ORCA & Niagara Senior Services Network. Licensed under the Retirement Homes Act.
STAFFING: *Available Staff/Services*: Social Work (CCAC), Recreation Therapy, Occupational Therapy (CCAC), Visiting Dentist, Physiotherapy (CCAC), Denturist, Dietitian (CCAC), Companions, Podiatry (CCAC), Chaplaincy, Speech Pathology (CCAC), Chiropody and Audiology/Hearing Clinic. *External services arranged by:* residence and/or family/resident. Staff trained *re*: visually, hearing and cognitively impaired. Visiting MD (on call). Can retain own MD. Staff members are bonded. Police Check or Vulnerable Person Screening is done for all new staff.
HEALTH SERVICES: Will accept (but not provide special assistance for) residents who require oxygen, catheters, ostomies and feeding tubes. Lab service (on-site). Residents can purchase outside resources and use agency of their choice. MD visits residents in their rooms/suites. Will help locate higher level of care if needed (St. Catharines Place staff members).
ACCOMMODATION: *Choice of suites available*: bachelor, 1-bedroom & 2-bedroom suites. *In all suites*: locks, full kitchen including full fridge, microwave, stove, patio/balcony, storage, window coverings, light fixtures, fire alarm, smoke detector, sprinkler, call bell, emergency response system with wearable pendant/bracelet, air conditioning (central), thermostats for heating & cooling and washer/dryer in suite. Private bathrooms with call bells, tubs and showers with non-slip surfaces. In-suite cable TV provided by residence (residence charges extra). Can have own phone number if resident arranges with phone company (residence charges extra $26.00/month). Unfurnished suites. Suites can be shared, roommate picked by resident. Pets allowed (only dogs under 30 lbs.; resident must be able to care for animals).
DINING SERVICE: All meals included in fee and served in dining room daily. *Sittings per meal:* Breakfast: 2, Lunch: 4, Dinner: 4. *Menu choices available:* Breakfast: 4, Lunch: 2, Dinner: 2. *Guest Meals*: Breakfast $7.95, Lunch $13.95, Dinner $19.95. *Special Diets*: Vegetarian, Low Salt and Diabetic. Tray service to room if ill (no charge for a maximum time of 21 days). Unlimited snacks available at any time. Open pantry. Party facilities.

AMENITIES AND ACTIVITIES: Parking available (outdoor, for visitors: free and indoor for residents: $50.00/month). *6 lounges with:* TVs (3), piano (1), theatre (1) and pub, café, spa (1). Guest suites available ($100.00/night). *Residence has a:* library, visiting library, chapel, barber/beauty shop, visiting hairdresser and laundry room(s) (no cost). Residence provides newspaper delivery to individual suite (extra cost). Mail delivered to main desk. *Recreation Facilities*: pool table, exercise room, craft room and card room. Posted schedule of activities. Internal newsletter for residents. *Recreational Programs*: exercise, shopping, theatre, parties, entertainment, art classes, pet visiting and day trips.
OTHER SERVICES: *Housekeeping*: weekly. *Laundry*: linen & towel (included in fee); personal ($10.00/ week). Wash/dryer in suite. Transportation for group social activities. Nightly security checks. Telephone & Cable TV (extra cost). Utilities (included in fee).
RENTAL INFORMATION: Rates may vary. Extra cost for 2nd person sharing suite ($450.00/month). Rent paid monthly. *Payment Options*: cheques, post-dated cheques and pre-authorized payments. Rent increases indexed to inflation, annual with 3 months' notice given.

◆ ST. THOMAS ◆

METCALFE GARDENS

45 Metcalfe Street, St. Thomas, ON N5R 5Y1
Tel: (519) 631-9393 • Fax: (519) 631-2563
Email: **info.metcalfe@diversicare.ca**
Website: **www.diversicare.ca**
Contact: **Marketing Manager**
Capacity: **104 residents**
Subsidies: **through DVA for eligible veterans**
Price: **$2,099.00 - $4,908.00/month**

Metcalfe Gardens is a beautiful retirement residence surrounded by lovely gardens. Our residence is celebrating 25 years in our community. We have 97 private suites and offer Full Service Lifestyle Packages. Our 24-hour health care staff are available to ensure you a safe, secure environment. We also provide a variety of daily recreational activities, beautiful lounges, physiotherapy, and spiritual comfort in our own chapel. Recent renovations to our entire residence proves our commitment to quality for the seniors who reside here. Our home-cooked meals make us the next best thing to home! We are situated close to downtown within walking distance to pharmacies, shops and grocery stores. **Metcalfe Gardens is owned/managed by Diversicare, who is the proud recipient of the 2003, 2006, 2009 and 2012 Order of Excellence Award presented by Excellence Canada.** This award was received for the exceptional quality and customer service we provide to our residents every day.

RESIDENCE INFORMATION: 25 years in operation. *Near:* Wellington Street and Elgin Street. Decorated in 2011. Handrails in hallways. 5 floors, 2 elevators. Wheelchair accessible. *Funding Base:* Corporate/for profit. *Owned and managed by:* Diversicare Canada Management Services Co., Inc. 97 units. *Average Waiting Period*: varies. *Average Age*: 85. Can sometimes accommodate cognitively impaired people (assessment required). Can accommodate physically challenged people (assessment required). Smoking allowed (designated outside of building). Alcohol allowed (in own suite). *Procedures to leave the premises on a temporary basis*...notify Front Desk. *Languages:* English. Main doors of residence secured at night only. *Close to:* Public Transit, Shopping, Churches, Seniors' Centre, Library, Major Highway and Local Hospital (St. Thomas-Elgin General Hospital). Member of ORCA & Chamber of Commerce. Licensed under the Retirement Homes Act.
STAFFING: *Available Staff/Services*: Pharmacy, Social Work (CCAC), Recreation Therapy, Occupational Therapy (CCAC), Physiotherapy (CCAC), Dietitian (CCAC), Companions, Chaplaincy, Speech Pathology

(CCAC), Chiropody and Audiology/Hearing Clinic. *External services arranged by:* residence and/or family/resident. Staff trained *re*: visually, hearing and cognitively impaired. 24-hour nursing and other staff. RNs, RPNs, HCAs, PSWs and UCPs on staff. Can retain own MD. Police Check or Vulnerable Person Screening is done for all new staff.
HEALTH SERVICES: Medication administration (if administered by our staff, our pharmacy is used) and/or supervision. Vitals monitored if required. Will accept and provide special assistance for residents who require oxygen, catheters and ostomies. Assistance with dressing available. Weekly assistance with bathing available. *Extra baths:* $15.00/half hour. Care plans done. Different levels of care available. Private Duty/Extra Care available ($25.00/hour). Lab service (visiting, $25.00/visit). Residents can purchase outside resources and use agency of their choice. MD visits residents in their rooms/suites. Will help locate higher level of care if needed (through CCAC).
ACCOMMODATION: *Choice of suites available*: standard bedsitting (14), deluxe bedsitting (48), luxury bedsitting (8), standard 1-bedroom (11), deluxe 1-bedroom (4) & luxury 1-bedroom (9) suites. *In all suites*: locks, storage, window coverings, smoke detector, sprinkler, call bell, air conditioning (central) and thermostats for heating & cooling. Private bathrooms (4-piece) with call bells, grab bars, tubs and showers with non-slip surfaces. In-suite cable TV if resident arranges with cable company (residence charges extra). Can have own phone number if resident arranges with phone company. Unfurnished suites, furnished suites available for short (respite, vacation or trial) stays. *Restrictions on electrical appliances*: must be checked by Maintenance; power bars with surge protectors only permitted. Suites can be shared (by couples only). Pets allowed (cats only - must be kept in suite).
DINING SERVICE: Supportive Service includes 2 meals/day (resident's choice); Full Service includes 3 meals/day. All meals served in dining room daily. *Sittings per meal:* Breakfast: 2, Lunch: 2, Dinner: 2. *Menu choices available:* Breakfast: 4, Lunch: 2, Dinner: 2. *Guest Meals*: Breakfast $6.00, Lunch $8.00, Dinner $10.00. *Special Diets*: Vegetarian and Diabetic (inquire re special needs). Tray service to suite at nurse's discretion (no charge as long as doctor orders). Unlimited snacks available at any time. Snacks are provided in a continental-style. Party facilities.
AMENITIES AND ACTIVITIES: Parking available (outdoor, for visitors and residents). *7 lounges with:* TV (1) and pianos (2). Guest suites available ($65.00/night). *Residence has a:* library, chapel, barber/beauty shop, laundry room(s) ($3.00/washer load, $3.00/dryer load) and tuck/gift shop (open bi-weekly). Banking services on premises (weekly). Resident can arrange newspaper delivery to main desk (extra cost). Mail delivered to main desk. *Recreation Facilities*: pool table, shuffleboard, exercise room, craft room, card room, auditorium, sun lounges and patio. Posted schedule of activities. *Recreational Programs*: exercise, shopping, theatre, parties, entertainment, art classes, pet visiting, day trips, Brain Gym® & More, computer programs, current events, games, bingo, mystery tours and dinners out, etc.
OTHER SERVICES: *Housekeeping*: daily and weekly. *Laundry*: linen, towel & personal (weekly laundry service included in fee); dry cleaning (seniors' discount applies). Resident provides own linen & towels. Transportation for group social activities. 24-hour security. Nightly security checks. Utilities (included in fee). Separate rates for service available if these services need to be increased for short periods.
RENTAL INFORMATION: Price varies per service package and suite size. Extra cost for 2nd person sharing suite ($833.00/month; varies per suite size and service package). Rent paid monthly. *Payment Options*: cheques, post-dated cheques and pre-authorized payments. Rent increases as per Provincial Tenancy Legislation, annual for resident with 3 months' notice given. Short-term respite and trial stays available.

Did you know?

The Government of Canada has created a series of publications on communication with and for seniors, their caregivers and medical personnel. For a series of downloadable documents, visit **www.publications.gc.ca/collections/Collection/H88-3-30-2001/html/p_com_e.htm.**

♦ STAYNER ♦

REVERA - BLUE MOUNTAIN MANOR

236 Weir Street, Box 140, Stayner, ON L0M 1S0
Tel: (855) 573-8372 • Toll Free: (855) 573-8372
Email: **bluemountain@reveraliving.com**
Website: **www.reveraliving.com/bluemountain**
Contact: **Executive Director or Lifestyle Consultant**
Capacity: **56 residents** • Subsidies: **none**
Price: **$2,496.00/month and up**

Keep living your life, your way, at Blue Mountain Manor. You'll find the range of services, amenities and choices that fit your lifestyle and requirements – all in a warm, safe and scenic environment. Located on a quiet street within walking distance of downtown Stayner, Blue Mountain Manor has what you need to keep living in freedom and comfort. Everything is designed to enable you to maintain your independence, have a full social life, enjoy private relaxation, and participate in the activities that you love. We offer 52 suites, nestled amidst a beautiful wooded area. The caring and friendly staff, along with the appealing accommodations, support who you are and how you want to live. With retirement living at Blue Mountain Manor, you change your address, not your life. *Blue Mountain Manor is part of the Revera family, one of North America's leading and most trusted providers of seniors' accommodation, care and services since 1961.*

RESIDENCE INFORMATION: 28 years in operation. *Near:* Highway 91 and Highway 26. Decorated in 2013. Handrails in hallways. 3 floors, 1 elevator. Wheelchair accessible. Central PA system. *Funding Base:* Corporate/for profit. *Owned and managed by:* Revera Inc. 52 units. *Average Waiting Period*: varies. *Average Age*: 85. Can accommodate cognitively impaired people with restrictions (non-exit seeking, amiable). Residents have a dress code (casual). Smoke-free residence. Alcohol allowed ('social'). *Procedures to leave the premises on a temporary basis...*sign out/in; take necessary medications; notify Dietary. *Languages:* English. Main doors of residence secured at all times. *Close to:* Shopping, Churches, Library, Major Highway and Local Hospital (Collingwood General and Marine). Member of ORCA. Licensed under the Retirement Homes Act.
STAFFING: *Available Staff/Services*: Pharmacy, Social Work (CCAC), Recreation Therapy, Occupational Therapy (CCAC), Physiotherapy (CCAC), Hairdresser and RPN Foot Care Service. *External services arranged by:* residence and/or family/resident. Staff trained *re*: visually and hearing impaired. 24-hour nursing and other staff. RNs, RPNs and UCPs on staff. Visiting MD (every 2 weeks & as needed). Can retain own MD. Police Check or Vulnerable Person Screening is done for all new staff.
HEALTH SERVICES: Medication administration (no I.V.s) and/or supervision. Vitals monitored if required. Will accept (but not provide special assistance for) residents who require catheters and ostomies. Will accept and provide special assistance for residents who require oxygen. Weekly assistance with bathing available ($72.00/month). Care plans done. Lab service (visiting, $25.00/visit). Residents can purchase outside resources and use agency of their choice. MD visits residents in their rooms/suites. Will help locate higher level of care if needed (via CCAC/physician).
ACCOMMODATION: *Choice of suites available*: 'luxury' full apartment (4), 'deluxe' suite with kitchenette corner (5) & 'standard' private (43) suites. *In all suites*: locks, storage, window coverings, light fixtures, linens, smoke detector, sprinkler, call bell, air conditioning (window units in most suites) and thermostats for heating. Central air conditioning in halls and common areas. Private bathrooms with call bells, grab bars, tubs and showers with non-slip surfaces and elevated toilet seats. In-suite cable TV provided by residence (residence charges extra). Can have own phone number if resident arranges with phone company. Unfurnished suites, furnished suites available for short stays. *Restrictions on electrical appliances*:

must be auto shut-off, in deluxe & luxury only; CSA approved and inspected by Maintenance before use. Suites can be shared (by couples only). Pets allowed (as per Pet Policy).
DINING SERVICE: All meals included in fee and served in dining room daily. *Sittings per meal:* Breakfast: 1, Lunch: 1, Dinner: 1. *Menu choices available:* Breakfast: 2, Lunch: 2, Dinner: 2. *Guest Meals*: Available. *Special Diets*: Vegetarian, Low Salt, Diabetic and Low Cholesterol/Renal. Tray service to room if ill (no charge for a maximum time of 4 days). 3 snacks/day. Party facilities. Open pantry. Daily comfort corner with refreshments.
AMENITIES AND ACTIVITIES: Parking available (outdoor, for visitors and residents). *3 lounges with:* TVs (3), pianos (2), bookcases (1) and gas fireplace (1). Guest suites available. *Residence has a:* library, barber/beauty shop, visiting hairdresser and laundry room(s) (no cost). Resident can arrange newspaper delivery to main desk. Mail delivered to individual suite. *Recreation Facilities*: shuffleboard, craft room, card room, raised garden, 2 lovely patios and van for local tours. Posted schedule of activities. Internal newsletter for residents. *Recreational Programs*: exercise, shopping, theatre, parties, entertainment, art classes, day trips and theme days.
OTHER SERVICES: *Housekeeping*: weekly (included in fee). *Laundry*: linen & towel (included in fee); personal (extra cost; may do their own). Transportation for group social activities. 24-hour security. Nightly security checks. Telephone (extra cost). Cable TV (extra cost added to monthly statement). Utilities (included in fee). Optional services available.
RENTAL INFORMATION: Rates may vary. Studio - $2,496.00/month & up; deluxe kitchenette - $2,596.00/month & up; luxury 1-bedroom apartment - $3,999.00/month & up. Extra cost for 2nd person sharing suite (optional services available for a fee). Rent paid monthly. *Payment Options*: post-dated cheques and pre-authorized payments. Rent increases as per Provincial Tenancy Legislation, annual for resident with 3 months' notice given. Short-term respite and trial stays subject to availability.

♦ STONEY CREEK ♦

NEW VILLAGE RETIREMENT HOME

490 #8 Highway, Stoney Creek, ON L8G 1G6
Tel: (905) 573-4940 • Fax: (905) 662-0833
Email: **nthomasmorgan@thomashealthcare.com**
Website: **www.thomashealthcare.com**
Contact: **Natalie Thomas-Morgan**
Capacity: **70 residents**
Subsidies: **DVA will fund eligible veterans; specific insurance coverage**
Price: **$1,800.00 - $3,600.00/month**

New Village is owned and operated by Thomas Health Care, a committed professional health care provider with over 45 years' experience. The home is nestled under the Niagara escarpment offering beautiful mountain views and views to Lake Ontario. Our home's location offers full access to public transportation and all amenities. We pride ourselves with having wonderful, kind and caring staff who are dedicated to our clients.

RESIDENCE INFORMATION: 36 years in operation. *Near:* Dewitt Road and Highway 8. Decorated in 2013. Handrails in hallways. 3 floors, 1 elevator. Wheelchair accessible. Central PA system. *Funding Base:* Corporate/for profit. *Owned by:* Thomas Health Care. 65 units. *Average Waiting Period*: varies. *Average Age*: 80. Smoking allowed (outside only). Alcohol allowed (unless directed otherwise by healthcare professionals). *Restrictions around Visitors/Visiting Hours:* security access throughout the night. *Procedures to leave the premises on a temporary basis...*inform staff. *Languages:* English, Italian,

Portuguese, Serbian, Croatian, Dutch, Filipino & German. Will accept Public Guardian and Trustee clients. Main doors of residence secured at night only. *Close to:* Public Transit, Shopping, Churches, Seniors' Centre, Library, Major Highway and Local Hospital (St. Joseph's Centre for Ambulatory Health Services). Member of ORCA. Licensed under the Retirement Homes Act.

STAFFING: *Available Staff/Services*: Pharmacy, Social Work (CCAC), Recreation Therapy, Occupational Therapy (CCAC), Physiotherapy (CCAC), Denturist, Dietitian (CCAC), Companions, Podiatry, Chaplaincy, Speech Pathology (CCAC), Chiropody, Audiology/Hearing Clinic, Hair Care, Aromatherapy and Esthetics. *External services arranged by:* residence and/or family/resident. Staff trained *re*: visually, hearing and cognitively impaired. 24-hour nursing and other staff. RNs, RPNs, PSWs and UCPs on staff. Can retain own MD (each resident has own attending physician). Police Check or Vulnerable Person Screening is done for all new staff.

HEALTH SERVICES: Medication administration and/or supervision. Vitals monitored if required. Will accept and provide special assistance for residents who require oxygen and ostomies. Assistance with dressing available. Weekly assistance with bathing available ($25.00/bath). Care plans done. Different levels of care available. Lab service (visiting, $35.00/visit). Residents can purchase outside resources and use agency of their choice. Will help locate higher level of care if needed (in association with CCAC).

ACCOMMODATION: *Choice of suites available*: small, medium, large private rooms & 1-bedroom suites with kitchenette. *In all suites*: locks, storage, window coverings, light fixtures, linens, fire alarm, smoke detector, sprinkler, emergency response system with wearable pendant/bracelet, air conditioning (central) and thermostats for heating. Kitchenette & bar fridge in some suites. Private bathrooms with call bells, grab bars, tubs and showers with non-slip surfaces and elevated toilet seats. In-suite cable TV if resident arranges with cable company. Can have own phone number if resident arranges with phone company. Unfurnished suites, furnished suites available for short stays. *Restrictions on electrical appliances*: must be CSA approved. Suites can be shared, roommate picked by resident. Pets allowed (no large dogs).

DINING SERVICE: All meals included in fee and served in dining room daily. *Sittings per meal:* Breakfast: 1, Lunch: 1, Dinner: 1. *Menu choices available:* Breakfast: 2, Lunch: 2, Dinner: 2. *Guest Meals*: Breakfast $5.00, Lunch $7.00, Dinner $11.00. *Special Diets*: Vegetarian, Low Salt, Diabetic and Medically Required Modified Diet. 3 snacks/day. Open pantry 24-hour café with toaster, microwave, fridge, hot water, juice and coffee machines. Party facilities.

AMENITIES AND ACTIVITIES: Parking available (outdoor, for visitors and residents). *3 lounges with:* TVs (2), piano (1), quiet spaces (1) and fireplaces (2). Guest suites available ($45.00/night). *Residence has a:* library, visiting library, chapel, barber/beauty shop, visiting hairdresser, laundry room(s) ($1.25/washer load, $1.25/dryer load) and tuck/gift shop (open 24-hours/day). Resident can arrange newspaper delivery to individual suite (extra cost). Mail delivered to individual suite. *Recreation Facilities*: exercise room, craft room, card room and free Wi-Fi in lounge. Posted schedule of activities. Internal newsletter for residents. *Recreational Programs*: exercise, shopping, theatre, parties, entertainment, art classes, pet visiting, day trips, baking and cooking for resident private dinner parties.

OTHER SERVICES: *Housekeeping*: daily (included in fee). *Laundry*: linen, towel & personal (included in fee); dry cleaning (extra cost). Either staff or resident label clothing (clothing labels $35.00). 24-hour security. Nightly security checks. Utilities (included in fee).

RENTAL INFORMATION: Rates may vary. Small - $1,800.00/month; medium - $2,500.00/month; large - $2,600.00 to $2,900.00/month; suite - $3,200.00 to $3,600.00/month. Extra cost for 2nd person sharing suite ($900.00/month). Option to purchase unit available Rent paid monthly. *Payment Options*: pre-authorized payments. Rent increases as per Provincial Tenancy Legislation, annual for resident with 3 months' notice given. Short-term respite and trial stays available (both $90.00/day).

◆ STOUFFVILLE ◆

BUCKINGHAM MANOR

6257 Main Street, Stouffville, ON L4A 4J3
Tel: (905) 640-6660 • Fax: (905) 640-4772
Toll Free: (866) 640-6660
Email: **info@buckinghammanor.ca**
Website: **www.buckinghammanor.ca**
Contact: **Cindi Ross**
Capacity: **65 residents** • Subsidies: **none**
Price: **$1,725.00 - $3,760.00/month**

Buckingham Manor is conveniently located on Main Street in the heart of Stouffville, within walking distance of shops, churches, libraries, banks, restaurants, beauty salons and many other services.

RESIDENCE INFORMATION: 29 years in operation. *On:* Main Street and O'Brien Avenue. Decorated in 2006. Handrails in hallways. 4 floors, 2 elevators. Wheelchair accessible. Central PA system. *Funding Base:* Corporate/for profit. *Owned by:* Eldercare Equities Inc. *Managed by:* Eldercare Management & Consulting Corp. 59 units. *Average Waiting Period*: none. *Average Age*: 85. Can sometimes accommodate cognitively impaired people (depending on assessment of level of care required). Can accommodate physically challenged people (wheelchair-friendly suites available). Smoking allowed (fully licensed Smoking Room compliant with *2006 Smoke Free Ontario Act*). Alcohol allowed. *Procedures to leave the premises on a temporary basis...*resident sign in/sign out register at Reception Desk. *Languages:* English. Main doors of residence secured at night only. *Close to:* Public Transit, Shopping, Churches, Seniors' Centre, Library, Major Highway and Local Hospital (Markham-Stouffville Hospital). Member of ORCA & Whitchurch-Stouffville Chamber of Commerce. Licensed under the Retirement Homes Act.
STAFFING: *Available Staff/Services*: Pharmacy, Social Work (CCAC), Recreation Therapy, Occupational Therapy (CCAC), Physiotherapy (CCAC), Denturist, Dietitian, Companions, Podiatry, Chaplaincy, Speech Pathology (CCAC), Chiropody, Audiology/Hearing Clinic and Hair Salon/Barber. *External services arranged by:* residence and/or family/resident. Staff trained *re*: visually, hearing and cognitively impaired. 24-hour staff. RPNs, HCAs, PSWs and UCPs on staff. Visiting MD (weekly and on-call). Can retain own MD. Police Check or Vulnerable Person Screening is done for all new staff.
HEALTH SERVICES: Medication administration and/or supervision. Vitals monitored if required. Will accept and provide special assistance for residents who require oxygen, catheters and ostomies.

Assistance with dressing available. Weekly assistance with bathing available. *Extra baths:* $125.00/month. Care plans done. Different levels of care available. Enhanced Care Program available for residents who require additional care. Private Duty/Extra Care available ($18.00 to $21.00/hour). Lab service (visiting). Residents can purchase outside resources and use agency of their choice. MD visits residents in their rooms/suites. Clinic area for medical visits. Will help locate higher level of care if needed.
ACCOMMODATION: *Choice of suites available*: semi-private (2), private bedsitting (45), 1-bedroom (8), 1-bedroom + den (1) & 2-bedroom (3) units. *In all suites*: locks, storage, window coverings, light fixtures, linens, fire alarm, smoke detector, sprinkler, emergency nurse call with wireless wristband or pendant & voice communication, air conditioning (central & window units) and thermostats for heating. Private bathrooms with call bells, grab bars, tubs and showers. In-suite cable TV provided by residence (residence charges extra $32.00/month). Can have own phone extension number provided by residence (residence charges extra $29.00/month). Furnished & unfurnished suites available. *Restrictions on electrical appliances*: must meet safety requirements. Suites can be shared (pending availability of beds), roommate picked by resident & residence staff. Pets allowed (on a case-by-case basis).
DINING SERVICE: All meals included in fee and served in dining room daily. *Sittings per meal:* Breakfast: 1, Lunch: 1, Dinner: 1. *Menu choices available:* Breakfast: 2, Lunch: 2, Dinner: 2. *Guest Meals*: Breakfast $5.00, Lunch $6.00, Dinner $7.00. *Special Diets*: Vegetarian, Low Salt and Diabetic. All therapeutic diets accommodated. Tray service to room if ill (no charge as long as doctor orders). 3 snacks/day. Open pantry. Party facilities. Private dining area available for family gatherings & special occasions.
AMENITIES AND ACTIVITIES: Parking available (outdoor, for visitors and residents). *4 lounges with:* TVs (3) and pianos (2). Guest suites available ($75.00/night). *Residence has a:* library, visiting library, barber/beauty shop, visiting hairdresser, laundry room(s) (no cost) and tuck/gift shop. Residence provides newspaper delivery to individual suite. Mail delivered to dining room. *Recreation Facilities*: craft room, card room, large-screen theatre, patio garden and Nintendo Wii. Posted schedule of activities. Internal newsletter for residents. *Recreational Programs*: exercise, shopping, theatre, parties, entertainment, art classes, pet visiting, day trips, games and Happy Hour.
OTHER SERVICES: *Housekeeping*: weekly (included in fee). *Laundry*: linen, towel & personal (included in fee). 24-hour security. Nightly security checks. Telephone ($29.00/month). Cable TV ($32.00/month). Utilities (included in fee). Hairdresser & Barber. Foot Care.
RENTAL INFORMATION: Rates may vary. Semi-private - $1,725.00/month & up; private - $2,350.00 to $3,760.00/month. Extra cost for 2nd person sharing suite ($600.00/month). Rent paid monthly. *Payment Options*: cheques and post-dated cheques. Rent increases as per Provincial Tenancy Legislation, annual for resident with 3 months' notice given. Will help resident move into residence. Short-term respite and trial stays (2 - 4 weeks recommended minimum trial) available (both $75.00/day; cost ranges depending on care needs).

STOUFFVILLE CREEK RETIREMENT RESIDENCE

40 Freel Lane, Stouffville, ON L4A 0P5
Tel: (905) 642-2902 • Fax: (905) 642-8580
Email: **mkg.mgr.stouffville@diversicare.ca**
Website: **www.stouffvillecreek.ca**
Contact: **Marketing Manager**
Capacity: **130 residents** • Subsidies: **none**
Price: **$2,884.00 - $5,021.00/month**

Stouffville Creek combines a luxurious, yet relaxed atmosphere as an Independent and Full Service Retirement Residence. We are located in the heart of Stouffville just off Main Street and steps away from buses and trains. A quiet oasis in the midst of a vibrant community. Come and discover farmlands, an amazing country market, gallery, museum and art centre. **Stouffville Creek is managed/owned by Diversicare, who is the recipient of the 2003, 2006, 2009 and 2012 Order of Excellence Award**

presented by Excellence Canada. This award was received for the exceptional quality and customer service we provide to our residents every day.

RESIDENCE INFORMATION: 5 years in operation. *Near:* Main Street and Freel Lane. Decorated in 2009. Handrails in hallways. 5 floors, 2 elevators. Wheelchair accessible. Central PA system. *Funding Base:* Corporate/for profit. *Owned and managed by:* Diversicare Canada Management Services Co., Inc. 118 units. *Average Waiting Period*: none. *Average Age*: 84. Can accommodate cognitively impaired & physically challenged people (assessment must be conducted). Smoke-free residence. Alcohol allowed. *Restrictions around Visitors/Visiting Hours:* visitor sign in/out required. *Procedures to leave the premises on a temporary basis...*resident sign in/out required. *Languages:* English. Main doors of residence secured at night only. *Close to:* Public Transit, Shopping, Churches, Seniors' Centre, Library, Major Highway and Local Hospital (Markham-Stouffville Hospital). *Predominant Cultural Group:* Canadian. Member of ORCA, Whitchurch-Stouffville Chamber of Commerce, Markham Board of Trade & Silver Jubilee. Licensed under the Retirement Homes Act.
STAFFING: *Available Staff/Services*: Pharmacy, Social Work (CCAC), Recreation Therapy, Occupational Therapy, Visiting Dentist, Physiotherapy, Denturist, Chaplaincy, Speech Pathology (CCAC), Audiology/Hearing Clinic and Brain Gym® & More program. *External services arranged by:* residence and/or family/resident. Staff trained *re*: visually, hearing and cognitively impaired. 24-hour staff. RNs, RPNs, PSWs and UCPs on staff. Visiting MD (bi-weekly). Can retain own MD. Staff members are bonded. Police Check or Vulnerable Person Screening is done for all new staff.
HEALTH SERVICES: Medication administration and/or supervision. Vitals monitored if required. Will accept (but not provide special assistance for) residents who require catheters, ostomies and feeding tubes. Will accept and provide special assistance for residents who require oxygen. Assistance with dressing available ($15.00/half hour). Assistance with bathing available as needed ($17.00/half hour). Care plans done. Different levels of care available. Lab service (visiting, $25.00/visit). Residents can purchase outside resources and use agency of their choice. MD visits residents in their rooms/suites. Clinic area for medical visits. Will help locate higher level of care if needed (long-term care process is reviewed with resident and family).
ACCOMMODATION: *Choice of suites available*: studio, 1-bedroom & 2-bedroom suites. *In all suites*: locks, kitchenette, bar fridge, patio/balcony, storage, window coverings, light fixtures, fire alarm, smoke detector, sprinkler, call bell, emergency response system with wearable pendant/bracelet & emergency pull cord, air conditioning (central) and thermostats for heating & cooling. Most suites with balconies. Private bathrooms with call bells, grab bars, showers with non-slip surfaces and elevated toilet seats. In-suite cable TV if resident arranges with cable company. Can have own phone number if resident arranges with phone company. Unfurnished suites, furnished suites available for short stays. *Restrictions on electrical appliances*: no toasters. Suites can be shared (by couples only), roommate picked by resident. Small pets allowed (must be able to care for the pet).
DINING SERVICE: All meals included in fee; lunch and dinner in dining room with daily features and à la carte menu, separate breakfast room. Alcohol available in dining room and bistro. *Sittings per meal:* Breakfast: 1, Lunch: 2, Dinner: 2. *Menu choices available:* Lunch: 2, Dinner: 2. *Guest Meals*: Lunch $8.00, Dinner $15.00. *Special Diets*: Vegetarian, Low Salt, Diabetic and Limited Therapeutic. Tray service to room if ill (no charge for a maximum time of 5 days). Unlimited snacks available at any time. Open pantry. Party facilities.
AMENITIES AND ACTIVITIES: Parking available (outdoor, for visitors and residents). *4 lounges with:* TVs (2) and piano (1). Guest suites available ($75.00/night). *Residence has a:* library, chapel, barber/beauty shop, visiting hairdresser, laundry room(s) (no cost) and tuck/gift shop. Mail delivered to private mailbox with key. *Recreation Facilities*: pool table, billiards, exercise room, craft room, card room and media room. Posted schedule of activities. Internal newsletter for residents. *Recreational Programs*: exercise, shopping, theatre, parties, entertainment, art classes, pet visiting, day trips and Brain Gym® & More programs.

OTHER SERVICES: *Housekeeping*: weekly (included in fee; daily tidy up extra cost). *Laundry*: linen & towel (included in fee); personal ($20.00/load). Staff label clothing (included in fee). Complimentary laundry facilities. Transportation for group social activities. 24-hour security. Nightly security checks. Telephone & Cable TV (extra cost). Utilities (included in fee). Full Service Lifestyle ($500.00/month) includes medication management, administration/assistance with personal care as per contract & weekly laundering of personal clothing.
RENTAL INFORMATION: Rates may vary. Studio - $2,884.00/month & up; 1-bedroom - $3,708.00/month & up; 2-bedroom - $4,635.00/month & up. Extra cost for 2nd person sharing suite ($600.00/month; current Move-In Incentive, call to inquire). Rent paid monthly. *Payment Options*: cheques, post-dated cheques and pre-authorized payments. Rent increases as per Provincial Tenancy Legislation with 3 months' notice given. Will help resident move into residence (extra cost). Short-term respite and trial stays available (both $85.00/day).

◆ STRATFORD ◆

ROYAL PALISADE

200 McCarthy Road, Stratford, ON N5A 0B6
Tel: (519) 271-9800 • Fax: (519) 271-9809
Email: **info@royalpalisade.com**
Website: **www.royalpalisade.com**
Contact: **Valerie Trudgeon**
Capacity: **150 residents** • Subsidies: **none**
Price: **$2,562.00/month and up**

Opened in May 2011, Royal Palisade is a charming four-storey residence in Stratford — Canada's home to the theatre and arts. You can choose to rent your suite, or own a condominium. Immediate occupancy. All rental suites contain a kitchen, separate bedroom, and balcony. A variety of condo layouts to choose from. A wide selection of amenities & services, such as; 24-hour emergency response, restaurant-style dining, library/computer room, movie theatre, hair salon, billiards room, health & wellness clinic, gym, fireside lounge, large dining room overlooking the courtyard, housekeeping & laundry and van transportation.

RESIDENCE INFORMATION: 3 years in operation. *Near:* Mornington Street and McCarthy Road. Decorated in 2011. Handrails in hallways. 4 floors, 3 elevators. Wheelchair accessible. *Funding Base:* Corporate/for profit. *Owned and managed by:* Retirement Life Communities. 124 units. *Average Waiting Period*: none. *Average Age*: 78. Can accommodate physically challenged people. Smoking allowed (within private unit, with Administration's approval). Alcohol allowed. *Procedures to leave the premises on a temporary basis...*notify Administration. *Languages:* English. Main doors of residence secured at night only. *Close to:* Public Transit, Shopping, Churches, Seniors' Centre, Major Highway and Local Hospital (Stratford General Hospital). Licensed under the Retirement Homes Act.
STAFFING: *Available Staff/Services*: Pharmacy, Recreation Therapy, Physiotherapy (CCAC), Chaplaincy and Audiology/Hearing Clinic. *External services arranged by:* residence and/or family/resident. Staff trained *re*: visually, hearing and cognitively impaired. 24-hour nursing and other staff. RPNs, PSWs and UCPs on staff. Can retain own MD. Police Check or Vulnerable Person Screening is done for all new staff.
HEALTH SERVICES: Medication administration (included in some packages & at an additional fee) and/or supervision. Vitals monitored if required. Will accept and provide special assistance for residents who require oxygen, catheters and ostomies. Assistance with dressing available ($30.00/hour). Assistance with bathing available as needed ($20.00/bath). Massage Therapy. Care plans done. Different levels of

care available. Lab service (visiting, $26.50/visit). Residents can purchase outside resources and use agency of their choice. MD visits residents in their rooms/suites. Clinic area for medical visits. Will help locate higher level of care if needed (via CCAC).

ACCOMMODATION: *Choice of suites available*: 1-bedroom & 2-bedroom condominiums for sale or 1-bedroom & 2-bedroom rental units. *In all suites*: locks, kitchenette, bar fridge, microwave, patio/balcony, storage, window coverings, light fixtures, stove, fire alarm, smoke detector, sprinkler, call bell, emergency response system with wearable pendant/bracelet, air conditioning (electrical forced air - resident can control temperature from own unit) and thermostats for heating & cooling. All condominium & rental units have full kitchens. Private bathrooms with call bells, grab bars, showers with non-slip surfaces and elevated toilet seats. In-suite cable TV if resident arranges with cable company. Can have own phone number if resident arranges with phone company. Unfurnished suites, furnished suites available for short stays. Suites can be shared (by couples only). Pets allowed (cats and small dogs).

DINING SERVICE: All meals included in fee and served in dining room daily. *Guest Meals*: Breakfast $6.00, Lunch $12.00, Dinner $17.00. *Special Diets*: Vegetarian, Low Salt, Diabetic and Gluten Free. Tray service to room if ill (no charge for a maximum time of 5 days). Unlimited snacks available at any time. Open pantry. On-site chef-prepared meals. Party facilities.

AMENITIES AND ACTIVITIES: Parking available (outdoor, for visitors and residents). *4 lounges with:* TV (1) and piano (1). Guest suites available ($80.00/night). *Residence has a:* library, visiting library, barber/ beauty shop, visiting hairdresser and laundry room(s) (no cost). Residence provides newspaper delivery to individual suite. Mail delivered to private mailbox with key. *Recreation Facilities*: pool table, billiards, shuffleboard, exercise room, craft room, card room and sewing room. Posted schedule of activities. Internal newsletter for residents. *Recreational Programs*: exercise, shopping, theatre, parties, art classes, entertainment, pet visiting, day trips and special themed events.

OTHER SERVICES: *Housekeeping*: daily and weekly (included in fee; according to service level). *Laundry*: linen & towel (extra cost; included in Care Free Package); personal (extra cost; included in Helping Hand Package) & dry cleaning (extra cost; Front Desk arranges service). Transportation for group social activities. 24-hour security. Nightly security checks. Utilities (included in fee; extra cost for condominium owners).

RENTAL INFORMATION: Rates may vary. Extra cost for 2nd person sharing suite ($791.00/month for Select Service Care Package). Option to purchase unit available (1-bedroom and 2-bedroom condominiums available for sale). Rent paid monthly. *Payment Options*: cheques and post-dated cheques. Rent increases as per Provincial Tenancy Legislation, annual for resident with 3 months' notice given. Will help resident move into residence (extra cost). Short-term respite and trial stays available (both $80.00/day).

◆ SUDBURY ◆

PALAMBRO RETIREMENT RESIDENCE

1315 Regent Street, Sudbury, ON P3E 3Z1
Tel: (705) 523-5295 • Fax: (705) 523-5295
Email: **info@palambro.com**
Website: **www.palambro.com**
Contact: **Marijo Fegarty**
Capacity: **54 residents** • Subsidies: **none**
Price: **$1,700.00 - $2,700.00/month**

Palambro is the small and friendly retirement community in Sudbury's south end. Residents enjoy spacious, attractive suites, delicious and nutritious home-cooked meals and the opportunity to participate in optional trips, hobbies and entertainment, all within a truly caring community.

RESIDENCE INFORMATION: 29 years in operation. *Near:* Regent Street and Walford Road. Decorated in 2009. Handrails in hallways. 3 floors, no elevator. *Funding Base:* Corporate/for profit. *Owned by:* Marijo and Andrew Fegarty. 29 units. *Average Waiting Period*: none. Can sometimes accommodate cognitively impaired people. Can accommodate physically challenged people (mobility challenged and visually impaired welcome). Smoking allowed (outside, as per by-laws). Alcohol allowed (In resident's own suite; alcoholic drinks are provided at special monthly dinners). *Procedures to leave the premises on a temporary basis...*Short-term: inform Supervisor of Resident Care. Overnight & Holidays: inform on-duty care staff. *Languages:* English & French. Will accept Public Guardian and Trustee clients. Main doors of residence secured at night only. *Close to:* Public Transit, Shopping, Churches, Seniors' Centre, Library and Local Hospitals (Health Sciences North (Sudbury Regional Hospital) 1.8 km & St. Joseph's Health Centre 2.3 km). Member of ORCA. Licensed under the Retirement Homes Act.
STAFFING: *Available Staff/Services*: Pharmacy, Recreation Therapy, Physiotherapy (CCAC), Chaplaincy, Hair Care, Nail Care, Exercise Class and Activities. *External services arranged by:* residence and/or family/resident. Staff trained *re*: visually, hearing and cognitively impaired. 24-hour staff. RNs, RPNs, PSWs and UCPs on staff. Visiting MD (every 6 weeks, as required). Can retain own MD. Police Check or Vulnerable Person Screening is done for all new staff.
HEALTH SERVICES: Medication administration and/or supervision. Vitals monitored if required. Will accept (but not provide special assistance for) residents who require oxygen. Care plans done. Residents can purchase outside resources and use agency of their choice. MD visits residents in their rooms/suites. Will help locate higher level of care if needed.
ACCOMMODATION: *Choice of suites available*: private suites (26) & larger suites (2). *In all suites*: locks, window coverings, light fixtures, linens, smoke detector, air conditioning (window units) and thermostats for heating & cooling. Private bathrooms with grab bars, tubs and showers. In-suite cable/satellite TV if resident arranges with cable/satellite company. Can have own phone number if resident arranges with phone company. Furnished & unfurnished suites available. Restrictions on electrical appliances. Suites can be shared (by couples only). No pets allowed.
DINING SERVICE: All meals included in fee and served in dining room daily. *Sittings per meal:* Breakfast: 1, Lunch: 1, Dinner: 1. *Menu choices available:* Breakfast: 2, Lunch: 2, Dinner: 2. *Guest Meals*: Breakfast $3.00, Lunch $5.00, Dinner $7.00. *Special Diets*: Vegetarian, Low Salt and Diabetic. Catering staff can accommodate dietary restriction. Tray service to room if ill (no charge or restrictions). 2 snacks/day. Party facilities.
AMENITIES AND ACTIVITIES: Parking available (outdoor, for visitors and residents). *2 lounges with:* TVs (2). *Residence has a:* visiting hairdresser and laundry room(s) (no cost). Resident can arrange newspaper delivery to main desk. Mail delivered to main desk. *Recreation Facilities*: craft room and card room. Posted schedule of activities. *Recreational Programs*: exercise, shopping, theatre, parties, entertainment, pet visiting and day trips.
OTHER SERVICES: *Housekeeping*: weekly (included in fee). *Laundry*: linen, towel & personal (included in fee). Transportation to medical appointments (will book Handi-Trans or arrange taxi) and for group social activities (extra cost). 24-hour security. Nightly security checks. Telephone (regular Bell fees apply). Cable TV (extra cost). Utilities (included in fee).
RENTAL INFORMATION: Price varies by size and whether suite has balcony and modernized bathroom. Extra cost for 2nd person sharing suite ($300.00/month). Rent paid monthly. *Payment Options*: cheques and post-dated cheques. Rent increases as per Provincial Tenancy Legislation, annual for resident with 3 months' notice given. Will help resident move into residence (extra cost). Short-term respite and trial stays available (both $80.00/day).

Pricing information for homes listed in The *Guide* may vary slightly.
Please verify rates with the residences you are interested in directly.

RED OAK VILLA

20 Ste. Anne Road, Sudbury, ON P3E 5N4
Tel: (705) 673-0050 • Fax: (705) 673-5123
Email: **bconlin@autumnwood.ca**
Website: **www.autumnwood.ca**
Contact: **Brenda Conlin**
Capacity: **100 residents •** Subsidies: **none**
Price: **$2,000.00/month and up**

Red Oak Villa is situated in a historic landmark in the heart of Sudbury. Step back into old world charm and architecture while being surrounded by all of the downtown amenities. Red Oak Villa boasts home-cooked meals and a very caring, professional and skilled staff to help with all your needs and services. ***Red Oak Villa was voted Sudbury's Best Retirement Home 2009 – 2012!***

RESIDENCE INFORMATION: 8 years in operation. *Near:* Notre Dame Avenue and Ste. Anne Road. Decorated in 2006. 4 floors, 1 elevator. Wheelchair accessible. Central PA system. *Funding Base:* Corporate/for profit. *Owned and managed by:* Autumnwood Mature Lifestyle Communities. 84 units. *Average Waiting Period*: varies. *Average Age*: 79. Can accommodate cognitively impaired & physically challenged people with restrictions. Smoking allowed (outside designated area). Alcohol allowed (served at special functions and special dinners). *Procedures to leave the premises on a temporary basis*...notify staff and record it in a sign out book. *Languages:* English & French. Main doors of residence secured at all times. *Close to:* Public Transit, Shopping, Churches, Seniors' Centre, Library and Local Hospital (Health Sciences North – St. Joseph's Health Centre). Member of ORCA. Licensed under the Retirement Homes Act.
STAFFING: *Available Staff/Services*: Pharmacy, Social Work (CCAC), Occupational Therapy (CCAC), Physiotherapy (CCAC), Dietitian (CCAC), Podiatry (CCAC), Chaplaincy and Speech Pathology (CCAC). *External services arranged by:* family/resident. Staff trained *re*: visually and hearing impaired. 24-hour staff. RPNs and PSWs on staff. Visiting MD (twice/month). Can retain own MD. Police Check or Vulnerable Person Screening is done for all new staff.
HEALTH SERVICES: Medication administered if required (will not administer medications via G-tube). Vitals monitored if required. Will accept (but not provide special assistance for) residents who require feeding tubes. Will accept and provide special assistance for residents who require oxygen. Assistance with dressing available ($15.00/hour). Weekly assistance with bathing available. *Extra baths:* $30.00/bath. Care plans done. Different levels of care available. Lab service (on-site, $20.00/visit). Residents can purchase outside resources and use agency of their choice. Clinic area for medical visits. Will help locate higher level of care if needed (CCAC, Bayshore, Discharge Planners).
ACCOMMODATION: *Choice of suites available*: studios, 1-bedroom & 2-bedroom units. *In all suites*: locks, kitchenette, window coverings, light fixtures, linens, fire alarm, smoke detector, sprinkler, call bell & nurse call on phones, air conditioning (central - individually controlled in newer wings) and thermostats for heating & cooling. Can bring own microwave & bar fridge. Private bathrooms with call bells, grab

bars, tubs and showers with non-slip surfaces. In-suite cable TV provided by residence (residence charges extra). Can have own phone extension number provided by residence (residence charges extra $35.00/month). Unfurnished suites, furnished suites available for short stays. *Restrictions on electrical appliances*: no toasters or hot plates; all appliances must be auto shut-off; must be checked by Maintenance. Suites can be shared. No pets allowed.
DINING SERVICE: All meals included in fee and served in dining room daily. *Sittings per meal:* Breakfast: 1, Lunch: 1, Dinner: 1. *Menu choices available:* Lunch: 2, Dinner: 2. *Guest Meals*: Breakfast $5.00, Lunch $8.00, Dinner $12.00. *Special Diets*: Vegetarian, Low Salt and Diabetic. Tray service to room if ill. Open pantry. Party facilities. A private dining room is available for residents who may want to have a special occasion or just a private dinner with their relatives and or friends.
AMENITIES AND ACTIVITIES: Parking available (outdoor, for visitors and residents). *1 lounge with:* TV (1), piano (1) and breakfast nooks with TVs (2). Guest suites available ($75.00/night). *Residence has a:* library, barber/beauty shop, visiting hairdresser, laundry room(s) (no cost) and tuck/gift shop (open Friday). Resident can arrange newspaper delivery to individual suite. Mail delivered to private mailbox with key. *Recreation Facilities*: pool table, exercise room, craft room and card room. Posted schedule of activities. *Recreational Programs*: exercise, shopping, theatre, parties, entertainment, art classes, pet visiting and day trips.
OTHER SERVICES: *Housekeeping*: weekly (light housekeeping includes linen & towel laundry). *Laundry*: linen & towel (included in fee); personal ($15.00/load). Laundry machines on each floor. Transportation for group social activities. 24-hour security. Nightly security checks. Telephone (extra cost; telephone is mandatory). Cable TV (extra cost). Utilities (included in fee).
RENTAL INFORMATION: Rates may vary; price ranges are influenced by size and amenities. Extra cost for 2nd person sharing suite ($650.00/month). Rent paid monthly. *Payment Options*: pre-authorized payments. Rent increases as per Provincial Tenancy Legislation with 3 months' notice given. Short-term respite and trial stays available (both $75.00/day, all meals included).

THE AMBERWOOD SUITES

1385 Regent Street South, Sudbury, ON P3E 3Z1
Tel: (705) 522-5682 • Fax: (705) 522-0040
Email: **blanthier@autumnwood.ca**
Website: **www.autumnwood.ca**
Contact: **Brenda Lanthier**
Capacity: **87 units** • Subsidies: **none**
Price: **$2,225.00 - $4,050.00/month**

The new Amberwood Suites, is situated in the south end of the city, close to public transportation, banking, shopping, restaurants, churches and other community amenities. With this in mind, many seniors are choosing to seek a new and different lifestyle; a lifestyle that allows them to remain independent and still enjoy all the things they love while living in a supportive community. Amberwood is now open with a complete expansion - large bright studios, 1-bedroom & 2-bedroom suites, with kitchenettes, 3 meals/day, housekeeping, medication administration, and activities. *Sudbury's newest full service retirement residence.* Call for your visit.

RESIDENCE INFORMATION: 17 years in operation. *Near:* Regent Street South and Bouchard Street. Renovated in 2012. Handrails in hallways. 3 floors, 2 elevators. Wheelchair accessible. Central PA system. *Funding Base:* Corporate/for profit. *Owned and managed by:* Autumnwood Mature Lifestyle Communities. *Average Waiting Period*: currently none. *Average Age*: 82. Can sometimes accommodate cognitively impaired people (depending on level of care required). Can accommodate physically challenged people. Smoke-free building. Alcohol allowed. *Procedures to leave the premises on a temporary basis...*notify staff and record it in a sign out book. *Languages:* English & French. Secured

entrance. *Close to:* Public Transit, Shopping, Churches, Library, Major Highway and Local Hospitals (Health Sciences North). Licensed under the Retirement Homes Act.
STAFFING: *Available Staff/Services:* Pharmacy, Social Work (CCAC), Occupational Therapy (CCAC), Physiotherapy (CCAC), Dietitian (CCAC), Podiatry (CCAC) and Speech Pathology (CCAC). *External services arranged by:* residence and/or family/resident. 24-hour staff. RPNs and PSWs on staff. Visiting MD (once/month). Can retain own MD. Police Check or Vulnerable Person Screening is done for all new staff.
HEALTH SERVICES: Medication administration and/or supervision. Vitals monitored if required. Will accept (but not provide special assistance for) residents who require oxygen, catheters, ostomies and feeding tubes. Weekly assistance with bathing available. Care plans done. Different levels of care available. Additional care services available for a fee. Residents can purchase outside resources and use agency of their choice. Will help locate higher level of care if needed (CCAC, Social Workers, Discharge Planners).
ACCOMMODATION: *Choice of suites available:* bachelor (55), 1-bedroom (30) & 2-bedroom (5) suites. *In all suites:* locks, kitchenette, bar fridge, window coverings, light fixtures, linens & towels, fire alarm, smoke detector, sprinkler, call bell and thermostats for heating & cooling. Private bathrooms with call bells, grab bars, seated showers with non-slip surfaces. Telephone and cable TV provided for a nominal fee. Unfurnished suites, furnished suites available for short stays. No pets allowed.
DINING SERVICE: All meals included in fee and served in dining room daily. *Sittings per meal:* Breakfast: 1, Lunch: 1, Dinner: 1. *Menu choices available:* Breakfast: 1, Lunch: 2, Dinner: 2. *Guest Meals:* Breakfast $8.00, Lunch $10.00, Dinner $15.00. *Special Diets:* Vegetarian, Low Salt and Diabetic. Tray service to room if ill. Unlimited snacks available at any time. Private dining room.
AMENITIES AND ACTIVITIES: Parking available (outdoor, for visitors and residents). *1 lounge with:* TV (1). *Residence has a:* library area, barber/beauty shop, visiting hairdresser and laundry room(s) (no cost). Resident can arrange newspaper delivery to main desk. Mail delivered to main desk. *Recreation Facilities:* craft area and card area. Posted schedule of activities. *Recreational Programs:* exercise, shopping, parties, entertainment, pet visiting and day trips.
OTHER SERVICES: *Housekeeping:* weekly. *Laundry:* linen & towel (included in fee); personal (resident does own - soap provided). Transportation for group social activities. 24-hour security. Telephone & Cable TV (extra cost). Utilities (included in fee).
RENTAL INFORMATION: Rates may vary. Extra cost for 2nd person sharing suite ($650.00/month). Rent paid monthly. *Payment Options:* pre-authorized payments. Rent increases as per Provincial Tenancy Legislation with 3 months' notice given. Short-term respite subject to suite availability.

♦ THORNHILL ♦

FOUR ELMS RETIREMENT RESIDENCE

1500 Steeles Avenue West, Thornhill, ON L4J 4H6
Tel: (905) 738-0905 • Fax: (905) 738-6710
Email: **mktg1.fe@diversicare.ca**
Website: **www.fourelms.ca**
Contact: **Marketing Manager**
Capacity: **178 residents** • Subsidies: **none**
Price: **$3,080.00 - $5,675.00/month**

Four Elms Retirement Residence is a lovely new home located in Thornhill, at Dufferin and Steeles. With 160 suites we offer a variety of styles including studio, 1-bedroom & 2-bedroom suites, some with den and balcony. We provide Independent, Full Service and Assisted Living Lifestyles. We have 29 suites located on our Assisted Living Secure Floor. We are serviced by both TTC Wheel-Trans and Vaughan Mobility Plus. **Four Elms Retirement Residence is owned/managed by Diversicare, who is the proud**

recipient of the 2003, 2006, 2009 and 2012 Order of Excellence Award given by Excellence Canada. The award was received for the exceptional quality and customer service we provide to our residents every day.

RESIDENCE INFORMATION: 4 years in operation. *On:* Steeles Avenue and Dufferin Street. Decorated in 2010. Handrails in hallways. 6 floors, 3 elevators. Wheelchair accessible. Central PA system. *Funding Base:* Corporate/for profit. *Owned by:* Diversicare Canada Management Services Co., Inc. 160 units. *Average Waiting Period*: none. *Average Age*: 80. Can accommodate cognitively impaired people (secure access). Can accommodate physically challenged people (assessment by RN). Smoke-free residence. Alcohol allowed. *Procedures to leave the premises on a temporary basis...*notify staff. *Languages:* English, Hebrew, Italian, Russian, Filipino, Spanish & Portuguese. Will accept Public Guardian and Trustee clients. Main doors of residence secured at night only. *Close to:* Public Transit, Shopping, Churches, Synagogues, Seniors' Centre, Library, Major Highway and Local Hospital (North York General Hospital & MacKenzie Health). Member of ORCA. Licensed under the Retirement Homes Act.
STAFFING: *Available Staff/Services*: Pharmacy, Social Work (CCAC), Recreation Therapy, Occupational Therapy (CCAC), Visiting Dentist, Physiotherapy, Denturist, Dietitian, Companions, Chaplaincy, Speech Pathology (CCAC), Chiropody, Audiology/Hearing Clinic and Brain Gym® & More program. *External services arranged by:* family/resident. Staff trained *re*: visually, hearing and cognitively impaired. 24-hour nursing and other staff. RNs, RPNs, PSWs and UCPs on staff. Visiting MD (once/week). Can retain own MD. Police Check or Vulnerable Person Screening is done for all new staff.
HEALTH SERVICES: Medication administration and/or supervision. Vitals monitored if required. Will accept and provide special assistance for residents who require oxygen, catheters and ostomies. Assistance with dressing available. Assistance with bathing available twice a week. *Extra baths:* $30.00/bath. Care plans done. Different levels of care available. Private Duty/Extra Care available ($40.00 to $60.00/hour). Rates for Assisted Living vary based on size of suite; available throughout building. Assisted Living Area is secured to accommodate residents with dementia. Lab service (visiting). Residents can purchase outside resources and use agency of their choice. MD visits residents in their rooms/suites. Clinic area for medical visits. Will help locate higher level of care if needed (Residence Service Manager works with CCAC).
ACCOMMODATION: *Choice of suites available*: studio (25), alcove (16), 1-bedroom (32), 1-bedroom + den (40), 2-bedroom (4), 2-bedroom + den (14); Secure Floor - studio (14) & 1-bedroom (15) units. *In all suites*: locks, kitchenette, bar fridge, storage, window coverings, light fixtures, fire alarm, smoke detector, sprinkler, emergency response system with wearable pendant/bracelet, air conditioning (central) and thermostats for heating & cooling. Some suites with balconies. No kitchenettes on Secure Floor. Private bathrooms with call bells, grab bars, showers with non-slip surfaces and elevated toilet seats. In-suite cable TV if resident arranges with cable company. Can have own phone number if resident arranges with phone company. Unfurnished suites, furnished suites available for short stays. *Restrictions on electrical appliances*: automatic shut-off & CSA approved, no hot plates. Suites can be shared, roommate picked by resident. Small pets allowed (they must take care of them).
DINING SERVICE: All meals included in fee and served in dining room daily. *Sittings per meal:* Lunch: 2, Dinner: 2. Open Seating for Breakfast. *Guest Meals*: Breakfast $5.00, Lunch $8.00, Dinner $15.00. *Special Diets*: Vegetarian, Low Salt, Diabetic, Gluten Free, Lactose Free and Renal. Tray service to room if ill (no charge as long as doctor orders). Unlimited snacks available at any time. Party facilities.
AMENITIES AND ACTIVITIES: Parking available (outdoor, for visitors: free and indoor for residents: $50.00/month). *3 lounges with:* TVs (2) and piano (1). Guest suites available ($95.00/night). *Residence has a:* library, chapel, barber/beauty shop, laundry room(s) (no cost) and tuck/gift shop (open daily; 9:00 a.m. - 8:00 p.m.). Banking services on premises (once/month). Residence provides newspaper delivery to main desk. Mail delivered to private mailbox with key. *Recreation Facilities*: billiards, exercise room, greenhouse, craft room, card room, computer lounge, theatre, activity room, bistro, café and patio. Residence has its own bus. Posted schedule of activities. Internal newsletter for residents. *Recreational Programs*: exercise, shopping, theatre, parties, art classes, pet visiting, day trips, movies, card games, guest speakers and live entertainment.

OTHER SERVICES: *Housekeeping*: weekly (included in fee; Assisted Living & Secure Living includes daily tidy). *Laundry*: linen & towel (included in fee); personal (extra cost for independent only; included for full service & Assisted Living) & dry cleaning (extra cost). Resident laundry rooms available on each resident floor at no charge. Transportation for group social activities. 24-hour security (staff on duty 24/7). Nightly security checks (only for Assisted Living and on Secure Floor). Telephone & Cable TV (pay provider). Utilities (included in fee). Internet (arrange with provider).
RENTAL INFORMATION: Rates may vary. Studios - $3,080.00/month & up; alcoves - $3,690.00/month & up; 1-bedrooms - $3,710.00/month & up; 1-bedrooms + den - $4,345.00/month & up; 2-bedrooms - $5,265.00/month; 2-bedrooms + den - $5,525.00/month & up. Assisted Living - $4,230.00 to $6,825.00/month; Secured Floor - $4,400.00 to $5,800.00/month & up. Extra cost for 2nd person sharing suite ($675.00/month). Rent paid monthly. *Payment Options*: cheques, direct deposit and pre-authorized payments. Rent increases as per Provincial Tenancy Legislation, annual for resident with 3 months' notice given. Short-term respite and trial stays available (range is $90.00 - $140.00/day depending on care; up to 30 days).

REVERA - GLYNNWOOD

7700 Bayview Avenue, Thornhill, ON L3T 5W1
Tel: (855) 573-8372 • Toll Free: (855) 573-8372
Email: **glynnwood@reveraliving.com**
Website: **www.reveraliving.com/glynnwood**
Contact: **Executive Director or Lifestyle Consultant**
Capacity: **179 units** • Subsidies: **none**
Price: **$2,900.00/month and up**

Keep living your life, your way, at Glynnwood. You'll find the range of services, amenities and choices that fit your lifestyle – all in a warm, safe and elegant environment. Glynnwood is often compared to a country club or first class hotel. Nestled on 6 acres of woodland property, residents enjoy their own private park with a pond and picturesque gardens. Located in a beautiful area of Thornhill, it is also conveniently close to shopping, local amenities and community services, places of worship, highways, and public transit. Everything is designed for you to maintain your independence and privacy, enjoy a full social life, and participate in the activities that you love. With retirement living at Glynnwood, you change your address, not your life. *Glynnwood is part of the Revera family, one of North America's leading and most trusted providers of seniors' accommodation, care and services since 1961.*

RESIDENCE INFORMATION: 33 years in operation. *Near:* Bayview Avenue and John Street. Decorated in 2011. Handrails in hallways. 6 floors, 3 elevators. Wheelchair accessible. Central PA system. *Funding Base:* Corporate/for profit. *Owned and managed by:* Revera Inc. *Average Waiting Period*: varies. *Average Age*: 85. Can sometimes accommodate cognitively impaired people (please inquire for details). Can accommodate physically challenged people (please inquire for details). Smoke-free residence. Alcohol allowed. *Procedures to leave the premises on a temporary basis...*Short-term: inform reception of absence if you are away from a meal. Overnight & Holidays: inform Reception of absence and arrival date. *Languages:* English. Main doors of residence secured at night only. *Close to:* Public Transit, Shopping, Churches, Synagogues, Seniors' Centre, Library, Major Highway and Local Hospitals (MacKenzie Health, North York General Hospital & Sunnybrook Health Sciences Centre). Member of ORCA & Markham Board of Trade. Licensed under the Retirement Homes Act.
STAFFING: *Available Staff/Services*: Pharmacy, Social Work (CCAC), Recreation Therapy, Occupational Therapy (CCAC), Visiting Dentist, Physiotherapy (CCAC), Denturist, Dietitian (CCAC), Companions, Podiatry (CCAC), Chaplaincy, Speech Pathology (CCAC), Chiropody, Audiology/Hearing Clinic, Ophthalmology, Foot Care Nurse and Blood Lab Services. *External services arranged by:* residence and/or family/resident. Staff trained *re*: visually, hearing and cognitively impaired. 24-hour nursing and

other staff. RNs, RPNs, HCAs and PSWs on staff. Visiting MD. Can retain own MD. Staff members are bonded & insured. Police Check or Vulnerable Person Screening is done for all new staff.
HEALTH SERVICES: Medication administered if required. Vitals monitored if required. Will accept (but not provide special assistance for) residents who require catheters and ostomies. Will accept and provide special assistance for residents who require oxygen. Assistance with dressing available (cost). Weekly assistance with bathing available (cost). Care plans done. Different levels of care available. Assisted Living Area (1 month waiting period) is secured to accommodate residents with dementia. Lab service (visiting). Residents can purchase outside resources and use agency of their choice. Clinic area for medical visits. Will help locate higher level of care if needed (referral to Revera residences; assistance coordinating services through CCAC).
ACCOMMODATION: *Choice of suites available*: studio, 1-bedroom, deluxe 1-bedroom & 2-bedroom suites. *In all suites*: locks, kitchenette, bar fridge, patio/balcony, sheers & draperies, light fixtures, fire alarm, smoke detector, sprinkler, call bell, air conditioning (central) and thermostats for heating & cooling. Balconies/patios or solariums in suites. Private bathrooms with call bells, grab bars and showers. Unfurnished suites, furnished suites available for short stays. Suites can be shared (by couples or friends upon request). Pets allowed (as per Pet Policy in Residency Agreement).
DINING SERVICE: All meals included in fee and served in dining room daily. *Sittings per meal:* Breakfast: 2, Lunch: 2, Dinner: 2. *Menu choices available:* Lunch: 2, Dinner: 3. *Guest Meals*: Available. *Special Diets*: Vegetarian, Low Salt and Diabetic. Tray service to room if ill (no charge for a maximum time of 4 days). 1 snack/day. Party facilities. Separate Assisted Living dining room with walkout to patio overlooking pond. We now offer Lifestyle Choices which provides the resident with the choice to opt out of breakfast or lunch.
AMENITIES AND ACTIVITIES: Parking available (outdoor, for visitors: free and indoor for residents: $70.00/month). *7 lounges with:* TV (1) and piano (1). Guest suites available. *Residence has a:* library, barber/beauty shop, visiting hairdresser, laundry room(s) (no cost) and tuck/gift shop (open 3 days/week). Banking services on premises (monthly). Resident can arrange newspaper delivery to individual suite (extra cost). Mail delivered to private mailbox. *Recreation Facilities*: pool table, billiards, shuffleboard, exercise room, craft room, card room, large auditorium, private dining room, gardens, putting green, solarium and 16-passenger bus for scheduled trips. Posted schedule of activities. Internal newsletter for residents. *Recreational Programs*: exercise, shopping, theatre, parties, entertainment, art classes, pet visiting, day trips, current events, guest speakers and coach tour bus trips.
OTHER SERVICES: *Housekeeping*: weekly. *Laundry*: linen & towel (included in fee); personal (extra cost; included in Enhanced Living Package) & dry cleaning (extra cost; on-site service). Transportation for group social activities. 24-hour security. Nightly security checks (for residents receiving Assisted Living). Telephone & Cable TV (extra cost). Utilities (included in fee). Extensive recreation program. 3 meals/day with a variety of choices.
RENTAL INFORMATION: Rates may vary. Studios - $2,900.00/month & up; large studios - $3,800.00/month & up; 1-bedroom suites - $4,800.00/month & up; deluxe 1-bedroom suites - $5,500.00/month & up; 2-bedroom suites - $6,650.00/month & up. Extra cost for 2nd person sharing suite ($785.00/month). Rent paid monthly. *Payment Options*: pre-authorized payments. Rent increases as per Provincial Tenancy Legislation, annual for resident with 90 days' notice given. Will help resident move into residence. Short-term respite and trial stays (complimentary 3 day trial stay is available for qualified individuals) available.

See RICHMOND HILL & VAUGHAN for additional homes in this region.

◆ TILBURY ◆

HUDSON MANOR

36 Lawson Street, Tilbury, ON N0P 2L0
Tel: (519) 682-3366 • Fax: (519) 682-0688
Email: **gm.hm@diversicare.ca**
Website: **www.diversicare.ca**
Contact: **Marketing Manager**
Capacity: **50 residents** • Subsidies: **none**
Price: **$2,659.00 - $4,459.00/month**

Hudson Manor Retirement Residence is a lovely home located in Tilbury. We offer Independent and Full Service Lifestyle Packages tailored to meet your needs. We also have curbside service to senior community members to come to Hudson Manor and enjoy fun activities, entertainment and meals for a minimal charge. **Hudson Manor is owned/managed by Diversicare, who is the proud recipient of the 2003, 2006, 2009 and 2012 Order of Excellence Award given by Excellence Canada.** This award was received for the exceptional quality and customer service we provide to our residents every day.

RESIDENCE INFORMATION: 26 years in operation. *Near:* Stewart Street and Ella Street. Decorated in 2011. Handrails in hallways. 1 floor, no elevators. Wheelchair accessible. Central PA system. *Funding Base:* Corporate/for profit. *Owned and managed by:* Diversicare Canada Management Services Co., Inc. 43 units. *Average Waiting Period*: none. *Average Age*: 86. Can accommodate cognitively impaired people (mildly impaired, no secured units). Can accommodate physically challenged people (individuals need to be able to transfer with minimal assistance). Smoking allowed (outdoor smoking area provided no smoking indoors). Alcohol allowed (no restrictions unless indicated by individuals attending physician). *Procedures to leave the premises on a temporary basis...*notify Health Care Department so that appropriate medications can be ordered to allow for the vacation. *Languages:* English & some French speaking residents and staff. Will accept Public Guardian and Trustee clients. Main doors of residence secured at night only. *Close to:* Shopping, Churches, Library and Major Highway. Member of ORCA & member in good standing with local Chamber of Commerce and Business Improvement Association. Licensed under the Retirement Homes Act.
STAFFING: *Available Staff/Services*: Recreation Therapy, Physiotherapy, Chiropody, Audiology/Hearing Clinic and Hairdresser. *External services arranged by:* residence and/or family/resident. Staff trained *re*: visually and hearing impaired. 24-hour staff. RNs, RPNs, HCAs, PSWs and UCPs on staff. Visiting MD (bi-weekly and on call 24/7). Can retain own MD. Staff members are bonded. Police Check or Vulnerable Person Screening is done for all new staff.
HEALTH SERVICES: Medication administration (medication is dispensed from Remedy Pharmacy) and/or supervision (medications is dispensed from Remedy Pharmacy). Vitals monitored if required. Will accept (but not provide special assistance for) residents who require catheters and ostomies. Will accept and provide special assistance for residents who require oxygen. Assistance with dressing available. Weekly assistance with bathing available. *Extra baths:* $6.00/bath. Care plans done. Different levels of care available. Private Duty/Extra Care available ($30.00/hour). Assisted Living Area ($75.00 to $350.00/month; less than 2 week waiting period). Lab service (visiting, $6.00/visit). Residents can purchase outside resources and use agency of their choice. MD visits residents in their rooms/suites. Will help locate higher level of care if needed (residence arranges for CCAC assessment for placement; residence staff meet with family members prior to arranging for placement assessment).
ACCOMMODATION: *Choice of suites available*: all private suites, 3 different sizes available. *In all suites*: locks, storage, light fixtures, smoke detector, call bell, thermostats for heating and ceiling fan. Private bathrooms with call bells, grab bars, tubs and showers with non-slip surfaces. In-suite cable TV (extra

cost). Can have own phone number if resident arranges with phone company. Unfurnished suites, furnished suites available for short stays. *Restrictions on electrical appliances*: all electrical appliances must be checked by the residence Maintenance Technician. Suites can be shared (by couples only). Pets allowed (must be maintained independently by residents and have all required shots).
DINING SERVICE: All meals included in fee and served in dining room daily. *Sittings per meal:* Breakfast: 1, Lunch: 1, Dinner: 1. *Menu choices available:* Breakfast: 2, Lunch: 2, Dinner: 2. *Guest Meals*: Breakfast $6.00, Lunch $7.50, Dinner $8.50. *Special Diets*: Low Salt and Diabetic. Tray service to room if ill (no charge for a maximum time of 5 days). Unlimited snacks available at any time. Party facilities. Open pantry.
AMENITIES AND ACTIVITIES: Parking available (outdoor, for visitors and residents). *3 lounges with:* TVs (2), pianos (2) and fireplaces (2). Guest suites available ($50.00/night). *Residence has a:* chapel, barber/beauty shop, visiting hairdresser and laundry room(s) (no cost). Resident can arrange newspaper delivery to main desk (extra cost). Mail delivered to private mailbox with key. Posted schedule of activities. Internal newsletter for residents. *Recreational Programs*: exercise, shopping, theatre, parties, entertainment, art classes and day trips.
OTHER SERVICES: *Housekeeping*: rotation of every 10 days (included in fee). *Laundry*: linen, towel & personal (included in fee); dry cleaning (cost as per local dry cleaners). Transportation to medical appointments ($5.00 to $30.00 dependent on location) and for group social activities (extra cost only if there is an admission cost to the program). 24-hour security. Nightly security checks. Telephone (as per phone company). Cable TV (as per cable company). Utilities (extra cost for window air conditioners).
RENTAL INFORMATION: Rates may vary. Small private - $2,659.00/month; regular private - $2,771.00/month; large private - $3,209.00/month; kitchenette suite - $4,459.00/month. Extra cost for 2nd person sharing suite ($600.00/month). Rent paid monthly. *Payment Options*: cheques and pre-authorized payments. Rent increases as per Provincial Tenancy Legislation, annual for resident with 3 months' notice given. Will help resident move into residence ($30.00/hour). Short-term respite and trial stays available (both $85.00/day).

◆ TILLSONBURG ◆

BAYBRIDGE - HARVEST RETIREMENT COMMUNITY

15 Harvest Avenue, Tillsonburg, ON N4G 0E2
Tel: (519) 688-0448 • Fax: (519) 688-1856
Email: **EPatenaude@harvestrc.ca**
Website: **www.harvestrc.ca**
Contact: **Erica Patenaude** • Subsidies: **none**
Price: **$3,144.00 - $4,300.00/month**

Tucked away in the peaceful community of Tillsonburg, Harvest Retirement Community is a vibrant senior residence offering deluxe amenities to active and independent retirees. Our unique, all-inclusive lifestyle allows you to enjoy retirement to its fullest with the benefit of a safety net of supportive services should your needs change over time. Harvest Retirement Community is one of several independent retirement communities owned and managed by BayBridge Senior Living. Our communities are designed to provide Canadian seniors with the services and amenities needed so they may create the independent lifestyle they have always wanted.

RESIDENCE INFORMATION: 4 years in operation. Handrails in hallways. Wheelchair accessible. *Funding Base:* Corporate/for profit. *Owned and managed by:* BayBridge Senior Living. *Average Waiting Period*: varies. *Average Age*: 83. Can accommodate cognitively impaired & physically challenged people with restrictions. Residents have a dress code. Smoking allowed (outside only). Alcohol allowed. *Languages:*

English. Main doors of residence secured at night only. *Close to:* Public Transit, Shopping, Churches, Seniors' Centre and Library. Member of ORCA. Licensed under the Retirement Homes Act.
STAFFING: *Available Staff/Services*: Social Work (CCAC), Recreation Therapy, Occupational Therapy (CCAC), Physiotherapy (CCAC), Dietitian (CCAC), Podiatry (CCAC) and Speech Pathology (CCAC). RNs and PSWs on staff. Visiting MD. Can retain own MD. Police Check or Vulnerable Person Screening is done for all new staff.
HEALTH SERVICES: Medication administration and/or supervision. Vitals monitored if required. Will accept (but not provide special assistance for) residents who require oxygen, catheters, ostomies and feeding tubes. Weekly assistance with bathing available. Different levels of care available. Lab service (visiting). MD visits residents in their rooms/suites. Will help locate higher level of care if needed (through CCAC).
ACCOMMODATION: *Choice of suites available*: 1-bedroom & 2-bedroom apartments. *In all suites*: kitchenette, bar fridge, patio/balcony, window coverings, light fixtures, fire alarm, smoke detector, sprinkler and thermostats for heating & cooling. Private bathrooms with grab bars, showers with non-slip surfaces and elevated toilet seats. In-suite cable TV provided by residence (residence charges extra). Unfurnished suites, furnished suites available for short stays. Pets allowed (under 20 lbs.).
DINING SERVICE: All meals included in fee and served in dining room daily. *Sittings per meal:* Breakfast: 1, Lunch: 2, Dinner: 2. *Menu choices available:* Breakfast: 2, Lunch: 2, Dinner: 2. *Guest Meals*: Breakfast $6.00, Lunch $6.00, Dinner $6.00. *Special Diets*: Vegetarian, Low Salt and Diabetic. Tray service to room if ill. Unlimited snacks available at any time. Party facilities. Open pantry.
AMENITIES AND ACTIVITIES: Parking available (outdoor, for visitors and residents). *1 lounge with:* TV (1) and piano (1). *Residence has a:* library, barber/beauty shop, visiting hairdresser and laundry room(s) (no cost). Residence provides newspaper delivery to main desk. Mail delivered to private mailbox with key. *Recreation Facilities*: craft room and card room. Posted schedule of activities. Internal newsletter for residents. *Recreational Programs*: exercise, shopping, theatre, parties, entertainment, art classes, pet visiting and day trips.
OTHER SERVICES: *Housekeeping*: weekly. *Laundry*: linen, towel & personal (included in fee); dry cleaning (extra cost). Transportation to medical appointments and for group social activities. 24-hour security. Nightly security checks. Telephone & Cable TV (extra cost). Utilities (included in fee).
RENTAL INFORMATION: Rates may vary. Extra cost for 2nd person sharing suite ($650.00/month). Rent paid monthly. *Payment Options*: pre-authorized payments. Rent increases indexed to inflation as per Provincial Tenancy Legislation, annual with 3 months' notice given. Short-term respite ($85.00/day) available.

◆ TIMMINS ◆

ST. MARY'S GARDENS

225 Fifth Avenue, Timmins, ON P4N 0B2
Tel: (705) 267-5000 • Fax: (705) 267-3100
Toll Free: (866) 206-2220
Email: **aafonso@autumnwood.ca**
Website: **www.autumnwood.ca**
Contact: **Ann Afonso**
Capacity: **65 units** • Subsidies: **none**
Price: **$1,550.00 - $2,150.00/month**

Originally built in the early part of the century this building once St. Mary's Hospital, cared for much of Timmins' population is now enjoying a re-birth and caring for the very people it helped bring into the world. Located in the heart of downtown, St. Mary's Gardens will provide its residence with a strong and

secure home where the only requirement is carefree living. Presently serving 65 independent 1-bedroom & 2-bedroom apartments only with housekeeping, all appliances and air conditioning. Assisted Living suites will follow in late 2013.

RESIDENCE INFORMATION: 3 years in operation. 6 floors, 2 elevators. Wheelchair accessible. Central PA system. *Funding Base:* Corporate/for profit. *Owned by:* Autumnwood Mature Lifestyle Communities. *Average Waiting Period*: none. Smoke-free residence. *Languages:* English. *Close to:* Public Transit, Shopping, Churches and Library.
STAFFING: *Available Staff/Services*: Recreation Therapy. *External services arranged by:* family/resident. PSWs on staff.
ACCOMMODATION: *Choice of suites available*: only independent apartments. *In all suites*: storage, window coverings, full-size fridge, dishwasher, microwave, stove, light fixtures, fire alarm, smoke detector, sprinkler, call bell, air conditioning (HVAC) and thermostats for heating & cooling. Private bathrooms with call bells, grab bars, tubs and showers. In-suite cable TV provided by residence (residence charges extra $25.00/month). Can have own phone extension number provided by residence (residence charges extra $30.00/month). Unfurnished suites. No pets allowed.
AMENITIES AND ACTIVITIES: Parking available (outdoor, for visitors and residents). *Residence has a:* laundry room(s) (no cost). Mail delivered to resident. *Recreation Facilities*: exercise room and card room.
OTHER SERVICES: *Housekeeping*: weekly (included in fee).
RENTAL INFORMATION: Rates may vary. Rent paid monthly. *Payment Options*: direct deposit. Rent increases as per Provincial Tenancy Legislation, annual for resident with 3 months' notice given.

◆ TORONTO REGION ◆

TORONTO REGION (pages 288 - 353) – in an effort to assist our readers looking for a home in a particular part of Toronto, due to the number of homes in this region and the size of the amalgamated city of Toronto, residences in this section are divided into 4 sub-sections based on former municipalities – Etobicoke, North York and Scarborough. All other areas and residences within them are grouped together in the Toronto (Central) section. Within each section, homes are listed alphabetically.

◆ TORONTO (CENTRAL) ◆

BAYBRIDGE - LIVING LIFE ON THE AVENUE

1066 Avenue Road, Toronto, ON M5N 2C6
Tel: (416) 483-9900 • Fax: (416) 483-9977
Email: **bstroll@livinglifeontheavenue.com**
Website: **www.livinglifeontheavenue.com**
Contact: **Bev Stroll**
Capacity: **95 residents** • Subsidies: **none**
Price: **$4,251.00 - $8,289.00/month**

Avenue Road and Eglinton has a new landmark address. Where the architecture and design are a fitting expression of all you have achieved. Where service reaches the level of a 5-star hotel and your needs are not just answered but anticipated. You'll have the convenience of individualized wellness service plans. The sheer pleasure of a gourmet meal. The comfort of housekeeping and laundry services. The private

lounge with live entertainment. The reassurance of 24-hour security. The convenience of scheduled outings. There's a world of things to do here, in a neighbourhood where you're connected to everything.

RESIDENCE INFORMATION: 3 years in operation. *Near:* Avenue Road and Eglinton Avenue. Decorated in 2011. Handrails in hallways. 8 floors, 2 elevators. Wheelchair accessible. Central PA system. *Funding Base:* Corporate/for profit. *Owned and managed by:* BayBridge Senior Living. 75 units. *Average Waiting Period*: none. *Average Age*: 83. Can accommodate cognitively impaired people with restrictions (subject to individualized assessment). Can accommodate physically challenged people (subject to individualized assessment). Residents have a dress code (appropriate dinner attire). Smoke-free residence. Alcohol allowed. *Procedures to leave the premises on a temporary basis...*Short-term & Overnight: sign out at Concierge. Holidays: inform Concierge. *Languages:* English. Main doors of residence secured at night only. *Close to:* Public Transit, Shopping, Churches, Synagogues, Seniors' Centre, Library, Major Highway and Local Hospitals (Sunnybrook Health Sciences Centre and downtown area hospitals). Licensed under the Retirement Homes Act.
STAFFING: *Available Staff/Services*: Pharmacy, Social Work (CCAC), Recreation Therapy, Occupational Therapy (CCAC), Visiting Dentist, Physiotherapy (CCAC), Dietitian (CCAC), Companions, Podiatry (CCAC), Chaplaincy and Audiology/Hearing Clinic. *External services arranged by:* residence and/or family/resident. Staff trained *re*: visually, hearing and cognitively impaired. 24-hour staff. RNs, RPNs and PSWs on staff. Can retain own MD. Police Check or Vulnerable Person Screening is done for all new staff.
HEALTH SERVICES: Medication administration and/or supervision. Vitals monitored if required. Will accept and provide special assistance for residents who require oxygen. Assistance with dressing available (cost). Assistance with bathing available as needed (cost). Care plans done. Different levels of care available. Private Duty/Extra Care available. Assisted Living Area. Lab service (visiting). Residents can purchase outside resources and use agency of their choice. Clinic area for medical visits. Will help locate higher level of care if needed (referral to CCAC for assessment).
ACCOMMODATION: *Choice of suites available*: junior, 1-bedroom, 1-bedroom + den & 2-bedroom units. *In all suites*: locks, kitchenette, full-size refrigerator, microwave, window coverings, light fixtures, fire alarm, smoke detector, sprinkler, emergency response system with wearable pendant/bracelet, air conditioning (central) and thermostats for heating & cooling. Private bathrooms with grab bars and showers with non-slip surfaces. In-suite cable/satellite TV if resident arranges with cable/satellite company (residence charges extra). Can have own phone number if resident arranges with phone company (residence charges extra). Unfurnished suites, furnished suites available for short stays. Suites can be shared (by couples only). Small pets allowed (pending approval of Administration).
DINING SERVICE: All meals included in fee and served in dining room daily. *Sittings per meal:* Breakfast: 1, Lunch: 1, Dinner: 1. *Menu choices available:* Breakfast: 12, Lunch: 12, Dinner: 12. *Guest Meals*: Available. *Special Diets*: Vegetarian, Low Salt and Diabetic. Tray service to room if ill. Unlimited snacks available at any time. Party facilities.
AMENITIES AND ACTIVITIES: Parking available (indoor & outdoor, for visitors and indoor for residents). *4 lounges with:* TVs (2), piano (1) and fireplace (1). Guest suites available. *Residence has a:* library, barber/beauty shop and laundry room(s) (no cost). Mail delivered to main desk. *Recreation Facilities*: exercise room, craft room, card room, swimming pool, library, pub/café and Fitness & Yoga Centre. Posted schedule of activities. Internal newsletter for residents. *Recreational Programs*: exercise, shopping, theatre, parties, entertainment, art classes, day trips, intellectual programs & speakers and internet café.
OTHER SERVICES: *Housekeeping*: daily and weekly (included in fee). *Laundry*: linen & towel (included in fee); dry cleaning (extra cost). Transportation to medical appointments (via car service) and for group social activities (in some cases). 24-hour security. Nightly security checks. Telephone & Cable TV (extra cost). Utilities (included in fee).
RENTAL INFORMATION: Rates may vary. Extra cost for 2nd person sharing suite ($750.00/month). Rent paid monthly. *Payment Options*: cheques, post-dated cheques, direct deposit and pre-authorized payments. Rent increases as per Provincial Tenancy Legislation, annual for resident with 3 months' notice given. Will help resident move into residence. Short-term respite and trial stays available.

BEACH ARMS RETIREMENT RESIDENCE

505 Kingston Road, Toronto, ON M4L 1V5
Tel: (416) 698-0414 • Fax: (416) 698-9839
Email: **info@beacharms.com**
Website: **www.beacharms.com**
Contact: **Susan Turner**
Capacity: **84 residents** • Subsidies: **none**
Price: **$1,450.00 - $3,100.00/month**

Home-like ambiance. Attentive Staff. Central location. Bus available for outings. Near the lake.

RESIDENCE INFORMATION: 27 years in operation. *Near:* Main Street on Kingston Road. Decorated in 2012. Handrails in hallways. 6 floors, 1 elevator. Wheelchair accessible. Central PA system. *Funding Base:* Corporate/for profit. *Owned by:* Rahul Kuckreja. 73 units. *Average Waiting Period*: varies. *Average Age*: 87. Can accommodate cognitively impaired people (early stages of dementia). Can accommodate physically challenged people (strokes). Smoke-free residence. Alcohol allowed (unless they are a danger to themselves or others). *Procedures to leave the premises on a temporary basis...*Short-term & Overnight: notify the front security office. Holidays: notify Front Security Office. *Languages:* English, Greek, Macedonian, French & Filipino. Will accept Public Guardian and Trustee clients. Main doors of residence secured at all times. *Close to:* Public Transit, Shopping, Churches, Seniors' Centre, Library, Major Highway and Local Hospital (The Toronto East General Hospital). Member of ORCA. Licensed under the Retirement Homes Act.
STAFFING: *Available Staff/Services*: Pharmacy, Social Work (CCAC), Recreation Therapy, Occupational Therapy (CCAC), Physiotherapy (CCAC), Denturist, Dietitian (CCAC), Chaplaincy, Speech Pathology (CCAC), Audiology/Hearing Clinic and Dental, Eye & Foot Clinic. *External services arranged by:* residence and/or family/resident. Staff trained *re*: visually, hearing and cognitively impaired. 24-hour nursing and other staff. RNs, RPNs, HCAs, PSWs and UCPs on staff. Visiting MD (twice/week and on call 24-hours/day). Can retain own MD. Staff members are bonded. TB testing required. Police Check or Vulnerable Person Screening is done for all new staff.
HEALTH SERVICES: Medication administration and/or supervision. Vitals monitored if required. Will accept and provide special assistance for residents who require oxygen. Assistance with dressing available. Weekly assistance with bathing available. Care plans done. Different levels of care available. Lab service (visiting, $30.00/visit). Residents can purchase outside resources and use agency of their choice. MD visits residents in their rooms/suites. Will help locate higher level of care if needed (long-term care facilities).
ACCOMMODATION: *Choice of suites available*: semi-private (14), small private (29), medium private (25) & large private (12) suites. *In all suites*: locks, bar fridge, window coverings, light fixtures, linens, fire alarm, smoke detector, CO detectors, call bell, air conditioning (window units) and ceiling fan. Balcony (5 units only). Private bathrooms with call bells, grab bars, tubs and showers with non-slip surfaces. In-suite cable TV if resident arranges with cable company. Furnished & unfurnished suites available. *Restrictions on electrical appliances*: automatic shut-off valve kettle & no irons. Suites can be shared (pending availability of beds), roommate picked by residence staff. Pets allowed (resident must be able to care for pet).
DINING SERVICE: All meals included in fee and served in dining room daily. *Sittings per meal:* Breakfast: 2, Lunch: 2, Dinner: 2. *Menu choices available:* Breakfast: 2, Lunch: 2, Dinner: 2. *Guest Meals*: Breakfast $5.00, Lunch $5.00, Dinner $7.00. *Special Diets*: Vegetarian, Low Salt, Diabetic and Lactose Free. Tray Service To Suite: no charge for medical reasons; $2.00/meal by choice. 2 snacks/day. Party facilities.
AMENITIES AND ACTIVITIES: Parking available (outdoor, for visitors and residents). *3 lounges with:* TVs (2), piano (1), phone (1) and fireplaces (3). Guest suites available. *Residence has a:* library, visiting library, chapel, barber/beauty shop, visiting hairdresser and tuck/gift shop (open 5 days/week; 9:00 a.m. – 9:00 p.m.). Banking services on premises (Monday to Friday, 9:00 a.m. - 5:00 p.m.). Resident can

arrange newspaper delivery to main desk. Mail delivered to dining room. *Recreation Facilities*: exercise room, craft room, card room and sunroom. Posted schedule of activities. Internal newsletter for residents. *Recreational Programs*: exercise, shopping, theatre, parties, entertainment, art classes, pet visiting, day trips, bingo, card/word games, church services and current events, etc.

OTHER SERVICES: *Housekeeping*: daily and weekly. *Laundry*: linen, towel & personal (included in fee); dry cleaning (arrangements with the front desk). Clothing must be labeled only on washable items. Transportation to medical appointments (extra cost - only by community agency) and for group social activities. 24-hour security. Nightly security checks. Telephone & Cable TV (make own arrangements). Utilities (included in fee). Security cameras monitoring each hallway.

RENTAL INFORMATION: Rates may vary. Rent is paid on the first of every month; last month's rent deposit required for permanent residents. Extra cost for 2nd person sharing suite (total cost per couple - $3,450.00/month). Rent paid monthly. *Payment Options*: cheques, post-dated cheques and pre-authorized payments. Rent increases as per Provincial Tenancy Legislation, annual with 90 days' notice given. Short-term respite and trial stays available (costs vary according to suite size).

BELMONT HOUSE

55 Belmont Street, Toronto, ON M5R 1R1
Tel: (416) 964-9231 • Fax: (416) 964-1448
Email: **information@belmonthouse.com**
Website: **www.belmonthouse.com**
Contact: **Gail Walker**
Capacity: **87 residents** • Subsidies: **none**
Price: **$2,910.00 - $5,180.00/month**

Belmont House is a charitable, non-profit, Christian retirement home for seniors offering Independent, Enhanced and Assisted Living. Situated in one of the last remaining green spaces in the heart of downtown Toronto, Belmont House provides a wide range of programs, services, and resources for both our residents and the community.

RESIDENCE INFORMATION: 162 years in operation. *Near:* Yonge Street and Davenport Avenue. Handrails in hallways. 7 floors, 3 elevators. Wheelchair accessible. Central PA system. *Funding Base:* Not-for-profit. 81 units. *Average Waiting Period*: varies. Can sometimes accommodate physically challenged people. Smoke-free residence. Alcohol allowed. *Procedures to leave the premises on a temporary basis...* Overnight & Holidays: inform Reception. *Languages:* English. Main doors of residence secured at all times. *Close to:* Public Transit, Shopping, Churches, Synagogues, Library and Local Hospital. *Predominant Cultural Group:* English-speaking Christian. Member of OANHSS. Licensed under the Retirement Homes Act.

STAFFING: *Available Staff/Services*: Pharmacy, Social Work, Recreation Therapy, Occupational Therapy, Visiting Dentist, Physiotherapy, Denturist, Dietitian, Companions, Podiatry, Chaplaincy, Speech Pathology,

Chiropody and Audiology/Hearing Clinic. *External services arranged by:* residence and/or family/ resident. Staff trained *re*: visually and hearing impaired. 24-hour nursing and other staff. RNs, RPNs, HCAs and PSWs on staff. Visiting MD (weekly). Can retain own MD. Police Check or Vulnerable Person Screening is done for all new staff.

HEALTH SERVICES: Medication administration (and treatments available - costs may be applicable) and/or supervision. Vitals monitored if required. Will accept (but not provide special assistance for) residents who require oxygen and catheters. Weekly assistance with bathing available. Care plans done. Different levels of care available. Lab service. Residents can purchase outside resources and use agency of their choice. MD visits residents in their rooms/suites. Clinic area for medical visits. Will help locate higher level of care if needed.

ACCOMMODATION: *Choice of suites available*: studio (15), 1-bedroom (60) & 2-bedroom (6) units. *In all suites*: locks, kitchenette, bar fridge, storage, window coverings, light fixtures, fire alarm, smoke detector, sprinkler, air conditioning (central) and thermostats for heating & cooling. Full kitchen with 3 appliances in apartments. Private bathrooms with call bells, grab bars, tubs and showers with non-slip surfaces. In-suite cable TV if resident arranges with cable company. Can have own phone number if resident arranges with phone company. Unfurnished suites. *Restrictions on electrical appliances*: must be CSA approved. Suites can be shared in larger retirement suites and 2-bedroom apartments (by couples only). Pets allowed (cats).

DINING SERVICE: All meals included in fee and served in dining room daily. *Sittings per meal:* Breakfast: 1, Lunch: 1, Dinner: 1. *Menu choices available:* Breakfast: 2, Lunch: 2, Dinner: 2. *Guest Meals*: Breakfast $7.50, Lunch $12.50, Dinner $20.00. *Special Diets*: Vegetarian, Low Salt and Diabetic. Will accommodate any dietary needs. Tray service to room if ill. Party facilities.

AMENITIES AND ACTIVITIES: Parking available (outdoor, for visitors: free and residents: $120.00/month). *7 lounges with:* TV (1) and pianos (3). *Residence has a:* library, visiting library, chapel, barber/beauty shop, laundry room(s) ($1.25/washer load, $1.25/dryer load) and tuck/gift shop (open Monday to Friday; 10:00 a.m. - 12:00 p.m.). Banking services on premises (daily). Residence provides newspaper delivery to individual suite. Mail delivered to private mailbox with key. *Recreation Facilities*: pool table, billiards, shuffleboard, exercise room, greenhouse, craft room and card room. Posted schedule of activities. Internal newsletter for residents. *Recreational Programs*: exercise, shopping, theatre, parties, entertainment, art classes, pet visiting and day trips.

OTHER SERVICES: *Housekeeping*: weekly (included in fee). *Laundry*: linen & towel (extra cost; included in Enhanced and Assisted Living Packages); personal ($130.00/month) & dry cleaning (extra cost - available). Staff label clothing (one-time cost for labeling all clothes). Transportation for group social activities. 24-hour security. Utilities (included in fee).

RENTAL INFORMATION: Rates may vary. Extra cost for 2nd person sharing suite ($2,205.00/month). Rent paid monthly. *Payment Options*: cheques, post-dated cheques and pre-authorized payments. Rent increases as per Provincial Tenancy Legislation, annual for resident with 3 months' notice given.

BRITON HOUSE RETIREMENT CENTRE (THE)

720 Mount Pleasant Road, Toronto, ON M4S 2N6
Tel: (416) 487-3392 • Fax: (416) 482-0469
Toll Free: (877) 487-3392
Email: **info@britonhouse.com**
Website: **www.britonhouse.com**
Contact: **Karen Lantela, Family Consultant**
Capacity: **240 residents** • Subsidies: **none**
Price: **$2,650.00 - $7,470.00/month**

Lavish year round English garden, indoor swimming pool, fitness room, elegant recital hall, and Thai Breezes Sunspace. To arrange a tour of our Residence, please contact Karen Lantela at **(416) 487-3392 ext. 2004**.

RESIDENCE INFORMATION: 39 years in operation. *Near:* Eglinton Avenue East and Mount Pleasant Road. Decorated in 2003. Handrails in hallways. 21 floors, 5 elevators. Wheelchair accessible. Central PA system. *Funding Base:* Corporate/for profit. *Owned by:* Wells Gordon Ltd. 220 units. *Average Waiting Period*: varies. *Average Age*: 85. Can accommodate cognitively impaired people (flexible/independent living with assistance or secure). Can accommodate physically challenged people (depends on situation). Residents have a dress code. Smoke-free residence. Alcohol allowed. *Procedures to leave the premises on a temporary basis...*Short-term: notify Front Desk. Overnight & Holidays: notify Management. *Languages:* English. Will accept Public Guardian and Trustee clients. Main doors of residence secured at night only. *Close to:* Public Transit, Shopping, Churches, Seniors' Centre, Library and Local Hospital (Sunnybrook Health Sciences Centre). *Predominant Cultural Group:* Anglo-Saxon. Licensed under the Retirement Homes Act.
STAFFING: *Available Staff/Services*: Pharmacy, Social Work (CCAC), Recreation Therapy, Occupational Therapy (CCAC), Physiotherapy, Dietitian (CCAC), Companions, Podiatry, Speech Pathology (CCAC), Chiropody and Audiology/Hearing Clinic. *External services arranged by:* residence and/or family/resident. Staff trained *re*: visually, hearing and cognitively impaired. 24-hour nursing staff. RNs, RPNs, HCAs and PSWs on staff. Visiting MD (3 days/week). Can retain own MD. Police Check or Vulnerable Person Screening is done for all new staff.
HEALTH SERVICES: Medication administration and/or supervision. Vitals monitored if required. Will accept and provide special assistance for residents who require oxygen, catheters, ostomies and feeding tubes. Assistance with dressing available ($7.50/half hour). Assistance with bathing available as needed ($22.00/bath). Care plans done. Different levels of care available. Separate unit for residents with dementia. Lab service (visiting, $25.00/visit). Residents can purchase outside resources and use agency of their choice. Clinic area for medical visits. Will help locate higher level of care if needed (discussions and assistance with CCAC).
ACCOMMODATION: *Choice of suites available*: bachelor (15), bedsitting (74), 1-bedroom (52) & 2-bedroom (16) suites. *In all suites*: locks, storage, window coverings, light fixtures, linens, fire alarm, smoke detector, sprinkler, call bell, air conditioning (central) and thermostats for heating & cooling. Fridge and balcony in most tower suites. Private bathrooms with call bells, grab bars, tubs and showers with non-slip surfaces. In-suite cable TV if resident arranges with cable company. Can have own phone number if resident arranges with phone company. Unfurnished suites, furnished suites available for short stays. *Restrictions on electrical appliances*: subject to approval of Management. Pets allowed (individual approval required, must be able to care for pet).
DINING SERVICE: All meals included in fee and served in dining room daily. *Sittings per meal:* Breakfast: 1, Lunch: 1, Dinner: 1. *Menu choices available:* Breakfast: 3, Lunch: 2, Dinner: 2. *Guest Meals*: Breakfast $6.00, Lunch $11.00, Dinner $14.00. *Special Diets*: Vegetarian, Low Salt and Diabetic. Tray service to room if ill (no charge as long as doctor orders). Party facilities. Snacks upon request. Coffee station.
AMENITIES AND ACTIVITIES: Parking available (indoor & outdoor, for visitors: free and indoor for residents: $100.00/month). *5 lounges with:* TV (1), piano (1), fireplace (1) and library (2). Guest suites available ($75.00/night + HST). *Residence has a:* library, chapel, barber/beauty shop, laundry room(s) ($2.25/washer load and $1.50/dryer load). Resident can arrange newspaper delivery to individual suite. Mail delivered to private mailbox with key. *Recreation Facilities*: pool table, billiards, exercise room, card room, swimming pool, concert hall and large sky lit atrium with English Garden & mini-golf. Posted schedule of activities. Internal newsletter for residents. *Recreational Programs*: exercise, shopping, theatre, parties, entertainment, art classes, pet visiting, day trips, bridge, bingo and gardening.
OTHER SERVICES: *Housekeeping*: weekly (included in fee). *Laundry*: linen & towel (included in fee); personal ($18.00/load or coin laundry) & dry cleaning (dry cleaner nearby). 24-hour security. Nightly security checks. Telephone & Cable TV (extra cost). Utilities (included in fee). Guest Suites available ($75.00/night + HST).
RENTAL INFORMATION: Rates may vary. Extra cost for 2nd person sharing suite ($600.00/month; extra cost is for certain units). Rent paid monthly. *Payment Options*: cheques and direct debit. Rent increases

as per Provincial Tenancy Legislation, annual for resident with 3 months' notice given. Will help resident move into residence. Short-term respite and trial stays available (price depends on unit rented + phone & cable, furnished rooms, minimum stay of 1 month).

CHRISTIE GARDENS APARTMENTS AND CARE

600 Melita Crescent, Toronto, ON M6G 3Z4
Tel: (416) 530-1330 • Fax: (416) 530-1686
Email: **diana.sweatman@christiegardens.org**
Website: **www.christiegardens.org**
Contact: **Marketing Coordinator**
Capacity: **300 units** • Subsidies: **none**
Price: **$2,400.00 - $4,000.00/month**

Christie Gardens is a community you can have faith in. For over 25 years Christie has made a notable difference in the lives of many mature adults and their families. Christie Gardens offers you a choice of personal accommodation options. The Terrace Life Lease Suites with services takes independence to a whole new level. *We invite you to come explore, discover and thrive at Christie Gardens - Toronto's Distinctive Retirement Community.*

RESIDENCE INFORMATION: 31 years in operation. *Near:* Christie Street and Dupont Avenue. Handrails in some of the hallways. 10 floors, 4 elevators. Wheelchair accessible. *Funding Base:* Not-for-profit. *Average Waiting Period*: varies. *Average Age*: 81. Smoke-free residence. *Languages:* English. Main doors of residence secured at all times. *Close to:* Public Transit, Shopping, Churches, Library and Local Hospital (University Health Network -Toronto Western Hospital Site). *Predominant Cultural Group:* Anglo-Canadians. Member of Willow Creek Canada & CARF. Licensed under the Retirement Homes Act.
STAFFING: *Available Staff/Services*: Pharmacy, Recreation Therapy, Occupational Therapy, Visiting Dentist, Physiotherapy, Denturist, Dietitian, Companions, Podiatry, Chaplaincy, Chiropody and Audiology/Hearing Clinic. *External services arranged by:* residence and/or family/resident. 24-hour nursing staff. RNs on staff. Visiting MD (2 GPs provide on-site support). Can retain own MD.
HEALTH SERVICES: Different levels of care available. 24/7 nursing care now available without relocation. Assisted Living Area. Lab service (visiting). Residents can purchase outside resources. On-site Wellness Centre.
ACCOMMODATION: *Choice of suites available*: apartment rental suites with services & Market Value Life Lease suites with services. *In all suites*: fire alarm, smoke detector, sprinkler, air conditioning (central air conditioning in the Life Lease Suites) and thermostats for heating & cooling. Self-contained suites up to 1,600 sq. ft. Independent living rental apartments have kitchen with fridge and stove; Life Lease has full kitchen with appliances. Private bathrooms with grab bars, tubs and showers with non-slip surfaces. In-suite cable TV provided by residence. Can have own phone number if resident arranges with phone company. Unfurnished suites. No pets allowed.
DINING SERVICE: 15 meals/month included in monthly fee for Independent Living; extra meals can be purchased. All meals included in fee and served in dining rooms for Retirement Residents including private dining. *Guest Meals*: Available. *Special Diets*: Vegetarian, Low Salt and Diabetic. Tray service to room if ill.
AMENITIES AND ACTIVITIES: Parking available (outdoor, for visitors and indoor for residents). Guest suites available. *Residence has a:* library, chapel, barber/beauty shop, laundry room(s) (cost), tuck/gift shop (open 6 days/week; 9:00 a.m. - 5:00 p.m.). Mail delivered to private mailbox with key. *Recreation Facilities*: pool table, craft room, card room and café (open 7 days/week). Posted schedule of activities. Internal newsletter for residents. *Recreational Programs*: exercise, shopping, theatre, parties, entertainment, art classes and day trips. A wide & varied range of activities offered daily.

OTHER SERVICES: *Housekeeping*: included for Retirement Residents; extra cost for Independent Residents. *Laundry*: linen, towel & personal (extra cost for Independent Residents; included for Retirement Residents.); dry cleaning (extra cost). Cable TV (included in fee). Retirement Residents – meals/refreshments included.
RENTAL INFORMATION: Rates may vary. Independent living - $2,400.00 to $4,000.00/month; Retirement Living - $4,500.00/month & up; Life Lease - price per unit varies, determined by market value. Rent paid monthly (for independent & retirement residents). Extra cost for 2nd person sharing suite. 3 months' notice given for rent increases.

FELLOWSHIP TOWERS RETIREMENT COMMUNITY

877 Yonge Street, Toronto, ON M4W 3M2
Tel: (416) 923-8887 • Fax: (416) 923-1343
Email: **inquiries@fellowshiptowers.com**
Website: **www.fellowshiptowers.com**
Contact: **Dot Hayes**
Capacity: **250 residents** • Subsidies: **none**
Price: **$2,249.00 - $3,399.00/month**

A not-for-profit retirement community for seniors looking to call a vibrant, friendly, urban neighbourhood home.

RESIDENCE INFORMATION: 32 years in operation. *Near:* Davenport Road and Yonge Street. Decorated in 2011. Handrails in hallways. 15 floors, 3 elevators. Central PA system. *Funding Base:* Not-for-profit. Independently Owned. 240 units. *Average Waiting Period*: 4 - 6 months. *Average Age*: 80. Can accommodate physically challenged people with restrictions (no wheelchairs). Residents have a dress code (no dressing gowns in dining room). Smoke-free residence. Alcohol allowed (no alcohol served in dining room). *Restrictions around Visitors/Visiting Hours:* overnight guests can stay in furnished guest rooms. *Procedures to leave the premises on a temporary basis...*sign out. *Languages:* English. Will accept Public Guardian and Trustee clients. Main doors of residence secured at all times. *Close to:* Public Transit, Shopping, Churches, Library, Major Highway and Local Hospital (St. Michael's Hospital). Member of ORCA. Licensed under the Retirement Homes Act.
STAFFING: *Available Staff/Services*: Pharmacy, Social Work (CCAC), Recreation Therapy, Occupational Therapy (CCAC), Physiotherapy, Dietitian (CCAC), Companions, Podiatry, Chaplaincy, Speech Pathology (CCAC), Chiropody, Massage Therapy and Reflexology. *External services arranged by:* residence and/or family/resident. Staff trained *re*: visually, hearing and cognitively impaired. 24-hour nursing and other staff. RNs, HCAs, PSWs and UCPs on staff. Visiting MD (once/week). Can retain own MD. Police Check or Vulnerable Person Screening is done for all new staff.
HEALTH SERVICES: Medication administered if required (some restrictions apply; $78.00/month). Vitals monitored if required. Assistance with bathing available as needed ($30.00/bath). Care plans done. Different levels of care available. Extra care services ($85.00 to $1,035.00/month). Private Duty/Extra Care available ($23.00/hour). ERS (emergency response system) available ($25.00/month). Assisted Living Area (3 - 4 week waiting period). Lab service (visiting, $20.00/visit). Residents can purchase outside resources and use agency of their choice. Clinic area for medical visits. Will help locate higher level of care if needed (medical department will help fill out placement papers).
ACCOMMODATION: *Choice of suites available*: self-contained 1-bedroom apartments (98) with the option for services or residential rooms (170) which include window coverings and shared kitchenette with bar fridge. *In all suites*: locks, storage, light fixtures, smoke detector, emergency response system with wearable pendant/bracelet, air conditioning (window units available on rental basis) and thermostats for heating. Shared kitchen/bar fridge in residential rooms and full kitchen including full size oven/stove

in apartments. Private bathrooms with grab bars. In-suite cable TV provided by residence. Can have own phone number provided by residence (residence charges extra $24.50/month). Unfurnished suites, furnished suites available for short stays. Suites can be shared (2 people can reside in an apartment), roommate picked by resident & residence staff. No pets allowed.
DINING SERVICE: All meals included in fee and served in dining room daily. *Sittings per meal:* Breakfast: 2, Lunch: 2, Dinner: 2. *Menu choices available:* Breakfast: 2, Lunch: 3, Dinner: 2. *Guest Meals*: Breakfast $7.00, Lunch $11.00, Dinner $15.00. *Special Diets*: Vegetarian, Low Salt and Diabetic. Tray service to room if ill. Party facilities. Complimentary tea, coffee and cookies served from 10:00 a.m. to 4:00 p.m. in Tea Room.
AMENITIES AND ACTIVITIES: Parking available (outdoor, for visitors: $8.00/day and indoor for residents: $65.00/month). *2 lounges with:* TV (1) and piano (1). Guest suites available ($65.00/night). *Residence has a:* library, visiting library, chapel, barber/beauty shop, visiting hairdresser, laundry room(s) ($1.50/washer load and $1.50/dryer load). Banking services on premises (weekly). Resident can arrange newspaper delivery to individual suite. Mail delivered to private mailbox with key. *Recreation Facilities*: shuffleboard, exercise room, craft room and computer centre. Posted schedule of activities. Internal newsletter for residents. *Recreational Programs*: exercise, shopping, theatre, parties, entertainment, art classes, day trips, games, cards, walking groups, sing-alongs and organized outings.
OTHER SERVICES: *Housekeeping*: weekly. *Laundry*: linen & towel (included in fee); personal ($15.00/ load). Transportation for group social activities. 24-hour security. Nightly security checks. Cable TV & Utilities (included in fee). Meals. In-house activities. Insurance.
RENTAL INFORMATION: Rates may vary. Extra cost for 2nd person sharing suite (fee based on service package). Rent paid monthly. *Payment Options*: cheques, post-dated cheques and pre-authorized payments. Rent increases indexed to inflation as per Provincial Tenancy Legislation, annual for resident with 90 days' notice given. Will help resident move into residence. Short-term respite ($88.33/day) and trial stays ($2,650.00/month; shorter stays will be pro-rated) available.

HAROLD AND GRACE BAKER CENTRE

1 Northwestern Avenue, Toronto, ON M6M 2J7
Tel: (416) 654-2889 • Fax: (416) 654-0217
Email: **bakercentre@reveraliving.com**
Website: **www.bakercentre.com**
Contact: **Lifestyle Consultant or Executive Director**
Capacity: **91 units** • Subsidies: **none**
Price: **$1,850.00/month and up**

The Harold and Grace Baker Centre is a non-profit residence situated on park-like grounds in a quiet area of West Toronto. The Harold & Grace Baker Centre is overseen by a volunteer Board of Directors and managed by Revera Inc. The Harold and Grace Baker Centre offers a warm and friendly social environment, with a wide array of recreational interests and twice weekly outings on the Buttercup Coach. Entertainment, movie nights, and cocktail hour in the beautifully renovated Steele Lounge are all part of the fun. Personalized care and services are available to meet the unique and changing needs of each resident. Trial, respite and short-term stay options are available. We also have a long-term care centre on-site.

RESIDENCE INFORMATION: 30 years in operation. *Near:* Keele Street and Eglinton Avenue. Decorated in 2012. Handrails in hallways. 6 floors, 3 elevators. Wheelchair accessible. Central PA system. *Funding Base:* Not-for-profit. Voluntary Board of Directors. *Managed by:* Revera Inc. *Average Waiting Period*: 1 month. *Average Age*: 84. Can accommodate cognitively impaired people (3rd floor is a designated care unit). Can accommodate physically challenged people (on assessment). Smoke-free residence. Alcohol allowed. *Procedures to leave the premises on a temporary basis...*sign out. *Languages:* English, Italian, Portuguese, Tagalog, Slovenian, Croatian, Spanish, Hungarian, Greek,

German, Polish & Hebrew. Will accept Public Guardian and Trustee clients. Main doors of residence secured at all times. *Close to:* Public Transit, Shopping, Churches, Seniors' Centre, Library, Major Highway and Local Hospital (Humber River Regional Hospital – Church Street Site). *Predominant Cultural Group:* Italian & Jewish. Member of ORCA, OLTCA & Accreditation Canada. Licensed under the Retirement Homes Act.

STAFFING: *Available Staff/Services*: Pharmacy, Social Work, Recreation Therapy, Occupational Therapy (CCAC), Visiting Dentist, Physiotherapy (CCAC), Denturist, Dietitian, Podiatry (CCAC), Chaplaincy, Speech Pathology (CCAC) and Foot Care Nurse. *External services arranged by:* residence and/or family/resident. Staff trained *re*: visually, hearing and cognitively impaired. 24-hour nursing staff. RNs, RPNs, HCAs and PSWs on staff. Visiting MD (3 physicians on staff and on call 24-hours/day). Can retain own MD. Police Check or Vulnerable Person Screening is done for all new staff.

HEALTH SERVICES: Medication administered if required (additional cost). Vitals monitored if required. Will accept and provide special assistance for residents who require oxygen, catheters and ostomies. Assistance with dressing available (cost). Weekly assistance with bathing available (cost). Care plans done. Different levels of care available. Care Packages available from $470.00/month. Assisted Living Area (less than 2 week waiting period). Lab service (visiting). Residents can purchase outside resources and use agency of their choice. Clinic area for medical visits. Will help locate higher level of care if needed (referral for long-term care placement on-site via Community Care Access Centre).

ACCOMMODATION: *Choice of suites available*: 1-bedroom suite (3), deluxe private (24), private (46) & private with shared bath (18). *In all suites*: locks, window coverings, light fixtures, linens, fire alarm, smoke detector, sprinkler, call bell and air conditioning (central). Private bathrooms (shared 2-piece bathroom in shared private room) with call bells and grab bars. In-suite cable TV if resident arranges with cable company. Can have own phone number if resident arranges with phone company. Furnished & unfurnished suites available. *Restrictions on electrical appliances*: no stoves, no microwaves, no kettles; equipment must be CSA approved. Suites can be shared (pending availability of beds), roommate picked by resident & residence staff. Pets allowed (dogs, cats and birds subject to approval).

DINING SERVICE: All meals included in fee and served in dining room daily. *Sittings per meal:* Breakfast: 1, Lunch: 1, Dinner: 1. *Menu choices available:* Breakfast: 2, Lunch: 2, Dinner: 3. *Guest Meals*: Breakfast $5.00, Lunch $5.00, Dinner $7.00. *Special Diets*: Vegetarian, Low Salt and Diabetic. Tray service to room if ill (no charge as long as doctor orders). 2 snacks/day. Party facilities. Open pantry. Each floor has a kitchenette, tea & coffee service available twice daily.

AMENITIES AND ACTIVITIES: Parking available (outdoor, for visitors and residents). *7 lounges with:* TVs (6), piano (1) and craft rooms (2). Guest suites available. *Residence has a:* library, visiting library, chapel, barber/beauty shop, laundry room(s) (no cost), tuck/gift shop (open daily; 11:00 a.m. - 3:00 p.m.). Resident can arrange newspaper delivery to main desk. Mail delivered to individual suite. *Recreation Facilities*: exercise room, craft room, card room, Buttercup Coach for recreational trips, Steele Lounge for cocktail hour/movies and courtyard gardens. Posted schedule of activities. Internal newsletter for residents. *Recreational Programs*: exercise, shopping, theatre, parties, entertainment, art classes, pet visiting, day trips, outdoor gardening, spiritual services in chapel, music programs and intergenerational programs.

OTHER SERVICES: *Housekeeping*: weekly. *Laundry*: linen & towel (included in fee); personal ($20.00/ week). Staff label clothing (included in fee; $8.00 for labels). Washer/dryer on floor for personal laundry at no charge. 24-hour security. Nightly security checks. Telephone & Cable TV (available through service provider). Utilities (included in fee).

RENTAL INFORMATION: Rates may vary. Retirement - private room with shared bathroom - $1,850.00/ month & up; private room - $2,320.00/month & up; deluxe private - $2,600.00/month & up; couples suite - $2,600.00/month & up plus extra person cost; 1-bedroom suites - $3,700.00/month & up. Extra cost for 2nd person sharing suite ($800.00/month). Rent paid monthly. *Payment Options*: cheques, post-dated cheques, direct deposit and pre-authorized payments. Rent increases as per Provincial Tenancy Legislation, annual for resident with 3 months' notice given. Will help resident move into residence. Short-term respite and trial stays available (from $75.00/day).

HAZELTON PLACE RETIREMENT RESIDENCE

111 Avenue Road, Toronto, ON M5R 3J8
Tel: (416) 928-0111 • Fax: (416) 928-0118
Email: **info.hazelton@diversicare.ca**
Website: **www.hazeltonplace.ca**
Contact: **Marketing Manager**
Capacity: **185 residents •** Subsidies: **none**
Price: **$3,595.00 - $7,196.00/month**

Located in the heart of the city in Yorkville, close to the arts, shops, restaurants & the entertainment district, Hazelton Place offers full service retirement living; providing our residents with unparalleled service, comfort and superb chef-prepared dining. 24-hour health care team & state-of-the-art security system. Assisted Living and Independent living. Respite and trial stays welcome. **Hazelton Place is managed by Diversicare, who is the proud recipient of the 2003, 2006, 2009 and 2012 Order of Excellence Award given by Excellence Canada.** This award was received for the exceptional quality and customer service we provide to our residents every day.

RESIDENCE INFORMATION: 14 years in operation. *Near:* Avenue Road and Bloor Street. Decorated in 2012. Handrails in hallways. 8 floors, 3 elevators. Wheelchair accessible. Central PA system. *Funding Base:* Corporate/for profit. *Owned by:* BC Pension Fund - Great West Life. *Managed by:* Diversicare Canada Management Services Co., Inc. 161 units. *Average Waiting Period*: varies. *Average Age*: 85. Can accommodate cognitively impaired & physically challenged people (with assessment). Smoke-free residence. Alcohol allowed. *Procedures to leave the premises on a temporary basis...*sign out. *Languages:* English. Will accept Public Guardian and Trustee clients. Main doors of residence secured at all times. *Close to:* Public Transit, Shopping, Churches, Synagogues, Seniors' Centre, Library, Major Highway and Local Hospitals (University Health Network - Toronto General Hospital Site, Princess Margaret Hospital Site & Toronto Western Hospital Site, Mount Sinai Hospital, Toronto Rehabilitation Institute & Holland Orthopaedic and Arthritic Centre). *Predominant Cultural Group:* English-speaking. Member of ORCA, Yonge-Bloor-Bay Business Association, Ontario Gerontology Association, Orthopaedic & Arthritic Institute. Licensed under the Retirement Homes Act.
STAFFING: *Available Staff/Services*: Pharmacy, Social Work (CCAC), Recreation Therapy, Occupational Therapy (CCAC), Visiting Dentist, Physiotherapy, Denturist, Dietitian (CCAC), Companions, Podiatry, Speech Pathology (CCAC), Chiropody, Audiology/Hearing Clinic and Visiting Chaplain. *External services arranged by:* residence and/or family/resident. Staff trained *re*: visually, hearing and cognitively impaired. 24-hour nursing staff. RNs, RPNs, HCAs, PSWs and UCPs on staff. Visiting MD (1 x/week & on call). Can retain own MD. Staff members are bonded. Police Check or Vulnerable Person Screening is done for all new staff.
HEALTH SERVICES: Medication administration and/or supervision. Vitals monitored if required. Will accept (but not provide special assistance for) residents who require oxygen, catheters and ostomies. Assistance with dressing available ($14.00/half hour). Assistance with bathing available as needed ($14.00/half hour). Care plans done. Different levels of care available. Private Duty/Extra Care available ($26.00/hour). Assisted Living Area ($1,100.00/month; 1 - 2 month waiting period) is secured to accommodate residents with dementia. Lab service (visiting, $30.00/visit). Residents can purchase outside resources and use agency of their choice. MD visits residents in their rooms/suites. Clinic area for medical visits. Will help locate higher level of care if needed (co-ordination with family, Resident Care Manager and CCAC).
ACCOMMODATION: *Choice of suites available*: 1-bedroom & 2-bedroom suites - various sizes and styles. *In all suites*: locks, kitchenette, bar fridge, storage, window coverings, light fixtures, fire alarm, smoke detector, CO alarm/detector, sprinkler, emergency response system with wearable pendant/bracelet,

air conditioning (central) and thermostats for heating & cooling. Private bathrooms with call bells, grab bars and showers. In-suite cable TV if resident arranges with cable company. Can have own phone number if resident arranges with phone company. Unfurnished suites, furnished suites available for short stays. *Restrictions on electrical appliances*: approved appliances only, no burners or toasters. Suites can be shared (by couples only), roommate picked by resident. Pets allowed (cats, birds, small dogs on approval).
DINING SERVICE: All meals included in fee and served in dining room daily. *Sittings per meal:* Breakfast: 1, Lunch: 2, Dinner: 2. *Menu choices available:* Breakfast: 6, Lunch: 4, Dinner: 5. *Guest Meals*: Breakfast $10.95, Lunch $16.95, Dinner $18.95. *Special Diets*: Vegetarian, Low Salt, Diabetic and Limited Therapeutic Diet. Tray service to room if ill (no charge as long as doctor orders). 2 snacks/day. Party facilities. Elegant restaurant, private dining room, both with wait service, cathedral ceiling, full window views and private dining. Open seating. Sunday brunch. Licensed Bar.
AMENITIES AND ACTIVITIES: Parking available (outdoor, for visitors: free and indoor for residents: $65.00/month). *6 lounges with:* TVs (3), pianos (3), gas fireplaces (2), games, bridge and ping pong (1). Guest suites available ($130.00/night). *Residence has a:* library, barber/beauty shop, visiting hairdresser, laundry room(s) (no cost), tuck/gift shop (open 3 x/week; 3:30 p.m. - 4:30 p.m.). Resident can arrange newspaper delivery to individual suite (extra cost). Mail delivered to private mailbox with key. *Recreation Facilities*: pool table, billiards, craft room, card room, gym, spa, landscaped garden, hobby/art studio and resident kitchen. Posted schedule of activities. Internal newsletter for residents. *Recreational Programs*: exercise, shopping, theatre, parties, entertainment, art classes, pet visiting, day trips, Brain Gym® & More program, internet access and one-on-one & individualized recreation programs.
OTHER SERVICES: *Housekeeping*: daily and weekly (included in fee; daily at an additional cost if independent). *Laundry*: linen & towel (included in fee); personal ($85.00/month/single or $120.00/month/ double for Independent; no charge for Assisted Living) & dry cleaning (pick up & delivery available from local dry cleaners). Transportation for group social activities. 24-hour security. Nightly security checks. Telephone & Cable TV (client responsible). Utilities (included in fee).
RENTAL INFORMATION: Rates may vary. Extra cost for 2nd person sharing suite ($765.00/month; $1,275.00/month for Assisted Living). Rent paid monthly. *Payment Options*: post-dated cheques, direct deposit and pre-authorized payments. Rent increases indexed to inflation as per Provincial Tenancy Legislation, annual for resident with 3 months' notice given. Short-term respite and trial stays available (both $125.00/day; full service for trials, respite).

Did you know?

There are several ways in which you can keep your home safe to avoid the risk of falling both inside and out. To view and print a checklist of ways to avoid injury visit **www.phac-aspc.gc.ca/seniors-aines/publications/public/injury-blessure/safelive-securite/chap4-eng.php.**

MEIGHEN RETIREMENT RESIDENCE

84 Davisville Avenue, Toronto, ON M4S 1G1
Tel: (416) 481-5557 • Fax: (416) 481-8540
Email: **marie_osborne@can.salvationarmy.org**
Website: **www.sa-mhc.ca**
Contact: **Marie Osborne**
Capacity: **89 residents** • Subsidies: **none**
Price: **$2,275.00 - $3,825.00/month**

A retirement community within a community.

RESIDENCE INFORMATION: 42 years in operation. *Near:* Yonge Street and Mount Pleasant Avenue. Decorated in 2008. Handrails in hallways. 6 floors, 3 elevators. Central PA system. *Funding Base:* Not-for-profit. *Owned by:* The Salvation Army. *Managed by:* The Meighen Health Centre. 72 units. *Average Waiting Period*: 2 - 4 months. *Average Age*: 87. Can accommodate cognitively impaired & physically challenged people with restrictions. Residents have a dress code (no night clothes in the dining room). Smoke-free residence. *Procedures to leave the premises on a temporary basis...*Short-term: sign in/out at Reception. Overnight: sign in/out and inform Care Department. Holidays: written notice of time away to Administration and Care Departments. *Languages:* English. Will accept Public Guardian and Trustee clients. Main doors of residence secured at all times. *Close to:* Public Transit, Shopping, Churches, Seniors' Centre, Library and Local Hospital (Sunnybrook Health Sciences Centre). *Predominant Cultural Group:* Second Generation Canadians.
STAFFING: *Available Staff/Services*: Pharmacy, Recreation Therapy, Visiting Dentist, Physiotherapy, Dietitian, Chaplaincy, Chiropody, Housekeeping, Nursing and 24-hour Care Staff. *External services arranged by:* family/resident. Staff trained *re*: visually and hearing impaired. 24-hour nursing staff. RNs, RPNs, HCAs and PSWs on staff. Visiting MD (visits 1 day/week and is on call). Can retain own MD. Police Check or Vulnerable Person Screening is done for all new staff.
HEALTH SERVICES: Medication administration and/or supervision. Vitals monitored if required. Assistance with bathing available twice a week. Care plans done. Lab service (visiting, $25.00/visit). Clinic area for medical visits. Will help locate higher level of care if needed.
ACCOMMODATION: *Choice of suites available*: single rooms with 2-piece bathroom (36), single room with 3-piece bathroom (19) & 2-room suite (17). *In all suites*: locks, storage, window coverings, light fixtures, linens, smoke detector, sprinkler, call bell, air conditioning (central) and thermostats for heating. Private bathrooms with call bells and grab bars. In-suite cable TV if resident arranges with cable company. Can have own phone number if resident arranges with phone company. Furnished & unfurnished suites available. Suites can be shared. No pets allowed.
DINING SERVICE: All meals included in fee and served in dining room daily. *Sittings per meal:* Breakfast: 1, Lunch: 1, Dinner: 1. *Menu choices available:* Breakfast: 2, Lunch: 2, Dinner: 2. *Guest Meals*: Breakfast $4.35, Lunch $6.50, Dinner $5.00. *Special Diets*: Low Salt and Diabetic. Tray service to room if ill (no charge or restrictions). Room service when ordered by the Care Department. 1 snack/day and unlimited snacks available at any time. Party facilities. Party and outside meeting space available at no charge except for refreshments, food and staff.
AMENITIES AND ACTIVITIES: Parking available (outdoor, for visitors and residents). *6 lounges with:* TVs (6) and pianos (5). *Residence has a:* library, chapel, barber/beauty shop, visiting hairdresser, laundry room(s) (no cost) and tuck/gift shop (open 8:00 a.m. - 10:00 p.m.). Mail delivered to main desk. *Recreation Facilities*: activity room and large screen TV area. Posted schedule of activities. Internal newsletter for residents. *Recreational Programs*: exercise, shopping, parties, entertainment, pet visiting, day trips, walking programs, games, outings and craft program.
OTHER SERVICES: *Housekeeping*: daily and weekly (included in fee). *Laundry*: linen & towel (included in fee); personal ($25.00/month). Extra charge for dry cleaning services. Staff label clothing (included in fee).

24-hour security. Nightly security checks. Utilities (included in fee). Maintenance. Meals/snacks. Nursing & personal support/attendant if necessary. Care monitoring.
RENTAL INFORMATION: Rates may vary. Single private, 2-piece bathroom - $2,275.00/month; single private, 3-piece bathroom - $2,337.00/month; Suite/1 person - $3,053.00/month; Suite/2 people - $3,825.00/month. Extra cost for 2nd person sharing suite ($773.00/month). Rent paid monthly on the first day of each month. *Payment Options*: cheques, post-dated cheques and pre-authorized payments. Rent increases are annual with 90 days' notice given.

NEW HORIZONS TOWER

1140 Bloor Street West, Toronto, ON M6H 4E6
Tel: (416) 536-6111 • Fax: (416) 536-6748
Email: **Ian.Anderson@newhorizonstower.com**
Website: **www.newhorizonstower.com**
Contact: **Ian Anderson**
Capacity: **140 residents •** Subsidies: **none**
Price: **$2,500.00 - $3,150.00/month**

New Horizons
TOWER

New Horizons Tower is a seniors community excelling in accommodation and services inspired by a foundation of love, hope and faith. The congregation of Dovercourt Baptist Church wanted to make a contribution to their neighbourhood and believed that the establishment of a retirement community would be a lasting legacy. New Horizons Tower has become that legacy as one of the city's well established not-for-profit senior housing providers. Operating since 1974 as a charitable organization, we are committed to reinvest in the community we serve, to enhance and enrich the lives of seniors who choose to live in the heart of Bloordale Village. From gracious dining to new suites and lounges, residents are enjoying the new management and upgrades found at 1140 Bloor Street West.

RESIDENCE INFORMATION: 40 years in operation. *On:* Bloor Street and Dufferin Street. Decorated in 2013. Handrails in hallways. 16 floors, 3 elevators. Wheelchair accessible. Central PA system. *Funding Base:* Not-for-profit. 140 units. *Average Waiting Period*: 1 - 2 months. *Average Age*: 80. Can sometimes accommodate physically challenged people. Residents have a dress code. Smoke-free residence. *Languages:* English. Will accept Public Guardian and Trustee clients. Main doors of residence secured at all times. *Close to:* Public Transit, Shopping, Churches, Seniors' Centre, Library and Local Hospital. Licensed under the Retirement Homes Act.
STAFFING: *Available Staff/Services*: Pharmacy, Recreation Therapy, Visiting Dentist, Physiotherapy, Denturist, Dietitian, Companions, Chaplaincy, Chiropody and Audiology/Hearing Clinic. *External services arranged by:* residence and/or family/resident. 24-hour nursing and other staff. RPNs and PSWs on staff. Visiting MD (available once/week and on call). Can retain own MD. Police Check or Vulnerable Person Screening is done for all new staff.
HEALTH SERVICES: Medication administration supervised. Vitals monitored if required. Will accept and provide special assistance for residents who require oxygen, catheters and ostomies. Assistance with dressing available. Assistance with bathing available as needed. Care plans done. Different levels of care available. Assisted Living Area (6 - 12 month waiting period). Oasis Floor provides Enhanced Support for those struggling with independence due to memory loss. Separate unit for residents with dementia. Residents can purchase outside resources and use agency of their choice. Clinic area for medical visits. Will help locate higher level of care if needed.
ACCOMMODATION: *Choice of suites available*: studios and suites, complete with built-in cabinetry. *In all suites*: locks, kitchenette, bar fridge, window coverings, light fixtures, linens, fire alarm, smoke detector, air conditioning (window units) and thermostats for heating. Private bathrooms with grab bars, showers with non-slip surfaces and elevated toilet seats. In-suite cable TV if resident arranges with cable company. Can have own phone number if resident arranges with phone company. Unfurnished suites. *Restrictions*

on electrical appliances: Maintenance must check all incoming appliances. Suites can be shared (by couples only). Pets allowed.
DINING SERVICE: All meals included in fee and served in dining room daily. *Menu choices available:* Breakfast: 2, Lunch: 3, Dinner: 3. *Guest Meals*: Breakfast $7.50, Lunch $10.00, Dinner $15.00. *Special Diets*: Vegetarian, Low Salt and Diabetic. Tray service to room if ill (no charge for a maximum time of 5 days). Unlimited snacks available at any time. Party facilities. All Meals are served as open dining. Residents may dine at the time of their choice without needing reservations.
AMENITIES AND ACTIVITIES: *14 lounges with:* TVs (14) and pianos (2). Guest suites available ($100.00/night). *Residence has a:* library, chapel, barber/beauty shop and laundry room(s) (no cost). Resident can arrange newspaper delivery to main desk. Mail delivered to private mailbox with key. *Recreation Facilities*: shuffleboard, exercise room, craft room, card room, Wii Sports, computer lab, rooftop garden, walkout terrace, concert auditorium and by Dufferin Subway. Posted schedule of activities. Internal newsletter for residents. *Recreational Programs*: exercise, theatre, parties, art classes, entertainment, pet visiting and day trips.
OTHER SERVICES: *Housekeeping*: weekly (included in fee). *Laundry*: linen & towel (included in fee); personal ($25.00/load or $100.00/month). Staff label clothing (included in fee, if resident opts for full personal laundry). Transportation to medical appointments (extra cost - PSW will accompany the client via cab) and for group social activities. 24-hour security. Nightly security checks. Utilities (included in fee). 24-hour nursing staff.
RENTAL INFORMATION: Rates may vary. Extra cost for 2nd person sharing suite ($750.00/month). Rent paid monthly. *Payment Options*: post-dated cheques and pre-authorized payments. Rent increases as per Provincial Tenancy Legislation, annual for resident with 90 days' notice given. Short-term respite and trial stays available.

REVERA - BRADGATE ARMS

54 Foxbar Road, Toronto, ON M4V 2G6
Tel: (855) 573-8372 • Toll Free: (855) 573-8372
Email: **bradgate@reveraliving.com**
Website: **www.reveraliving.com/bradgate**
Contact: **Lifestyle Consultant or Executive Director**
Capacity: **95 residents** • Subsidies: **none**
Price: **$3,500.00/month and up**

Keep living your life, your way, at Bradgate Arms. Once an exclusive hotel, Bradgate Arms is now Toronto's premier choice for luxurious retirement living. Bradgate Arms has been part of the historic Toronto community for more than 100 years. Near Avenue Road and St. Clair Avenue, you'll find services and amenities to fit your lifestyle, from valet parking to room service. Many suites have architectural details like wood beams and fireplaces, echoing features of fine homes in Forest Hill and Rosedale. Step outside, and you're near great shopping, community services, a seniors' centre, and public transit. Everything is designed to help you maintain your independence and privacy, enjoy a full social life, and participate in the activities you love. With retirement living at Bradgate Arms, you change your address, not your life. *Bradgate Arms is part of the Revera family, one of North America's leading and most trusted providers of seniors' accommodation, care and services since 1961.*

RESIDENCE INFORMATION: 18 years in operation. *Near:* Avenue Road and St. Clair Avenue. Decorated in 2010. Handrails in hallways. 6 floors, 2 elevators. Wheelchair accessible. Central PA system. *Funding Base:* Corporate/for profit. *Owned and managed by:* Revera Inc. 81 units. *Average Waiting Period*: varies. *Average Age*: 82. Can sometimes accommodate cognitively impaired & physically challenged people. Residents have a dress code (while there is no formal dress code the residents do dress up for dinner). Smoke-free residence. Alcohol allowed. *Procedures to leave the premises on a temporary basis...*

Overnight & Holidays: residents sign a form with the receptionist outlining who they are with in case of emergency. *Languages:* English. Will accept Public Guardian and Trustee clients. Main doors of residence secured at night only. *Close to:* Public Transit, Shopping, Churches, Seniors' Centre, Library and Local Hospitals (University Health Network - Toronto General Hospital Site & Mount Sinai Hospital). Member of ORCA. Licensed under the Retirement Homes Act.

STAFFING: *Available Staff/Services*: Pharmacy, Recreation Therapy, Occupational Therapy (CCAC), Visiting Dentist, Physiotherapy (CCAC), Denturist, Companions, Podiatry, Chaplaincy, Audiology/Hearing Clinic, Foot Care Clinic and Massage Therapist. *External services arranged by:* residence and/or family/ resident. Staff trained *re*: visually, hearing and cognitively impaired. 24-hour nursing staff. RNs, RPNs, HCAs and PSWs on staff. Visiting MD (weekly/on call 24/7). Can retain own MD. Staff members are bonded. Police Check or Vulnerable Person Screening is done for all new staff.

HEALTH SERVICES: Medication administration and/or supervision. Will accept and provide special assistance for residents who require oxygen, catheters and ostomies. Assistance with dressing available (cost). Weekly assistance with bathing available. Care plans done. Different levels of care available. Private Duty/Extra Care available. Assisted Living Area. Lab service (visiting). Residents can purchase outside resources and use agency of their choice. MD visits residents in their rooms/suites. Clinic area for medical visits. Will help locate higher level of care if needed (referrals to Revera residences; assistance with contacting CCAC for services).

ACCOMMODATION: *Choice of suites available*: studios & 3 very unique layouts of 1-bedroom suites. *In all suites*: locks, kitchenette, bar fridge, storage, window coverings, light fixtures, linens, fire alarm, smoke detector, sprinkler, call bell, emergency response system with wearable pendant/bracelet, air conditioning (central) and thermostats for heating & cooling. Private bathrooms with call bells, grab bars and walk-in showers with non-slip surfaces. In-suite cable TV provided by residence (residence charges extra). Can have own phone number provided by residence (residence charges extra). Unfurnished suites, furnished suites available for short stays. Short-term guest stays can be arranged. *Restrictions on electrical appliances*: no open elements. Pets allowed (as per Pet Policy within the Tenancy Agreement).

DINING SERVICE: All meals included in fee and served in our full service dining room between 7:30 a.m. - 8:00 p.m. *Sittings per meal:* Breakfast: 1, Lunch: 1, Dinner: 1. *Guest Meals*: Available. *Special Diets*: Available. Tray service to room if ill (no charge or restrictions). 2 snacks/day. Party facilities. Unlimited complimentary room service is available upon request.

AMENITIES AND ACTIVITIES: Parking available (indoor, for visitors and residents). *3 lounges with:* TVs (2) and piano (1). Guest suites available. *Residence has a:* library, barber/beauty shop, laundry room(s) (no cost) and tuck/gift shop. Residence provides newspaper delivery to individual suite (extra cost). Mail delivered to main desk. *Recreation Facilities*: exercise room, card room, salon and whirlpool. Posted schedule of activities. Internal newsletter for residents. *Recreational Programs*: exercise, shopping, theatre, parties, entertainment, art classes, pet visiting, day trips, Yoga, lectures and music appreciation.

OTHER SERVICES: *Housekeeping*: daily and weekly (included in fee). *Laundry*: linen, towel & personal (included in fee); dry cleaning (extra cost based on the item). Free washer/dryer on 2nd and 4th floor for resident use. Transportation for group social activities. 24-hour security. Nightly security checks. Telephone & Cable TV (extra cost). Utilities (included in fee). Valet Parking (no additional cost).

RENTAL INFORMATION: Prices vary depending on suite size and services provided. Extra cost for 2nd person sharing suite ($800.00/month). Rent paid monthly. *Payment Options*: pre-authorized payments. Rent increases as per Provincial Tenancy Legislation, annual for resident with 3 months' notice given. Will help resident move into residence. Short-term respite and trial stays available (cost depends on care and services). Hotel suites are available and are fully furnished.

Pricing information for homes listed in *The Guide* may vary slightly.
Please verify rates with the residences you are interested in directly.

REVERA - FOREST HILL PLACE

645 Castlefield Avenue, Toronto, ON M5N 3A5
Tel: (855) 573-8372 • Toll Free: (855) 573-8372
Email: **foresthill@reveraliving.com**
Website: **www.reveraliving.com/foresthill**
Contact: **Executive Director or Lifestyle Consultant**
Capacity: **156 residents** • Subsidies: **none**
Price: **$2,499.00/month and up**

Keep living your life, your way, at Forest Hill Place. You'll find the range of services, features and choices that fit your lifestyle and requirements – all in a refined, friendly and safe environment. Located in one of Toronto's premier residential neighbourhoods, we feature landscaped gardens, high calibre entertainment and cultural programs. Our central location, proximity to shopping and other amenities, and warm atmosphere all make us the residence of choice for many retired members of the Forest Hill community. Everything is designed for you to maintain your independence and privacy, enjoy a full social life, and participate in the activities that you love. With retirement living at Forest Hill Place, you change your address, not your life. *Forest Hill Place is part of the Revera family, one of North America's leading and most trusted providers of seniors' accommodation, care and services since 1961.*

RESIDENCE INFORMATION: 24 years in operation. *Near:* Bathurst Street and Eglinton Avenue. Decorated in 2012. Handrails in hallways. 8 floors, 3 elevators. Wheelchair accessible. Central PA system. *Funding Base:* Corporate/for profit. *Owned and managed by:* Revera Inc. 156 units. *Average Waiting Period*: none. *Average Age*: 87. Can accommodate cognitively impaired people (moderate dementia). Can accommodate physically challenged people (1-person transfer). Residents have a dress code (proper attire at all times). Smoke-free residence (specified outdoor smoking amenities). Alcohol allowed. *Procedures to leave the premises on a temporary basis...*give notice from a security perspective. *Languages:* English. Will accept Public Guardian and Trustee clients. Main doors of residence secured at night only. *Close to:* Public Transit, Shopping, Churches, Synagogues, Seniors' Centre, Library, Major Highway and Local Hospitals (North York General Hospital & Sunnybrook Health Sciences Centre). *Predominant Cultural Group:* Jewish. Member of ORCA. Associated with Hadassah Group and National Council of Jewish Women. Licensed under the Retirement Homes Act.
STAFFING: *Available Staff/Services*: Pharmacy, Social Work (CCAC), Recreation Therapy, Occupational Therapy (CCAC), Visiting Dentist, Physiotherapy (CCAC), Denturist, Dietitian (CCAC), Companions, Podiatry, Chiropody, Audiology/Hearing Clinic, RMT, Foot Clinic, Optometrist and Blood Work Clinic. *External services arranged by:* residence and/or family/resident. Staff trained *re*: visually, hearing and cognitively impaired. 24-hour nursing and other staff. RNs, RPNs, HCAs and PSWs on staff. Visiting MD (2x/weekly). Can retain own MD. Police Check or Vulnerable Person Screening is done for all new staff.
HEALTH SERVICES: Medication administered if required. Vitals monitored if required. Will accept and provide special assistance for residents who require oxygen, catheters and ostomies. Assistance with dressing available ($30.00/half hour). Weekly assistance with bathing available ($79.00/month). Care plans done. Different levels of care available. Private Duty/Extra Care available. Assisted Living Area. Lab service (visiting). Residents can purchase outside resources and use agency of their choice. MD visits residents in their rooms/suites. Clinic area for medical visits. Will help locate higher level of care if needed (referral to Revera Residence or assistance with obtaining services from CCAC).
ACCOMMODATION: *Choice of suites available*: Apartments – various studios & 1- bedroom units with full kitchen/3 full-sized appliances; Independent Living – studio, 1-bedroom & 2-bedroom units with kitchenette & fridge; Assisted - studio, 1-bedroom & 2-bedroom units. *In all suites*: locks, kitchenette, bar fridge, microwave, storage, walk-in closets, window coverings, light fixtures, fire alarm, smoke detector, sprinkler, call bell, emergency response system with wearable pendant/bracelet, air conditioning (central), thermostats for heating & cooling and underground parking. Private bathrooms with call bells, grab bars,

tubs and showers with non-slip surfaces and elevated toilet seats. In-suite cable TV provided by residence (residence charges extra). Can have own phone number if resident arranges with phone company (residence charges extra). Furnished & unfurnished suites available. *Restrictions on electrical appliances*: no hot plates. Suites can be shared (by couples only). Pets allowed (as per Pet Policy within Tenancy Agreement).
DINING SERVICE: Three meals/day included in fee and served in dining room daily (for Independent Living and Assisted Living); Apartment Living dining available à la carte. *Sittings per meal:* Breakfast: 1, Lunch: 1, Dinner: 1. *Menu choices available:* Breakfast: 10, Lunch: 15, Dinner: 15. *Guest Meals*: Breakfast $8.50, Lunch $12.00, Dinner $18.00. *Special Diets*: Vegetarian, Low Salt, Diabetic, Gluten Free and Lactose Intolerance. Tray service to room if ill (no charge for a maximum time of 4 days). 2 snacks/day. Coffee and tea available all day. Party facilities.
AMENITIES AND ACTIVITIES: Parking available (outdoor, for visitors and indoor for residents). *10 lounges with:* TVs (3) and pianos (2). Guest suites available ($119.00/night). *Residence has a:* library, visiting library, barber/beauty shop, visiting hairdresser, laundry room(s) (no cost) and tuck/gift shop (open 9:30 a.m. - 5:00 p.m.). Resident can arrange newspaper delivery to individual suite (extra cost). Mail delivered to private mailbox with key. *Recreation Facilities*: pool table, billiards, exercise room, craft room, card room, kitchen centre, LLBO bar, library, media room, theatre and garden patio. Posted schedule of activities. Internal newsletter for residents. *Recreational Programs*: exercise, shopping, theatre, parties, entertainment, art classes, pet visiting, day trips and computer email/internet use.
OTHER SERVICES: *Housekeeping*: weekly (included in fee; daily on Assisted Living). *Laundry*: linen & towel (included in fee); personal (weekly - extra cost; included in Assisted Living) & dry cleaning (as per dry cleaning service). Transportation to medical appointments (can be arranged for extra cost) and for group social activities. 24-hour security. Nightly security checks (extra cost). Telephone & Cable TV (extra cost). Utilities (extra cost - Gas and Hydro). Medication administration (extra cost). Diabetes management (extra cost).
RENTAL INFORMATION: Rates may vary. Senior Apartments: studios - $2,499.00/month & up; Independent Living: studios - $3,180.00/month & up; 1-bedrooms - $4,560.00/month & up ; 2-bedrooms - $6,995.00/month & up; Assisted Living: studios - $3,755.00/month & up; 1-bedroom - $5,355.00/month & up; 2-bedroom - $8,705.00/month & up. Extra cost for 2nd person sharing suite. Rent paid monthly. *Payment Options*: cheques, post-dated cheques, direct deposit and pre-authorized payments. Credit card payment available for short-term stays. Rent increases as per Provincial Tenancy Legislation, annual for resident with 90 days' notice given. Will help resident move into residence (extra cost). Short-term respite ($99.00/day) and trial stays ($109.00/day) available.

REVERA - LEASIDE

10 & 14 William Morgan Drive, Toronto, ON M4H 1E7
Tel: (855) 573-8372 • Toll Free: (855) 573-8372
Email: **leaside@reveraliving.com**
Website: **www.reveraliving.com/leaside**
Contact: **Executive Director or Lifestyle Consultant**
Capacity: **300 residents** • Subsidies: **none**
Price: **$1,915.00/month and up**

Keep living your life, your way, at Leaside. You'll find the range of services, amenities and choices that fit your lifestyle and requirements – all in a warm, safe and stylish environment. Located in the Leaside community, we are nestled in a lush ravine setting backing onto beautiful Taylor Creek. Our quiet court location, featuring an expansive courtyard and gardens, is also conveniently close to great restaurants, shopping, a library, a seniors' centre, churches, hospitals and public transportation. Everything is designed for you to maintain your independence and privacy, enjoy a full social life, and participate in the activities you love. Our caring and friendly staff and appealing accommodations support who you are and how you want to live. With retirement living at Leaside, you change your address, not your life. *Leaside is part of*

the Revera family, one of North America's leading and most trusted providers of seniors' accommodation, care and services since 1961.

RESIDENCE INFORMATION: 49 years in operation. *Near:* Don Mills Road and Overlea Boulevard. Decorated in 2011. Handrails in hallways. 7 floors, 5 elevators. Wheelchair accessible. Central PA system. *Funding Base:* Corporate/for profit. *Owned and managed by:* Revera Inc. 285 units. *Average Waiting Period*: varies. *Average Age*: 83. Can accommodate cognitively impaired people (separate Secured Memory Care accommodation). Can accommodate physically challenged people (can accommodate walkers and wheelchairs). Smoking allowed (outside designated smoking area). Alcohol allowed. *Restrictions around Visitors/Visiting Hours:* Receptionist on duty until 9:00 p.m. 7 days/week, buzzer to get in after 9:00pm. *Procedures to leave the premises on a temporary basis...*Short-term: sign in/out at Reception. Overnight & Holidays: inform staff and sign in/out at reception. *Languages:* English. Will accept Public Guardian and Trustee clients. Main doors of residence secured at night only. *Close to:* Public Transit, Shopping, Churches, Seniors' Centre, Library, Major Highway and Local Hospitals (Sunnybrook Health Sciences Centre, North York General Hospital & The Toronto East General Hospital). Member of ORCA. Licensed under the Retirement Homes Act.
STAFFING: *Available Staff/Services*: Pharmacy, Social Work (CCAC), Recreation Therapy, Occupational Therapy (CCAC), Physiotherapy (CCAC), Companions, Chaplaincy, Chiropody, Audiology/Hearing Clinic, Massage Therapy, Esthetician and Hair Salon. *External services arranged by:* family/resident. Staff trained *re*: visually, hearing and cognitively impaired. 24-hour nursing staff. RNs, RPNs, HCAs, PSWs and UCPs on staff. Visiting MD (5 physicians on-site 4 times/week & on call 24-hours). Can retain own MD. Police Check or Vulnerable Person Screening is done for all new staff.
HEALTH SERVICES: Medication administration and/or supervision. Vitals monitored if required. Will accept (but not provide special assistance for) residents who require catheters and feeding tubes. Will accept and provide special assistance for residents who require oxygen and ostomies. Assistance with dressing available (cost). Assistance with bathing available (cost). Care plans done. Different levels of care available. Private Duty/Extra Care available. Assisted Living Area (less than 2 week waiting period). Separate unit for residents with dementia. Lab service (visiting). Residents can purchase outside resources and use agency of their choice. MD visits residents in their rooms/suites. Clinic area for medical visits. Will help locate higher level of care if needed (referral to Revera residence; assistance coordinating services through CCAC).
ACCOMMODATION: *Choice of suites available*: private studio, 1-bedroom & 2-bedroom suites. *In all suites*: locks, storage, window coverings, light fixtures, smoke detector, sprinkler, call bell, 24/7 emergency response system with wearable pendant/bracelet, air conditioning (central) and thermostats for heating & cooling. Kitchenettes, step-in showers & walk-in closets in many suites. Recently renovated. Private bathrooms with call bells/emergency pull cord, grab bars, tubs and showers with non-slip surfaces and elevated toilet seats. In-suite cable TV provided by residence (residence charges extra). Can have own phone number if resident arranges with phone company (residence charges extra). Unfurnished suites, furnished suites available for short stays. *Restrictions on electrical appliances*: auto shut-off appliances only. Suites can be shared (no restrictions). Pet-friendly residence (cats, birds and small to medium sized dogs all welcome).
DINING SERVICE: All meals included in fee and served in dining room daily. *Sittings per meal:* Breakfast: 1, Lunch: 4, Dinner: 4. *Menu choices available:* Breakfast: 5, Lunch: 2, Dinner: 2. *Guest Meals*: Available. *Special Diets*: Vegetarian, Low Salt, Diabetic and Heart Smart Choices. Tray service to room if ill (no charge for a maximum time of 4 days). 2 snacks/day. Party facilities.
AMENITIES AND ACTIVITIES: Parking available (outdoor, for visitors and residents). *21 lounges with:* TV (1), pianos (2) and Grand Piano (1). Guest suites available. *Residence has a:* library, visiting library, chapel, barber/beauty shop, laundry room(s) (no cost) and tuck/gift shop (open 9:00 a.m. - 3:00 p.m.). Banking services on premises. Resident can arrange newspaper delivery to individual suite (extra cost). Mail delivered to resident. *Recreation Facilities*: pool table, billiards, exercise room, craft room, card

room, bar/pub, games room, recreation area, sunrooms, outdoor patios, walking path, theatre and party room. Posted schedule of activities. Internal newsletter for residents. *Recreational Programs*: exercise, shopping, theatre, parties, entertainment, art classes, pet visiting, day trips, dining club, excursions/trips, church services, lectures, socials and happy hour.

OTHER SERVICES: *Housekeeping*: daily and weekly (weekly included in fee for all). *Laundry*: linen & towel (included in fee); personal (extra cost - option do to own personal laundry, lowers rent) & dry cleaning (extra cost - arrange with reception). Either staff or resident label clothing. Weekly linen, towel and personal laundry included for Retirement, Assisted Living & Memory Care. Transportation to medical appointments (WheelTrans or taxi service) and for group social activities (cost of admission only; transportation included). 24-hour security. Nightly security checks. Telephone & Cable TV (extra cost). Utilities (included in fee). Optional services available.

RENTAL INFORMATION: Rates may vary. Extra cost for 2nd person sharing suite. Rent paid monthly. *Payment Options*: post-dated cheques and pre-authorized payments. Rent increases as per Provincial Tenancy Legislation, annual for resident with 3 months' notice given. Will help resident move into residence. Short-term respite and trial stays available. Vacation & respite stays easily arranged.

REVERA - PINE VILLA

1035 Eglinton Avenue West, Toronto, ON M6C 2C8
Tel: (855) 573-8372 • Toll Free: (855) 573-8372
Email: **pinevilla@reveraliving.com**
Website: **www.reveraliving.com/pinevilla**
Contact: **Executive Director or Lifestyle Consultant**
Capacity: **74 residents** • Subsidies: **none**
Price: **$1,999.00/month and up**

Keep living your life, your way, at Pine Villa. You'll find the range of services, amenities and choices that fit your lifestyle and requirements – all in a warm and safe environment. Pine Villa is a boutique-style residence located in the heart of Forest Hill's Jewish community. This vibrant area is conveniently close to shopping, restaurants, medical services, parks, public transportation, and more, with numerous synagogues within walking distance. Everything is designed to enable you to maintain your independence and privacy, enjoy a full social life, and participate in the activities that you love. Our caring and friendly staff, along with beautiful accommodations, support your lifestyle choice and comfort. With retirement living at Pine Villa, you change your address, not your life. *Pine Villa is part of the Revera family, one of North America's leading and most trusted providers of seniors' accommodation, care and services since 1961.*

RESIDENCE INFORMATION: 33 years in operation. *Near:* Allen Road and Eglinton Avenue West. Decorated in 2009. Handrails in hallways. 4 floors, 1 elevator. Wheelchair accessible. Central PA system. *Funding Base:* Corporate/for profit. *Owned and managed by:* Revera Inc. 74 units. *Average Waiting Period*: none. *Average Age*: 85. Can accommodate cognitively impaired people (various levels of care for those with dementia). Can accommodate physically challenged people (wheelchair ramp at entrance; easy access showers and bathrooms). Smoke-free residence. Alcohol allowed. *Procedures to leave the premises on a temporary basis...*Short-term: inform Reception. Overnight & Holidays: inform charge staff or RN. *Languages:* English, Hungarian, Yiddish, Hebrew, Polish, French, Russian & Romanian. Will accept Public Guardian and Trustee clients. Main doors of residence secured at all times. *Close to:* Public Transit, Shopping, Churches, Synagogues, Seniors' Centre, Library, Major Highway and Local Hospitals (Sunnybrook Health Sciences Centre, North York General Hospital, Humber River Regional Hospital – Finch Street & Church Street Sites, Baycrest Hospital & Mount Sinai Hospital). *Predominant Cultural Group:* Jewish. Member of ORCA. Licensed under the Retirement Homes Act.

STAFFING: *Available Staff/Services:* Pharmacy, Social Work (CCAC), Physiotherapy (CCAC), Recreation Therapy, Occupational Therapy (CCAC), Visiting Dentist, Denturist, Dietitian (CCAC), Companions,

Podiatry, Chaplaincy, Speech Pathology (CCAC), Chiropody, Audiology/Hearing Clinic and 24-hour Supervised Staff. *External services arranged by:* residence and/or family/resident. Staff trained *re*: visually, hearing and cognitively impaired. 24-hour staff. RNs, RPNs, HCAs and PSWs on staff. Visiting MD (once/week and when needed). Can retain own MD. Staff members are bonded. Police Check or Vulnerable Person Screening is done for all new staff.

HEALTH SERVICES: Medication administration and/or supervision. Vitals monitored if required. Will accept and provide special assistance for residents who require oxygen, catheters and ostomies. Assistance with dressing available (cost). Weekly assistance with bathing available (cost). Care plans done. Different levels of care available. Private Duty/Extra Care available. Lab service (visiting). Residents can purchase outside resources and use agency of their choice. MD visits residents in their rooms/suites. Clinic area for medical visits. Will help locate higher level of care if needed (assistance with obtaining services from CCAC).

ACCOMMODATION: *Choice of suites available*: private studios and 1-bedroom suites with various layouts. *In all suites*: locks, kitchenette, bar fridge, storage, window coverings, light fixtures, linens, fire alarm, smoke detector, carbon monoxide detector, sprinkler, call bell, emergency response system with wearable pendant/bracelet, air conditioning (central) and thermostats for heating & cooling. Private bathrooms with call bells, grab bars and showers with non-slip surfaces. In-suite cable TV provided by residence (residence charges extra). Can have own phone number provided by residence (residence charges extra). Furnished & unfurnished suites available. *Restrictions on electrical appliances*: no stoves or hot plates; kettles with automatic shut-off and microwaves are allowed. Suites can be shared (by couples, companions). Pets allowed (as per Pet Policy within Tenancy Agreement).

DINING SERVICE: All meals included in fee and served in dining room daily. *Sittings per meal:* Breakfast: 2, Lunch: 2, Dinner: 2. *Menu choices available:* Breakfast: 5, Lunch: 2, Dinner: 2. *Guest Meals*: Available. *Special Diets*: Vegetarian, Low Salt, Diabetic, Pre-Cut, Mashed and Kosher-Style (no mashgiach). Tray service to room if ill (no charge for a maximum time of 3 days). 2 snacks/day. Party facilities. Food prepared fresh for every meal.

AMENITIES AND ACTIVITIES: Parking available (outdoor, for visitors and residents). *4 lounges with:* TV (1), piano (1), library/fireplace (1) and patios (2). Guest suites available. *Residence has a:* library, visiting library, barber/beauty shop and visiting hairdresser. Resident can arrange newspaper delivery to main desk. Mail delivered to private mailbox with key. *Recreation Facilities*: exercise room, craft room, card room, game room and computer study. Posted schedule of activities. Internal newsletter for residents. *Recreational Programs*: exercise, shopping, theatre, parties, entertainment, art classes, pet visiting, day trips, live music, walking groups, bingo, lectures and outings.

OTHER SERVICES: *Housekeeping*: weekly (included in fee). *Laundry*: linen, towel & personal (included in fee); dry cleaning (dry cleaners across the street). Transportation to medical appointments (extra cost) and for group social activities (included in fee). 24-hour security. Nightly security checks. Telephone & Cable TV (extra cost). Utilities (included in fee). Additional care available for dressing, bathing, eating, toileting if necessary (extra cost).

RENTAL INFORMATION: Rates vary depending on size of the apartment. Studios - $1,999.00/month & up; 1-bedrooms - $3,650.00/month & up. Additional costs for extra care vary depending on level of care package required - items can be purchased separately or bundled in a package. Extra cost for 2nd person sharing suite ($650.00/month). Rent paid monthly. *Payment Options*: post-dated cheques, direct deposit and pre-authorized payments. Rent increases are a set percentage indexed to inflation as per Provincial Tenancy Legislation, annual for resident with 3 months' notice given. Will help resident move into residence (extra cost). Short-term respite, hotel and trial stays available ($99.00/day & up depending on suite size).

Do you need information on retirement residences, long term care homes or seniors resources in other provinces?

www.senioropolis.com is National!! Click on the link to the province you are interested in and explore the wealth of information available.

REVERA - THE ANNEX

123 Spadina Road, Toronto, ON   M5R 2T1
Tel: (855) 573-8372 • Toll Free: (855) 573-8372
Email: **annex@reveraliving.com**
Website: **www.reveraliving.com/annex**
Contact: **Executive Director Lifestyle Consultant**
Capacity: **100 residents** • Subsidies: **none**
Price: **$2,400.00/month and up**

Keep living your life, your way, at The Annex. You'll find the range of services, amenities and choices that fit your lifestyle and requirements – all in a warm, safe and intimate environment. The renovated Annex residence is located in one of the most historic and unique neighbourhoods in Toronto, right on the subway line. We provide a full spectrum of care – independent living, memory care, and short-term stays – with the convenience of a downtown location. Everything here is designed to enable you to maintain your independence and privacy, enjoy a full social life and participate in activities you love. Our caring and friendly staff and appealing accommodations support who you are and how you want to live. With retirement living at The Annex, you change your address, not your life. *The Annex is part of the Revera family, one of North America's leading and most trusted providers of seniors' accommodation, care and services since 1961.*

RESIDENCE INFORMATION: 42 years in operation. *Near:* Spadina Road and Bloor Street. Decorated in 2009. Handrails in hallways. 5 floors, 2 elevators. Wheelchair accessible. Central PA system. *Funding Base:* Corporate/for profit. *Owned and managed by:* Revera Inc. 98 units. *Average Waiting Period*: varies. *Average Age*: 82. Can accommodate cognitively impaired people with restrictions (depending on level of impairment). Can sometimes accommodate physically challenged people (depending on level of care required). Residents have a dress code (appropriate casual dress). Smoking allowed (outdoors only in designated area). Alcohol allowed (bar/pub also on-site). *Restrictions around Visitors/Visiting Hours:* family may come anytime - building is locked at 9:00 p.m., visitors after 9:00 p.m. should call ahead. *Procedures to leave the premises on a temporary basis...*Short-term: notify Reception. Overnight & Holidays: notify Nursing or Administration. *Languages:* English. Will accept Public Guardian and Trustee clients. Main doors of residence secured at night only. *Close to:* Public Transit, Shopping, Churches, Seniors' Centre, Library and Local Hospitals (Mt. Sinai Hospital, University Health Network - Princess Margaret Hospital Site, Toronto General Hospital Site, Toronto Western Hospital Site, Women's College Hospital & St. Michael's Hospital). Member of ORCA. Licensed under the Retirement Homes Act.
STAFFING: *Available Staff/Services*: Pharmacy, Social Work (CCAC), Recreation Therapy, Occupational Therapy (CCAC), Visiting Dentist, Physiotherapy (CCAC), Denturist, Dietitian (CCAC), Companions, Podiatry, Chaplaincy, Speech Pathology (CCAC), Manicurist, Hair Stylist and Barber. *External services arranged by:* residence and/or family/resident. Staff trained *re*: visually, hearing and cognitively impaired. 24-hour nursing and other staff. RNs, RPNs, PSWs and UCPs on staff. Visiting MD (2 visiting MDs available 3 days/week). Can retain own MD. Staff members are bonded. Police Check or Vulnerable Person Screening is done for all new staff.
HEALTH SERVICES: Medication administration (Medication Management Program available at extra charge) and/or supervision. Vitals monitored if required. Will accept and provide special assistance for residents who require oxygen and catheters. Assistance with dressing available (cost). Assistance with bathing available as needed (cost). Care plans done. Different levels of care available. Separate unit for residents with dementia. Lab service (visiting). Residents can purchase outside resources and use agency of their choice. MD visits residents in their rooms/suites. Clinic area for medical visits. Will help locate higher level of care if needed (referrals to Revera residences; will help apply for long-term care if required).
ACCOMMODATION: *Choice of suites available*: studios with private bath & 1-bedroom suites. *In all suites*: locks, storage, window coverings, light fixtures, smoke detector, CO detector, sprinkler, call bell,

emergency response system with wearable pendant/bracelet, air conditioning (HVAC heat/air conditioning units in rooms, central in building) and thermostats for heating & cooling. Kitchenettes & balcony in some suites only. Each floor has a kitchenette and heat detector. Private bathrooms with call bells, grab bars and showers with non-slip surfaces. In-suite cable TV provided by residence (residence charges extra). Can have own phone number provided by residence (residence charges extra). Furnished & unfurnished suites available. *Restrictions on electrical appliances*: acceptable appliances are small fridges, microwaves, auto shut-off kettles. Suites can be shared, roommate picked by resident. Pets allowed (as per Pet Policy within Tenancy Agreement).
DINING SERVICE: All meals included in fee and served in dining room daily. *Sittings per meal:* Breakfast: 2, Lunch: 2, Dinner: 2. *Menu choices available:* Breakfast: 3, Lunch: 3, Dinner: 3. *Guest Meals*: Available. *Special Diets*: Vegetarian, Low Salt, Diabetic and Therapeutic. Tray service to room if ill (no charge for a maximum time of 4 days). 2 snacks/day. Common pantry/kitchenette on every floor. Some suites have their own kitchenette. Party facilities.
AMENITIES AND ACTIVITIES: Parking available (outdoor, for visitors). *3 lounges with:* TV (1), piano (1), fireside private dining (1) and internet computer (1). Guest suites available. *Residence has a:* library, barber/beauty shop, visiting hairdresser and laundry room(s) (no cost). Resident can arrange newspaper delivery to individual suite (extra cost). Mail delivered to main desk. *Recreation Facilities*: craft room, card room, outdoor patio & garden, fireside lounge and health & wellness centre. Posted schedule of activities. Internal newsletter for residents. *Recreational Programs*: exercise, shopping, theatre, parties, entertainment, art classes, pet visiting, day trips, restaurants and lectures.
OTHER SERVICES: *Housekeeping*: weekly (included in fee; extra cost for daily tidy). *Laundry*: linen & towel (included in fee); personal (extra cost; weekly laundering of all linens and personal items). Either staff or resident label clothing. Dry cleaner picks up and delivers to residence (extra cost). Transportation for group social activities. Nightly security checks. Telephone & Cable TV (extra cost). Utilities (included in fee). Optional services available.
RENTAL INFORMATION: Rates vary depending on suite type and service package. Extra cost for 2nd person sharing suite. Rent paid monthly. *Payment Options*: post-dated cheques and pre-authorized payments. Credit card payment available for short-term stays. Rent increases as per Provincial Tenancy Legislation, annual for resident with 3 months' notice given. Will help resident move into residence (extra cost). Short-term respite, vacation and trial stays available.

REVERA - THE CLAREMONT

305 Balliol Street, Toronto, ON M4S 3H5
Tel: (855) 573-8372 • Toll Free: (855) 573-8372
Email: **claremont@reveraliving.com**
Website: **www.reveraliving.com/claremont**
Contact: **Lifestyle Consultant or Executive Director**
Capacity: **77 residents** • Subsidies: **none**
Price: **$3,140.00/month and up**

Keep living your life, your way, at The Claremont. You'll find the range of services, amenities and choices that fit your lifestyle and requirements – all in a warm and safe environment. Located in the neighbourhood of Mt. Pleasant and Davisville, The Claremont is one of Toronto's premier choices for luxurious retirement living – a haven of tranquility, elegance and care. Conveniently located near shops, great restaurants, galleries, and public transit. Everything is designed to enable you to maintain your independence and privacy, enjoy a full social life and participate in the activities you love. The vibrancy here is evident in the annual Claremont calendar, where stereotype-smashing photos highlight the fun-loving spirit of residents. With retirement living at The Claremont, you change your address, not your life. *The Claremont is part of the Revera family, one of North America's leading and most trusted providers of seniors' accommodation, care and services since 1961.*

RESIDENCE INFORMATION: 12 years in operation. *Near:* Mount Pleasant Avenue and Davisville Avenue. Decorated in 2012. Handrails in hallways. 8 floors, 2 elevators. Wheelchair accessible. Central PA system. *Funding Base:* Corporate/for profit. *Owned and managed by:* Revera Inc. 77 units. *Average Waiting Period*: varies. *Average Age*: 86. Can accommodate cognitively impaired people with restrictions. Smoke-free residence. Alcohol allowed. *Procedures to leave the premises on a temporary basis...*sign out. *Languages:* English. Main doors of residence secured at night only. *Close to:* Public Transit, Shopping, Churches, Seniors' Centre, Library, Major Highway and Local Hospital (Sunnybrook Health Sciences Centre). Member of ORCA. Licensed under the Retirement Homes Act.
STAFFING: *Available Staff/Services*: Pharmacy, Social Work (CCAC), Recreation Therapy, Occupational Therapy (CCAC), Physiotherapy (CCAC), Denturist, Dietitian (CCAC), Companions, Podiatry and Audiology/Hearing Clinic. *External services arranged by:* residence and/or family/resident. Staff trained *re*: visually and hearing impaired. 24-hour nursing staff. RNs, RPNs, PSWs and UCPs on staff. Visiting MD (weekly visits, 24/7 emergency calls). Can retain own MD.
HEALTH SERVICES: Medication administration and/or supervision. Vitals monitored if required. Will accept and provide special assistance for residents who require oxygen. Assistance with dressing available (cost). Assistance with bathing available as needed (cost). Care plans done. Different levels of care available. Private Duty/Extra Care available. Lab service (visiting). Residents can purchase outside resources and use agency of their choice. Clinic area for medical visits. Will help locate higher level of care if needed.
ACCOMMODATION: *Choice of suites available*: various sizes of 1-bedroom suites. *In all suites*: locks, kitchenette, bar fridge, storage, window coverings, light fixtures, linens, fire alarm, smoke detector, sprinkler, call bell, air conditioning (central) and thermostats for heating & cooling. Private bathrooms with call bells, grab bars and showers with non-slip surfaces. In-suite cable TV provided by residence (residence charges extra). Can have own phone number if resident arranges with phone company (residence charges extra). Unfurnished suites, furnished suites available for short stays. *Restrictions on electrical appliances*: no toasters or toaster ovens. Suites can be shared (by couples only). Pets allowed (as per Pet Policy within the Residency Agreement).
DINING SERVICE: All meals included in fee and served in dining room daily. *Menu choices available:* Breakfast: 2, Lunch: 2, Dinner: 2. *Guest Meals*: Available. *Special Diets*: Low Salt, Diabetic and Others (as required). Tray service to room if ill (no charge as long as doctor orders). 2 snacks/day. Afternoon Tea. Party facilities. Private dining room available for catered events.
AMENITIES AND ACTIVITIES: Parking available (outdoor, for visitors and residents). *3 lounges with:* TV (1) and piano (1). *Residence has a:* library, visiting library, chapel, barber/beauty shop, visiting hairdresser and laundry room(s) (no cost). Resident can arrange newspaper delivery to individual suite. Mail delivered to private mailbox with key. *Recreation Facilities*: exercise room, craft room and card room. Posted schedule of activities. Internal newsletter for residents. *Recreational Programs*: exercise, shopping, theatre, parties, entertainment, art classes, day trips and other activities as requested by residents.
OTHER SERVICES: *Housekeeping*: daily and weekly. *Laundry*: dry cleaning (extra cost). Laundry facilities are available on each floor for resident use. Transportation for group social activities. 24-hour security. Utilities (included in fee).
RENTAL INFORMATION: Rates may vary. Extra cost for 2nd person sharing suite. Rent paid monthly. *Payment Options*: pre-authorized payments. Rent increases as per Provincial Tenancy Legislation, annual for resident with 3 months' notice given. Short-term respite and trial stays available.

Did you know?

There is a website to assist people going through a joint replacement experience that contains helpful tips and videos as well as an opportunity to gain support from others who have, and are going through, the same experience. Visit **www.myjointreplacement.ca/**

ST. HILDA'S RETIREMENT & ASSISTED LIVING / ST. HILDA'S TOWERS

2339 Dufferin Street at Eglinton Avenue, Toronto, ON M6E 4Z5
Tel: (416) 256-6536 • Fax: (416) 781-5058
Email: **wanttomovein@sthildastowers.com**
Website: **www.sthildastowers.com**
Contact: **Director of Marketing**
Capacity: **225 residents** • Subsidies: **none**
Price: **$1,795.00 - $3,695.00/month**

St. Hilda's has been the leader in not-for-profit, full service Retirement and Assisted Living for over 38 years. We take pride in our positive commitment to the care of seniors and in making an outstanding difference in the lives we touch. St. Hilda's offers a safe, secure and welcoming environment with private accommodation, 24-hour care, delicious and nutritious meals and a variety of on-site activities and amenities. Our notable Safe Harbour Program provides an immediate alternative for seniors who have been approved for long-term care, but must wait until the facility of their choice become available. Our Respite Care Program is an ideal option when family/primary caregivers need a break or when individuals need time to rest and recover after an illness or surgery. St. Hilda's is a friendly community of seniors living in 3 urban buildings near mid-town Toronto at Dufferin Street and Eglinton Avenue West, easily accessible by TTC.

RESIDENCE INFORMATION: 39 years in operation. *Near:* Dufferin Street and Eglinton Avenue. Decorated in 2012. Handrails in hallways. 15 floors, 4 elevators. Wheelchair accessible. *Funding Base:* Not-for-profit. *Average Waiting Period*: none. *Average Age*: 85. Can accommodate physically challenged people. Smoke-free residence. Alcohol allowed. *Procedures to leave the premises on a temporary basis...* Short-term: notify Medical Office or Main Reception. Overnight & Holidays: notify Medical Office. *Languages:* English, Italian, Portuguese & Spanish. Will accept Public Guardian and Trustee clients. Main doors of residence secured at all times. *Close to:* Public Transit, Shopping, Churches, Synagogues, Seniors' Centre, Library, Major Highway and Local Hospitals (University Health Network, St. Joseph's Health Centre, St. Michael's Hospital, Sunnybrook Health Science Centre & Humber River Regional Hospital). Member of ORCA & AASHA. Licensed under the Retirement Homes Act.
STAFFING: *Available Staff/Services*: Pharmacy, Social Work, Recreation Therapy, Occupational Therapy (CCAC), Physiotherapy (CCAC), Denturist, Dietitian, Companions, Podiatry (CCAC), Chaplaincy, Speech Pathology (CCAC), Audiology/Hearing Clinic and Spa Room (with accessible shower). *External services arranged by:* residence. 24-hour nursing and other staff. RNs, RPNs, HCAs and PSWs on staff. Visiting MD (on-call 24-hours). Can retain own MD. Staff members are bonded. Police Check or Vulnerable Person Screening is done for all new staff.
HEALTH SERVICES: Medication administration and/or supervision. Vitals monitored if required. Will accept and provide special assistance for residents who require oxygen, catheters and ostomies. Assistance with dressing available. Weekly assistance with bathing available. Care plans done. Different levels of care available. Private Duty/Extra Care available ($25.00 to $35.00/hour). Assisted Living Area (less than 2 week waiting period). Lab service (visiting, $12.00/visit). Residents can purchase outside resources and use agency of their choice. Clinic area for medical visits. Will help locate higher level of care if needed (on-site Social Worker will assist with applications for CCAC services or long-term care).
ACCOMMODATION: *Choice of suites available*: bachelor & 1-bedroom units with private bathroom. *In all suites*: locks, kitchenette, bar fridge, storage, window coverings, light fixtures, linens, stove, fire alarm, smoke detector, sprinkler, new state-of-the-art communication system/emergency call bell system, emergency response system with wearable pendant/bracelet, air conditioning (central & window units), thermostats for heating & cooling and closed circuit TV (able to see guests in lobby). Private bathrooms with grab bars, tubs and showers with non-slip surfaces and elevated toilet seats. In-suite cable TV provided by residence. Can have own phone number provided by residence. Unfurnished suites, furnished suites available for short stays. Small pets only allowed.

DINING SERVICE: All meals included in fee and served in dining room daily. *Guest Meals*: Available. *Special Diets*: Vegetarian, Low Salt, Diabetic, Kosher-Style and Pureed. Tray service to room if ill.
AMENITIES AND ACTIVITIES: Parking available (indoor & outdoor, for visitors: free and indoor for residents: $50.00/month). *5 lounges with:* TV (1), pianos (3) and tranquil spot (1). Guest suites available ($65.00/night). *Residence has a:* library, visiting library, chapel, barber/beauty shop, laundry room(s) ($1.25/washer load, $1.25/dryer load) and tuck/gift shop. Resident can arrange newspaper delivery to individual suite. Mail delivered to private mailbox with key. *Recreation Facilities*: pool table, billiards, greenhouse, craft room and exercise area. Posted schedule of activities. Internal newsletter for residents. *Recreational Programs*: exercise, shopping, theatre, parties, entertainment, art classes, pet visiting, day trips, gardening and Resident Council.
OTHER SERVICES: *Housekeeping*: daily and weekly. *Laundry*: linen & towel (included in fee); personal (weekly - $48.00/month). 24-hour security. Telephone (local calls only included in fee. Long Distance Plan $8.00/month). Cable TV & Utilities (included in fee).
RENTAL INFORMATION: Rates may vary. Bachelor with1 meal daily - $1,895.00/month; bachelor with 3 meals & 24-hour personal care - $2,495.00/month; bachelor with 3 meals & full assistance with daily living - $3,195.00/month; 1-bedroom with 3 meals & full assistance with daily living - $3,695.00/month. Extra cost for 2nd person sharing suite ($1,000.00/month). Rent paid monthly. *Payment Options*: cheques, post-dated cheques and direct deposit. Rent increases indexed to inflation, annual for resident with 3 months' notice given. Short-term respite and trial stays (both $99.00/day) available.

THE DUNFIELD

77 Dunfield Avenue, Toronto, ON M4S 2H3
Tel: (416) 481-8524 • Fax: (416) 481-3041
Email: **khen@thedunfield.com**
Website: **www.thedunfield.com**
Contact: **Karen Hen**
Capacity: **200 residents** • Subsidies: **none**
Price: **$4,000.00/month and up**

THE DUNFIELD is Toronto's newest and most exciting senior's retirement residence. Centred in the vibrant Yonge & Eglinton neighbourhood, The Dunfield's exceptional location offers restaurants, entertainment, shopping, and transportation at its doorstep. The Dunfield establishes a new standard in senior living with fully equipped kitchens including washers and dryers in our studios, 1-bedroom or 2-bedroom suites. The Dunfield appeals to seniors by offering services personalized to meet and exceed their every expectation. *Welcome to The Dunfield, Un-Retirement Residence!*

RESIDENCE INFORMATION: 5 years in operation. *On:* Yonge Street and Eglinton Avenue. Decorated in 2009. Handrails in hallways. 17 floors, 3 elevators. Wheelchair accessible. Central PA system. *Funding Base:* Corporate/for profit. *Owned by:* Shiplake Dunfield Ltd. 177 units. *Average Waiting Period*: 1 month. *Average Age*: 84. Can accommodate cognitively impaired & physically challenged people (as assessed by

Director of Care Services). Residents have a dress code (casual). Smoking allowed (in designated areas - this is a smoke free residence). Alcohol allowed. *Procedures to leave the premises on a temporary basis...* notify Resident Service Manager/Director of Care Services. *Languages:* English, French, Italian & Dutch - residents. Main doors of residence secured at night only. *Close to:* Public Transit, Shopping, Churches, Synagogues, Seniors' Centre, Library, Major Highway and Local Hospital (Sunnybrook Health Sciences Centre). *Predominant Cultural Group:* multicultural. Member of ORCA. Licensed under the Retirement Homes Act.

STAFFING: *Available Staff/Services*: Pharmacy, Recreation Therapy, Occupational Therapy, Visiting Dentist, Physiotherapy, Companions, Podiatry, Chaplaincy, Audiology/Hearing Clinic and Eye Clinic. *External services arranged by:* residence and/or family/resident. Staff trained *re*: visually, hearing and cognitively impaired. 24-hour nursing and other staff. RNs, RPNs, HCAs and PSWs on staff. Visiting MD (1 day/week). Can retain own MD. Police Check or Vulnerable Person Screening is done for all new staff.

HEALTH SERVICES: Medication administration and/or supervision. Vitals monitored if required. Will accept and provide special assistance for residents who require oxygen, catheters and ostomies. Assistance with dressing available (cost). Weekly assistance with bathing available. *Extra baths:* $65.00/month. Care plans done. Different levels of care available. Private Duty/Extra Care available. Assisted Living Area ($450.00 to $2,250.00/month). Separate unit for residents with dementia. Lab service (visiting, $30.00/visit). Residents can purchase outside resources and use agency of their choice. Clinic area for medical visits. Will help locate higher level of care if needed (in consultation with the Resident Care Manager).

ACCOMMODATION: *Choice of suites available*: studio (11), 1-bedroom (101), 2-bedroom (38) & Assisted (27) units. *In all suites*: locks, kitchenette, storage, window coverings, light fixtures, fire alarm, smoke detector, sprinkler, emergency response system with wearable pendant/bracelet, air conditioning (central) and thermostats for heating & cooling. Fridge, dishwasher, washer/dryer and stove in all 1-bedroom & 2-bedroom units. Private bathrooms with grab bars, tubs and showers with non-slip surfaces. In-suite cable TV provided by residence. Can have own phone number provided by residence. Unfurnished suites, furnished suites available for short stays. *Restrictions on electrical appliances*: must be approved by Environmental Services Manager. Suites can be shared (by couples only). Pets allowed (residents can only have 1 pet at a time).

DINING SERVICE: All meals included in fee and served in dining room daily. *Sittings per meal:* Breakfast: 1, Lunch: 1, Dinner: 1. *Guest Meals*: Available. *Special Diets*: Vegetarian, Low Salt and Diabetic. Kosher can be arranged. Tray service to room if ill (no charge for a maximum time of 4 days). Unlimited snacks available at any time. Party facilities. Meal options available; à la carte menu, 3 special items every day for lunch & dinner.

AMENITIES AND ACTIVITIES: Parking available (indoor, for visitors: free and residents: $150.00/month). *15 lounges with:* TVs (3) and pianos (2). Guest suites available ($179.00/night). *Residence has a:* library, visiting library, chapel, barber/beauty shop, visiting hairdresser and tuck/gift shop (open 4 hours/week). Resident can arrange newspaper delivery to main desk. Mail delivered to private mailbox with key. *Recreation Facilities*: pool table, billiards, shuffleboard, exercise room, greenhouse, craft room, card room, swimming pool, Nintendo Wii and computer room. Posted schedule of activities. Internal newsletter for residents. *Recreational Programs*: exercise, shopping, theatre, parties, entertainment, art classes, pet visiting and day trips.

Did you know?

The RCMP has created the *Seniors Guidebook to Safety and Security* containing valuable information on a host of topics including: elder abuse, fraud and scams and various safety topics. Visit **www.rcmp-grc.gc.ca/pubs/ccaps-spcca/seniors-aines-eng.htm** to download your copy.

OTHER SERVICES: *Housekeeping*: weekly (included in fee; daily quick clean extra charge, weekly included). *Laundry*: linen & towel (included in fee; suites have washers/dryers); personal (extra cost; only on Assisted Living & Memory Care) & dry cleaning (residents responsibility). Bed linens & towels are provided. Transportation for group social activities. 24-hour security. Nightly security checks. Telephone, Cable TV & Utilities (included in fee). Rebate of monthly service charge for Internet.
RENTAL INFORMATION: Rates may vary. Studio - $4,000.00/month & up; 1-bedroom - $5,200.00/month. & up; 2-bedroom - $8,500.00/month & up. Extra cost for 2nd person sharing suite ($800.00/month). Rent paid monthly. *Payment Options*: pre-authorized payments. Rent increases as per Provincial Tenancy Legislation, annual for resident with 3 months' notice given. Will help resident move into residence. Short-term respite and trial stays available (both $179.00/day).

THE GRENADIER RETIREMENT RESIDENCE

2100 Bloor Street West, Toronto, ON M6S 1M7
Tel: (416) 769-2885 • Fax: (416) 769-7238
Email: **mrkt.thegrenadier@diversicare.ca**
Website: **www.thegrenadier.com**
Contact: **Marketing Manager**
Capacity: **246 residents** • Subsidies: **none**
Price: **$2,940.00 - $4,975.00/month**

Enjoy the elegant, friendly lifestyle you've been searching for at The Grenadier! Located a short walk to High Park and Bloor West Village, we provide exceptional service, focusing on your comfort, wellness and security. Our spacious suites are offered in studio, 1-bedroom & 2-bedroom sizes. From Independent to Assisted Living, our 24-hour registered staff are available to meet all of your needs. Take advantage of our various amenities and recreational activities. Respite and short-term stays are available. **The Grenadier is managed by Diversicare, who is the proud recipient of the 2003, 2006, 2009 and 2012 Order of Excellence Award given by Excellence Canada.** This award was received for the exceptional quality and customer service we provide to our residents every day.

RESIDENCE INFORMATION: 27 years in operation. *Near:* Bloor Street and Keele Street. Decorated in 2011. Handrails in hallways. 7 floors, 6 elevators. Wheelchair accessible. Central PA system. *Funding Base:* Corporate/for profit. *Owned by:* Assante Management Services. *Managed by:* Diversicare Canada Management Services Co., Inc. 246 units. *Average Waiting Period*: varies. *Average Age*: 82. Can accommodate cognitively impaired & physically challenged people (assessment required). Smoking allowed (in suites or outdoors). Alcohol allowed. *Procedures to leave the premises on a temporary basis...*notify Reception Desk. *Languages:* English. Will accept Public Guardian and Trustee clients. Main doors of residence secured at all times. *Close to:* Public Transit, Shopping, Churches, Seniors' Centre, Library, Major Highway and Local Hospital (St. Joseph's Health Centre). *Predominant Cultural Group:* English-speaking. Licensed under the Retirement Homes Act.
STAFFING: *Available Staff/Services*: Pharmacy, Social Work (CCAC), Recreation Therapy, Occupational Therapy (CCAC), Physiotherapy, Denturist, Dietitian (CCAC), Companions, Chaplaincy, Speech Pathology (CCAC), Audiology/Hearing Clinic, Nurse Practitioner (on-site) and Foot Care (via RPN). *External services arranged by:* residence and/or family/resident. Staff trained *re*: visually, hearing and cognitively impaired. 24-hour nursing and other staff. RNs, RPNs, HCAs, PSWs and UCPs on staff. Can retain own MD. Police Check or Vulnerable Person Screening is done for all new staff (staff are required to have a clear criminal record check prior to hiring).
HEALTH SERVICES: Medication administration and/or supervision (when required). Vitals monitored if required. Will accept and provide special assistance for residents who require oxygen, catheters and ostomies. Assistance with dressing available (cost). Weekly assistance with bathing available. Care plans done. Different levels of care available. Private Duty/Extra Care available. Assisted Living Area is secured

to accommodate residents with dementia. Lab service (visiting). Residents can purchase outside resources and use agency of their choice. MD visits residents in their rooms/suites. Clinic area for medical visits. Will help locate higher level of care if needed (CCAC Care Coordinator visits weekly).
ACCOMMODATION: *Choice of suites available*: studio,1-bedroom & 2-bedroom suites. *In all suites*: locks, kitchenette, bar fridge, storage, window coverings, light fixtures, fire alarm, smoke detector, call bell, air conditioning (central air throughout home and window units in suites) and thermostats for heating. Private bathrooms with call bells, grab bars, tubs and showers with non-slip surfaces and elevated toilet seats. In-suite cable TV if resident arranges with cable company. Can have own phone number if resident arranges with phone company. Unfurnished suites, furnished suites available for short stays. *Restrictions on electrical appliances*: no stoves or hot plates. Suites can be shared, roommate picked by resident. Pets allowed (small dogs, cats, and birds; must be able to manage care of pet).
DINING SERVICE: Dinner included in fee and served in dining room daily. *Sittings per meal:* Breakfast: 2, Lunch: 1, Dinner: 2. *Menu choices available:* Breakfast: 2, Lunch: 2, Dinner: 2. *Guest Meals*: Breakfast $9.00, Lunch $11.50, Dinner $19.25. *Special Diets*: Vegetarian, Low Salt and Diabetic. Alternate options available at all meals. À la carte options available. Tray service to room if ill (no charge as long as doctor orders). 3 snacks/day. Party facilities. Full service dining.
AMENITIES AND ACTIVITIES: Parking available (indoor, for visitors: free and residents: $110.00/month). *2 lounges with:* TVs (2), pianos (2) and pool table (1). Guest suites available ($85.00/night). *Residence has a:* library, visiting library, chapel, laundry room(s) (no cost) and tuck/gift shop (open daily; 7:00 a.m. - 11:00 p.m.). Resident can arrange newspaper delivery to individual suite (extra cost). Mail delivered to private mailbox with key. *Recreation Facilities*: pool table, exercise room, craft room, card room, theatre room, horseshoe pitch, health club and various outdoor spaces. Posted schedule of activities. Internal newsletter for residents. *Recreational Programs*: exercise, shopping, theatre, parties, entertainment, art classes, pet visiting, day trips, Brain Gym® & More, crafts, gardening, book club and fitness programs.
OTHER SERVICES: *Housekeeping*: weekly (included in fee). *Laundry*: linen & towel (extra cost; included in Full Service Retirement option); personal (extra cost; included in Assisted Living option) & dry cleaning (extra cost). Transportation for group social activities. 24-hour security. Nightly security checks. Utilities (included in fee).
RENTAL INFORMATION: Rates may vary. Assisted Living - $4,760.00/month. Extra cost for 2nd person sharing suite ($660.00/month). Rent paid monthly. *Payment Options*: cheques, post-dated cheques and pre-authorized payments. Rent increases as per Provincial Tenancy Legislation, annual for resident with 3 months' notice given. Will help resident move into residence (extra cost). Short-term respite and trial stays available (both $100.00/day, daily rate is based on care and services required).

THE RUSSELL HILL RETIREMENT RESIDENCE

262 St. Clair Avenue West, Toronto, ON M4V 1R8
Tel: (416) 922-8005
Email: **info@therussellhill.com**
Website: **www.therussellhill.com**
Contact: **Executive Director or Marketing Manager**
Capacity: **90 residents** • Subsidies: **none**
Price: **$4,730.00 - $7,930.00/month**

Centrally located at Russell Hill Road & St. Clair Avenue. The Russell Hill Retirement Residence offers high service levels, beautiful suites, and is quality built by Great Gulf Homes. Some of the special services included are unlimited room service for meals not taken in our dining room, a Driver for appointments and social outings, medications administered, all laundry, superb music, outings and exercise programs. All of this in a smaller, distinctive residence. *Experience vibrant seniors living.*

RESIDENCE INFORMATION: 5 years in operation. *Near:* St. Clair Avenue and Russell Hill Road. Decorated in 2009. Handrails in hallways. 7 floors, 2 elevators. Wheelchair accessible. *Funding Base:* Corporate/for profit. *Managed by:* Signature Retirement Living. 69 units. *Average Waiting Period*: varies. *Average Age*: 86. Can sometimes accommodate cognitively impaired people. Residents have a dress code (residents must be dressed in common areas). Smoke-free residence. Alcohol allowed. *Procedures to leave the premises on a temporary basis...*sign out with Concierge. *Languages:* English. Main doors of residence secured at night only. *Close to:* Public Transit, Shopping, Churches, Seniors' Centre, Library and Local Hospitals (short drive to major downtown hospitals). Member of ORCA. Licensed under the Retirement Homes Act.

STAFFING: *Available Staff/Services*: Pharmacy, Social Work, Recreation Therapy, Occupational Therapy, Visiting Dentist, Physiotherapy, Podiatry, Speech Pathology, Chiropody, Audiology/Hearing Clinic and Foot Care Nurse. *External services arranged by:* family/resident. Staff trained *re*: visually, hearing and cognitively impaired. 24-hour nursing and other staff. RNs, RPNs and PSWs on staff. Visiting MD (24-hours/day). Can retain own MD. Police Check or Vulnerable Person Screening is done for all new staff.

HEALTH SERVICES: Medication administered if required (included in monthly rates). Vitals monitored if required. Assistance with dressing available (cost). Assistance with bathing available as needed (cost). Care plans done. Different levels of care available. Private Duty/Extra Care available. Assisted Living Area. Lab service (visiting). Residents can purchase outside resources and use agency of their choice. Clinic area for medical visits. Will help locate higher level of care if needed (our Director of Care & Wellness will assist with this process).

ACCOMMODATION: *Choice of suites available*: 1-bedroom, 1-bedroom + den & 2-bedroom units. *In all suites*: locks, kitchenette, fridges are almost full-size (much larger than a bar fridge), microwave, storage, window coverings, light fixtures, linens, fire alarm, smoke detector, sprinkler, call bell, emergency response system with wearable pendant/bracelet (included in monthly rates), air conditioning (central) and thermostats for heating & cooling. Private bathrooms with call bells, grab bars and showers. In-suite cable TV provided by residence. Can have own phone number provided by residence. Unfurnished suites, furnished suites available for short stays. *Restrictions on electrical appliances*: no open elements. Pets allowed (with approval of Executive Director).

DINING SERVICE: All meals included in fee and served in dining room daily. *Guest Meals*: Available. *Special Diets*: Low Salt and Diabetic. Selection of Gluten Free products available. Open pantry. Room Service (no charge or restrictions). Snacks, fresh fruit, coffee, tea and fruit juice, available all day. Party facilities.

AMENITIES AND ACTIVITIES: Parking available (indoor & outdoor, for visitors: free and indoor for residents: $85.00/month). *3 lounges with:* TV (1), piano (1) and fireplace (1). Guest suites available. *Residence has a:* library, barber/beauty shop and laundry room(s) (no cost). Banking services on premises. Residence provides newspaper delivery to individual suite. Mail delivered to private mailbox (no key). *Recreation Facilities*: exercise room and card room. Posted schedule of activities. Internal newsletter for residents. *Recreational Programs*: exercise, shopping, theatre, parties, entertainment, art classes, day trips, Stratford & Shaw Festival outings and outdoor barbecues.

OTHER SERVICES: *Housekeeping*: daily and weekly (included in fee). *Laundry*: linen, towel & personal (included in fee); dry cleaning (extra cost). Resident laundry room on each floor. Transportation to medical appointments (Driver available first come first serve) and for group social activities. 24-hour security. Nightly security checks. Telephone (included in fee; long distance is extra). Cable TV (basic cable) & Utilities (included in fee). Internet (included; one-time cost for modem).

RENTAL INFORMATION: Rates may vary - prices are subject to change. Extra cost for 2nd person sharing suite ($800.00/month). Rent paid monthly. *Payment Options*: cheques, post-dated cheques, direct deposit and pre-authorized payments. Rent increases as per Provincial Tenancy Legislation, annual for resident with 3 months' notice given. Short-term respite and trial stays available.

WESTON GARDENS RETIREMENT RESIDENCE

303 Queens Drive, Toronto, ON M6L 3C1
Tel: (416) 241-1113 • Fax: (416) 241-1801
Email: **myhome@westongardens.ca or info@westongardens.ca**
Website: **www.westongardens.ca**
Contact: **Heidi Naroui, Director of Community Relations**
Capacity: **152 residents** • Subsidies: **none**
Price: **$1,999.00/month and up**

Keep living your life, your way, at Weston Gardens. You'll find the range of services, amenities and choices that fit your lifestyle and requirements – all in a warm and safe environment. Weston Gardens is nestled on the banks of Black Creek. We offer the best of both worlds: a central city location – conveniently close to shopping, places of worship, medical services, a library, highways, public transit and more – and a picturesque natural setting with spectacular grounds. Everything here is designed to enable you to maintain your independence and privacy, enjoy a full social life, and participate in the activities that you love. With retirement living at Weston Gardens, you change your address, not your life.

RESIDENCE INFORMATION: 39 years in operation. *Near:* Jane Street and Lawrence Avenue. Decorated in 2010. Handrails in hallways. 5 floors, 2 elevators. Wheelchair accessible. Central PA system. *Funding Base:* Corporate/for profit. 152 units. *Average Waiting Period*: varies. *Average Age*: 82. Can accommodate cognitively impaired people (dementia). Can accommodate physically challenged people (must be able to self-transfer). Residents have a dress code (appropriate attire in the common areas). Smoking allowed (designated area - exterior of building). Alcohol allowed. *Procedures to leave the premises on a temporary basis...*sign out & alert Front Desk. *Languages:* English, Polish, Italian, German, Spanish, Filipino, French, Turkish & Farsi. Will accept Public Guardian and Trustee clients. Main doors of residence secured at night only. *Close to:* Public Transit, Shopping, Churches, Synagogues, Seniors' Centre, Library, Major Highway and Local Hospital (Humber River Regional Hospital - Church Street Site). Member of ORCA. Licensed under the Retirement Homes Act.

STAFFING: *Available Staff/Services*: Pharmacy, Social Work (CCAC), Recreation Therapy, Occupational Therapy (CCAC), Visiting Dentist, Physiotherapy (CCAC), Denturist, Podiatry, Chaplaincy, Speech Pathology (CCAC), Chiropody and Audiology/Hearing Clinic. *External services arranged by:* residence and/or family/resident. Staff trained *re*: visually, hearing and cognitively impaired. 24-hour nursing staff. RPNs, PSWs and UCPs on staff. Visiting MD (twice/week). Can retain own MD. Staff members are bonded. Police Check or Vulnerable Person Screening is done for all new staff.

HEALTH SERVICES: Medication administration (at an additional fee) and/or supervision. Vitals monitored if required. Will accept (but not provide special assistance for) residents who require catheters and ostomies. Will accept and provide special assistance for residents who require oxygen. Assistance with dressing available (cost). Weekly assistance with bathing available (cost). Care plans done. Different levels of care available. Optional services available. Private Duty/Extra Care available. Lab service (visiting). Residents can purchase outside resources and use agency of their choice. MD visits residents in their rooms/suites. Clinic area for medical visits. Will help locate higher level of care if needed (family conference arranged to assist family).

ACCOMMODATION: *Choice of suites available*: junior, standard and deluxe studios, 1-bedroom & 2-bedroom suite. *In all suites*: locks, kitchenette, bar fridge, window coverings, light fixtures, fire alarm, smoke detector, sprinkler, call bell, emergency response system with wearable pendant/bracelet, air conditioning (central) and thermostats for heating & cooling. Kitchenettes available in many suites. Private bathrooms with call bells and showers. In-suite cable TV if resident arranges with cable company (residence charges extra). Can have own phone number if resident arranges with phone company (residence charges extra). Unfurnished suites, furnished suites available for short stays. *Restrictions on*

electrical appliances: no stoves or burner elements. Suites can be shared (by couples only), roommate picked by resident. Pets allowed (with assessment - as per Pet Policy within Tenancy Agreement).
DINING SERVICE: All meals included in fee and served in dining room daily. *Sittings per meal:* Breakfast: 1, Lunch: 2, Dinner: 2. *Menu choices available:* Breakfast: 2, Lunch: 2, Dinner: 2. *Guest Meals*: Available. *Special Diets*: Vegetarian, Low Salt, Diabetic and Soft/Puree. Tray service to room if ill (no charge for a maximum time of 3 days). 3 snacks/day and unlimited snacks available at any time. Party facilities. Barbeques in summer, outdoor patio overlooking fountain and gardens.
AMENITIES AND ACTIVITIES: Parking available (outdoor, for visitors and residents). *14 lounges with:* TV (1) and piano (1). Guest suites available. *Residence has a:* library, chapel, barber/beauty shop, visiting hairdresser and laundry room(s) (no cost). Mail delivered to private mailbox with key. *Recreation Facilities*: pool table, billiards, shuffleboard, exercise room, craft room and card room. Posted schedule of activities. Internal newsletter for residents. *Recreational Programs*: exercise, shopping, theatre, parties, entertainment, art classes, pet visiting and day trips.
OTHER SERVICES: *Housekeeping*: weekly (included in fee). *Laundry*: linen & towel (extra cost; weekly); personal (extra cost). Transportation for group social activities. 24-hour security. Nightly security checks. Utilities (included in fee).
RENTAL INFORMATION: Rates vary depending on suite type. Extra cost for 2nd person sharing suite ($500.00/month). Rent paid monthly. *Payment Options*: pre-authorized payments. Rent increases as per Provincial Tenancy Legislation, annual for resident with 3 months' notice given. Will help resident move into residence. Short-term respite and trial stays available.

♦ TORONTO (ETOBICOKE) ♦

DELMANOR PRINCE EDWARD

4180 Dundas Street West, Toronto, ON M8X 1X8
Tel: (416) 233-0725
Email: **nlewis@delmanor.com or jshuster@delmanor.com**
Website: **www.delmanor.com**
Contact: **Nikki Lewis or Julie Shuster**
Capacity: **160 residents**
Subsidies: **none**

OPENING LATE SPRING 2014! Located in the prestigious Kingsway neighbourhood in Etobicoke, the newest Tridel-inspired retirement community will back directly onto the spectacular Humber River. Extensive amenities to include a fitness centre, movie theatre, full service spa and salon, bar, café, library, gourmet test kitchen and a fully landscaped rooftop terrace complete with extensive seating areas, a putting green and shuffleboard court. Full Service Independent and Assisted Living services, along with state-of-the art building security and emergency response systems. Spacious and well-appointed studio, 1-bedroom & 2-bedroom suites - most with balconies or terraces. Breathtaking, panoramic views of the Humber River or downtown Toronto. Luxury suite features to include granite countertops, full-size stainless steel fridge, microwave oven and front loading washer and dryer for your added convenience.

RESIDENCE INFORMATION: New residence. *Near:* Dundas Street and Prince Edward Drive. Decorated in 2014. Handrails in hallways. 8 floors, 2 elevators. Wheelchair accessible. Central PA system. *Funding Base:* Corporate/for profit. *Owned by:* Tridel Inc. *Managed by:* Delmanor Seniors Communities Inc. 139 units. *Average Waiting Period*: none. Can accommodate cognitively impaired people (mild dementia, Assisted Living Services). Can accommodate physically challenged people. Residents have a dress code (no shorts at dinner service). Smoke-free residence. Alcohol allowed. *Procedures to leave the premises*

on a temporary basis...notify Concierge. *Languages:* English. Main doors of residence secured at night only. *Close to:* Public Transit, Shopping, Churches, Seniors' Centre, Library, Major Highway and Local Hospital (St. Joseph's Health Centre).

STAFFING: *Available Staff/Services*: Pharmacy, Recreation Therapy, Occupational Therapy, Visiting Dentist, Physiotherapy, Podiatry, Chiropody and Massage Therapist (upon opening). *External services arranged by:* residence and/or family/resident. Staff trained *re*: visually, hearing and cognitively impaired. 24-hour nursing and other staff. RNs, RPNs and PSWs on staff. Visiting MD (1 day/week). Can retain own MD. Police Check or Vulnerable Person Screening is done for all new staff. Additional information upon community opening.

HEALTH SERVICES: Medication administered if required. Vitals monitored if required. Will accept and provide special assistance for residents who require oxygen. Assistance with dressing available (cost). Weekly assistance with bathing available (cost). Care plans done. Different levels of care available. Assisted Living Area. Lab service (visiting). Residents can purchase outside resources and use agency of their choice. Clinic area for medical visits. Will help locate higher level of care if needed (CCAC). Additional information upon community opening.

ACCOMMODATION: *Choice of suites available*: studio, 1-bedroom & 2-bedroom suites. Independent and Assisted Living Suites. *In all suites*: locks, kitchenette, full-size stainless steel fridge, microwave, in-suite washer & dryer, window coverings, light fixtures, fire alarm, smoke detector, sprinkler, emergency response system with wearable pendant/bracelet, air conditioning (central) and thermostats for heating & cooling. Private bathrooms with grab bars, showers with non-slip surfaces and elevated toilet seats. In-suite cable TV provided by residence. Can have own phone extension number provided by residence. Unfurnished suites, furnished suites available for short stays. *Restrictions on electrical appliances*: no hot plates. Suites can be shared (by couples only), roommate picked by resident. Small pets allowed (20 lbs. or less).

DINING SERVICE: Lunch and Dinner included in fee and served in dining room daily. *Sittings per meal:* Lunch: 2, Dinner: 2. *Menu choices available:* Lunch: 2, Dinner: 2. *Guest Meals*: Available. *Special Diets*: Vegetarian, Low Salt, Diabetic, Heart Healthy Options and Gluten Free. Tray service to room if ill (no charge as long as doctor orders). Party facilities. Private dining room to host family and friends.

AMENITIES AND ACTIVITIES: Parking available (indoor & outdoor, for visitors and indoor for residents). Guest suites available. *Residence has a:* library, chapel, barber/beauty shop, visiting hairdresser, laundry room(s) (no cost) and tuck/gift shop. Resident can arrange newspaper delivery to individual suite. Mail delivered to private mailbox with key. *Recreation Facilities*: pool table, billiards, shuffleboard, exercise room, greenhouse, craft room, card room, movie theatre, rooftop terrace and putting green. Posted schedule of activities. Internal newsletter for residents. *Recreational Programs*: exercise, shopping, theatre, parties, entertainment, art classes, day trips and Living***Well*** personal coach.

OTHER SERVICES: *Housekeeping*: weekly (included in fee; daily cleaning also available at an extra cost). *Laundry*: linen & towel (included in fee); personal & dry cleaning (extra cost). In-suite washer and dryer in all units. Transportation for group social activities. 24-hour security. Nightly security checks. Telephone, Cable TV & Utilities (included in fee).

RENTAL INFORMATION: Extra cost for 2nd person sharing suite. Rent paid monthly. *Payment Options*: post-dated cheques and pre-authorized payments. Rent increases as per Provincial Tenancy Legislation, annual for resident with 3 months' notice given. Will help resident move into residence. Short-term respite and trial stays available.

Moving Day Tip

On 'Moving Day' ensure you have a small hand bag with items you might need throughout the day including medications, toiletries and important papers. Arrange with a friend or family member to accompany you and help you settle into your new home.

HEARTHSTONE BY THE BAY

3 Marine Parade Drive, Toronto, ON M8V 3Z5
Tel: (416) 259-4466 • Fax: (416) 259-4077
Email: **info@hearthstonebythebay.com**
Website: **www.HearthstoneByTheBay.com**
Contact: **Cindy Flanagan**
Capacity: **145 units**
Subsidies: **none**

The Hearthstone Difference! Owning your own home has always made good economic sense and it still does in retirement. At Hearthstone, you will own a beautiful condominium with a full kitchen and for a minimal monthly fee have access to health and wellness services, social programs, a full service dining room and so much more. Imagine surrounding yourself with gourmet dining, house cleaning, state-of-the-art fitness and wellness facilities. Plus, a full social calendar organized by your on-site Recreation Director who is always available to keep you thoroughly entertained. Including a gourmet kitchen, each suite comes with ensuite laundry, balcony/terrace, parking space, locker and 24-hour emergency response. Meet with friends, entertain family and stroll along the waterfront trails. Invest in your future. Come for a personal visit today and see what better retirement living looks like at Hearthstone by the Bay.

RESIDENCE INFORMATION: *Near:* Parklawn Road and Lake Shore Boulevard. Handrails in hallways. 21 floors, 2 elevators. Wheelchair accessible. Central PA system. *Managed by:* Hearthstone Communities Ltd. *Average Waiting Period*: varies. *Average Age*: 78. Can accommodate physically challenged people (all suites are accessible). Smoke-free residence. Alcohol allowed. *Languages:* English. Main doors of residence secured at all times. *Close to:* Public Transit, Shopping, Churches, Seniors' Centre, Library, Major Highway and Local Hospital.
STAFFING: *Available Staff/Services*: Social Work, Recreation Therapy, Occupational Therapy, Physiotherapy, Denturist, Dietitian, Companions, Podiatry, Speech Pathology, Chiropody and Audiology/Hearing Clinic. *External services arranged by:* residence and/or family/resident. Staff trained *re*: visually, hearing and cognitively impaired. 24-hour nursing and other staff. RNs, RPNs and PSWs on staff. Visiting MD (visitations to be determined). Can retain own MD.
HEALTH SERVICES: Medication administration and/or supervision. Vitals monitored if required. Will accept and provide special assistance for residents who require oxygen, catheters, ostomies and feeding tubes. Assistance with dressing available (cost). Weekly assistance with bathing available (cost). Care plans done. Different levels of care available. Private Duty/Extra Care available. Lab service (visiting). Residents can purchase outside resources and use agency of their choice. Clinic area for medical visits. Will help locate higher level of care if needed.
ACCOMMODATION: *Choice of suites available*: condominium suites ranging from 1-bedroom to 2-bedroom + den. *In all suites*: locks, patio/balcony, storage, fire alarm, smoke detector, sprinkler, emergency response system with wearable pendant/bracelet, air conditioning (central), thermostats for heating & cooling, separately metered hydro, full kitchen with 4 appliances (fridge, stove, dishwasher & microwave), washer/dryer, sunroom, balcony or terrace and security system. Private bathrooms with call bells. In-suite cable TV if resident arranges with cable company (residence charges extra). Can have own phone number if resident arranges with phone company. Unfurnished suites, furnished suites available for short stays. Pets allowed.
DINING SERVICE: The Lakeview Dining Room (restaurant) and outdoor Terrace. *Guest Meals*: Available. *Special Diets*: Vegetarian, Low Salt and Diabetic. Tray service to room if ill. Party facilities.
AMENITIES AND ACTIVITIES: Parking available (indoor, for visitors and residents). 3 lounges. *Residence has a:* library, chapel, barber/beauty shop, visiting hairdresser and tuck/gift shop. Mail delivered to private mailbox with key. *Recreation Facilities*: pool table, billiards, exercise room, greenhouse, card room, swimming pool, Humber Arms Pub, Lakeview Dining Room, outdoor terrace, cinema and wellness centre.

Posted schedule of activities. Internal newsletter for residents. *Recreational Programs*: exercise, shopping, theatre, parties, entertainment, art classes and day trips.
OTHER SERVICES: *Housekeeping*: included in Basic Service Package. *Laundry*: personal (extra cost). Private laundry in each condominium. Transportation to medical appointments (depends on service package) and for group social activities (included/extra - dependent on activity). 24-hour security. Nightly security checks. Telephone & Cable TV (extra cost). Utilities (extra cost for hydro; water, heat/cooling system included). 24-hour emergency response. Building insurance & maintenance of common elements (included in fee).
RENTAL INFORMATION: Please speak with sales representative for more details. Extra cost for 2nd person sharing suite ($170.00/month; fees vary as per service package). Option to purchase unit available (full condominium ownership). Monthly club service fees range. Condominium fees based on square footage. Mortgage payments would be additional. Hearthstone provides notice for fee increases. Will help resident move into residence (extra cost). Trial stays available (see sales representative for details).

REVERA - CENTENNIAL PARK PLACE

25 Centennial Park Road, Toronto, ON M9C 5H1
Tel: (855) 573-8372 • Toll Free: (855) 573-8372
Email: **centennial@reveraliving.com**
Website: **www.reveraliving.com/centennial**
Contact: **Executive Director or Lifestyle Consultant**
Capacity: **47 residents** • Subsidies: **none**
Price: **$2,224.00/month and up**

Keep living your life, your way, at Centennial Park Place. You'll find the range of services, amenities and choices that fit your lifestyle and requirements – in a warm and safe environment. Nestled right in the heart of Centennial Park in Etobicoke, our charming single-storey residence is conveniently located close to shopping, churches, community centres and services, medical services, an art gallery, public transportation, and more. Everything here is designed to enable you to maintain your independence and privacy, enjoy a full social life, and participate in the activities that you love. Our caring and friendly staff, along with appealing accommodations, support who you are and how you want to live in freedom and comfort. With retirement living at Centennial Park Place, you change your address, not your life. *Centennial Park Place is part of the Revera family, one of North America's leading and most trusted providers of seniors' accommodation, care and services since 1961.*

RESIDENCE INFORMATION: 33 years in operation. *Near:* Renforth Drive and Rathburn Road. Decorated in 2012. Handrails in hallways. 1 floor, no elevators. Wheelchair accessible. *Funding Base:* Corporate/for profit. *Owned and managed by:* Revera Inc. 46 units. *Average Waiting Period*: varies. *Average Age*: 80. Can accommodate cognitively impaired people (mild dementia). Can accommodate physically challenged people (wheelchair bound). Residents have a dress code (casual). Smoking allowed (outside in the front, away from the entrance). Alcohol allowed. *Procedures to leave the premises on a temporary basis...*Short-term: inform staff. Overnight & Holidays: notify Management. *Languages:* English, Polish, Croatian, German, Hindi, Punjabi, Ukrainian, French & Slovak. Will accept Public Guardian and Trustee clients. Main doors of residence secured at all times. *Close to:* Public Transit, Shopping, Churches, Seniors' Centre, Library, Major Highway and Local Hospitals (Trillium Health Partners, Humber River Regional Hospital, William Osler Health Centre - Etobicoke General Site & St. Joseph's Health Centre). Member of ORCA. Licensed under the Retirement Homes Act.
STAFFING: *Available Staff/Services*: Pharmacy, Social Work (CCAC), Recreation Therapy, Occupational Therapy (CCAC), Visiting Dentist, Physiotherapy (CCAC), Denturist, Podiatry, Chaplaincy, Speech Pathology (CCAC), Audiology/Hearing Clinic and Visiting Lab Technicians. *External services arranged by:* residence and/or family/resident. Staff trained *re*: visually, hearing and cognitively impaired. 24-hour nursing and

other staff. RNs, RPNs, HCAs and PSWs on staff. Visiting MD (weekly visits & on call 24/7). Can retain own MD. Police Check or Vulnerable Person Screening is done for all new staff.
HEALTH SERVICES: Medication administration and/or supervision. Vitals monitored if required. Will accept and provide special assistance for residents who require oxygen, catheters and ostomies. Assistance with dressing available (cost). Weekly assistance with bathing available (cost). Care plans done. Different levels of care available. Assisted Living Area. Lab service (visiting). Residents can purchase outside resources and use agency of their choice. MD visits residents in their rooms/suites. Clinic area for medical visits. Will help locate higher level of care if needed (family conference arranged to determine future care needs).
ACCOMMODATION: *Choice of suites available*: studio suites (45) & semi-private (1) units. *In all suites*: locks, storage, window coverings, light fixtures, linens, smoke detector, sprinkler, emergency call bell system, air conditioning (central), thermostats for heating & cooling and wall to wall coverings. Private bathrooms with call bells, grab bars, tubs and showers with non-slip surfaces. In-suite cable TV provided by residence (residence charges extra). Can have own phone number if resident arranges with phone company. Furnished & unfurnished suites available. *Restrictions on electrical appliances*: no stoves, microwaves or heaters. Suites can be shared, roommate picked by residence staff. Pets allowed (cats, birds and small dogs).
DINING SERVICE: All meals included in fee and served in dining room daily. *Sittings per meal:* Breakfast: 1, Lunch: 1, Dinner: 1. *Menu choices available:* Breakfast: 2, Lunch: 2, Dinner: 2. *Guest Meals*: Available. *Special Diets*: Vegetarian, Low Salt, Diabetic and Textured. Tray service to room if ill (no charge for a maximum time of 3 days). 3 snacks/day. All meals are prepared on-site by trained cooks.
AMENITIES AND ACTIVITIES: Parking available (outdoor, for visitors and residents). *1 lounge with:* TV (1) and piano (1). Guest suites available. *Residence has a:* visiting library, barber/beauty shop, visiting hairdresser, tuck/gift shop (open Monday, Wednesday & Friday). Residence provides newspaper delivery to individual suite (extra cost). Mail delivered to resident. *Recreation Facilities*: shuffleboard, exercise room, craft room, card room and courtyard. Posted schedule of activities. Internal newsletter for residents. *Recreational Programs*: exercise, shopping, theatre, parties, entertainment, art classes, pet visiting, day trips and theme evenings.
OTHER SERVICES: *Housekeeping*: daily and weekly (included in fee). *Laundry*: linen & towel (included in fee); dry cleaning (extra cost). Transportation to medical appointments (extra cost; Transhelp, outside agency) and for group social activities. 24-hour security. Telephone & Cable TV (extra cost). Utilities (included in fee).
RENTAL INFORMATION: Rates may vary. Extra cost for 2nd person sharing suite. Rent paid monthly. *Payment Options*: pre-authorized payments. Rent increases as per Provincial Tenancy Legislation, annual for resident with 3 months' notice given. Will help resident move into residence (extra cost). Short-term respite and trial stays subject to availability.

REVERA - KINGSWAY

4251 Dundas Street West, Toronto, ON M8X 2Z5
Tel: (855) 573-8372 • Toll Free: (855) 573-8372
Email: **kingsway@reveraliving.com**
Website: **www.reveraliving.com/kingsway**
Contact: **Executive Director or Lifestyle Consultant**
Capacity: **107 units** • Subsidies: **none**
Price: **$2,999.00/month and up**

Keep living your life, your way, at Kingsway. Here, you'll find the range of services, amenities and choices that fit your lifestyle and requirements – all in a warm and safe environment, and the most established retirement residence in the community. With retirement living at Kingsway, you change your address, not your life. We're conveniently located near Royal York Road, with easy access to public transit, shopping, entertainment, parks, and churches. Everything here is designed to enable you to maintain your independence

and privacy, enjoy a full social life, and participate in the activities that you love. Our caring and friendly staff, appealing accommodations and our refined style and luxury support who you are and how you want to live. Explore what we have to offer, to keep you living in freedom and comfort. *Kingsway is part of the Revera family, one of North America's leading and most trusted providers of seniors' accommodation, care and services since 1961.*

RESIDENCE INFORMATION: 15 years in operation. *On:* Royal York Road and Dundas Street. Decorated in 2010. Handrails in hallways. 6 floors, 2 elevators. Wheelchair accessible. Central PA system. *Funding Base:* Corporate/for profit. *Owned and managed by:* Revera Inc. *Average Waiting Period*: varies. *Average Age*: 84. Can accommodate cognitively impaired people (secured floor for residents with dementia). Can accommodate physically challenged people. Residents have a dress code (smart, casual dress). Smoke-free residence. Alcohol allowed. *Procedures to leave the premises on a temporary basis...*Short-term: inform Reception. Overnight & Holidays: inform Nursing and Reception. *Languages:* English. Will accept Public Guardian and Trustee clients. Main doors of residence secured at night only. *Close to:* Public Transit, Shopping, Churches, Seniors' Centre, Library, Major Highway and Local Hospital (St Joseph's Heath Centre). Member of ORCA. Licensed under the Retirement Homes Act.
STAFFING: *Available Staff/Services*: Pharmacy, Social Work (CCAC), Recreation Therapy, Occupational Therapy (CCAC), Visiting Dentist, Physiotherapy (CCAC), Denturist, Dietitian, Companions, Podiatry, Chaplaincy, Speech Pathology (CCAC), Chiropody and Audiology/Hearing Clinic. *External services arranged by:* family/resident. Staff trained *re*: visually, hearing and cognitively impaired. 24-hour nursing and other staff. RPNs and PSWs on staff. Visiting MD (weekly visits & on call 24/7). Can retain own MD. Staff members are bonded. Police Check or Vulnerable Person Screening is done for all new staff.
HEALTH SERVICES: Medication administration and/or supervision. Vitals monitored if required. Will accept and provide special assistance for residents who require oxygen, catheters and ostomies. Assistance with dressing available (cost). Assistance with bathing available as needed (cost). Care plans done. Different levels of care available. Private Duty/Extra Care available. Assisted Living Area (less than 2 week waiting period). Separate unit for residents with dementia. Lab service (visiting). Residents can purchase outside resources and use agency of their choice. MD visits residents in their rooms/suites. Clinic area for medical visits. Will help locate higher level of care if needed (family conference arranged to determine future care needs).
ACCOMMODATION: *Choice of suites available*: studio, 1-bedroom & 2-bedroom suites. *In all suites*: locks, kitchenette, bar fridge, storage, window coverings, light fixtures, fire alarm, smoke detector, sprinkler, call bell, emergency response system with wearable pendant/bracelet, air conditioning (central) and thermostats for heating & cooling. Private bathrooms with call bells, grab bars, tubs or walk-in showers with non-slip surfaces. In-suite cable TV provided by residence (residence charges extra). Can have own phone number if resident arranges with phone company (residence charges extra). Unfurnished suites, furnished suites available for short stays. *Restrictions on electrical appliances*: microwaves and auto shut-off kettles permitted. Suites can be shared (by couples or family members only). Pets allowed (cats, birds and small dogs).
DINING SERVICE: All meals included in fee and served in dining room daily. *Sittings per meal:* Breakfast: 1, Lunch: 2, Dinner: 2. *Menu choices available:* Breakfast: 3, Lunch: 2, Dinner: 2. *Guest Meals*: Available. *Special Diets*: Vegetarian, Low Salt and Diabetic. Can assist with many types of diets. Tray service to room if ill (no charge for a maximum time of 4 days). 2 snacks/day. Party facilities. Private dining room or The Kingsway Lounge is available for private parties.
AMENITIES AND ACTIVITIES: Parking available (indoor & outdoor, for visitors and residents). *3 lounges with:* TV (1), piano (1) and double-sided fireplaces (2). Guest suites available. *Residence has a:* library, visiting library, chapel, barber/beauty shop, visiting hairdresser, laundry room(s) (no cost), tuck/gift shop (open every Friday; 1:00 p.m. - 1:30 p.m.). Banking services on premises (twice/month). Resident can arrange newspaper delivery to individual suite (extra cost). Mail delivered to private mailbox with key. *Recreation Facilities*: pool table, billiards, exercise room, craft room, card room, unique café, fireside

library & penthouse bar/theatre and residence bus. Posted schedule of activities. Internal newsletter for residents. *Recreational Programs*: exercise, shopping, theatre, parties, entertainment, art classes, pet visiting and day trips by bus to casino, shopping, theatre, winery tours, etc.
OTHER SERVICES: *Housekeeping*: daily and weekly (included in fee). *Laundry*: linen & towel (included in fee); personal (extra cost) & dry cleaning (extra cost; pick-up and delivery service available). Transportation for group social activities. 24-hour security. Nightly security checks. Telephone & Cable TV (extra cost). Utilities (included in fee). Optional services available.
RENTAL INFORMATION: Rates may vary. Extra cost for 2nd person sharing suite ($500.00/month). Rent paid monthly. *Payment Options*: cheques, post-dated cheques, direct deposit and pre-authorized payments. Rent increases as per Provincial Tenancy Legislation, annual for resident with 3 months' notice given. Will help resident move into residence.

TAPESTRY AT VILLAGE GATE WEST

15 Summerland Terrace, Toronto, ON M9A OB5
Tel: (416) 777-2911 • Fax: (416) 777-2888
Email: **VGW@discovertapestry.com**
Website: **www.discovertapestry.com**
Contact: **Tim Smale**
Capacity: **200 residents** • Subsidies: **none**
Price: **$3,170.00 - $6,200.00/month**

Tapestry at Village Gate West features full kitchens with fridge, stove and dishwashers. The well-appointed suites range from 344 – 1,039 sq. ft. offering a choice of floor plans from studios to 2-bedrooms with den - most of which offer balconies or terraces. 5-star restaurant dining for breakfast, lunch & dinner is offered in either Montgomery's or The Black Alder Pub. Fabulous amenities including a high definition golf simulator. Outstanding staff. Town car transportation services. Fun and exciting lifestyle.

RESIDENCE INFORMATION: 6 years in operation. *On:* Dundas Street near Kipling Avenue. Handrails in hallways. 11 floors, 3 elevators. Wheelchair accessible. Central PA system. *Funding Base:* Corporate/for profit. *Owned by:* Concert Properties. *Managed by:* Leisure Care Retirement Communities. 168 units. *Average Waiting Period*: none. *Average Age*: 80. Can accommodate physically challenged people with restrictions (1-person transfers only). Smoke-free residence. Alcohol allowed. *Procedures to leave the premises on a temporary basis*...inform the Front Desk. *Languages:* English. Main doors of residence secured at night only. *Close to:* Public Transit, Shopping, Churches, Synagogues, Seniors' Centre, Library, Major Highway and Local Hospitals (St. Joseph's Health Centre & Trillium Health Partners). Licensed under the Retirement Homes Act.
STAFFING: *Available Staff/Services*: Pharmacy, Physiotherapy, Podiatry and Audiology/Hearing Clinic. *External services arranged by:* residence and/or family/resident. Staff trained *re*: visually and hearing impaired. 24-hour staff. RPNs and PSWs on staff. Visiting MD (weekly). Can retain own MD. Police Check or Vulnerable Person Screening is done for all new staff.
HEALTH SERVICES: Medication administered if required (we provide medication assistance). Vitals monitored if required. Assistance with dressing available (cost). Assistance with bathing available as needed (cost). Care plans done. Different levels of care available. Assisted Living Area. Residents can purchase outside resources and use agency of their choice. MD visits residents in their rooms/suites. Clinic area for medical visits. Will help locate higher level of care if needed (referral services available).
ACCOMMODATION: *Choice of suites available*: studio, 1-bedroom, 1-bedroom + den, 2-bedroom & 2-bedroom + den; all suites with full kitchens with refrigerators, stoves and dishwashers. *In all suites*: window coverings, light fixtures, fire alarm, smoke detector, sprinkler, call bell, emergency response system with wearable pendant/bracelet, air conditioning (central) and thermostats for heating & cooling. Private bathrooms with call bells, showers with non-slip surfaces and elevated toilet seats. In-suite cable

TV provided by residence. Unfurnished suites, furnished suites available for short stays. Pets allowed (cats and dogs only).
DINING SERVICE: Residents receive a meal credit of $400.00 or $500.00/month which may be used in either the restaurant or pub. There are no seatings as menus are restaurant-style with countless choices. *Menu choices available:* Breakfast: 15, Lunch: 30, Dinner: 35. *Guest Meals*: Available. *Special Diets*: Vegetarian, Low Salt and Diabetic. Large selection on our menus plus daily specials. Tray service to room if ill (no charge or restrictions). 2 snacks/day. Party facilities.
AMENITIES AND ACTIVITIES: Parking available (indoor, for visitors: free and residents: $75.00/month). *3 lounges with:* TVs (2) and piano (1). Guest suites available ($99.00/night). *Residence has a:* library, barber/beauty shop, laundry room(s) (no cost) and tuck/gift shop (open 24-hours/day). Residence provides newspaper delivery to individual suite. Mail delivered to private mailbox with key. *Recreation Facilities*: pool table, billiards, shuffleboard, exercise room, craft room, card room, swimming pool and Posit Science Brain Fitness. Posted schedule of activities. Internal newsletter for residents. *Recreational Programs*: exercise, shopping, theatre, parties, entertainment, art classes, day trips, seminars & lectures, cooking demonstrations, jewelry making and extensive fitness programs including aquafit.
OTHER SERVICES: *Housekeeping*: weekly (included in fee). *Laundry*: linen & towel (included in fee); personal & dry cleaning (extra cost). Complimentary laundry facilities on each floor. Transportation to medical appointments (doctor's appointments, scheduled shopping via town car) and for group social activities (extensive social program). 24-hour security. Nightly security checks. Telephone (per provider costs with Bell/Rogers etc.). Cable TV & Utilities (included in fee).
RENTAL INFORMATION: Rates may vary. Studio - $3,170.00/month & up; 1-bedroom - $3,400.00/month & up; 2-bedroom - $4,800.00/month & up; 2-bedroom + den - $5,800.00/month & up. Extra cost for 2nd person sharing suite ($650.00/month). Rent paid monthly. *Payment Options*: cheques, post-dated cheques, direct deposit and pre-authorized payments. Rent increases as per Provincial Tenancy Legislation, annual for resident with 3 months' notice given. Will help resident move into residence. Short-term respite ($99.00 to $189.00/day) and trial stays ($99.00/day) available.

THE VILLAGE OF HUMBER HEIGHTS

2245 Lawrence Avenue West, Toronto, ON M9P 3W3
Tel: (416) 235-0201
Email: **Darla.Walker@schlegelvillages.com**
Website: **www.schlegelvillages.com**
Contact: **Darla Walker**
Capacity: **230 units** • Subsidies: **none**
Price: **$3,680.00/month and up**

The Village of Humber Heights is Etobicoke's unique continuum of care community for seniors and offers a full range of care support levels. Our residences are modern and attractive, set on beautifully landscaped grounds, without the institutional feeling of nursing and retirement homes of the past. Our signature indoor Main Street has all the conveniences of a small town, accessible for residents in any weather - summer, winter, rain or shine! Residents, both singles and couples, can choose from cozy studios that emphasize care to generous 1-bedroom apartments that emphasize independence. Five levels of care are offered at Humber Heights - Retirement Apartments, Assisted Care, Memory Care, Full Service Retirement Living and Long-Term Care.

RESIDENCE INFORMATION: 7 years in operation. *Near:* Lawrence Avenue and Royal York Road. Handrails in hallways. 5 floors, 3 elevators. Wheelchair accessible. Central PA system. *Funding Base:* Corporate/for profit. *Owned and managed by:* Schlegel Villages. *Average Waiting Period*: 1 - 2 months. Can accommodate cognitively impaired people (Memory Care Neighbourhood). Can accommodate physically challenged people (Assisted Care Neighbourhood). Smoke-free residence. Alcohol allowed.

Procedures to leave the premises on a temporary basis...inform the Director of Retirement Care or the Neighbourhood Coordinator. *Languages:* English. Will accept Public Guardian and Trustee clients. Main doors of residence secured at night only. *Close to:* Public Transit, Shopping, Churches, Seniors' Centre, Library, Major Highway and Local Hospital. Member of ORCA. Licensed under the Retirement Homes Act.
STAFFING: *Available Staff/Services*: Pharmacy, Social Work (CCAC), Recreation Therapy, Occupational Therapy (CCAC), Visiting Dentist, Physiotherapy, Dietitian, Companions, Podiatry, Chaplaincy, Speech Pathology (CCAC) and Chiropody. *External services arranged by:* residence and/or family/resident. Staff trained *re*: visually and cognitively impaired. 24-hour nursing and other staff. RNs, RPNs, HCAs, PSWs and UCPs on staff. Visiting MD (one day/week). Can retain own MD. Police Check or Vulnerable Person Screening is done for all new staff.
HEALTH SERVICES: Medication administration and/or supervision (Medication Program can be purchased in Retirement Apartments). Vitals monitored if required. Will accept and provide special assistance for residents who require oxygen, catheters and ostomies. Assistance with dressing available. Weekly assistance with bathing available. *Extra baths:* $27.00/hour. Care plans done. Different levels of care available. Private Duty/Extra Care available ($27.00/hour). Assisted Living Area. Separate unit for residents with dementia. Lab service (visiting). Residents can purchase outside resources and use agency of their choice. Will help locate higher level of care if needed.
ACCOMMODATION: *Choice of suites available*: studio & 1-bedroom suites. *In all suites*: locks, kitchenette, bar fridge, storage, window coverings, light fixtures, linens, fire alarm, smoke detector, sprinkler, call bell, emergency response system with wearable pendant/bracelet, air conditioning (central) and thermostats for heating & cooling. Full-size fridge & microwave in Apartments. Main floor suites have walk-out patios. No kitchenettes in Memory Care. Private bathrooms with call bells, grab bars, showers with non-slip surfaces and elevated toilet seats. In-suite cable TV provided by residence (residence charges extra $37.00/month). Can have own phone number provided by residence (residence charges extra $30.00/month). Unfurnished suites, furnished suites available for short stays. Suites can be shared. Pets allowed.
DINING SERVICE: All meals included in fee and served in dining room daily. Retirement Apartments include Lunch and Dinner only in base rate. *Guest Meals*: Available. *Special Diets*: Vegetarian, Low Salt and Diabetic. Tray service to room if ill. Unlimited snacks available at any time. Party facilities.
AMENITIES AND ACTIVITIES: Parking available (outdoor, for visitors and indoor & outdoor for residents). *Residence has a:* library, chapel, barber/beauty shop, laundry room(s) (no cost) and tuck/gift shop. Mail delivered to resident. *Recreation Facilities*: pool table, exercise room, greenhouse, craft room and card room. Posted schedule of activities. Internal newsletter for residents. *Recreational Programs*: exercise, shopping, theatre, parties, entertainment, art classes, pet visiting and day trips.
OTHER SERVICES: *Housekeeping*: weekly (included in fee). *Laundry*: linen & towel (included in fee); personal (extra cost). Staff label clothing (one-time fee of $60.00). Transportation for group social activities. Telephone & Cable TV (extra cost). Utilities (included in fee). Additional Care available in $27.00/hour increments spread out through a 24-hour period.
RENTAL INFORMATION: Rates may vary. Starting Rates: Retirement Suites - $3,680.00/month; Full Service Retirement - $3,599.00/month; Assisted Care - $4,373.00/month; Memory Care - $4,549.00/month. Extra cost for 2nd person sharing suite (couples have rate per person). Rent paid monthly. *Payment Options*: cheques and pre-authorized payments. Rent increases as per Provincial Tenancy Legislation, annual for resident with 3 months' notice given. Short-term respite and trial stays available.

♦ TORONTO (NORTH YORK) ♦

BAYBRIDGE - KENSINGTON PLACE RETIREMENT RESIDENCE

866 Sheppard Avenue West, Toronto, ON M3H 2T5
Tel: (416) 636-9555 • Fax: (416) 636-8211
Email: **manidjar@thekensingtonplace.com**
Website: **www.thekensingtonplace.com**
Contact: **Mira Anidjar**
Capacity: **120 residents •** Subsidies: **none**
Price: **$3,506.00 - $6,436.00/month**

For Jewish seniors looking for a beautiful atmosphere, first-rate service and accommodation options, the choice is simple. Kensington Place is the ideal blend of European-inspired architecture, delicious kosher cuisine and a haymish atmosphere that comes from being among good people. Our recreation program is unparalleled, with activities that include thought-provoking speakers, fitness and wellness programs, community involvement, theatrical and musical presentations, and weekly religious services. Dining services supervised under the KASHRUTH COUNCIL.

RESIDENCE INFORMATION: 10 years in operation. *Near:* Bathurst Street and Sheppard Avenue. Decorated in 2004. Handrails in hallways. 8 floors, 2 elevators. Wheelchair accessible. Central PA system. *Funding Base:* Corporate/for profit. *Owned and managed by:* BayBridge Senior Living. 101 units. *Average Waiting Period*: varies. *Average Age*: 80. Can accommodate cognitively impaired people (mild cases cared for on our Wellness Plus Floor). Can accommodate physically challenged people (health assessment completed to individualize care plan). Smoking allowed (exterior designated area). Alcohol allowed. *Procedures to leave the premises on a temporary basis...*notify Concierge & Wellness Nurse if medications are required. *Languages:* English, Hebrew & Yiddish. Will accept Public Guardian and Trustee clients. Main doors of residence secured at night only. *Close to:* Public Transit, Shopping, Churches, Synagogues, Seniors' Centre, Library, Major Highway and Local Hospital (North York General Hospital). *Predominant Cultural Group:* Jewish. Member of ORCA. Licensed under the Retirement Homes Act.
STAFFING: *Available Staff/Services*: Pharmacy, Social Work (CCAC), Recreation Therapy, Occupational Therapy (CCAC), Visiting Dentist, Physiotherapy (CCAC), Denturist, Companions, Chaplaincy, Speech Pathology (CCAC), Chiropody and Audiology/Hearing Clinic. *External services arranged by:* residence and/or family/resident. Staff trained *re*: visually, hearing and cognitively impaired. 24-hour nursing and other staff. RNs, RPNs, HCAs and PSWs on staff. Visiting MD (on call & twice/week). Can retain own MD. Police Check or Vulnerable Person Screening is done for all new staff.
HEALTH SERVICES: Medication administration and/or supervision. Vitals monitored if required. Will accept and provide special assistance for residents who require oxygen, catheters, ostomies and feeding tubes. Assistance with dressing available (cost). Assistance with bathing available as needed (cost). Care plans done. Different levels of care available. Assisted Living Area ($3,918.00 to $5,669.00/month). Lab service (visiting). Residents can purchase outside resources and use agency of their choice. Clinic area for medical visits. Will help locate higher level of care if needed (General Manager works with resident and family).
ACCOMMODATION: *Choice of suites available*: bachelor (20), 1-bedroom (71) & 2-bedroom (10) suites. *In all suites*: locks, kitchenette, bar fridge, microwave, storage, window coverings, light fixtures, fire alarm, smoke detector, sprinkler, call bell, air conditioning (central) and thermostats for heating & cooling. Some suites have balconies. Private bathrooms with call bells, grab bars, tubs and showers with non-slip surfaces and elevated toilet seats. In-suite cable/satellite TV if resident arranges with cable/satellite company. Furnished & unfurnished suites available. *Restrictions on electrical appliances*: no stoves/ovens. Suites

can be shared (couples or other family members), roommate picked by resident. Pets allowed (with General Manager review and approval).

DINING SERVICE: All meals Kosher under COR. All meals included in fee and served in dining room daily. *Sittings per meal:* Breakfast: 1, Lunch: 1, Dinner: 1. *Menu choices available:* Breakfast: 6, Lunch: 7, Dinner: 7. *Guest Meals*: Available. *Special Diets*: Vegetarian, Kosher, Low Salt and Diabetic. Some other diets accommodated. Tray service to room if ill (no charge as long as doctor orders). Unlimited snacks available at any time. Open pantry. European-style café open 7:00 a.m. to 7:00 p.m. with snacks/beverages. Separate Assisted Living dining room. Party facilities.

AMENITIES AND ACTIVITIES: Parking available (indoor & outdoor, for visitors: free and residents: $50.00/month). *8 lounges with:* TVs (4), piano (1), courtyards (2) and patio (1). Guest suites available. *Residence has a:* library, visiting library, chapel, barber/beauty shop, visiting hairdresser, laundry room(s) (no cost) and tuck/gift shop (open during the day hours). Resident can arrange newspaper delivery to main desk. Mail delivered to Concierge Desk. *Recreation Facilities*: pool table, billiards, shuffleboard, exercise room, craft room, card room, movie theatre, spa and resident kitchen. Posted schedule of activities. Internal newsletter for residents. *Recreational Programs*: shopping, theatre, parties, entertainment, art classes, pet visiting, day trips and Yoga & a variety of exercise classes.

OTHER SERVICES: *Housekeeping*: weekly (included in fee). *Laundry*: linen & towel (included in fee); personal (extra cost) & dry cleaning (external provider). Transportation for group social activities. 24-hour security. Nightly security checks. Cable TV (external provider). Telephone & Utilities (included in fee).

RENTAL INFORMATION: Rates may vary. Extra cost for 2nd person sharing suite ($650.00/month). Rent paid monthly. *Payment Options*: post-dated cheques and pre-authorized payments. Rent increases as per Provincial Tenancy Legislation, annual for resident with 3 months' notice given. Will help resident move into residence. Short-term respite and trial stays available (cost depends on suite chosen and assistance required).

CANTERBURY PLACE RETIREMENT RESIDENCE

1 Canterbury Place, Toronto, ON M2N 0G7
Tel: (416) 227-1643 • Fax: (416) 227-2344
Email: **mktg1.canterbury@diversicare.ca**
Website: **www.canterburyplaceretirement.ca**
Contact: **Marketing Manager**
Capacity: **180 residents** • Subsidies: **none**
Price: **$3,050.00 - $5,000.00/month**

Canterbury Place Retirement Residence is a new residence located in North York, north of Sheppard Avenue. This seventeen-storey residence has 165 suites ranging from studio to 2-bedroom accommodations. This beautiful retirement residence has Independent and Full Service Lifestyle Packages available. Additional care services are available if required. **Canterbury Place is owned & managed by Diversicare who is**

the proud recipient of the 2003, 2006, 2009 and 2012 Order of Excellence Award given by Excellence Canada. The award was received for the exceptional quality and customer service we provide to our residents every day.

RESIDENCE INFORMATION: New residence. *Near:* Yonge Street and Ellerslie Avenue. Decorated in 2012. Handrails in hallways. 17 floors, 3 elevators. Wheelchair accessible. Central PA system. *Funding Base:* Corporate/for profit. *Owned by:* Diversicare Canada Management Services Co., Inc. 165 units. *Average Waiting Period*: none. *Average Age*: 80. Can accommodate cognitively impaired people with restrictions (with assessment). Can accommodate physically challenged people (with assessment). Smoking allowed. Alcohol allowed. *Procedures to leave the premises on a temporary basis...*sign out. *Languages:* English, Spanish, Japanese & Tagalog. Will accept Public Guardian and Trustee clients. Main doors of residence secured at night only. *Close to:* Public Transit, Shopping, Churches, Synagogues, Seniors' Centre, Library, Major Highway and Local Hospital (North York General Hospital). Member of ORCA. Licensed under the Retirement Homes Act.
STAFFING: *Available Staff/Services*: Pharmacy, Social Work (CCAC), Recreation Therapy, Occupational Therapy (CCAC), Visiting Dentist, Physiotherapy (CCAC), Denturist, Dietitian (CCAC), Companions, Podiatry (CCAC), Chaplaincy, Speech Pathology (CCAC), Chiropody, Audiology/Hearing Clinic and Nurse Practitioner (available 24/7). *External services arranged by:* residence and/or family/resident. Staff trained *re*: visually, hearing and cognitively impaired. 24-hour staff. RNs, RPNs, HCAs, PSWs and UCPs on staff. Visiting MD (on call, visiting as needed). Can retain own MD. Staff members are bonded. Police Check or Vulnerable Person Screening is done for all new staff.
HEALTH SERVICES: Medication administration (no restrictions) and/or supervision. Vitals monitored if required. Will accept (but not provide special assistance for) residents who require oxygen, catheters, ostomies and feeding tubes. Assistance with dressing available. Assistance with bathing available twice a week (cost). Care plans done. Different levels of care available. Package includes all nursing, which includes Nurse Practitioner. Private Duty/Extra Care available. Lab service (visiting). Residents can purchase outside resources and use agency of their choice. MD visits residents in their rooms/suites. Clinic area for medical visits. Will help locate higher level of care if needed (our nursing staff will discuss with family and involve CCAC).
ACCOMMODATION: *Choice of suites available*: studio, 1-bedroom & 2-bedroom suites. *In all suites*: locks, kitchenette, bar fridge, patio/balcony, storage, window coverings, light fixtures, fire alarm, smoke detector, sprinkler, call bell, emergency response system with wearable pendant/bracelet, air conditioning (central & Geo Thermal HVAC in common areas) and thermostats for heating & cooling. Private bathrooms with call bells, grab bars, showers with non-slip surfaces and elevated toilet seats. In-suite cable TV if resident arranges with cable company. Can have own phone number if resident arranges with phone company. Unfurnished suites, furnished suites available for short stays. *Restrictions on electrical appliances*: approved appliances only, no burners. Suites can be shared (by couples only). Small pets allowed (on approval).
DINING SERVICE: All meals included in fee and served in dining room daily. *Menu choices available:* Breakfast: 1, Lunch: 2, Dinner: 2. *Guest Meals*: Available. *Special Diets*: Vegetarian, Low Salt, Diabetic and Limited Therapeutic. Tray service to room if ill (no charge as long as doctor orders). Unlimited snacks available at any time. Open pantry. Party facilities. Elegant, licensed dining room and private dining room, serving chef-prepared meals.
AMENITIES AND ACTIVITIES: Parking available (indoor & outdoor, for visitors: free and indoor for residents: $50.00/month). *3 lounges with:* TVs (2), fireplaces (3) and outdoor terraces (2). Guest suites available. *Residence has a:* library, visiting library, chapel, barber/beauty shop, visiting hairdresser, laundry room(s) (no cost) and tuck/gift shop (hours vary). Residence provides newspaper delivery to main desk. Mail delivered to private mailbox with key. *Recreation Facilities*: pool table, billiards, exercise room, craft room, card room, hair salon and spa. Posted schedule of activities. Internal newsletter for residents.

Recreational Programs: exercise, shopping, theatre, parties, entertainment, art classes, pet visiting, day trips, Pet Therapy, Brain Gym® & More program and internet access.
OTHER SERVICES: *Housekeeping*: weekly (included in fee). *Laundry*: linen & towel (included in fee); personal (extra cost). Transportation for group social activities. 24-hour security. Nightly security checks. Telephone & Cable TV (extra cost). Utilities (included in fee).
RENTAL INFORMATION: Rates may vary. Extra cost for 2nd person sharing suite ($700.00/month). Rent paid monthly. *Payment Options*: cheques, post-dated cheques, direct deposit and pre-authorized payments. Rent increases as per Provincial Tenancy Legislation, annual for resident with 3 months' notice given. Will help resident move into residence (extra cost). Short-term respite and trial stays available.

DELMANOR NORTHTOWN

5351 Yonge Street, Toronto, ON M2M 7L5
Tel: (416) 225-9146 • Fax: (416) 225-9185
Email: **lfortin@delmanor.com**
Website: **www.delmanor.com**
Contact: **Laurie Fortin**
Capacity: **150 residents** • Subsidies: **none**
Price: **$3,595.00 - $6,795.00/month**

Luxury awaits in this Tridel-inspired Retirement Community. Steps from the subway; Delmanor Northtown is located near shopping malls, Toronto Centre for the Performing Arts, parks, churches and medical services. Spacious 1-bedroom & 2-bedroom suites with private balconies or terraces, stainless steel appliances, granite countertops and in-suite washer and dryer. Building amenities include a dining room with garden views, fireplace lounges, a pub with billiards lounge and card room, fully stocked library with wireless internet, fitness centre and a state-of-the-art home theatre. There are 2 landscaped terraces. Enjoy the magnificent views from the rooftop terrace complete with a putting green. Guest stays offered, subject to availability.

RESIDENCE INFORMATION: 5 years in operation. *Near:* Yonge Street and Finch Avenue. Decorated in 2009. Handrails in hallways. 8 floors, 2 elevators. Wheelchair accessible. Central PA system. *Funding Base:* Corporate/for profit. *Owned by:* Tridel Corporation. *Managed by:* Delmanor Seniors Communities Inc. 112 units. *Average Waiting Period*: none. *Average Age*: 80. Can accommodate cognitively impaired people with restrictions (mild dementia). Can sometimes accommodate physically challenged people. Residents have a dress code (proper attire in dining room). Smoke-free residence. Alcohol allowed. *Procedures to leave the premises on a temporary basis...*sign in/out at Concierge. *Languages:* English. Main doors of residence secured at night only. *Close to:* Public Transit, Shopping, Churches, Synagogues, Seniors' Centre, Library, Major Highway and Local Hospital (North York General Hospital). Member of ORCA. Licensed under the Retirement Homes Act.
STAFFING: *Available Staff/Services*: Pharmacy, Occupational Therapy, Visiting Dentist, Physiotherapy, Podiatry, Chiropody, Audiology/Hearing Clinic and Registered Massage Therapy. *External services arranged by:* family/resident. Staff trained *re*: visually, hearing and cognitively impaired. 24-hour nursing and other staff. RPNs and PSWs on staff. Visiting MD (every week). Can retain own MD. Police Check or Vulnerable Person Screening is done for all new staff.
HEALTH SERVICES: Medication administered if required. Vitals monitored if required. Will accept and provide special assistance for residents who require oxygen. Assistance with dressing available. Assistance with bathing available as needed (cost). Care plans done. Different levels of care available. Lab service (visiting). Residents can purchase outside resources and use agency of their choice. Clinic area for medical visits. Will help locate higher level of care if needed (will assist with the CCAC application process).

ACCOMMODATION: *Choice of suites available*: 1 & 2-bedroom suites, some with dens; most with private balconies or terraces. *In all suites*: locks, kitchenette, full-size stainless steel fridge, microwave, window coverings, light fixtures, fire alarm, smoke detector, sprinkler, call bell, emergency response system with wearable pendant/bracelet, air conditioning (central), thermostats for heating & cooling and in-suite washer & dryer. Private bathrooms with call bells, grab bars, showers with non-slip surfaces and elevated toilet seats. In-suite cable TV provided by residence. Can have own phone number provided by residence. Unfurnished suites, furnished suites available for short stays. *Restrictions on electrical appliances*: no hot plates or other cooking surfaces. Suites can be shared (by couples only), roommate picked by resident. Pets allowed (must be 20 lbs. or under and resident must sign a Pet Waiver).
DINING SERVICE: Continental Breakfast served daily. Lunch and Dinner included in fee and served in dining room daily. *Sittings per meal:* Lunch: 2, Dinner: 2. *Menu choices available:* Lunch: 2, Dinner: 2. *Guest Meals*: Lunch $13.00, Dinner $17.00. *Special Diets*: Vegetarian, Low Salt and Diabetic. Alternative menu choices & 5 week seasonal menus. Special à la carte dining menu available to residents and their guests. Tray service to room if ill (no charge as long as doctor orders). Unlimited snacks available at any time. Open pantry. Party facilities.
AMENITIES AND ACTIVITIES: Parking available (indoor for residents: $100.00/month). *3 lounges with:* TVs (2), piano (1) and fireplaces (2). Guest suites available. *Residence has a:* library, chapel, barber/beauty shop, visiting hairdresser and laundry room(s) (no cost). Banking services on premises. Resident can arrange newspaper delivery to individual suite. Mail delivered to private mailbox with key. *Recreation Facilities*: pool table, billiards, shuffleboard, exercise room, greenhouse, craft room, card room and hobby gourmet kitchen. Posted schedule of activities. Internal newsletter for residents. *Recreational Programs*: exercise, shopping, theatre, parties, entertainment, art classes, day trips and Living***Well*** lecture series.
OTHER SERVICES: *Housekeeping*: weekly (included in fee). *Laundry*: linen & towel (included in fee); personal & dry cleaning (extra cost). Washers and dryers in each suite. Transportation for group social activities. 24-hour security. Telephone, Cable TV & Utilities (included in fee).
RENTAL INFORMATION: Rates may vary. Extra cost for 2nd person sharing suite ($775.00/month). Rent paid monthly. *Payment Options*: post-dated cheques and pre-authorized payments. Rent increases as per Provincial Tenancy Legislation, annual for resident with 3 months' notice given. Will help resident move into residence. Short-term respite/guest ($110.00/night & up) and trial stays available.

DELMANOR WYNFORD

187 Wynford Drive, Toronto, ON M3C 0C7
Tel: (416) 331-9797 • Fax: (416) 331-8815
Email: **ppalmer@delmanor.com**
Website: **www.delmanor.com**
Contact: **Pam Palmer**
Capacity: **150 residents** • Subsidies: **none**
Price: **$3,845.00 - $7,295.00/month**

Delmanor Wynford is a Tridel-inspired retirement community located in the heart of Don Mills, conveniently situated off Eglinton and the DVP. Delmanor Wynford offers many large, one-of-a-kind suites with balconies, stainless-steel full size fridges and microwaves, granite countertops and in-suite washers and dryers. Building amenities include a dining room with courtyard view, fireplace lounges, a pub with billiards lounge, ground-floor wireless internet, conservatory and a state-of-the-art home theatre. There are 2 landscaped terraces, one of them on the rooftop with shuffleboard and putting green.

RESIDENCE INFORMATION: 4 years in operation. *Near:* Eglinton Avenue and Don Valley Parkway. Decorated in 2010. Handrails in hallways. 6 floors, 2 elevators. Wheelchair accessible. Central PA system.

Funding Base: Corporate/for profit. *Owned by:* Tridel Corporation. *Managed by:* Delmanor Seniors Communities Inc. 120 units. *Average Waiting Period*: varies. *Average Age*: 84. Can sometimes accommodate cognitively impaired people (mild dementia). Can sometimes accommodate physically challenged people. Residents have a dress code (appropriate day/evening attire). Smoke-free residence. Alcohol allowed. *Procedures to leave the premises on a temporary basis...*sign out at Concierge. *Languages:* English. Will accept Public Guardian and Trustee clients. Main doors of residence secured at night only. *Close to:* Public Transit, Shopping, Churches, Synagogues, Seniors' Centre, Library, Major Highway and Local Hospital (North York General Hospital). Member of ORCA. Licensed under the Retirement Homes Act.
STAFFING: *Available Staff/Services*: Pharmacy, Recreation Therapy, Visiting Dentist, Physiotherapy, Denturist, Podiatry, Chaplaincy, Chiropody, Audiology/Hearing Clinic, Massage Therapy, Foot-Care Nurse and Reflexology. *External services arranged by:* residence and/or family/resident. Staff trained *re*: visually, hearing and cognitively impaired. 24-hour nursing and other staff. RNs, RPNs and PSWs on staff. Visiting MD (weekly). Can retain own MD. Staff members are bonded. Police Check or Vulnerable Person Screening is done for all new staff.
HEALTH SERVICES: Medication administered if required. Vitals monitored if required. Will accept and provide special assistance for residents who require oxygen and ostomies. Assistance with dressing available (cost). Weekly assistance with bathing available (cost). Care plans done. Different levels of care available. Private Duty/Extra Care available ($26.00/hour). Lab service (visiting, $30.00/visit). Residents can purchase outside resources and use agency of their choice. MD visits residents in their rooms/suites. Clinic area for medical visits. Will help locate higher level of care if needed (residence will work with CCAC Care Coordinator).
ACCOMMODATION: *Choice of suites available*: 1-bedroom, 1-bedroom + den & 2-bedroom suites. *In all suites*: locks, kitchenette, full-size fridge, microwave, granite counter tops, storage, window coverings, light fixtures, fire alarm, smoke detector, sprinkler, emergency response system with wearable pendant/bracelet, air conditioning (central), thermostats for heating & cooling, washer & dryer and in-suite safe. Most have balconies. Private bathrooms (2-bedroom suites have 2 bathrooms - walk-in shower & bathtub) with grab bars, showers with non-slip surfaces and elevated toilet seats. In-suite cable TV provided by residence. Can have own phone number provided by residence. Unfurnished suites, furnished suites available for short stays. *Restrictions on electrical appliances*: no hot plates in suite. Suites can be shared (by couples only). Pets allowed (20 lbs. and under).
DINING SERVICE: Continental Breakfast served daily. Lunch and Dinner included in fee and served in dining room daily. *Sittings per meal:* Lunch: 2, Dinner: 2. *Menu choices available:* Lunch: 2, Dinner: 2. *Guest Meals*: Lunch $11.00, Dinner $17.00. *Special Diets*: Vegetarian, Low Salt and Diabetic. Alternative choice available. Special à la carte dining menu available to residents and their guests. Tray service to room if ill (no charge as long as doctor orders). 2 snacks/day. Party facilities.
AMENITIES AND ACTIVITIES: Parking available (indoor & outdoor, for visitors: free and indoor for residents: $100.00/month). *4 lounges with:* TV (1), piano (1), computers (1) and fully-licensed bar (1). *Residence has a:* library, chapel, barber/beauty shop, visiting hairdresser, laundry room(s) (no cost) and tuck/gift shop (open 11:00 a.m. – 12:00 noon). Banking services on premises (ATM machine). Resident can arrange newspaper delivery to individual suite (extra cost). Mail delivered to private mailbox with key. *Recreation Facilities*: pool table, billiards, shuffleboard, exercise room, greenhouse, craft room, card room, rooftop putting green and outdoor shuffleboard. Posted schedule of activities. Internal newsletter for residents. *Recreational Programs*: exercise, shopping, theatre, parties, entertainment, art classes, pet visiting, day trips and Living***Well*** personal coach.
OTHER SERVICES: *Housekeeping*: weekly (included in fee). *Laundry*: linen & towel (included in fee); personal (extra cost; ensuite washer and dryer) & dry cleaning (extra cost; Dry Cleaner will pick up at the Concierge's Desk). Transportation for group social activities. 24-hour security. Telephone, Cable TV & Utilities (included in fee).
RENTAL INFORMATION: Rates may vary. Extra cost for 2nd person sharing suite ($775.00/month). Rent paid monthly. *Payment Options*: post-dated cheques and pre-authorized payments. Rent increases as per

Provincial Tenancy Legislation, annual for resident with 3 months' notice given. Short-term respite ($125.00/day) and trial stays available. Guest suites subject to availability.

GREENVIEW LODGE SENIOR CARE RESIDENCE

880 Lawrence Avenue East, Toronto, ON M3C 1P6
Tel: (416) 445-2255 • Fax: (416) 391-2397
Email: **gvlseniorcare@sympatico.ca**
Website: **www.greenviewlodge.com**
Contact: **Deborah Lafreniere**
Capacity: **80 residents** • Subsidies: **none**
Price: **$3,500.00 - $4,500.00/month**

- RHRA LICENSED TO OPERATE.
- PERFECT LOCATION: in the heart of Don Mills – walking distance from the Shops at Don Mills mall, Edwards Gardens, Public Library, Restaurants, Banks, Transit & Shoppers Drug Mart.
- PERFECT SIZE: Small enough to feel cozy yet large enough for many social activities & friends. The atmosphere is warm & relaxed.
- PRICE: ALL- INCLUSIVE & AFFORDABLE.
- OPTIMAL CARE is offered due to Registered Nursing Staff 24-hours/day, on-site Doctor's Clinic, Physiotherapy Clinic, Foot & Dental Care. Ministry Approved Smoking Room: a rare feature that accommodates the needs of both smokers & non-smokers.
- DEDICATION to provide high quality personalized service, wellness & vitality within an atmosphere of compassion, respect and security.

RESIDENCE INFORMATION: 35 years in operation. *On:* Don Mills Road and Lawrence Avenue East. Decorated in 2012. Handrails in hallways. 3 floors, 1 elevator. Wheelchair accessible. Central PA system. *Funding Base:* Corporate/for profit. 74 units. *Average Waiting Period*: varies. *Average Age*: 83. Can accommodate cognitively impaired people (Alzheimer's, Lewy Body, vascular, temporal dementias). Can accommodate physically challenged people (depends on level of care). Residents have a dress code (neat, clean, casual - no formal dress code; residents must be dressed for meals in the dining room). Smoking allowed (Government Approved Smoking Room & designated exterior areas). Alcohol allowed (medical restrictions). *Restrictions around Visitors/Visiting Hours:* visitors are required to sign in. *Procedures to leave the premises on a temporary basis...*Short-term: sign out. Overnight & Holidays: 24-hours' notice to arrange for medications. *Languages:* English. Will accept Public Guardian and Trustee clients. Main doors of residence secured at all times. *Close to:* Public Transit, Shopping, Churches, Synagogues, Seniors' Centre, Library, Major Highway and Local Hospitals (North York General Hospital & Sunnybrook Health Sciences Centre). Member of ORCA. Licensed under the Retirement Homes Act.
STAFFING: *Available Staff/Services*: Social Work (CCAC), Recreation Therapy, Occupational Therapy (CCAC), Visiting Dentist, Physiotherapy, Denturist, Dietitian, Companions, Podiatry, Chaplaincy, Speech Pathology (CCAC), Chiropody, Audiology/Hearing Clinic, Doctor, Massage Therapy and Hair Salon. *External services arranged by:* residence and/or family/resident. Staff trained *re*: visually, hearing and

Don't forget ...

When searching for a retirement home you must be an **Informed Consumer**. Ask questions, make notes, talk to residents and staff, try the food and arrange a trial stay. Review our section on **RETIREMENT RESIDENCE VISITING TIPS** before your visits.

cognitively impaired. Staff receive ongoing education to meet the needs of the residents. 24-hour nursing staff. RNs, RPNs and PSWs on staff. Visiting MD (1 day/week & on call). Can retain own MD. Staff members are bonded. Police Check or Vulnerable Person Screening is done for all new staff.
HEALTH SERVICES: Medication administration and/or supervision. Vitals monitored if required. Will accept and provide special assistance for residents who require oxygen. Assistance with dressing available (cost). Assistance with bathing available twice a week. Care plans done. Different levels of care available. Private Duty/Extra Care available. Separate unit for residents with dementia. Lab service (visiting). Residents can purchase outside resources and use agency of their choice. MD visits residents in their rooms/suites. Clinic area for medical visits. Registered staff supervision 24-hours/day. Nightly room/security checks. Will help locate higher level of care if needed (in consultation with families).
ACCOMMODATION: *Choice of suites available*: private & semi-private rooms. *In all suites*: locks, window coverings, light fixtures, linens, smoke detector, carbon monoxide detector, heat detector call bell emergency response, air conditioning (central & window units) and thermostats for heating. Private bathrooms with call bells, grab bars, tubs and showers with non-slip surfaces. In-suite cable/satellite TV if resident arranges with cable/satellite company (residence charges extra). Can have own phone number if resident arranges with phone company (residence charges extra). Furnished & unfurnished suites available. *Restrictions on electrical appliances*: items checked for safety - some restrictions apply. Suites can be shared (couples welcome), roommate picked by resident & residence staff. No pets allowed.
DINING SERVICE: All meals included in fee and served in dining room daily. *Sittings per meal:* Breakfast: 2, Lunch: 1, Dinner: 1. *Menu choices available:* Breakfast: 2, Lunch: 2, Dinner: 2. *Guest Meals*: Lunch $10.00, Dinner $15.00. *Special Diets*: Vegetarian, Low Salt, Diabetic, Kosher-Style, Low Fat and Heart Friendly. Tray service to room if ill. 3 snacks/day. Party facilities. BBQ's.
AMENITIES AND ACTIVITIES: Parking available (indoor, for visitors and indoor & outdoor for residents). *4 lounges with:* TVs (4), pianos (2) and large screen TVs (2). Guest suites available ($100.00/night). *Residence has a:* library, visiting library, chapel, barber/beauty shop, visiting hairdresser, tuck/gift shop (open Monday to Friday; 2:00 p.m. - 4:00 p.m.). Banking services on premises (Trust Account). Mail delivered to main desk. *Recreation Facilities*: pool table, billiards, shuffleboard, craft room, card room and outdoor patios. Posted schedule of activities. Internal newsletter for residents. *Recreational Programs*: exercise, shopping, theatre, parties, entertainment, art classes, pet visiting, day trips, religious services, holiday celebrations, discussion groups and inter-generational visits.
OTHER SERVICES: *Housekeeping*: daily and weekly (extra room cleaning at additional cost). *Laundry*: linen & towel (included in fee), personal (included in fee; 2 loads/week) & dry cleaning (extra cost). Transportation to medical appointments (can be arranged at additional cost) and for group social activities (extra cost; special outings e.g. theatre). 24-hour security. Nightly security checks. Telephone & Cable TV (extra cost). Utilities (included in fee).
RENTAL INFORMATION: Rates may vary. Extra cost for 2nd person sharing suite (based on care needs). Rent paid monthly. *Payment Options*: cheques and post-dated cheques. Rent increases as per Provincial Tenancy Legislation, annual for resident with 90 days' notice given. Will help resident move into residence (extra cost). Short-term respite, vacation stays, Day Care Program and trial stays available.

L'CHAIM RETIREMENT HOMES INC.

718 Sheppard Avenue West, Toronto, ON M3H 2S6
Tel: (416) 398-7898 • Fax: (416) 398-3909
Email: **lchaimretirement@rogers.com**
Website: **www.lchaimretirement.ca**
Contact: **Judy Cohen**
Capacity: **30 residents** • Subsidies: **none**
Price: **$4,500.00 - $5,000.00/month**

L'Chaim specialize in Alzheimer's/dementia care using the Montessori philosophy. Small and unique home that cares for our residents to the end of life.

RESIDENCE INFORMATION: 13 years in operation. *Near:* Bathurst Street and Sheppard Avenue. Decorated in 2012. Handrails in hallways. 3 floors, 1 elevator. Wheelchair accessible. *Funding Base:* Corporate/for profit. *Owned by:* Judy Cohen. 30 units. *Average Waiting Period*: varies. *Average Age*: 85. Can accommodate cognitively impaired people (specializing in dementia using the Montessori methods for dementia). Can accommodate physically challenged people. Smoke-free residence. *Restrictions around Visitors/Visiting Hours:* we welcome our visitors anytime other than mealtimes. *Procedures to leave the premises on a temporary basis*...inform our Administrative Office. *Languages:* English, Yiddish & Hebrew. Will accept Public Guardian and Trustee clients. Main doors of residence secured at night only. *Close to:* Public Transit, Shopping, Churches, Synagogues, Seniors' Centre, Library, Major Highway and Local Hospital (North York General Hospital). *Predominant Cultural Group:* Jewish. Member of ORCA. Licensed under the Retirement Homes Act.

STAFFING: *Available Staff/Services*: Pharmacy, Social Work (CCAC), Recreation Therapy, Occupational Therapy (CCAC), Visiting Dentist, Denturist, Dietitian (CCAC), Companions, Podiatry, Chaplaincy, Speech Pathology (CCAC), Chiropody and Audiology/Hearing Clinic. *External services arranged by:* residence and/or family/resident. Staff trained *re*: visually, hearing and cognitively impaired. 24-hour staff. RNs, HCAs and PSWs on staff. Visiting MD (once/week & when needed). Can retain own MD. Staff members are bonded. Police Check or Vulnerable Person Screening is done for all new staff.

HEALTH SERVICES: Medication administration and/or supervision. Vitals monitored if required. Will accept and provide special assistance for residents who require oxygen, catheters, ostomies and feeding tubes. Assistance with dressing available. Weekly assistance with bathing available. *Extra baths:* $15.00/bath. Care plans done. Different levels of care available. Private Duty/Extra Care available ($13.00 to $15.00/hour). Assisted Living Area is secured to accommodate residents with dementia. Lab service (visiting, $15.00/visit). Residents can purchase outside resources and use agency of their choice. MD visits residents in their rooms/suites. Clinic area for medical visits. Will help locate higher level of care if needed (we adjust the level of care as needed).

ACCOMMODATION: *Choice of suites available*: unfurnished single private rooms. *In all suites*: locks, window coverings, light fixtures, fire alarm, smoke detector, sprinkler, call bell, air conditioning (central & window units) and thermostats for heating & cooling. Private bathrooms with call bells, grab bars, walk-in showers with non-slip surfaces and elevated toilet seats. In-suite cable TV if resident arranges with cable company. Can have own phone number if resident arranges with phone company. Unfurnished suites. No pets allowed.

DINING SERVICE: All meals included in fee and served in dining room daily. *Sittings per meal:* Breakfast: 2, Lunch: 2, Dinner: 2. *Menu choices available:* Breakfast: 2, Lunch: 2, Dinner: 2. *Guest Meals*: Lunch $5.00, Dinner $10.00. *Special Diets*: Vegetarian, Low Salt and Diabetic. Kosher meat, poultry & dairy (no Mashgiach). Tray service to room if ill (no charge as long as doctor orders). Unlimited snacks available at any time. Open pantry. All meals are cooked on-site using only fresh ingredients. Party facilities.

AMENITIES AND ACTIVITIES: Parking available (outdoor, for visitors and residents). *3 lounges with:* TVs (2), piano (1) and fireplace (1). *Residence has a:* library, visiting library, barber/beauty shop, visiting

hairdresser and laundry room(s) (no cost). Residence provides newspaper delivery to dining room. Mail delivered to private mailbox (no key). *Recreation Facilities*: exercise room and card room. Posted schedule of activities. Internal newsletter for residents. *Recreational Programs*: exercise, shopping, theatre, parties, entertainment, art classes, pet visiting and day trips.
OTHER SERVICES: *Housekeeping*: daily (included in fee). *Laundry*: linen, towel & personal (included in fee). We provide individual laundry service! Transportation for group social activities. 24-hour security. Nightly security checks. Utilities (included in fee).
RENTAL INFORMATION: Rates may vary. No cost for sharing suite. Rent paid monthly. *Payment Options*: post-dated cheques. Rent increases as per Provincial Tenancy Legislation, annual with 3 months' notice given. Trial stays available.

REVERA - DON MILLS SENIORS' APARTMENTS

1055/1057 Don Mills Road, Toronto, ON M3C 1W9
Tel: (855) 573-8372 • Toll Free: (855) 573-8372
Email: **donmills@reveraliving.com**
Website: **www.reveraliving.com/donmills**
Contact: **Executive Director or Lifestyle Consultant**
Capacity: **143 units** • Subsidies: **none**
Price: **$2,414.00/month and up**

Keep living your life, your way, at Don Mills Seniors' Apartments. You'll find the range of services, features and choices that fit your lifestyle and requirements – all in a warm and safe environment. We offer luxury apartments and a 24-hour concierge service, and are close to shopping, grocery stores, places of worship, pharmacies, parks, public transportation, and much more. For added convenience, we are adjacent to the full service Donway Place residence, with its many amenities, accessible via a covered walkway. Everything is designed to enable you to maintain your independence and privacy, enjoy a full social life, and participate in the activities that you love. With retirement living at Don Mills Seniors' Apartments, you change your address, not your life. *Don Mills Seniors' Apartments is part of the Revera family, one of North America's leading and most trusted providers of seniors' accommodation, care and services since 1961.*

RESIDENCE INFORMATION: 27 years in operation. *Near:* Don Mills Road and Lawrence Avenue. Decorated in 2010. Handrails in hallways. 6 floors, 2 elevators. Wheelchair accessible. *Funding Base:* Corporate/for profit. *Owned and managed by:* Revera Inc. *Average Waiting Period*: varies. *Average Age*: 86. Smoke-free residence. Alcohol allowed. *Procedures to leave the premises on a temporary basis...* advise Concierge. *Languages:* English. *Close to:* Public Transit, Shopping, Churches, Seniors' Centre, Library, Major Highway and Local Hospitals (North York General Hospital & Sunnybrook Health Sciences Centre). Member of ORCA.
STAFFING: *Available Staff/Services*: Social Work (CCAC), Recreation Therapy, Visiting Dentist, Physiotherapy (CCAC), Podiatry, Audiology/Hearing Clinic and 24-hour Response System (connected to nurse at Donway). *External services arranged by:* residence and/or family/resident. Staff trained *re*: visually and hearing impaired. 24-hour nursing staff. RNs and RPNs on staff. Visiting MD (2 on call 7 days/week; clinic open 3 days/week). Can retain own MD.
HEALTH SERVICES: Will accept (but not provide special assistance for) residents who require oxygen. Lab service (visiting). Residents can purchase outside resources and use agency of their choice. Clinic area for medical visits. Will help locate higher level of care if needed (referral to Revera residences; support to inquire into CCAC).
ACCOMMODATION: *Choice of suites available*: bachelor (2), 1-bedroom (46), 2-bedroom (94) & 3-bedroom (1) apartments. *In all suites*: locks, patio/balcony, galley kitchen, full-size fridge, stove, dishwasher, storage, window coverings, light fixtures, stove, smoke detector, sprinkler, call bell, air conditioning (central) and thermostats for heating & cooling. Private bathrooms with call bells, grab bars,

showers with non-slip surfaces and elevated toilet seats. In-suite cable TV provided by residence (residence charges extra). Can have own phone number if resident arranges with phone company (residence charges extra). Unfurnished suites. Pets allowed (as per Pet Policy within the Tenancy Agreement).
DINING SERVICE: Meals are not included in fee, but there is a dining room where meals can be purchased in Donway Place (adjacent Retirement Residence). *Guest Meals*: Breakfast $7.75, Lunch $9.75, Dinner $13.75. *Special Diets*: Low Salt and Diabetic. Tray service to room if ill (no charge for a maximum time of 4 days). 1 snack/day. Party facilities.
AMENITIES AND ACTIVITIES: Parking available (outdoor, for visitors: free and indoor for residents: $70.00/month). *2 lounges with:* TV (1), piano (1) and fireplaces (2). *Residence has a:* library, barber/beauty shop, laundry room(s) ($2.25/washer load, $1.50/dryer load) and tuck/gift shop. Banking services on premises (bi-monthly). Resident can arrange newspaper delivery to individual suite. Mail delivered to private mailbox with key. *Recreation Facilities*: pool table, exercise room, craft room and card room. Posted schedule of activities. Internal newsletter for residents. *Recreational Programs*: exercise, shopping, theatre, parties, entertainment, art classes, pet visiting, day trips and outdoor gardening.
OTHER SERVICES: *Housekeeping*: weekly (included in fee). 24-hour security. Nightly security checks. Telephone & Cable TV (extra cost). Utilities (included in fee). 24-hour Emergency Response (included in fee).
RENTAL INFORMATION: Rates may vary. Studios - $2,414.00/month & up; 1-bedrooms - $2,749.00/month & up; 2-bedrooms - $2,896.00/month & up. Extra cost for 2nd person sharing suite ($140.00/month). Rent paid monthly. *Payment Options*: pre-authorized payments. Credit card option available for short-term stays. Rent increases are a set percentage as per Provincial Tenancy Legislation, annual for resident with 90 days' notice given. Short-term respite and trial stays available (at adjacent Donway Place).

REVERA - DONWAY PLACE

8 The Donway East, Toronto, ON M3C 3R7
Tel: (855) 573-8372 • Toll Free: (855) 573-8372
Email: **donway@reveraliving.com**
Website: **www.reveraliving.com/donway**
Contact: **Executive Director or Lifestyle Consultant**
Capacity: **230 units** • Subsidies: **none**
Price: **$2,889.00/month and up**

Keep living your life, your way, at Donway Place. Here you'll find the range of services, amenities and choices that fit your lifestyle and requirements – all in a warm and safe environment. We are a bustling residence, located within walking distance of shopping, grocery stores, places of worship, pharmacies, parks, public transportation, and much more. For added convenience, we are adjacent to the Don Mills Seniors' Apartments, accessible via a covered walkway. Everything is designed to enable you to maintain your independence and privacy, enjoy a full social life, and participate in the activities that you love. Our caring and friendly staff and luxury accommodations, support who you are and how you want to live in freedom and comfort. With retirement living at Donway Place, you change your address, not your life. *Donway Place is part of the Revera family, one of North America's leading and most trusted providers of seniors' accommodation, care and services since 1961.*

RESIDENCE INFORMATION: 27 years in operation. *Near:* Lawrence Avenue and Don Mills Road. Decorated in 2010. Handrails in hallways. 6 floors, 4 elevators. Wheelchair accessible. Central PA system. *Funding Base:* Corporate/for profit. *Owned and managed by:* Revera Inc. *Average Waiting Period*: varies. *Average Age*: 86. Can accommodate cognitively impaired people with restrictions (no secured unit). Can accommodate physically challenged people with restrictions. Smoke-free residence. Alcohol allowed. *Procedures to leave the premises on a temporary basis...*advise Reception Desk. *Languages:* English. Main doors of residence secured at night only. *Close to:* Public Transit, Shopping, Churches, Seniors' Centre, Library, Major Highway and Local Hospitals (North York General Hospital & Sunnybrook Health Sciences Centre). Member of ORCA. Licensed under the Retirement Homes Act.

STAFFING: *Available Staff/Services*: Pharmacy, Social Work (CCAC), Recreation Therapy, Occupational Therapy (CCAC), Visiting Dentist, Physiotherapy (CCAC), Companions, Podiatry, Chaplaincy, Audiology/ Hearing Clinic, Doctor's Clinic, Hair Salon and Foot Clinic. *External services arranged by:* residence and/or family/resident. Staff trained *re*: visually, hearing and cognitively impaired. 24-hour nursing staff. RNs, RPNs, HCAs and UCPs on staff. Visiting MD (2 on call 7 days/week; clinic open 3 days/week). Can retain own MD. Police Check or Vulnerable Person Screening is done for all new staff.
HEALTH SERVICES: Medication administered if required (additional cost/optional service). Vitals monitored if required. Will accept (but not provide special assistance for) residents who require oxygen and catheters. Assistance with dressing available (cost). Weekly assistance with bathing available ($91.00/ month). Care plans done. Different levels of care available. Private Duty/Extra Care available. Assisted Living Area ($490.00 to $1,960.00/month). Lab service (visiting). Residents can purchase outside resources and use agency of their choice. Clinic area for medical visits. Will help locate higher level of care if needed (Director of Health & Wellness to assist with resource information on CCAC and Revera residences).
ACCOMMODATION: *Choice of suites available*: studio (84), 1-bedroom (52), 2-bedroom (6); ADL - studio (60), 1-bedroom (25) & 2-bedroom (3) units. *In all suites*: locks, window coverings, fire alarm, smoke detector, sprinkler, call bell, PA system, air conditioning (central) and thermostats for heating & cooling. Some kitchenettes. Some balconies. Private bathrooms with call bells, grab bars, tubs and showers with non-slip surfaces and elevated toilet seats. In-suite cable TV provided by residence (residence charges extra). Can have own phone number if resident arranges with phone company (residence charges extra). Unfurnished suites, furnished suites available for short stays. *Restrictions on electrical appliances*: no hot plates. Suites can be shared (by couples only). Pets allowed (as per Pet Policy within Tenancy Agreement).
DINING SERVICE: All meals included in fee and served in dining room daily. *Sittings per meal:* Breakfast: 2, Lunch: 3, Dinner: 3. *Menu choices available:* Breakfast: 2, Lunch: 2, Dinner: 2. *Guest Meals*: Breakfast $8.25, Lunch $9.75, Dinner $13.75. *Special Diets*: Low Salt and Diabetic. Tray service to room if ill (no charge for a maximum time of 4 days). 2 snacks/day. Party facilities.
AMENITIES AND ACTIVITIES: Parking available (outdoor, for visitors and residents). *10 lounges with:* TVs (2), pianos (2) and fireplaces (4). Guest suites available ($120.00/night). *Residence has a:* library, visiting library, barber/beauty shop and laundry room(s) (no cost). Banking services on premises (bi-weekly). Mail delivered to private mailbox with key. *Recreation Facilities*: pool table, exercise room, craft room, card room, auditorium with stage and wellness centre. Recreation hotline for visually impaired residents. Posted schedule of activities. Internal newsletter for residents. *Recreational Programs*: exercise, shopping, theatre, parties, entertainment, art classes, pet visiting, day trips, religious services and volunteer opportunities.
OTHER SERVICES: *Housekeeping*: daily and weekly. *Laundry*: linen & towel (included in fee); personal (extra cost for Retirement Living; included on ADL unit only). 24-hour security. Telephone (extra cost - Revera Telco). Cable TV (extra cost). Utilities (included in fee).
RENTAL INFORMATION: Rates may vary. Studio - $2,889.00/month & up; 1-bedroom - $3,940.00/month & up; 2-bedroom - $5,985.00/month & up. Extra cost for 2nd person sharing suite ($721.00/month). Rent paid monthly. *Payment Options*: pre-authorized payments. Credit card option available for short-term stays. Rent increases are a set percentage as per Provincial Tenancy Legislation, annual for resident with 90 days' notice given. Short-term respite and trial stays available.

REVERA - RAYOAK PLACE

1340 York Mills Road, Toronto, ON M3A 3R1
Tel: (855) 573-8372 • Toll Free: (855) 573-8372
Email: **rayoak@reveraliving.com**
Website: **www.reveraliving.com/rayoak**
Contact: **Executive Director or Lifestyle Consultant**
Capacity: **68 residents** • Subsidies: **none**
Price: **$3,085.00/month and up**

Keep living your life, your way, at Rayoak Place. You'll find the range of services, amenities and choices that fit your lifestyle and requirements – all in a warm and safe environment. Rayoak Place is a beautiful single-storey residence, with natural light spilling from skylights, creating a bright and cheerful atmosphere. Our cozy community is conveniently close to shopping, churches, a seniors' centre, medical services, the highway and public transportation. Everything is designed to enable you to maintain your independence and privacy, enjoy a full social life, and participate in the activities you love. Our caring and friendly staff and appealing accommodations support who you are and how you want to live in freedom and comfort. With retirement living at Rayoak Place, you change your address, not your life. *Rayoak Place is part of the Revera family, one of North America's leading and most trusted providers of seniors' accommodation, care and services since 1961.*

RESIDENCE INFORMATION: 27 years in operation. *Near:* Victoria Park Avenue and York Mills Road. Decorated in 2010. Handrails in hallways. 1 floor, no elevators. Wheelchair accessible. Central PA system. *Funding Base:* Corporate/for profit. *Owned and managed by:* Revera Inc. 65 units. *Average Waiting Period*: none. *Average Age*: 81. Can accommodate cognitively impaired people (Assisted Living available). Can accommodate physically challenged people. Smoking allowed (designated area outside). *Procedures to leave the premises on a temporary basis...*notify staff & sign out at Reception. *Languages:* English, Greek, Macedonian, Arabic, Mandarin, Portuguese, Spanish & Tagalog. Will accept Public Guardian and Trustee clients. Main doors of residence secured at all times. *Close to:* Public Transit, Shopping, Churches, Seniors' Centre, Library, Major Highway and Local Hospital (North York General Hospital). Member of ORCA. Licensed under the Retirement Homes Act.
STAFFING: *Available Staff/Services*: Social Work (CCAC), Recreation Therapy, Occupational Therapy (CCAC), Visiting Dentist, Physiotherapy (CCAC), Denturist, Dietitian (CCAC), Companions, Podiatry, Chaplaincy, Speech Pathology (CCAC), Chiropody, Audiology/Hearing Clinic, Registered Health Care Professionals and Foot Care Nurse. *External services arranged by:* residence and/or family/resident. Staff trained *re*: visually, hearing and cognitively impaired. 24-hour nursing staff. RPNs and PSWs on staff. Visiting MD (1 physician weekly & on call as required). Can retain own MD. Police Check or Vulnerable Person Screening is done for all new staff and volunteers.
HEALTH SERVICES: Medication administration and/or supervision. Vitals monitored if required. Will accept and provide special assistance for residents who require oxygen. Assistance with dressing available (cost). Weekly assistance with bathing available (cost). Care plans done. Different levels of care available. Falls Prevention Program and exercise program. Lab service (visiting). Residents can purchase outside resources and use agency of their choice. MD visits residents in their rooms/suites. Clinic area for medical visits. Will help locate higher level of care if needed (referral to a Revera residence).
ACCOMMODATION: *Choice of suites available*: private studio suites (65). *In all suites*: locks, storage, window coverings, light fixtures, fire alarm, smoke detector, heat detector, sprinkler, call bell, emergency response system with wearable pendant/bracelet, air conditioning (central) and thermostats for heating & cooling. Private bathrooms with call bells, grab bars and showers with non-slip surfaces. In-suite cable TV provided by residence (residence charges extra). Can have own phone number if resident arranges with phone company (residence charges extra). Unfurnished suites, furnished suites available for short

stays. *Restrictions on electrical appliances*: appliances are welcome based on a safety assessment. Pets allowed (as per Pet Policy within Tenancy Agreement).

DINING SERVICE: All meals included in fee and served in dining room daily. *Sittings per meal:* Breakfast: 1, Lunch: 1, Dinner: 1. *Menu choices available:* Breakfast: 2, Lunch: 2, Dinner: 2. *Guest Meals*: Breakfast $5.00, Lunch $7.00, Dinner $10.00. *Special Diets*: Vegetarian, Low Salt and Diabetic. Tray service to room if ill (no charge for a maximum time of 4 days). 3 snacks/day. Party facilities. Skylights. Full view of, and entrance to protected courtyard. Aquarium.

AMENITIES AND ACTIVITIES: Parking available (outdoor, for visitors and residents). *3 lounges with:* TV (1), piano (1) and fireplace (1). Guest suites available. *Residence has a:* library, visiting library, barber/beauty shop, visiting hairdresser and laundry room(s) (no cost). Mail delivered to main desk. *Recreation Facilities*: craft room, card room, recreation/craft room and music lounge. Posted schedule of activities. Internal newsletter for residents. *Recreational Programs*: exercise, shopping, parties, entertainment, art classes, pet visiting, day trips and arts & recreational leisure programs.

OTHER SERVICES: *Housekeeping*: weekly (included in fee). *Laundry*: linen, towel & personal (included in fee). Either staff or resident label clothing (cost if done by staff). Family can purchase labels and apply to clothing themselves. Transportation for group social activities. 24-hour security. Nightly security checks. Telephone & Cable TV (extra cost). Utilities (included in fee).

RENTAL INFORMATION: Rates may vary. Private studio suite - $3,085.00/month & up. Extra cost for 2nd person sharing suite. Rent paid monthly. *Payment Options*: pre-authorized payments and credit card. Rent increases are a set percentage as per Provincial Tenancy Legislation, annual for resident with 3 months' notice given. Short-term respite and trial stays available.

REVERA - TERRACE GARDENS

3705 Bathurst Street, Toronto, ON M6A 2E8
Tel: (855) 573-8372 • Toll Free: (855) 573-8372
Email: **terracegardens@reveraliving.com**
Website: **www.reveraliving.com/terracegardens**
Contact: **Executive Director or Lifestyle Consultant**
Capacity: **78 residents** • Subsidies: **none**
Price: **$2,124.00/month and up**

Keep living your life, your way, at Terrace Gardens. Here, you'll find the range of services, amenities and choices that fit your lifestyle and requirements – all in a warm and safe environment. Enjoy all the conveniences of quality Jewish retirement. We're located in a beautiful and established residential neighbourhood within Toronto's Jewish community, close to a wide variety of stores, banks, synagogues, public transit, and the highway. Terrace Gardens is a kosher-certified residence offering a full range of care services, with the feel of a small and close community. Everything here is designed to enable you to maintain your independence and privacy, enjoy a full social life, and participate in the activities that you love. With retirement living at Terrace Gardens, you change your address, not your life. *Terrace Gardens is part of the Revera family, one of North America's leading and most trusted providers of seniors' accommodation, care and services since 1961.*

RESIDENCE INFORMATION: 29 years in operation. *On:* Bathurst Street and Wilson Avenue. Decorated in 2009. Handrails in hallways. 5 floors, 2 elevators. Wheelchair accessible. Central PA system. *Funding Base:* Corporate/for profit. *Owned and managed by:* Revera Inc. 62 units. *Average Waiting Period*: none. *Average Age*: 80. Can accommodate cognitively impaired people (various levels of care for individuals with Alzheimer's or other dementias). Can accommodate physically challenged people (residents using wheelchairs, walkers and scooters). Residents have a dress code (casual). Smoking allowed (exterior designated areas). Alcohol allowed. *Procedures to leave the premises on a temporary basis*...Short-term: inform Reception. Overnight & Holidays: inform charge staff or RN or Executive Director. *Languages:*

English, Hebrew, Yiddish, Russian, Polish, Spanish, Romanian, French & Hungarian. Will accept Public Guardian and Trustee clients. Main doors of residence secured at all times. *Close to:* Public Transit, Shopping, Synagogues, Seniors' Centre, Library, Major Highway and Local Hospitals (Sunnybrook Health Sciences Centre, North York General, Humber River Regional Hospital – Finch Street & Church Street Sites & Baycrest Hospital). *Predominant Cultural Group:* Jewish. Member of ORCA. Licensed under the Retirement Homes Act.

STAFFING: *Available Staff/Services*: Pharmacy, Social Work (CCAC), Recreation Therapy, Occupational Therapy (CCAC), Visiting Dentist, Physiotherapy (CCAC), Dietitian (CCAC), Companions, Podiatry, Chaplaincy, Speech Pathology (CCAC), Chiropody and 24-hour Supervision. *External services arranged by:* residence and/or family/resident. Staff trained *re*: visually, hearing and cognitively impaired. 24-hour nursing and other staff. RPNs, HCAs and PSWs on staff. Visiting MD (2 times/week with possible house calls available). Can retain own MD. Staff members are bonded. Police Check or Vulnerable Person Screening is done for all new staff.

HEALTH SERVICES: Medication administration and/or supervision. Vitals monitored if required. Will accept and provide special assistance for residents who require oxygen, catheters, ostomies and feeding tubes. Assistance with dressing available (cost). Weekly assistance with bathing available (cost). Care plans done. Different levels of care available. Private Duty/Extra Care available. Assisted Living Area. Separate unit for residents with dementia. Lab service (visiting). Residents can purchase outside resources and use agency of their choice. MD visits residents in their rooms/suites. Clinic area for medical visits. Will help locate higher level of care if needed (will provide higher level of care if needed or assist in finding other information; referral to other Revera residences).

ACCOMMODATION: *Choice of suites available*: private & shared suites. *In all suites*: locks, kitchenette, bar fridge, microwave, storage, window coverings, light fixtures, sprinkler, heat detector, carbon monoxide detector, call bell, emergency response system with wearable pendant/bracelet, air conditioning (central) and thermostats for heating & cooling. Private bathrooms (shared suites share 1 bathroom for 2 residents) with call bells, grab bars and showers with non-slip surfaces. In-suite cable TV provided by residence (residence charges extra). Can have own phone number if resident arranges with phone company (residence charges extra). Unfurnished suites, furnished suites available for short stays. *Restrictions on electrical appliances*: no hot plates or stove/ovens; microwave and automatic shut-off kettle welcome. Suites can be shared (married couples or roommate chosen by residence), roommate picked by residence staff. Pets allowed (as per Pet Policy within Tenancy Agreement).

DINING SERVICE: Certified COR Kosher. Cholov Yisroel Milk products available. All meals included in fee and served in dining room daily. *Sittings per meal:* Breakfast: 1, Lunch: 1, Dinner: 1. *Menu choices available:* Breakfast: 3, Lunch: 2, Dinner: 2. *Guest Meals*: Breakfast $8.00, Lunch $12.00, Dinner $18.00. *Special Diets*: Vegetarian, Kosher, Low Salt, Diabetic, Puree, Lactose Free, Renal and Others. Tray service to room if ill (no charge for a maximum time of 4 days). 2 snacks/day. Take out lunches and dinners available upon advance request. Party facilities.

AMENITIES AND ACTIVITIES: Parking available (outdoor, for visitors and residents). *8 lounges with:* TVs (2) and piano (1). *Residence has a:* library, chapel, barber/beauty shop and visiting hairdresser. Residence provides newspaper delivery to main desk. Mail delivered to private mailbox with key. *Recreation Facilities*: exercise room, craft room, card room, recreation lounge, computer area and theatre room. Posted schedule of activities. Internal newsletter for residents. *Recreational Programs*: exercise, shopping, theatre, parties, entertainment, art classes, pet visiting, day trips, bingo, baking, gardening, walking, special Shabbat & holiday dinners, movies and discussion groups.

OTHER SERVICES: *Housekeeping*: daily and weekly (included in fee). *Laundry*: linen, towel & personal (included in fee); dry cleaning (extra cost). Either staff or resident label clothing (cost if residence provides service). 24-hour security. Nightly security checks. Telephone & Cable TV (extra cost). Utilities (included in fee). Extra care available for dressing, bathing, eating & toileting, if necessary (extra cost).

RENTAL INFORMATION: Rates may vary. Shared - $2,124.00/month & up; private - $3,362.00/month & up. Extra cost for 2nd person sharing suite ($650.00/month). Rent paid monthly. *Payment Options*:

cheques, post-dated cheques, pre-authorized payments, cheque and charge card for short stay. Rent increases as per Provincial Tenancy Legislation, annual for resident with 3 months' notice given. Will help resident move into residence (extra cost). Short-term respite and trial stays available (both $120.00/day).

♦ TORONTO (SCARBOROUGH) ♦

ALEXIS LODGE RETIREMENT RESIDENCE

707 Ellesmere Road, Toronto, ON M1P 2W1
Tel: (416) 752-1923 • Fax: (416) 752-4750
Email: **alexislodge@on.aibn.com**
Website: **www.alexislodge.com**
Contact: **Christiana Egi**
Capacity: **50 residents**
Subsidies: **may be available through residence**
Price: **$1,600.00 - $3,000.00/month**

Beautiful non-institutional, home-like setting for people with Alzheimer's Disease and other forms of dementia. Residents use their own furnishings and mementos to assist in providing a familiar environment for them to live in. We provide a therapeutic program aimed at maintaining and prolonging their memory for as long as possible.

RESIDENCE INFORMATION: 15 years in operation. *Near:* Birchmount Road and Ellesmere Road. Decorated in 2010. Handrails in some of the hallways. 3 floors, no elevator. *Funding Base:* Corporate/for profit. 50 units. *Average Waiting Period*: varies. *Average Age*: 80. Can accommodate cognitively impaired people (Alzheimer's and brain injury). Smoke-free residence. *Procedures to leave the premises on a temporary basis*...Short-term: outings encouraged with staff permission. Overnight & Holidays: depends on the individual resident. *Languages:* English, Tamil, Hindi, Russian, Patua, Yoruba, Hausa, Ibo & Cantonese. Will accept Public Guardian and Trustee clients. Main doors of residence secured at all times. *Close to:* Public Transit, Shopping, Churches, Seniors' Centre, Library, Major Highway and Local Hospitals (The Scarborough Hospital - Grace & General Sites, Rouge Valley Health System - Centenary Health Centre Site). Member of ORCA. Licensed under the Retirement Homes Act.
STAFFING: *Available Staff/Services*: Pharmacy, Recreation Therapy, Occupational Therapy, Visiting Dentist, Denturist, Dietitian, Chaplaincy and Physiotherapy (available 3 times weekly). *External services arranged by:* residence and/or family/resident. Staff trained *re*: visually, hearing and cognitively impaired. 24-hour nursing and other staff. RNs and PSWs on staff. Visiting MD (bi-weekly or as required). Can retain own MD. Staff members are bonded. Police Check or Vulnerable Person Screening is done for all new staff.
HEALTH SERVICES: Medication administration and/or supervision. Vitals monitored if required. Will accept and provide special assistance for residents who require oxygen and catheters. Assistance with dressing available. Daily assistance with bathing available. Care plans done. Different levels of care available. Lab service (visiting, $25.00/visit). Residents can purchase outside resources and use agency of their choice. MD visits residents in their rooms/suites. Will help locate higher level of care if needed.
ACCOMMODATION: *Choice of suites available*: private, semi-private & shared rooms. *In all suites*: window coverings, light fixtures, linens, smoke detector and hardwood floors with matt finish. Shared bathrooms with grab bars, tubs and showers with non-slip surfaces and elevated toilet seats. In-suite cable TV provided by residence. Can have own phone extension number provided by residence. Furnished & unfurnished suites available. Suites can be shared. No pets allowed.
DINING SERVICE: All meals included in fee and served in dining room daily. *Menu choices available:* Breakfast: 2, Lunch: 2, Dinner: 2. *Guest Meals*: Breakfast $4.00, Lunch $4.00, Dinner $4.00. *Special Diets*: Vegetarian, Low Salt and Diabetic. Tray service to room if ill. 3 snacks/day. Party facilities. Open pantry.

AMENITIES AND ACTIVITIES: Parking available (outdoor, for visitors and residents). *3 lounges with:* TVs (3), piano (1) and computer (1). *Residence has a:* chapel and visiting hairdresser. Mail delivered to resident. Posted schedule of activities. *Recreational Programs*: exercise, parties, entertainment, art classes, pet visiting and walks.
OTHER SERVICES: *Housekeeping*: daily. *Laundry*: linen, towel & personal (included in fee). Transportation to medical appointments (through EMS). 24-hour security. Nightly security checks. Cable TV & Utilities (included in fee).
RENTAL INFORMATION: Rates may vary. We have shared rooms, semi-private and private rooms; the price reflects accordingly. Cost for sharing suite - fee is per person. Rent paid monthly. *Payment Options*: cheques, post-dated cheques, direct deposit and cash. Rent increases as per Provincial Tenancy Legislation. Short-term respite and trial stays available (both $65.00/day).

MCCOWAN RETIREMENT RESIDENCE

2881 Eglinton Avenue East, Toronto, ON M1J 0A2
Tel: (416) 266-4445 • Fax: (416) 264-8377
Email: **gina@mccowanrr.com**
Website: **www.mccowanRR.com**
Contact: **Gina Cook**
Capacity: **148 residents** • Subsidies: **none**
Price: **$2,800.00 - $6,550.00/month**

Located in the heart of Scarborough, offering a wide range of retirement living choices: from Independent to Supportive Living and featuring warm water aquafit, respite stays for short-term needs, or permanent residency. We also offer Memory Lane, a safe and secure residence option for those with Alzheimer's and dementia.

RESIDENCE INFORMATION: 10 years in operation. *Near:* McCowan Street and Eglinton Avenue. Decorated in 2005. 7 floors, 2 elevators. Wheelchair accessible. Central PA system. *Funding Base:* Corporate/for profit. *Managed by:* Greenwood Retirement Communities. 139 units. *Average Waiting Period*: none. *Average Age*: 85. Can accommodate cognitively impaired people (on Memory Lane, our secured 6th floor). Can accommodate physically challenged people with restrictions (1-person pivot transfer). Smoking allowed (designated area outside). Alcohol allowed. *Procedures to leave the premises on a temporary basis*...sign out at the Reception Desk. *Languages:* English. Will accept Public Guardian and Trustee clients. Main doors of residence secured at night only. *Close to:* Public Transit, Shopping, Churches, Synagogues, Seniors' Centre, Library, Major Highway and Local Hospital (The Scarborough Hospital – General Site). Member of ORCA. Licensed under the Retirement Homes Act.
STAFFING: *Available Staff/Services*: Pharmacy, Social Work (CCAC), Recreation Therapy, Occupational Therapy (CCAC), Visiting Dentist, Physiotherapy (CCAC), Dietitian, Companions and Podiatry. *External services arranged by:* family/resident. Staff trained *re*: visually, hearing and cognitively impaired. 24-hour nursing and other staff. RPNs, PSWs and UCPs on staff. Visiting MD (once/week). Can retain own MD. Staff members are bonded. Police Check or Vulnerable Person Screening is done for all new staff.
HEALTH SERVICES: Medication administration and/or supervision. Vitals monitored if required. Will accept and provide special assistance for residents who require oxygen, catheters and ostomies. Weekly assistance with bathing available (cost). *Extra baths:* $20.00/bath. Care plans done. Different levels of care available. Private Duty/Extra Care available ($40.00/hour). Separate unit for residents with dementia. Lab service (visiting). Residents can purchase outside resources and use agency of their choice. MD visits residents in their rooms/suites. Clinic area for medical visits. Will help locate higher level of care if needed (through care conferencing).
ACCOMMODATION: *Choice of suites available*: studio & 1-bedroom suites, all private. *In all suites*: locks, kitchenette, bar fridge, microwave, storage, window coverings, light fixtures, fire alarm, smoke

detector, sprinkler, call bell, emergency response system with wearable pendant/bracelet, air conditioning (each suite has their own air conditioning and heating unit) and thermostats for heating & cooling. Private bathrooms with call bells, grab bars and showers with non-slip surfaces. In-suite cable TV provided by residence (residence charges extra $59.36/month). Unfurnished suites, furnished suites available for short stays. *Restrictions on electrical appliances*: no hot plates or toaster ovens. Suites can be shared (by couples only). Pets allowed (looked after by resident).

DINING SERVICE: All meals included in fee and served in dining room daily. *Sittings per meal:* Breakfast: 1, Lunch: 2, Dinner: 2. *Menu choices available:* Breakfast: 2, Lunch: 2, Dinner: 2. *Guest Meals*: Breakfast $6.00, Lunch $10.00, Dinner $15.00. *Special Diets*: Vegetarian, Low Salt, Diabetic and Others (as resident requests). 2 snacks/day. Party facilities. Private dining room available for use by residents.

AMENITIES AND ACTIVITIES: Parking available (outdoor, for visitors and residents). *3 lounges with:* TV (1), pool table, exercise equipment (1) and library (1). Guest suites available ($90.00/night). *Residence has a:* library, visiting library, chapel, barber/beauty shop, laundry room(s) (no cost) and tuck/gift shop (open 2 days/week). Resident can arrange newspaper delivery to main desk (extra cost). Mail delivered to private mailbox with key. *Recreation Facilities*: pool table, billiards, exercise room, craft room, card room, swimming pool, movie theatre and internet lounge. Posted schedule of activities. Internal newsletter for residents. *Recreational Programs*: exercise, shopping, theatre, parties, entertainment/bi-weekly outside entertainers, art classes, pet visiting and day trips.

OTHER SERVICES: *Housekeeping*: daily and weekly (included in fee; weekly on Independent and daily on Supportive Care). *Laundry*: linen & towel (included in fee); personal (included on Supportive Care; $95.00/month for à la carte) & dry cleaning (extra cost). Either staff or resident label clothing (service provided if required for $50.00 including labels). Transportation for group social activities. 24-hour security. Nightly security checks. Telephone & Cable TV (extra cost). Utilities (included in fee).

RENTAL INFORMATION: Rates may vary. Extra cost for 2nd person sharing suite ($670.00/month; $1,670.00/month if Supportive Care). Rent paid monthly. *Payment Options*: post-dated cheques and pre-authorized payments. Rent increases indexed to inflation as per Provincial Tenancy Legislation, annual for resident with 3 months' notice given. Will help resident move into residence. Short-term respite ($100.00/day) and trial stays ($70.00/day) available (if Supportive Care with medication administration then $112.00/day).

RETIREMENT SUITES BY THE LAKE

2121 Kingston Road, Toronto, ON M1N 1T5
Tel: (416) 267-2121 • Fax: (416) 267-2213
Email: **info@rsbl.ca**
Website: **www.suitesbythelake.ca**
Contact: **Debbie Casquenette**
Capacity: **110 residents** • Subsidies: **none**
Price: **$2,800.00 - $5,000.00/month**

Retirement Suites By the Lake is truly one of Toronto's best kept secrets! This elegantly appointed residence, located between Rosetta McClain Gardens and the Scarborough Bluffs, boasts an assortment of exceptionally large, competitively priced resident suites. Retirement Suites By the Lake is the ideal location for comfortable convenient retirement living.

RESIDENCE INFORMATION: 9 years in operation. *Near:* Birchmount Road and Kingston Road. Decorated in 2007. Handrails in hallways. 4 floors, 2 elevators. Wheelchair accessible. *Funding Base:* Corporate/for profit. *Managed by:* Greenwood Retirement Communities. 92 units. *Average Waiting Period*: none. *Average Age*: 87. Can sometimes accommodate cognitively impaired people (assessment required). Can accommodate physically challenged people with restrictions (assessment required). Smoke-free residence. Alcohol allowed (assessment required). *Restrictions around Visitors/Visiting Hours:* sign in/out

register. *Procedures to leave the premises on a temporary basis*...communication to Management/staff. *Languages:* English, French, Italian, German & Filipino. Will accept Public Guardian and Trustee clients. Main doors of residence secured at night only. *Close to:* Public Transit, Shopping, Churches, Seniors' Centre, Library, Major Highway and Local Hospitals (The Toronto East General Hospital & Rouge Valley Health System). Member of ORCA. Licensed under the Retirement Homes Act.

STAFFING: *Available Staff/Services*: Pharmacy, Social Work (CCAC), Recreation Therapy, Occupational Therapy (CCAC), Visiting Dentist, Physiotherapy, Dietitian (CCAC), Podiatry (CCAC), Chaplaincy, Speech Pathology (CCAC), Chiropody, Audiology/Hearing Clinic, Physician (in-house), Physiotherapist and Chiropodist. *External services arranged by:* residence and/or family/resident. Staff trained *re*: visually, hearing and cognitively impaired. 24-hour nursing and other staff. RPNs, HCAs, PSWs and UCPs on staff. Visiting MD (once/week). Can retain own MD. Police Check or Vulnerable Person Screening is done for all new staff.

HEALTH SERVICES: Medication administration and/or supervision. Vitals monitored if required. Will accept (but not provide special assistance for) residents who require ostomies. Will accept and provide special assistance for residents who require oxygen. Assistance with dressing available (cost). Care plans done. Different levels of care available. Private Duty/Extra Care available ($180.00 to $650.00/month). Lab service (visiting, $25.00/visit). Residents can purchase outside resources and use agency of their choice. Clinic area for medical visits. Will help locate higher level of care if needed (will assist with locating a higher level care facility through CCAC; all residents are able to stay in our residence with appropriate care plan in place).

ACCOMMODATION: *Choice of suites available*: all private suites; 1- bedroom (77) & studio (15) suites. *In all suites*: locks, kitchenette, bar fridge, microwave, window coverings, light fixtures, fire alarm, smoke detector, sprinkler, call bell, air conditioning (individual heating/air conditioning) and thermostats for heating & cooling. Private bathrooms with call bells, grab bars, tubs and showers with non-slip surfaces. In-suite cable TV provided by residence (residence charges extra $35.00/month). Can have own phone extension number provided by residence (residence charges extra $35.00/month). Unfurnished suites, furnished suites available for short stays. *Restrictions on electrical appliances*: no electrical appliances allowed in suites of cognitively impaired residents. Pets allowed (dog owners occupy suites with a walkout to patio).

DINING SERVICE: All meals included in fee and served in dining room daily. *Sittings per meal:* Breakfast: 1, Lunch: 2, Dinner: 2. *Menu choices available:* Breakfast: 1, Lunch: 2, Dinner: 2. *Guest Meals*: Breakfast $6.50, Lunch $6.50, Dinner $10.00. *Special Diets*: Vegetarian, Low Salt, Diabetic, Calorie Reduced, Minced and Pureed. Tray service to room if ill (no charge as long as doctor orders). 1 snack/day. Party facilities. Spacious dining area with large windows providing extensive lighting.

AMENITIES AND ACTIVITIES: Parking available (outdoor, for visitors: free and residents: $25.00/month). *3 lounges with:* TVs (2), piano (1), fireplaces (2) and internet (1). Guest suites available ($89.00/night). *Residence has a:* library, chapel, barber/beauty shop, visiting hairdresser and laundry room(s) (no cost). Residence provides newspaper delivery to individual suite. Mail delivered to individual suite. *Recreation Facilities*: exercise room, craft room, card room, gazebo, patio and deck. Posted schedule of activities. Internal newsletter for residents. *Recreational Programs*: exercise, shopping, theatre, parties, entertainment, art classes, pet visiting, day trips, manicures, Happy Hour and pub.

OTHER SERVICES: *Housekeeping*: weekly (included in fee). *Laundry*: linen & towel (included in fee); personal & dry cleaning (extra cost). Laundry room available for residents to do personal laundry – soap and bounce sheets are free. Transportation for group social activities. 24-hour security. Nightly security checks. Telephone & Cable TV (extra cost). Utilities (included in fee). Inquire about current promotions.

RENTAL INFORMATION: Rates may vary. Studios - $2,800.00/month & up; 1-bedroom suites - $3,300.00/month & up. Extra cost for 2nd person sharing suite ($600.00/month). Rent paid monthly. *Payment Options*: pre-authorized payments. Rent increases indexed to inflation, annual for resident with 3 months' notice given. Will help resident move into residence. Short-term respite and trial stays available (both $89.00/day).

SCARBOROUGH RETIREMENT RESIDENCE

148 Markham Road, Toronto, ON M1M 2Z8
Tel: (416) 264-3566
Email: **mscordamaglia@clmi.ca**
Website: **www.scarboroughretirement.ca**
Contact: **Maureen Scordamaglia**
Capacity: **137 residents** • Subsidies: **none**
Price: **$2,470.00 - $4,000.00/month (rates may vary)**

Scarborough Retirement Residence has been voted the #1 Retirement Residence by the Scarborough community. It is a Premier Boutique Retirement Experience, offering accommodations in a full service community for seniors who wish to maintain their independence. This commitment is reflected by the number of our on-site amenities such as a chapel with daily mass, air purification system for promoting optimal health, in-house physiotherapy program, in-house physician and dynamic social planning. We pride ourselves on a level of excellence that comes from dedicated and caring staff. We also accommodate short-term residency for respite or trial stays.

RESIDENCE INFORMATION: 25 years in operation. *Near:* Markham Road and Kingston Road. Handrails in some of the hallways. 7 floors, 2 elevators. Wheelchair accessible. Central PA system. *Funding Base:* Corporate/for profit. *Owned by:* Josee Lafontaine. 124 units. *Average Waiting Period*: varies. *Average Age*: 84. Can sometimes accommodate cognitively impaired people (mild cognitive impairment). Can accommodate physically challenged people (some restrictions). Smoke-free residence. Alcohol allowed. *Restrictions around Visitors/Visiting Hours:* visitors are required to sign in/out of the building. *Procedures to leave the premises on a temporary basis...*notify Health & Wellness Department/Reception Desk. *Languages:* English & Filipino. Will accept Public Guardian and Trustee clients. Main doors of residence secured at all times. *Close to:* Public Transit, Shopping, Churches, Seniors' Centre, Library, Major Highway and Local Hospital (The Scarborough Hospital - General Site & Rouge Valley Health System - Centenary Health Centre Site). *Predominant Cultural Group:* Catholic. Member of ORCA. Licensed under the Retirement Homes Act.

STAFFING: *Available Staff/Services*: Pharmacy, Recreation Therapy, Occupational Therapy (CCAC), Physiotherapy, Companions, Chaplaincy, Audiology/Hearing Clinic, Foot Care and Wellness Programs. *External services arranged by:* residence and/or family/resident. Staff trained *re*: visually, hearing and cognitively impaired. 24-hour nursing staff. RPNs and PSWs on staff. Visiting MD (2 times/week & on call 24-hours/day for emergencies). Can retain own MD. Police Check or Vulnerable Person Screening is done for all new staff.

HEALTH SERVICES: Medication administration and/or supervision. Vitals monitored if required. Will accept and provide special assistance for residents who require oxygen. Assistance with dressing available (cost). Weekly assistance with bathing available ($62.00/month). Care plans done. Different levels of care available. Private Duty/Extra Care available ($386.25 to $772.50/month). Lab service (visiting, $20.00/visit). Residents can purchase outside resources and use agency of their choice. Clinic area for medical visits. Will help locate higher level of care if needed (CCAC & long-term care papers).

ACCOMMODATION: *Choice of suites available*: various sized studio (83) & 1-bedroom (41) suites. *In all suites*: locks, storage, window coverings, light fixtures, linens, fire alarm, smoke detector, emergency response system with wearable pendant/bracelet, air conditioning (central) and thermostats for heating & cooling. Some studios & all 1-bedroom suites include kitchenettes. Private bathrooms with grab bars, tubs and showers with non-slip surfaces. In-suite cable TV provided by residence (residence charges extra $45.14/month). Can have own phone number provided by residence (residence charges extra). Furnished & unfurnished suites available. *Restrictions on electrical appliances*: must pass inspection. Suites can be shared (by couples only). Pets allowed (pending the signing of a Pet Contract).

DINING SERVICE: All meals included in fee and served in dining room daily. *Sittings per meal:* Breakfast: 1, Lunch: 1, Dinner: 4. *Menu choices available:* Breakfast: 2, Lunch: 2, Dinner: 2. *Guest Meals*: Breakfast $10.00, Lunch $10.00, Dinner $12.00. *Special Diets*: Vegetarian, Low Salt, Diabetic, Low Potassium, Minced, Calorie Reduced and Celiac. Tray service to room if ill (no charge as long as doctor orders). Unlimited snacks available at any time. We offer a 24-hour Tea Room with cookies, fruit, tea and coffee available to our residents. Party facilities.
AMENITIES AND ACTIVITIES: Parking available (outdoor, for visitors and residents). *8 lounges with:* TVs (2), pianos (2) and stereo & records (1). Guest suites available ($95.00/night). *Residence has a:* visiting library, chapel, barber/beauty shop, visiting hairdresser, laundry room(s) (no cost) and tuck/gift shop (open various hours; 7 days/week). Resident can arrange newspaper delivery to main desk. Mail delivered to private mailbox with key. *Recreation Facilities*: pool table, billiards, exercise room, craft room, card room, resident's kitchen, auditorium, tea room, physiotherapy room and garden club room. Posted schedule of activities. Internal newsletter for residents. *Recreational Programs*: exercise, shopping, theatre, parties, entertainment, art classes, pet visiting, day trips, games room with billiard table, card games, social groups, bingo, Community Theatre, Social Teas and Happy Hour.
OTHER SERVICES: *Housekeeping*: daily and weekly (weekly is included in fee; daily extra cost). *Laundry*: linen & towel (included in fee); personal ($154.50/week) & dry cleaning (extra cost). Transportation for group social activities ($7.00/trip). 24-hour security. Telephone ($30.00 or $40.00/month). Cable TV ($45.14/month). Utilities (included in fee).
RENTAL INFORMATION: Rates may vary. Extra cost for 2nd person sharing suite ($670.00/month). Rent paid monthly. *Payment Options*: pre-authorized payments. Rent increases as per Provincial Tenancy Legislation, annual for resident with 3 months' notice given. Short-term respite and trial stays available (both $95.00/day).

SHEPHERD TERRACE RETIREMENT RESIDENCE

3760 Sheppard Avenue East, Toronto, ON M1T 3K9
Tel: (416) 609-5700 • Fax: (416) 609-8329
Email: **nbrooker@shepherdvillage.org**
Website: **www.shepherdvillage.org**
Contact: **Noreen Brooker**
Capacity: **160 residents** • Subsidies: **none**
Price: **$3,000.00 - $6,500.00/month**

Warm and caring Christian environment. Access to swimming pool, wellness centre, salon and spa, pharmacy, tuck shop, adult day program, church in the village. Smoke-free environment. This residence is part of a retirement community that offers 5 different lifestyles from independent living to long-term care.

RESIDENCE INFORMATION: 23 years in operation. *Near:* Kennedy Road and Sheppard Avenue. Decorated in 2009. Handrails in hallways. 6 floors, 4 elevators. Wheelchair accessible. Central PA system. *Funding Base:* Not-for-profit. *Owned and managed by:* Shepherd Village Inc. 141 units. *Average Waiting Period*: varies. *Average Age*: 85. Can accommodate cognitively impaired people with restrictions (no wandering). Can accommodate physically challenged people. Smoke-free residence. Alcohol allowed (no alcohol in public areas). *Procedures to leave the premises on a temporary basis*...inform staff and sign out. *Languages:* English. Will accept Public Guardian and Trustee clients. Main doors of residence secured at all times. *Close to:* Public Transit, Shopping, Churches, Seniors' Centre, Library, Major

Did you know?

The phone number for Telehealth Ontario, a free, confidential health advice & information line staffed 24/7 by Registered Nurses is **(866) 797-0000.**

Highway and Local Hospitals (The Scarborough Hospital - Grace & General Sites). Member of ORCA. Joint long-term care CARF accreditation; long-term care is OLTCA accredited. Licensed under the Retirement Homes Act.

STAFFING: *Available Staff/Services*: Pharmacy, Social Work, Recreation Therapy, Occupational Therapy, Visiting Dentist, Physiotherapy, Denturist, Dietitian, Companions, Podiatry, Chaplaincy, Speech Pathology, Chiropody, Audiology/Hearing Clinic, Ophthalmologist, Optician and Massage Therapist. *External services arranged by:* residence and/or family/resident. Staff trained *re*: visually, hearing and cognitively impaired. 24-hour nursing and other staff. RNs, RPNs and PSWs on staff. In-house MDs available 3 days/week on-site & on 24-hour call. Can retain own MD. Police Check or Vulnerable Person Screening is done for all new staff.

HEALTH SERVICES: Medication administration and/or supervision. Vitals monitored if required. Will accept and provide special assistance for residents who require oxygen and ostomies. Assistance with dressing available. Weekly assistance with bathing available. Care plans done. Different levels of care available. Private Duty/Extra Care available ($40.00 to $70.00/day). Assisted Living Area (1 month waiting period). Lab service (visiting, $20.00/visit). Residents can purchase outside resources and use agency of their choice. MD visits residents in their rooms/suites. Clinic area for medical visits. Will help locate higher level of care if needed (assistance with completing CCAC papers; we also have a long-term care facility).

ACCOMMODATION: *Choice of suites available*: private suites, choice of sizes available (231 to 757 sq. ft.). *In all suites*: locks, storage, window coverings, light fixtures, linens, fire alarm, smoke detector, sprinkler, call bell, emergency response system with wearable pendant/bracelet, air conditioning (central) and thermostats for heating & cooling. Either private or shared kitchenette & bar fridge. Stove in some suites. Private bathrooms with call bells, grab bars, tubs and showers with non-slip surfaces. In-suite cable TV provided by residence. Can have own phone number if resident arranges with phone company. Furnished & unfurnished suites available. *Restrictions on electrical appliances*: must be tested. Suites can be shared (with spouse or sibling). Pets allowed (resident must be able to provide total care, Pet Policy Agreement).

DINING SERVICE: All meals included in fee and served in dining room daily. *Sittings per meal:* Breakfast: 2, Lunch: 2, Dinner: 2. *Menu choices available:* Breakfast: 2, Lunch: 2, Dinner: 2. *Guest Meals*: Breakfast $5.00, Lunch $6.00, Dinner $10.00. *Special Diets*: Vegetarian, Low Salt, Diabetic, Gluten Free and Others.

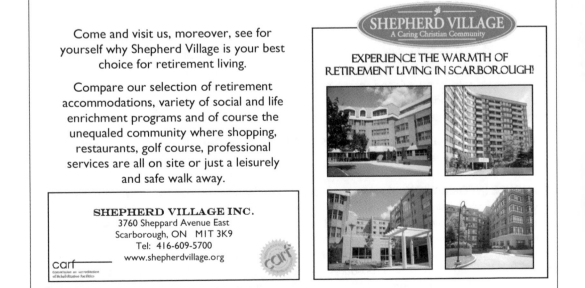

Tray service to room if ill (no charge as long as doctor orders). 3 snacks/day. Party facilities. Special area for private dining; restaurant, café and convenience store open to the public.

AMENITIES AND ACTIVITIES: Parking available (outdoor, for visitors and residents). *10 lounges with:* TVs (2), piano (1), pool table and ping pong (1). Guest suites available ($70.00/night). *Residence has a:* library, chapel, barber/beauty shop, laundry room(s) ($1.50/washer load, $1.50/dryer load), tuck/gift shop (open Monday to Friday; 9:00 a.m. - 5:00 p.m.). Banking services on premises (cash machine and cash advance service). Residence provides newspaper delivery to individual suite. Mail delivered to private mailbox with key. *Recreation Facilities*: pool table, billiards, shuffleboard, exercise room, craft room, card room, swimming pool, computer, games room, art studio and 3 hole mini-golf. Posted schedule of activities. Internal newsletter for residents. *Recreational Programs*: exercise, shopping, theatre, parties, entertainment, art classes, pet visiting, day trips, crafts, games, spiritual programming, movies and entertainment.

OTHER SERVICES: *Housekeeping*: weekly (included in fee). *Laundry*: linen & towel (included in fee); personal ($20.00/load or self-serve coin operated machines). Either staff or resident label clothing (included in fee). Transportation for group social activities (cost varies by outing). 24-hour security. Nightly security checks. Cable TV & Utilities (included in fee).

RENTAL INFORMATION: Rates may vary. Extra cost for 2nd person sharing suite (varies). Rent paid monthly. *Payment Options*: cheques, post-dated cheques and pre-authorized payments. Rent increases indexed to inflation as per Provincial Tenancy Legislation, annual for resident with 90 days' notice given. Short-term respite and trial stays available if space permits (both $120.00/day; fee prorated to number of days of occupancy).

STS. PETER AND PAUL RESIDENCE

221 Milner Avenue, Toronto, ON M1S 4P4
Tel: (416) 291-3900 • Fax: (416) 291-3918
Email: **office@stspeterandpaulresidence.com**
Website: **www.stspeterandpaulresidence.com**
Contact: **Marta Smalley**
Capacity: **63 units** • Subsidies: **none**
Price: **$2,352.00 - $2,410.00/month**

Sts. Peter and Paul Residence is a not-for-profit retirement residence operated by Sts. Peter and Paul Ukrainian Community Homes. We are located close to the 401 and easily accessed by TTC. For close to 30 years, the Residence has been offering seniors a choice of fully Independent Apartment Living or Assisted Living services in the retirement home. Amenities available to all residents include: banking, hairdresser, tuck shop, physiotherapy, foot care, voting day polling station. Retirement home care services include nutritious meals and snacks, medication administration, bathing assistance, and weekly housekeeping and laundry services and access to registered nursing staff 24-hours/day. Short-term trial and respite stays minimum 2 weeks are available. Facility tours available; book in advance.

INFORMATION PROVIDED BELOW APPLIES ONLY TO THE RETIREMENT HOME, and not to the Independent Living Apartment Wing.

RESIDENCE INFORMATION: 31 years in operation. *Near:* Markham Road and Highway 401. Decorated in 2003. Handrails in hallways. 6 floors, 2 elevators. Wheelchair accessible. Central PA system. *Funding Base:* Not-for-profit. *Owned by:* Sts. Peter and Paul Ukrainian Community Homes. *Average Waiting Period*: 2 - 3 weeks. *Average Age*: 88. Can accommodate cognitively impaired people with restrictions. Can accommodate physically challenged people (Assisted Living). Smoke-free residence. Alcohol allowed (bar lounge area and rooms only). *Procedures to leave the premises on a temporary basis*...notify Office/ Nursing Station. *Languages:* English & Ukrainian. Will accept Public Guardian and Trustee clients. Main doors of residence secured at all times. *Close to:* Public Transit, Shopping, Churches, Library, Major

Highway and Local Hospitals (Rouge Valley Health System & The Scarborough Hospital – General Site). *Predominant Cultural Group:* Ukrainian. Member of ORCA, ONPHA & OANHSS. Licensed under the Retirement Homes Act.

STAFFING: *Available Staff/Services*: Social Work (CCAC), Occupational Therapy (CCAC), Physiotherapy, Podiatry, Chaplaincy, Visiting Eye Clinic, Visiting Denturist and Lab Work. *External services arranged by:* residence and/or family/resident. 24-hour nursing staff. RNs, RPNs and PSWs on staff. Visiting MD (once/week & on call). Can retain own MD. Staff members are bonded. TB screening for all new staff. Police Check or Vulnerable Person Screening is done for all new staff.

HEALTH SERVICES: Medication administration and/or supervision (no IVs, no catheters). Vitals monitored if required. Will accept (but not provide special assistance for) residents who require oxygen and catheters. Assistance with dressing available ($152.00/month). Weekly assistance with bathing available. *Extra baths:* $25.00/half hour. Care plans done. Different levels of care available. Private Duty/Extra Care available. Assisted Living Area (2 - 3 week waiting period). Lab service (on-site). Residents can purchase outside resources and use agency of their choice. MD visits residents in their rooms/suites. Clinic area for medical visits. Will help locate higher level of care if needed (via CCAC).

ACCOMMODATION: *Choice of suites available*: private (63). *In all suites*: locks, window coverings, light fixtures, linens, fire alarm, smoke detector, call bell, air conditioning (incremental units) and thermostats for heating. Furniture if required - beds, lamps, dresser & night tables. Bathrooms (some shared, some private) with call bells and grab bars. In-suite cable TV if resident arranges with cable company. Can have own phone number if resident arranges with phone company. Furnished suites available on request. *Restrictions on electrical appliances*: no hot plates, toasters or microwaves. Suites can be shared (couples only; only cost of room is shared). Small and quiet pets only allowed.

DINING SERVICE: All meals included in fee and served in dining room daily. *Sittings per meal:* Breakfast: 1, Lunch: 1, Dinner: 1. *Menu choices available:* Breakfast: 2, Lunch: 2, Dinner: 2. *Guest Meals*: Breakfast $3.50, Lunch $10.00, Dinner $6.50. *Special Diets*: Vegetarian, Low Salt and Diabetic. Tray service to room if ill (no charge as long as doctor orders). 3 snacks/day. Party facilities.

AMENITIES AND ACTIVITIES: Parking available (outdoor, for visitors: free and residents: $20.00/month). *6 lounges with:* TVs (5) and day lounges (5). *Residence has a:* library, visiting library, chapel, barber/beauty shop, visiting hairdresser, laundry room(s) (no cost) and tuck/gift shop (open 10:00 a.m. - 12:00 p.m.). Banking services on premises (once/week). Resident can arrange newspaper delivery to individual suite. Mail delivered to private mailbox with key. *Recreation Facilities*: pool table, billiards, exercise room, greenhouse, craft room, card room, LLBO licensed bar and events room. Posted schedule of activities. *Recreational Programs*: exercise, parties, entertainment, pub nights, socials and guest speakers/seminars.

OTHER SERVICES: *Housekeeping*: weekly (included in fee; weekly and as needed). *Laundry*: linen, towel & personal (included in fee). Staff label clothing (included in fee). Dry cleaning is the resident's responsibility. 24-hour security. Nightly security checks. Utilities (included in fee).

RENTAL INFORMATION: Rates may vary. Private room/shared washroom - $2,352.00/month; private room/private washroom - $2,410.00/month. Cost for sharing suite - fee is per person. Rent paid monthly. *Payment Options*: cheques, post-dated cheques, cash and money order. Rent increases as per Provincial Tenancy Legislation, annual for resident with 3 months' notice given. Short-term respite and trial stays available (both $87.00/day, minimum 2 week stay).

Did you know?

The Government of Canada has produced *The Safe Living Guide: A Guide to Home Safety for Seniors*. It contains valuable tips on keeping your home safe as well as checklists for nutrition, physical activity and medications. It can be downloaded at: **www.phac-aspc.gc.ca/seniors-aines/publications/public/injury-blessure/safelive-securite/index-eng.php.**

VILLA PUGLIESE ASSISTED LIVING FACILITY

50 Gooderham Drive, Toronto, ON M1R 3G7
Tel: (416) 757-0836 • Fax: (416) 757-0836
Email: **r.volpe@rogers.com**
Website: **www.villapugliese.com**
Contact: **Rocchina Volpe**
Capacity: **10 residents** • Subsidies: **none**
Price: **$1,800.00 - $3,100.00/month**

A new Assisted Living residence complete with elevator, lift and ramp. Offering various levels of care and is an alternative to institutionalized living. We welcome brain injury residents. We provide comfort and supervision, assistance with daily tasks. Also offering transitional care after hospitalization or surgery. Long-term care, activities of daily living, respite care.

RESIDENCE INFORMATION: 9 years in operation. *Near:* Lawrence Avenue and Victoria Park Avenue. Decorated in 2008. 2 floors, 1 elevator. Wheelchair accessible. *Funding Base:* Corporate/for profit. *Owned by:* Rocchina Volpe. 7 units. *Average Waiting Period*: none. *Average Age*: 45. Can sometimes accommodate cognitively impaired people (mild dementia, brain injury, no wanderers). Can accommodate physically challenged people (brain injury, MS, stroke survivors). Smoking allowed (enclosed sunroom or outdoors). Alcohol allowed (strictly monitored). Visitors are encouraged to visit at any time. *Procedures to leave the premises on a temporary basis...*advance notice to staff. *Languages:* English, Italian, French & Russian. Will accept Public Guardian and Trustee clients. Main doors of residence secured at all times. *Close to:* Public Transit, Shopping, Churches, Seniors' Centre, Library, Major Highway and Local Hospitals (The Scarborough Hospital – Grace & General Sites & North York General Hospital).
STAFFING: *Available Staff/Services*: Pharmacy, Social Work (CCAC), Recreation Therapy, Occupational Therapy (CCAC), Physiotherapy (CCAC), Dietitian (CCAC), Podiatry (CCAC), Speech Pathology (CCAC) and Visiting Volunteers. *External services arranged by:* residence and/or family/resident. Staff trained *re*: visually, hearing and cognitively impaired. 24-hour staff. PSWs on staff. Visiting MD (as necessary). Can retain own MD. Staff members are bonded. Police Check or Vulnerable Person Screening is done for all new staff.
HEALTH SERVICES: Medication administration and/or supervision. Vitals monitored if required. Will accept and provide special assistance for residents who require catheters, ostomies and feeding tubes. Assistance with dressing available. Assistance with bathing available as needed. Care plans done. Different levels of care available. Residents can purchase outside resources and use agency of their choice. MD visits residents in their rooms/suites. Will help locate higher level of care if needed (refer to CCAC).
ACCOMMODATION: *Choice of suites available*: private (4) & shared (3) accommodation. *In all suites*: locks, storage, window coverings, light fixtures, linens, smoke detector and air conditioning (central). Bathrooms (2 bedrooms for each bathroom, 1 private bathroom) with grab bars, tubs and showers with non-slip surfaces and elevated toilet seats. In-suite cable TV provided by residence. Can have own phone number if resident arranges with phone company. Furnished & unfurnished suites available. Restrictions on electrical appliances. Suites can be shared, roommate picked by resident & residence staff. Pets allowed.
DINING SERVICE: All meals included in fee and served in dining room daily. *Sittings per meal:* Breakfast: 1, Lunch: 1, Dinner: 1. *Menu choices available:* Breakfast: 2, Lunch: 2, Dinner: 2. *Guest Meals*: Breakfast $5.00, Lunch $5.00, Dinner $5.00. *Special Diets*: Vegetarian, Low Salt, Diabetic and Others (as needed). Tray service to room if ill. 3 snacks/day. Party facilities. Open pantry.
AMENITIES AND ACTIVITIES: Parking available (outdoor, for visitors and residents). *1 lounge with:* TV (1). *Residence has a:* visiting hairdresser. Residence provides newspaper delivery to individual suite. Mail delivered to resident. *Recreation Facilities*: craft room. Posted schedule of activities. *Recreational Programs*: exercise, shopping, parties and day trips. Other activities can be arranged at resident's request.

OTHER SERVICES: *Housekeeping*: daily (included in fee). *Laundry*: linen, towel & personal (included in fee); dry cleaning (extra cost). Either staff or resident label clothing. Transportation to medical appointments. 24-hour security. Nightly security checks. Telephone (resident pays phone company). Cable TV & Utilities (included in fee).
RENTAL INFORMATION: Rates may vary. Shared accommodation starts at $60.00/day; private is $100.00/day. Extra cost for 2nd person sharing suite (couples rate available). Rent paid monthly. *Payment Options*: cheques and direct deposit. Rent increases as per Provincial Tenancy Legislation, annual for resident with 3 months' notice given. Will help resident move into residence (extra cost). Short-term respite and trial stays available (starting at $60.00/day).

♦ TRENTON ♦

THE CARRINGTON RETIREMENT RESIDENCE

114 Whites Road, Trenton, ON K8V 5P5
Tel: (613) 392-1615 • Fax: (613) 392-3879
Toll Free: (877) 392-1615
Email: **carrington@cogeco.net**
Website: **www.thecarringtonretirement.com**
Contact: **Patrice Murrant**
Capacity: **45 residents** • Subsidies: **none**
Price: **$1,650.00 - $2,850.00/month**

The Carrington Retirement serves the communities of Quinte West, in a relaxed country setting. *At The Carrington, warmth and caring are a way of life.*

RESIDENCE INFORMATION: 23 years in operation. *On:* Whites Road near CFB Trenton. Decorated in 2008. Handrails in hallways. 1 floor, no elevators. Wheelchair accessible. Central PA system. *Funding Base:* Corporate/for profit. *Owned by:* Carrington Properties Inc. *Managed by:* Eldercare Management & Consulting Corp. 38 units. *Average Waiting Period*: varies. *Average Age*: 85. Can sometimes accommodate cognitively impaired & physically challenged people (depending on assessment of level of care). Smoking allowed (outdoors). Alcohol allowed (Happy Hour). *Procedures to leave the premises on a temporary basis...*inform staff and have/take all medications. *Languages:* English. Will accept Public Guardian and Trustee clients. Main doors of residence secured at night only. *Close to:* Shopping, Churches, Seniors' Centre, Library, Major Highway and Local Hospital (Quinte Healthcare Corporation). Member of ORCA & Quinte West Chamber of Commerce. Licensed under the Retirement Homes Act.
STAFFING: *Available Staff/Services*: Pharmacy, Social Work (CCAC), Recreation Therapy, Occupational Therapy (CCAC), Physiotherapy (CCAC), Dietitian (CCAC), Companions, Podiatry, Chaplaincy, Speech Pathology (CCAC) and Audiology/Hearing Clinic. *External services arranged by:* residence and/or family/resident. Staff trained *re*: visually, hearing and cognitively impaired. 24-hour staff. RPNs, PSWs and UCPs on staff. Visiting MD (weekly). Can retain own MD. Police Check or Vulnerable Person Screening is done for all new staff.
HEALTH SERVICES: Medication administration and/or supervision. Vitals monitored if required. Will accept and provide special assistance for residents who require oxygen, catheters and ostomies. Assistance with dressing available. Weekly assistance with bathing available. Care plans done. Different levels of care available. Private Duty/Extra Care available ($19.00 to $25.00/hour). Lab service (on-site). Residents can purchase outside resources. MD visits residents in their rooms/suites. Will help locate higher level of care if needed (through the CCAC).

ACCOMMODATION: *Choice of suites available*: small private, large private & large suites. *In all suites*: locks, window coverings, light fixtures, linens, fire alarm, smoke detector, sprinkler, call bell, air conditioning (some suites have central, others have window units) and thermostats for heating. Private bathrooms with call bells and grab bars. In-suite cable TV provided by residence (residence charges extra $30.00/month). Can have own phone number if resident arranges with phone company. Furnished & unfurnished suites available. *Restrictions on electrical appliances*: pending safety assessment. Suites can be shared (pending availability of beds), roommate picked by resident & residence staff. Pets allowed (on a case-by-case basis).
DINING SERVICE: All meals included in fee and served in dining room daily. *Sittings per meal:* Breakfast: 1, Lunch: 1, Dinner: 1. *Menu choices available:* Breakfast: 1, Lunch: 2, Dinner: 2. *Guest Meals*: Breakfast $5.00, Lunch $7.00, Dinner $5.00. *Special Diets:* Vegetarian, Low Salt, Diabetic, Therapeutic and Gluten Free. Tray service to room if ill (no charge as long as doctor orders). 3 snacks/day. Party facilities. Private dining area for families available.
AMENITIES AND ACTIVITIES: Parking available (outdoor, for visitors and residents). *4 lounges with:* TVs (2) and piano (1). Guest suites available ($75.00/night). *Residence has a:* visiting library, barber/beauty shop and visiting hairdresser. Resident can arrange newspaper delivery to individual suite. Mail delivered to individual suite. *Recreation Facilities*: exercise room, craft room and card room. Posted schedule of activities. Internal newsletter for residents. *Recreational Programs*: exercise, shopping, entertainment, parties, pet visiting and day trips.
OTHER SERVICES: *Housekeeping*: daily and weekly (included in fee). *Laundry*: linen, towel & personal (included in fee). Transportation for group social activities. Nightly security checks. Telephone (per Bell Canada). Cable TV ($30.00/month). Utilities (included in fee). Internet access available through various providers.
RENTAL INFORMATION: Rates may vary. Private suites - $1,825.00/month & up. Extra cost for 2nd person sharing suite ($650.00/month). Rent paid monthly. *Payment Options*: cheques and post-dated cheques. Rent increases as per Provincial Tenancy Legislation, annual for resident with 3 months' notice given. Short-term respite (rate depends on suite availability) and trial stays ($65.00/day) available.

♦ UNIONVILLE ♦

BAYBRIDGE - THE MARLEIGH RETIREMENT RESIDENCE

34 Main Street, Unionville, ON L3R 2E4
Tel: (905) 947-9990 • Fax: (905) 305-6810
Email: **alison.gross@themarleigh.ca**
Website: **www.themarleighunionville.ca**
Contact: **Alison Gross**
Capacity: **180 residents** • Subsidies: **none**
Price: **$3,200.00 - $5,500.00/month**

Newly constructed and offering a broad range of sophisticated amenities and premium services, The Marleigh is a retirement living community like none other. As Unionville's premier retirement residence, we are situated close to the historic downtown and Main Street of the city. Residents of our community enjoy the convenience that comes from never having to worry about the daily tasks of life, such as housekeeping, meal preparation, shopping or home maintenance. The Marleigh is one of several independent retirement communities owned and managed by BayBridge Senior Living. Our communities are designed to provide Ontario seniors with the services and amenities needed so they may create the independent lifestyle they have always wanted.

RESIDENCE INFORMATION: New residence. *Near:* Main Street and Highway 7. Decorated in 2013. Handrails in hallways. 9 floors, 3 elevators. Wheelchair accessible. Central PA system. *Funding Base:* Corporate/for profit. *Owned and managed by:* BayBridge Senior Living. 150 units. *Average Waiting Period*: none. Can accommodate cognitively impaired & physically challenged people. Smoke-free residence. Alcohol allowed. *Languages:* English. Will accept Public Guardian and Trustee clients. Main doors of residence secured at night only. *Close to:* Public Transit, Shopping, Churches, Synagogues, Seniors' Centre, Library, Major Highway and Local Hospital (Markham-Stouffville Hospital). Licensed under the Retirement Homes Act.

STAFFING: *Available Staff/Services*: Pharmacy, Recreation Therapy, Visiting Dentist, Denturist, Podiatry, Chaplaincy, Chiropody and Audiology/Hearing Clinic. *External services arranged by:* residence and/or family/resident. Staff trained *re*: hearing and cognitively impaired. 24-hour nursing staff. RNs, RPNs, PSWs and UCPs on staff. Visiting MD (weekly). Can retain own MD. Police Check or Vulnerable Person Screening is done for all new staff.

HEALTH SERVICES: Medication administration and/or supervision. Vitals monitored if required. Will accept and provide special assistance for residents who require oxygen, catheters, ostomies and feeding tubes. Assistance with dressing available. Weekly assistance with bathing available. Care plans done. Different levels of care available. Private Duty/Extra Care available. Assisted Living Area. Separate unit for residents with dementia. Lab service (visiting, $25.00/visit). Residents can purchase outside resources and use agency of their choice. MD visits residents in their rooms/suites. Clinic area for medical visits. Will help locate higher level of care if needed (Aging in Place residence – no need to go elsewhere for higher care).

ACCOMMODATION: *Choice of suites available*: studio, companion, 1-bedroom, 1-bedroom + den & 2-bedroom suites. *In all suites*: locks, kitchenette, bar fridge, window coverings, light fixtures, fire alarm, smoke detector, sprinkler, call bell, emergency response system with wearable pendant/bracelet, air conditioning (central) and thermostats for heating & cooling. Private bathrooms (companion suites share 1 bathroom) with call bells, grab bars and showers with non-slip surfaces. In-suite cable TV provided by residence (residence charges extra). Can have own phone number if resident arranges with phone company (residence charges extra). Unfurnished suites, furnished suites available for short stays. *Restrictions on electrical appliances*: no cooktops. Suites can be shared. Pets allowed.

DINING SERVICE: All meals included in fee and served in dining room daily. *Menu choices available:* Breakfast: 3, Lunch: 3, Dinner: 3. *Guest Meals*: Available. *Special Diets*: Vegetarian, Low Salt and Diabetic. Tray service to room if ill (no charge or restrictions). Unlimited snacks available at any time. Party facilities. Open pantry. Separate dining for care floors; 4 dining rooms in total.

AMENITIES AND ACTIVITIES: *7 lounges with:* TVs (5) and pianos (2). Guest suites available. *Residence has a:* library, barber/beauty shop, visiting hairdresser and tuck/gift shop. Residence provides newspaper delivery to main desk. Mail delivered to private mailbox with key. *Recreation Facilities*: exercise room, greenhouse and craft room. Posted schedule of activities. Internal newsletter for residents. *Recreational Programs*: exercise, shopping, theatre, parties, entertainment, art classes, pet visiting and day trips.

OTHER SERVICES: *Housekeeping*: weekly. *Laundry*: linen & towel (included in fee); personal & dry cleaning (extra cost). Either staff or resident label clothing. Transportation to medical appointments and for group social activities. 24-hour security. Nightly security checks. Telephone & Cable TV (extra cost). Utilities (included in fee).

RENTAL INFORMATION: Rates may vary. Extra cost for 2nd person sharing suite ($700.00/month). Rent paid monthly. *Payment Options*: pre-authorized payments. Rent increases as per Provincial Tenancy Legislation, annual for resident with 3 months' notice given. Will help resident move into residence. Short-term respite and trial stays available (both $95.00/day).

◆ UXBRIDGE ◆

BUTTERNUT MANOR

3 Norm Goodspeed Drive, Uxbridge, ON L9P 0B7
Tel: (905) 852-6777 • Fax: (905) 852-2399
Toll Free: (888) 852-6778
Email: **info@butternutmanor.com**
Website: **www.butternutmanor.com**
Contact: **Stacey Sellery**
Capacity: **80 residents** • Subsidies: **none**
Price: **$2,935.00 - $4,860.00/month**

UXBRIDGE'S PREMIER RETIREMENT RESIDENCE. Set in the rural Historic Town of Uxbridge. Unique Garden Courtyard, adjacent park. Our gardens are connected to Uxbridge's walking trail system. Warm and friendly building with a variety of suites to choose from. TOLL FREE NUMBER: **(888) 852-6778**.

RESIDENCE INFORMATION: 6 years in operation. *Near:* Brock Street West and Toronto Street. Decorated in 2008. Handrails in hallways. 2 floors, 1 elevator. Wheelchair accessible. *Funding Base:* Corporate/for profit. *Owned by:* Butternut Manor Uxbridge Inc. *Managed by:* Eldercare Consulting Inc. 63 units. *Average Waiting Period*: varies. *Average Age*: 81. Can accommodate cognitively impaired people with restrictions (based on assessment). Can accommodate physically challenged people (based on assessment). Smoke-free residence. Alcohol allowed (in moderation). *Procedures to leave the premises on a temporary basis*...to be arranged with staff. *Languages:* English. Main doors of residence secured at night only. *Close to:* Public Transit, Shopping, Churches, Seniors' Centre, Library and Local Hospital (Markham-Stouffville Hospital - Uxbridge The Cottage Hospital Site). Member of ORCA & Uxbridge Chamber of Commerce. Licensed under the Retirement Homes Act.
STAFFING: *Available Staff/Services*: Pharmacy, Social Work (CCAC), Recreation Therapy, Occupational Therapy (CCAC), Visiting Dentist, Physiotherapy (CCAC), Denturist, Dietitian (CCAC), Companions, Podiatry (CCAC), Chaplaincy, Speech Pathology (CCAC), Chiropody, Audiology/Hearing Clinic, Hairdresser, Barber and Pet Therapy. *External services arranged by:* residence and/or family/resident. Staff trained *re:* visually, hearing and cognitively impaired. 24-hour staff. RPNs, HCAs, PSWs and UCPs on staff. Visiting MD (weekly). Can retain own MD. Police Check or Vulnerable Person Screening is done for all new staff.
HEALTH SERVICES: Medication administration (must use residence pharmacy) and/or supervision. Vitals monitored if required. Will accept and provide special assistance for residents who require oxygen. Assistance with dressing available (cost). Weekly assistance with bathing available. *Extra baths:* $100.00/month. Care plans done. Additional/different levels of care available. Palliative care available. Private Duty/Extra Care available ($19.00 to $25.00/hour). Lab service (visiting, $30.00/visit). Residents can purchase outside resources and use agency of their choice. MD visits residents in their rooms/suites. Clinic area for medical visits. Will help locate higher level of care if needed (via CCAC).
ACCOMMODATION: *Choice of suites available*: studio & 1-bedroom suites. *In all suites*: locks, window coverings, light fixtures, fire alarm, smoke detector, sprinkler, call bell, emergency response system with wearable pendant/bracelet, air conditioning (individual built in units in each suite) and thermostats for heating & cooling. Private bathrooms with call bells, grab bars and showers with non-slip surfaces. In-suite cable TV provided by residence (residence charges extra $30.00/month). Can have own phone extension number provided by residence (residence charges extra $30.00/month). Unfurnished suites, furnished suites available for short stays. *Restrictions on electrical appliances*: must be checked by staff and conform to code and safety. Suites can be shared, roommate picked by resident & residence staff. Pets allowed (on a case-by-case basis following residence policies).

DINING SERVICE: All meals included in fee and served in dining room daily. *Sittings per meal:* Breakfast: 1, Lunch: 1, Dinner: 1. *Menu choices available:* Breakfast: 2, Lunch: 2, Dinner: 2. *Guest Meals*: Breakfast $7.00, Lunch $7.00, Dinner $9.00. *Special Diets*: Vegetarian, Low Salt and Diabetic. Most therapeutic diets can be accommodated. Tray service to room if ill (no charge as long as doctor orders). 3 snacks/day and unlimited snacks available at any time. Open pantry. Party facilities. Private dining room for families or groups - seats up to 16 guests.
AMENITIES AND ACTIVITIES: Parking available (outdoor, for visitors and residents). *3 lounges with:* TVs (3), pianos (2) and fireplace (1). Guest suites available ($125.00/night). *Residence has a:* library, visiting library, barber/beauty shop, visiting hairdresser, laundry room(s) (no cost) and tuck/gift shop. Residence provides newspaper delivery to individual suite. Mail delivered to dining room. *Recreation Facilities*: exercise room, craft room, card room, courtyard flower & herb garden, walking trails, furnished outdoor patio and Nintendo Wii. Posted schedule of activities. Internal newsletter for residents. *Recreational Programs*: exercise, shopping, theatre, parties, entertainment, art classes, pet visiting, day trips, gardening, bird feeding, BBQ's, card clubs and sports clubs.
OTHER SERVICES: *Housekeeping*: weekly (included in fee). *Laundry*: linen, towel & personal (included in fee). Each resident's laundry is done separately. Transportation to medical appointments and for group social activities (extra cost for restaurant meals, tickets). Nightly security checks. Telephone ($30.00/month). Cable TV ($30.00/month). Utilities (included in fee). Esthetics (various services available).
RENTAL INFORMATION: Rates may vary. Studio suites - $2,935.00/month & up; 1-bedroom suites - $4,530.00/month & up. Extra cost for 2nd person sharing suite ($650.00/month). Rent paid monthly. *Payment Options*: cheques and post-dated cheques. Rent increases as per Provincial Tenancy Legislation, annual for resident with 3 months' notice given. Will help resident move into residence. Short-term respite ($75.00/day) and trial stays ($2,935.00/month) subject to availability.

♦ VAUGHAN ♦

RICHVIEW MANOR

10500 Dufferin Street, Vaughan, ON L6A 4R1
Tel: (905) 585-5000 • Fax: (905) 585-5555
Email: **mdimaria@richviewmanor.com**
Website: **www.richviewmanor.com**
Contact: **Magdalena Di Maria**
Capacity: **160 residents** • Subsidies: **none**
Price: **$3,100.00 - $4,699.00/month**

Richview Manor is located at Eagles Nest Golf Club offering over 137 suites for seniors who wish to be in a community that provides both Independent and Assisted Living accommodations. The all-inclusive 5-star style resort living offered by Richview Manor is unlike any other senior retirement living accommodations. We believe our seniors should not be troubled with additional à la carte expenditures for care services, which cause unnecessary stress and added expensive costs both to the resident and their family.

RESIDENCE INFORMATION: 3 years in operation. *Near:* Major Mackenzie Road and Dufferin Street. Decorated in 2011. Handrails in some of the hallways. 6 floors, 3 elevators. Wheelchair accessible. *Funding Base:* Corporate/for profit. Privately Owned. *Managed by:* UniversalCare Inc. 137 units. *Average Waiting Period*: none. *Average Age*: 80. Can accommodate cognitively impaired people. Can accommodate physically challenged people. Smoking allowed (outdoors only in designated areas). Alcohol allowed. *Restrictions around Visitors/Visiting Hours:* all guests must check in with our Concierge. *Languages:* English. Will accept Public Guardian and Trustee clients. Main doors of residence secured at night only.

Close to: Public Transit, Shopping, Churches, Synagogues, Seniors' Centre, Library, Major Highway and Local Hospital (MacKenzie Health formerly York Central Hospital). Licensed under the Retirement Homes Act.

STAFFING: *Available Staff/Services*: Pharmacy, Recreation Therapy, Occupational Therapy, Visiting Dentist, Physiotherapy, Denturist, Chiropody and Audiology/Hearing Clinic. *External services arranged by:* family/resident. 24-hour nursing staff. RNs, RPNs and PSWs on staff. Visiting MD (every 2 weeks and available via telephone daily). Can retain own MD. Police Check or Vulnerable Person Screening is done for all new staff.

HEALTH SERVICES: Medication administration and/or supervision. Vitals monitored if required. Will accept and provide special assistance for residents who require oxygen. Assistance with dressing available. Weekly assistance with bathing available. Care plans done. Different levels of care available. Private Duty/Extra Care available ($25.00/hour). Assisted Living Area. Lab service (visiting, $5.00/visit). Residents can purchase outside resources and use agency of their choice. Clinic area for medical visits. Will help locate higher level of care if needed (Clinical Director works with family & CCAC).

ACCOMMODATION: *Choice of suites available*: 2-bedroom (19), 1-bedroom (60), 1-bedroom + den (8), studio (48) & studio + den (2) suites. *In all suites*: locks, kitchenette, bar fridge, microwave, storage, window coverings, fire alarm, smoke detector, sprinkler, call bell, emergency response system with wearable pendant/bracelet, air conditioning (central) and thermostats for heating & cooling. Full-size condominium-style fridge/freezer on Independent Living. Private bathrooms with call bells, grab bars, tubs and showers with non-slip surfaces and elevated toilet seats. In-suite cable TV provided by residence (residence charges extra $50.00/month). Can have own phone number if resident arranges with phone company (residence charges extra $50.00/month). Furnished & unfurnished suites available. *Restrictions on electrical appliances*: CSA approved and home assessment. Suites can be shared. Pets allowed (depending on size and resident's ability to care for the pet).

DINING SERVICE: All meals included in fee and served in dining room daily. *Sittings per meal:* Breakfast: 1, Lunch: 1, Dinner: 1. *Menu choices available:* Breakfast: 2, Lunch: 2, Dinner: 2. *Guest Meals*: Breakfast $6.00, Lunch $8.00, Dinner $10.00. *Special Diets*: Vegetarian, Low Salt and Diabetic. Tray service to room if ill (no charge for a maximum time of 1 days). 3 snacks/day. Party facilities. Mealtimes for Independent Living resident's are flexible within a pre-set time.

AMENITIES AND ACTIVITIES: Parking available (indoor & outdoor, for visitors: free and residents: $50.00/month). *6 lounges with:* TVs (5) and pianos (2). Guest suites available. *Residence has a:* library, visiting library, barber/beauty shop, visiting hairdresser, laundry room(s) (no cost) and tuck/gift shop (open 24/7). Banking services on premises (ever 2 weeks by certain banks). Residence provides newspaper delivery to Concierge Desk. Mail delivered to private mailbox with key. *Recreation Facilities*: pool table, billiards, craft room, card room, swimming pool, theatre room, private dining areas, Bluewater Spa, fitness centre and outdoor patio (2,000 sq. ft.) on Assisted Living. Posted schedule of activities. Internal newsletter for residents. *Recreational Programs*: exercise, shopping, theatre, parties, entertainment, pet visiting, day trips and aquafit.

OTHER SERVICES: *Housekeeping*: daily and weekly (included in fee). *Laundry*: linen & towel (included in fee; weekly - residence provides linens & towels), personal (extra cost; included for Assisted Living Residents only). Complimentary laundry room on every floor (includes washers/dryers, ironing & folding table). Transportation for group social activities (weekly outings 2 x week). 24-hour security. Nightly security checks (only if resident requires). Telephone ($50.00/month). Cable TV ($50.00/month). Utilities (included in fee).

RENTAL INFORMATION: Rates may vary. Extra cost for 2nd person sharing suite ($650.00/month). Rent paid monthly. *Payment Options*: pre-authorized payments. Rent increases as per Provincial Tenancy Legislation, annual for resident with 3 months' notice given. Short-term respite, vacation and trial stays available (all $125.00/day).

V!VA THORNHILL WOODS RETIREMENT COMMUNITY

9700 Bathurst Street (at Lebovic Campus Drive),
Vaughan, ON L6A 4V2
Tel: (905) 417-8585
Email: **thornhillwoods@vivalife.ca**
Website: **www.vivalife.ca**
Capacity: **134 units**
Subsidies: **none**

Located directly across from the brand-new Schwartz/Reisman Community Centre and Mt. Sinai Medical Clinic, V!VA Thornhill Woods features a wellness spa with an indoor saltwater pool, pub, movie theatre, concierge services and more. With options for Independent and Assisted Living, suites range from studio to 2-bedroom. Three healthy and delicious meals are prepared fresh daily featuring Jewish-style dining.

RESIDENCE INFORMATION: New residence. *Near:* Bathurst Street and Lebovic Campus Drive. Decorated in 2013. Handrails in some of the hallways. 7 floors, 3 elevators. Wheelchair accessible. Central PA system. *Funding Base:* Corporate/for profit. *Owned and managed by:* V!VA Retirement Communities. *Average Waiting Period*: none. Can accommodate cognitively impaired people (early Alzheimer's and dementia). Can accommodate physically challenged people. Smoke-free residence. Alcohol allowed. *Procedures to leave the premises on a temporary basis*...advise Concierge. *Languages:* English. Will accept Public Guardian and Trustee clients. Main doors of residence secured at night only. *Close to:* Public Transit, Shopping, Churches, Synagogues, Seniors' Centre, Library, Major Highway and Local Hospital (MacKenzie Health formerly York Central Hospital). Member of ORCA. Licensed under the Retirement Homes Act.

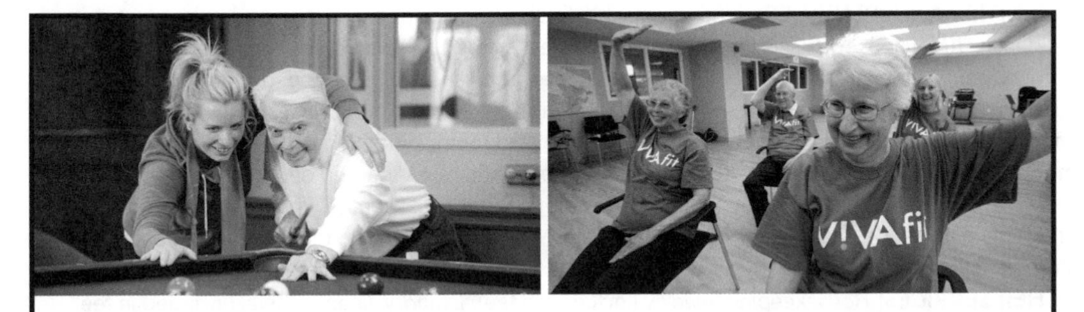

STAFFING: *Available Staff/Services*: Pharmacy, Social Work (CCAC), Recreation Therapy, Occupational Therapy (CCAC), Visiting Dentist, Physiotherapy (CCAC), Denturist, Dietitian (CCAC), Companions, Podiatry (CCAC), Chaplaincy, Speech Pathology (CCAC), Chiropody and Audiology/Hearing Clinic. *External services arranged by:* residence and/or family/resident. Staff trained *re*: visually, hearing and cognitively impaired. 24-hour nursing and other staff. RNs, RPNs, HCAs and PSWs on staff. Visiting MD (weekly & as needed). Can retain own MD. Police Check or Vulnerable Person Screening is done for all new staff.
HEALTH SERVICES: Medication administration and/or supervision. Vitals monitored if required. Will accept and provide special assistance for residents who require oxygen, catheters and ostomies. Assistance with dressing available. Weekly assistance with bathing available. Care plans done. Different levels of care available. Private Duty/Extra Care available. Assisted Living Area. Lab service (visiting). Residents can purchase outside resources and use agency of their choice. Clinic area for medical visits. Will help locate higher level of care if needed.
ACCOMMODATION: *Choice of suites available*: studio, 1-bedroom, 1-bedroom + den & 2-bedroom suites. *In all suites*: locks, storage, bar fridge, microwave, window coverings, light fixtures, stove, fire alarm, smoke detector, sprinkler, emergency response system with wearable pendant/bracelet, air conditioning (central) and thermostats for heating & cooling. Kitchenettes with stainless steel full-size fridge and microwave provided in Independent Living suites only. Private bathrooms with call bells, grab bars, showers with non-slip surfaces and elevated toilet seats. Can have own phone number if resident arranges with phone company. Furnished & unfurnished suites available. *Restrictions on electrical appliances*: CSA approved products. Suites can be shared, roommate picked by resident. Pets allowed (size restrictions).
DINING SERVICE: All meals included in fee and served in dining room daily. *Guest Meals*: Available. *Special Diets*: Vegetarian, Low Salt and Diabetic. Jewish-style dining/menu is available. Tray service to room if ill (no charge as long as doctor orders). Unlimited snacks available at any time. Party facilities. Open pantry. Children's menu available.
AMENITIES AND ACTIVITIES: Parking available (indoor & outdoor, for visitors and indoor for residents). *10 lounges with:* TVs (7) and piano (1). Guest suites available. *Residence has a:* library, chapel, barber/beauty shop and laundry room(s) (no cost). Resident can arrange newspaper delivery to individual suite (extra cost). Mail delivered to private mailbox with key. *Recreation Facilities*: pool table, billiards, shuffleboard, exercise room, greenhouse, craft room, card room, swimming pool, fully licensed pub, movie theatre, stretch & strength studios, massage room and raised garden beds. Posted schedule of activities. Internal newsletter for residents. *Recreational Programs*: exercise, shopping, theatre, parties, entertainment, art classes, pet visiting, day trips and V!VAfit program with focus on cardio, balance, strength & flexibility.
OTHER SERVICES: *Housekeeping*: weekly (included in fee). *Laundry*: linen & towel (included in fee); personal & dry cleaning (extra cost). Transportation for group social activities (aboard shuttle bus). Nightly security checks. Telephone (extra cost). Cable TV & Utilities (included in fee).
RENTAL INFORMATION: Call **(905) 417-8585** for pricing details. Extra cost for 2nd person sharing suite. Rent paid monthly. *Payment Options*: cheques, post-dated cheques, direct deposit and pre-authorized payments. Rent increases as per Provincial Tenancy Legislation, annual for resident with 3 months' notice given. Will help resident move into residence (extra cost). Short-term respite and trial stays available.

Did you know?

www.senioropolis.com is now a portal for information for seniors ... we are constantly adding new articles, information on resources, jobs, special events, promotions, retirement residences, long-term care homes and even apartments ***...visit us often to see what's new ...***

♦ WATERLOO ♦

BAYBRIDGE - THE COURT AT LAURELWOOD

605 Laurelwood Drive, Waterloo, ON N2V 2W7
Tel: (519) 725-2442 • Fax: (519) 725-1526
Email: **Wendy.Davila-Hill@CourtatLaurelwood.com**
Website: **www.courtatlaurelwood.com**
Contact: **Wendy Davila-Hill**
Capacity: **118 units** • Subsidies: **none**
Price: **$2,389.00/month and up**

At The Court at Laurelwood we believe retirement living should be relaxing and carefree, spent doing the things you love. That's why our community provides a unique independent retirement lifestyle in a warm and welcoming environment. In one affordable, all-inclusive month-to-month rent, residents enjoy 3 delicious chef-prepared meals daily, enriching activities to share with friendly neighbours, housekeeping service, complimentary transportation, and much more. We do not provide health care services; however, residents are welcome to receive services from an outside home health care provider of their choice to continue enjoying life independently at our community. Discover the peace-of-mind, happiness and fulfillment you deserve. Contact us today to schedule your personal tour!

RESIDENCE INFORMATION: 9 years in operation. *Near:* Erbsville Road and Laurelwood Drive. Decorated in 2005. Handrails in hallways. 3 floors, 1 elevator. Wheelchair accessible. Central PA system. *Funding*

Base: Corporate/for profit. *Owned and managed by:* BayBridge Senior Living. *Average Waiting Period*: varies. *Average Age*: 83. Can accommodate cognitively impaired people with restrictions. Can accommodate physically challenged people (must be independent; wheelchairs, walkers, scooters are welcome). Residents have a dress code (casual). Smoking allowed (on balcony or patio only). Alcohol allowed (in apartments and dining room). *Procedures to leave the premises on a temporary basis*...let Front Office know. *Languages:* English. Will accept Public Guardian and Trustee clients. Main doors of residence secured at night only. *Close to:* Public Transit, Shopping, Churches, Seniors' Centre, Library, Major Highway and Local Hospitals (Grand River Hospital Corporation & St. Mary's General Hospital).
STAFFING: *Available Staff/Services*: Social Work (CCAC), Recreation Therapy, Occupational Therapy (CCAC), Physiotherapy (CCAC), Dietitian (CCAC), Podiatry (CCAC) and Speech Pathology (CCAC). *External services arranged by:* family/resident. Can retain own MD. Police Check or Vulnerable Person Screening is done for all new staff.
HEALTH SERVICES: Will accept (but not provide special assistance for) residents who require oxygen, catheters, ostomies and feeding tubes. Residents can purchase outside resources and use agency of their choice. Will help locate higher level of care if needed (information provided by Managers and CCAC).
ACCOMMODATION: *Choice of suites available*: studio, 1-bedroom & 2-bedroom suites. *In all suites*: locks, kitchenette, window coverings, light fixtures, linens, fire alarm, smoke detector, sprinkler, call bell, air conditioning (through the wall unit) and thermostats for heating & cooling. Most have patios/balcony. Full-size fridge in all apartments. Private bathrooms with call bells, grab bars, tubs and showers with non-slip surfaces and elevated toilet seats. In-suite cable TV provided by residence. Can have own phone number if resident arranges with phone company (residence charges extra). Unfurnished suites, furnished suites available for short stays. *Restrictions on electrical appliances*: no hot plates or stoves. Suites can be shared, roommate picked by resident. Pets allowed (small dogs only).
DINING SERVICE: All meals included in fee and served in dining room daily. *Sittings per meal:* Breakfast: 1, Lunch: 1, Dinner: 1. *Menu choices available:* Breakfast: 5, Lunch: 6, Dinner: 5. *Guest Meals*: Breakfast $10.00, Lunch $12.00, Dinner $10.00. *Special Diets*: Vegetarian, Low Salt and Diabetic. Tray service to room if ill (no charge for a maximum time of 5 days). Unlimited snacks available at any time. Fruit available all day. Party facilities. Private Dining Area. Large meal served at noon-time.
AMENITIES AND ACTIVITIES: Parking available (outdoor, for visitors and residents). *4 lounges with:* TV (1), piano (1), fireplace (1) and computers (1). *Residence has a:* library, chapel, barber/beauty shop and laundry room(s) (no cost). Resident can arrange newspaper delivery to individual suite. Mail delivered to private mailbox with key. *Recreation Facilities*: pool table, billiards, shuffleboard, exercise room, craft room and card room. Posted schedule of activities. Internal newsletter for residents. *Recreational Programs*: exercise, shopping, parties, entertainment, pet visiting, day trips and resident requests.
OTHER SERVICES: *Housekeeping*: weekly. *Laundry*: linen & towel (included in fee). Free laundry rooms for personal use. Transportation to medical appointments and for group social activities. 24-hour security. Cable TV & Utilities (included in fee). Free outdoor parking (cost for indoor parking).
RENTAL INFORMATION: Rates may vary. Rate listed above is based on single occupancy. Extra cost for 2nd person sharing suite (please call for specifics). Rent paid monthly. *Payment Options*: cheques, post-dated cheques, direct deposit and pre-authorized payments. Rent increases indexed to inflation as per Provincial Tenancy Legislation, annual for resident with 3 months' notice given. Will help resident move into residence (extra cost). Short-term respite and trial stays available (see Managers).

CLAIR HILLS RETIREMENT COMMUNITY

530 Columbia Street West, Waterloo, ON N2T 0B1
Tel: (519) 880-8444 • Fax: (519) 603-3025
Email: **info@clairhillsretirement.com**
Website: **www.clairhillsretirement.com**
Contact: **Executive Director or Marketing Manager**
Capacity: **160 residents •** Subsidies: **none**
Price: **$3,300.00 - $5,300.00/month**

Looking for more energy every day? Ready to step out with a new sense of positive vitality? Clair Hills in Waterloo is a community devoted to helping you bring positive energy to everything you do, with a comprehensive program of activities and services designed to help make every day fantastic! Independent Living, personal on-site care, and Assisted Living options available. Now Open! Full Service Dining Room. Spectacular Views. Movie Theatre. Saltwater Swimming Pool. Wellness Care.

RESIDENCE INFORMATION: New residence. *On:* Columbia Street and Erbsville Road. Decorated in 2012. Handrails in some of the hallways. 4 floors, 3 elevators. Wheelchair accessible. Central PA system. *Funding Base:* Corporate/for profit. *Owned and managed by:* Signature Retirement Living. 120 units. *Average Waiting Period*: none. *Average Age*: 79. Can sometimes accommodate cognitively impaired people. Can sometimes accommodate physically challenged people (motorized scooters are not permitted within the building). Smoke-free residence. Alcohol allowed. *Procedures to leave the premises on a temporary basis...*Overnight & Holidays: inform the Concierge. *Languages:* English. Main doors of residence secured at night only. *Close to:* Public Transit, Shopping, Churches, Synagogues, Seniors' Centre, Library, Major Highway and Local Hospitals (St. Mary's General Hospital and Grand River Hospital Corporation). Member of ORCA. Licensed under the Retirement Homes Act.
STAFFING: *Available Staff/Services*: Pharmacy, Social Work (CCAC), Recreation Therapy, Occupational Therapy (CCAC), Physiotherapy, Companions, Podiatry, CLUBfit and Religious Services. *External services arranged by:* residence and/or family/resident. Staff trained *re*: visually, hearing and cognitively impaired. 24-hour nursing and other staff. RPNs and PSWs on staff. Visiting MD (weekly). Can retain own MD. Police Check or Vulnerable Person Screening is done for all new staff.
HEALTH SERVICES: Medication administered if required. Vitals monitored if required. Assistance with dressing available ($25.00/hour). Weekly assistance with bathing available ($85.00/month). *Extra baths:* $25.00/hour. Care plans done. Different levels of care available. Private Duty/Extra Care available ($25.00/hour). Assisted Living Area. Residents can purchase outside resources and use agency of their choice. Clinic area for medical visits. Will help locate higher level of care if needed (Our Director of Care will meet with family members to assist with planning and information).
ACCOMMODATION: *Choice of suites available*: all private suites. 100 Independent Living Suites from studios to 2-bedroom + den; 20 Assisted Living Suites near the Nursing Office. *In all suites*: locks, kitchenette, bar fridge, microwave, patio/balcony, storage, window coverings, light fixtures, fire alarm, smoke detector, sprinkler, call bell, emergency response system with wearable pendant/bracelet, air conditioning (central) and thermostats for heating & cooling. Kitchenettes in Independent Living. Private bathrooms with call bells, grab bars, showers with non-slip surfaces and elevated toilet seats. In-suite cable TV if resident arranges with cable company. Can have own phone number if resident arranges with phone company. Unfurnished suites, furnished suites available for short stays. Suites can be shared, roommate picked by resident. Pets allowed (under 30 lbs. with approval of Management).
DINING SERVICE: All meals included in fee and served in dining room daily. *Guest Meals*: Available. *Special Diets*: Vegetarian, Low Salt and Diabetic. Other special diets may be available in consultation. Tray service to room if ill (no charge for a maximum time of 3 days). Unlimited snacks available at any time. Freestyle Dining. Party facilities. Private dining room available for parties.

AMENITIES AND ACTIVITIES: Parking available (outdoor, for visitors and residents). *4 lounges with:* TVs (2), piano (1) and outdoor patio (1). Guest suites available ($95.00/night). *Residence has a:* library, chapel, barber/beauty shop, visiting hairdresser and laundry room(s) (no cost). Resident can arrange newspaper delivery to individual suite. Mail delivered to private mailbox with key. *Recreation Facilities*: shuffleboard, exercise room, craft room, card room, swimming pool, community shuttle bus, CLUBfit program (included), licensed pub and more to come! Posted schedule of activities. Internal newsletter for residents. *Recreational Programs*: exercise, shopping, theatre, parties, entertainment, art classes, pet visiting, day trips, aquafit and raised flower beds in garden.
OTHER SERVICES: *Housekeeping*: weekly (included in fee). *Laundry*: linen & towel (included in fee). 24-hour security. Nightly security checks. Telephone & Cable TV (extra cost). Utilities (included in fee).
RENTAL INFORMATION: Rates may vary. Ranging from studios @ $3,300.00/month to 2-bedroom + den @ $5,300.00/month. Extra cost for 2nd person sharing suite ($650.00/month). Rent paid monthly. *Payment Options*: cheques and pre-authorized payments. Rent increases as per Provincial Tenancy Legislation, annual for resident with 3 months' notice given. Short-term respite and trial stays available (both $95.00/day).

LUTHER VILLAGE ON THE PARK

139 Father David Bauer Drive, Waterloo, ON N2L 6L1
Tel: (519) 783-3710 • Fax: (519) 884-9071
Email: **cdaniel@luthervillage.org**
Website: **www.luthervillage.org**
Contact: **Charlotte Daniel**
Capacity: **178 residents** • Subsidies: **none**
Price: **$3,470.00 - $4,995.00/month**

Luther Village on the Park is a world class retirement community that includes Life Lease Suites and Townhomes as well as Assisted Living Rental Suites. Life in the Village is carefree knowing that as needs change, a continuum of care is available. Independence and choice are key as residents enjoy an array of amenities and wellness services as well as endless activities for every interest.

The information provided below outlines the care and services offered within The Assisted Living Centre and common amenities available to all residents at Luther Village on the Park.

RESIDENCE INFORMATION: 11 years in operation. *Near:* Erb Street and Westmount Avenue. Decorated in 2011. Handrails in hallways. 5 floors, 2 elevators. Wheelchair accessible. *Funding Base:* Not-for-profit. *Owned by:* Lutherwood. 148 units. *Average Waiting Period*: 2 - 4 months. *Average Age*: 81. Can sometimes accommodate cognitively impaired people (early stage Alzheimer's only). Can accommodate physically challenged people. Smoking allowed (outside of building as specified by city of Waterloo by-law). Alcohol allowed. *Procedures to leave the premises on a temporary basis*...notify Front Reception. *Languages:* English, German, Dutch, French, Italian, Spanish & Eastern European Languages. *Close to:* Public Transit, Shopping, Churches, Seniors' Centre, Library and Local Hospital (Grand River Hospital Corporation). Member of OANHSS, ORCA & CARF. *Predominant Cultural Group:* White Anglo-Saxon. Licensed under the Retirement Homes Act.
STAFFING: *Available Staff/Services*: Social Work (CCAC), Recreation Therapy, Occupational Therapy (CCAC), Physiotherapy, Denturist, Dietitian (CCAC), Companions, Podiatry (CCAC), Chaplaincy, Speech Pathology (CCAC), Chiropody, Audiology/Hearing Clinic, Massage, Reflexology and Optometry. *External services arranged by:* residence and/or family/resident. Staff trained *re*: visually, hearing and cognitively impaired. 24-hour nursing staff. RNs, RPNs and PSWs on staff. Visiting MD (twice/week & on call). Can retain own MD. Police Check or Vulnerable Person Screening is done for all new staff.

HEALTH SERVICES: Medication administration (no IV medications) and/or supervision. Vitals monitored if required. Will accept and provide special assistance for residents who require oxygen, catheters and ostomies. Assistance with dressing available. Weekly assistance with bathing available. *Extra baths:* $15.00/bath. Care plans done. Different levels of care available. Private Duty/Extra Care available. Lab service (on-site, $15.00/visit). Residents can purchase outside resources and use agency of their choice. Clinic area for medical visits. Will help locate higher level of care if needed (through referrals to appropriate agencies).

ACCOMMODATION: *Choice of suites available*: private (148), 2-bedroom apartment (20), 1-bedroom apartment (88) & studio (40) suites. *In all suites*: locks, kitchenette, bar fridge, window coverings, light fixtures, fire alarm, smoke detector, sprinkler, emergency response system with wearable pendant/bracelet, air conditioning (central) and thermostats for heating & cooling. Laundry facilities on each floor. Private bathrooms with grab bars, tubs and showers with non-slip surfaces. In-suite cable TV if resident arranges with cable company. Can have own phone number provided by residence. Unfurnished suites, furnished suites available for short stays. Suites can be shared, roommate picked by resident. Pets allowed (must be capable of caring for the pet; pet must be on a leash in common areas).

DINING SERVICE: Three meals daily included in fee and served in dining room. *Sittings per meal:* Breakfast: 1, Lunch: 2, Dinner: 2. *Menu choices available:* Breakfast: 2, Lunch: 2, Dinner: 2. *Guest Meals*: Breakfast $7.00, Lunch $10.00, Dinner $15.00. *Special Diets*: Vegetarian, Low Salt, Diabetic and Others (upon consultation). Tray service to room if ill (no charge or restrictions). 2 snacks/day. Party facilities. Theme dinners. Buffets & Sunday brunch. Two cafés.

AMENITIES AND ACTIVITIES: Parking available (outdoor, for visitors: free and residents: $35.00/month). *8 lounges with:* TVs (2), pianos (2), water feature (1), library (1) and outdoor gardens (3). Guest suites available ($70.00/night). *Residence has a:* chapel, barber/beauty shop, laundry room(s) (no cost), tuck/gift shop (open Monday to Saturday; 10:00 a.m. - 2:00 p.m.). Banking services on premises (weekly). Resident can arrange newspaper delivery to individual suite. Mail delivered to private mailbox with key. *Recreation Facilities*: pool table, billiards, shuffleboard, exercise room, greenhouse, craft room, card room, swirl pool, 2 libraries, business centre, woodworking shop, quilting room and gardening. Posted schedule of activities. Internal newsletter for residents. *Recreational Programs*: exercise, shopping, theatre, parties, entertainment, art classes, pet visiting, day trips, 30+ resident run clubs, committees, concerts, movie night and speakers series.

OTHER SERVICES: *Housekeeping*: daily and weekly (à la carte only is pay per use). *Laundry*: linen, towel & personal (included in fee); dry cleaning (extra cost). 24-hour security. Cable TV (extra cost). Telephone & Utilities (included in fee). Guest meals. Emergency response system. Assessments. Medication management. Recreation. Pastoral care.

RENTAL INFORMATION: Rates may vary. Extra cost for 2nd person sharing suite ($575.00/month to $1,165.00/month). Option to purchase unit available (Independent Life Lease Apartments and Townhomes available on-site). Rent paid monthly. *Payment Options*: pre-authorized payments. Rent increases as per Provincial Tenancy Legislation, annual for resident with 3 months' notice given. Short-term respite ($90.00/day) and trial stays ($115.00/day) available (Enhanced Care is $140.00/day).

Did you know?

The Ontario Seniors' Secretariat has prepared a series downloadable of 'Fact Sheets' on Financial Security and Planning for Seniors including information on financial planning, income benefits, protecting your assets, financial abuse and other topics. To download your choice of documents visit **www.seniors.gov.on.ca/en/moneymatters/factsheets_home.php.**

PINEHAVEN RETIREMENT RESIDENCE

229 Lexington Road, Waterloo, ON N2K 2E1
Tel: (519) 885-6990 • Fax: (519) 885-5052
Email: **sbarkshire@thecaringnetwork.ca**
Website: **www.thecaringnetwork.ca**
Contact: **Sandy Barkshire**
Capacity: **40 residents** • Subsidies: **none**
Price: **$1,783.00 - $3,735.00/month**

RESIDENCE INFORMATION: 18 years in operation. *Near:* Davenport Street. Handrails in hallways. 3 floors, 4 elevators. Wheelchair accessible. Central PA system. *Funding Base:* Corporate/for profit. *Owned by:* Deem Management. 34 units. *Average Waiting Period*: none. Can accommodate cognitively impaired & physically challenged people. Smoking allowed (outside patio area). Alcohol allowed. *Procedures to leave the premises on a temporary basis...*Short-term: sign out Front Desk. Overnight & Holidays: alert Charge Nurse/sign out Front Desk. *Languages:* English. Will accept Public Guardian and Trustee clients. Main doors of residence secured at night only. *Close to:* Public Transit, Shopping, Churches and Local Hospital (Grand River Hospital Corporation). Member of ORCA. Licensed under the Retirement Homes Act.
STAFFING: *Available Staff/Services*: Pharmacy, Social Work (CCAC), Recreation Therapy, Occupational Therapy (CCAC), Physiotherapy, Denturist, Dietitian, Companions, Chaplaincy, Audiology/Hearing Clinic and Resident Care Attendants. *External services arranged by:* residence and/or family/resident. Staff trained *re*: visually, hearing and cognitively impaired. 24-hour nursing and other staff. RPNs and UCPs on staff. Visiting MD (weekly). Can retain own MD. Police Check or Vulnerable Person Screening is done for all new staff.
HEALTH SERVICES: Medication administration and/or supervision. Vitals monitored if required. Will accept (but not provide special assistance for) residents who require catheters. Will accept and provide special assistance for residents who require oxygen. Assistance with dressing available. Weekly assistance with bathing available. *Extra baths:* $10.00/half hour. Care plans done. Different levels of care available. Private Duty/Extra Care available ($20.00/hour). Lab service (visiting, $10.90/visit). Residents can purchase outside resources and use agency of their choice. MD visits residents in their rooms/suites. Will help locate higher level of care if needed (CCAC).
ACCOMMODATION: Choice of suites available. *In all suites*: locks, window coverings, light fixtures, linens, smoke detector and thermostats for heating & cooling. Private bathrooms with call bells, grab bars, tubs and showers with non-slip surfaces. In-suite cable TV if resident arranges with cable company. Can have own phone extension number provided by residence. Furnished & unfurnished suites available. Restrictions on electrical appliances. Suites can be shared, roommate picked by residence staff. No pets allowed.
DINING SERVICE: All meals included in fee and served in dining room daily. *Sittings per meal:* Breakfast: 1, Lunch: 1, Dinner: 1. *Menu choices available:* Lunch: 2, Dinner: 2. *Guest Meals*: Available. *Special Diets*: Vegetarian, Low Salt and Diabetic. Tray service to room if ill (no charge as long as doctor orders). Unlimited snacks available at any time. Party facilities.
AMENITIES AND ACTIVITIES: Parking available (outdoor, for visitors and residents). *2 lounges with:* TVs (2). *Residence has a:* library, visiting library, chapel, barber/beauty shop, visiting hairdresser and tuck/gift shop (open the 2nd Sunday). Resident can arrange newspaper delivery to individual suite. Mail delivered to dining room. *Recreation Facilities*: exercise room, craft room and card room. Posted schedule of activities. Internal newsletter for residents. *Recreational Programs*: exercise, shopping, parties, entertainment, art classes, pet visiting and day trips.
OTHER SERVICES: *Housekeeping*: weekly (included in fee). *Laundry*: linen, towel & personal (included in fee). Transportation for group social activities. 24-hour security. Nightly security checks. Cable TV (extra cost). Telephone & Utilities (included in fee).
RENTAL INFORMATION: Rates may vary. Extra cost for 2nd person sharing suite. Rent paid monthly. *Payment Options*: cheques, post-dated cheques, direct deposit and pre-authorized payments. Rent

increases as per Provincial Tenancy Legislation, annual for resident with 3 months' notice given. Short-term respite and trial stays available (both $70.00/day).

♦ WHITBY ♦

LYNDE CREEK MANOR RETIREMENT RESIDENCE

50 Paul Burns Way, Whitby, ON L1R 2Y9
Tel: (905) 665-9227 • Fax: (905) 665-7018
Email: **jennifer@lyndecreekmanor.com**
Website: **www.lyndecreekmanor.com**
Contact: **Jennifer Sousa**
Capacity: **44 residents** • Subsidies: **none**
Price: **$1,900.00 - $4,300.00/month**

Lynde Creek Manor located in north Whitby, is a lively addition to Lynde Creek Village, a unique adult lifestyle retirement community. Nestled near the quiet banks of Lynde Creek, the Manor is close to shopping, banking, churches, seniors centre, golf courses and more. Lynde Creek Manor is now offering Assisted Living Services in the privacy of your own suite. We are owned by The Corporation of Convention Baptist Non-Profit Residences of Ontario and Quebec and proudly managed by Palladian Health Solutions Inc. Give us a call today to book your tour and complimentary lunch.

RESIDENCE INFORMATION: 10 years in operation. *Near:* Brock Street and Taunton Road. Decorated in 2004. 4 floors, 1 elevator. Wheelchair accessible. Central PA system. *Funding Base:* Not-for-profit. *Owned by:* Corporation of Convention Baptist Non-Profit Residences of Ontario and Quebec. *Managed by:* Palladian Health Solutions Inc. 37 units. *Average Waiting Period*: varies. *Average Age*: 80. Can accommodate cognitively impaired people with restrictions. Smoke-free residence. Alcohol allowed. *Procedures to leave the premises on a temporary basis...*notify Wellness Centre. *Languages:* English. Will accept Public Guardian and Trustee clients. Main doors of residence secured at all times. *Close to:* Public Transit, Shopping, Churches, Seniors' Centre, Library, Major Highway and Local Hospital (Lakeridge Health – Oshawa General Hospital Site). Licensed under the Retirement Homes Act.
STAFFING: *Available Staff/Services*: Pharmacy, Social Work (CCAC), Recreation Therapy, Occupational Therapy (CCAC), Physiotherapy (CCAC), Companions, Chaplaincy, Chiropody, Audiology/Hearing Clinic, Hair Salon and Chiropractor. *External services arranged by:* family/resident. Staff trained *re*: visually, hearing and cognitively impaired. 24-hour nursing and other staff. RNs, PSWs and UCPs on staff. Can retain own MD. Police Check or Vulnerable Person Screening is done for all new staff.
HEALTH SERVICES: Medication administration and/or supervision. Vitals monitored if required. Will accept (but not provide special assistance for) residents who require oxygen, catheters, ostomies and feeding tubes. Assistance with dressing available. Care plans done. Different levels of care available. Private Duty/Extra Care available. Assisted Living Area ($200.00 to $400.00/month). Lab service (visiting, $25.00/visit). Residents can purchase outside resources and use agency of their choice. Will help locate higher level of care if needed (referrals, paperwork).
ACCOMMODATION: *Choice of suites available*: bachelor, 1-bedroom, walk out, all with kitchenettes. *In all suites*: locks, kitchenette, bar fridge, microwave, patio/balcony, storage, window coverings, light fixtures, fire alarm, smoke/heat detector, sprinkler, call bell, cordless emergency response system with wearable pendant/bracelet, air conditioning (central), thermostats for heating & cooling (individual climate control) and lock box. Private bathrooms with grab bars, tubs and showers with non-slip surfaces. Can have own phone number if resident arranges with phone company. Unfurnished suites, furnished suites available for short stays. *Restrictions on electrical appliances*: no hot plates; all space heaters must

have auto shut-off. Suites can be shared (by couples only). Pets allowed (must follow Pet Policy & sign Agreement).

DINING SERVICE: All meals included in fee and served in dining room daily. *Sittings per meal:* Breakfast: 1, Lunch: 1, Dinner: 1. *Menu choices available:* Breakfast: 2, Lunch: 2, Dinner: 2. *Guest Meals*: Breakfast $4.00, Lunch $8.00, Dinner $10.00. *Special Diets*: Vegetarian, Low Salt and Diabetic. Tray service to room if ill (no charge as long as doctor orders). 2 snacks/day and unlimited snacks available at any time. Open pantry. Party facilities. Elegant private dining room.

AMENITIES AND ACTIVITIES: Parking available (outdoor, for visitors and residents). *2 lounges with:* TV (1), pianos (2), fireplaces (2) and balcony (2). Guest suites available ($75.00/night). *Residence has a:* library, chapel, barber/beauty shop, visiting hairdresser and laundry room(s) (no cost). Resident can arrange newspaper delivery to individual suite. Mail delivered to private mailbox (no key). *Recreation Facilities*: exercise room, craft room, card room and large activity room. Posted schedule of activities. Internal newsletter for residents. *Recreational Programs*: exercise, shopping, theatre, parties, entertainment, pet visiting, day trips, bingo, cards, Paraffin Hand Treatments, Brain Benders, and so much more.

OTHER SERVICES: *Housekeeping*: weekly (included in fee). *Laundry*: personal ($80.00/month). Transportation to medical appointments (family doctor only) and for group social activities. 24-hour security. Nightly security checks. Telephone (resident/family to arrange). Cable TV & Utilities (included in fee). Contact residence for details on other optional services.

RENTAL INFORMATION: Rates may vary. Extra cost for 2nd person sharing suite ($550.00/month). Life Lease Option is available (in our Village). Rent paid monthly. *Payment Options*: post-dated cheques and pre-authorized payments. Rent increases as per Provincial Tenancy Legislation, annual for resident with 3 months' notice given. Short-term respite and trial stays available (both $75.00/day).

THE COURT AT PRINGLE CREEK

3975 Anderson Street, Whitby, ON L1R 2Y8
Tel: (905) 665-4837 • Fax: (905) 665-4838
Email: **5411-manager@holidaytouch.com**
Website: **www.thecourtatpringlecreek.com**
Contact: **Community Managers**
Capacity: **119 units** • Subsidies: **none**
Price: **$2,995.00/month and up (rates may vary)**

Holiday Retirement believes retirement living should be relaxing and carefree, spent doing the things you love. That's why our communities provide a unique independent retirement lifestyle in a warm and welcoming environment. In one affordable, all-inclusive month-to-month rent, residents enjoy 3 delicious chef-prepared meals daily, enriching activities to share with friendly neighbours, housekeeping service, complimentary transportation, and so much more. Each Holiday community also features 2 sets of compassionate, dedicated live-in Managers available 24/7 to ensure safety and security. We do not provide any health care services; however, residents are welcome to receive services from any outside home health care provider of their choice to help them continue enjoying life at our community. Discover the peace-of-mind, happiness and fulfillment you deserve. Contact us today to schedule your personal tour!

RESIDENCE INFORMATION: 14 years in operation. *Near:* Anderson Street and Taunton Road. Handrails in hallways. 3 floors, 1 elevator. Wheelchair accessible. Central PA system. *Funding Base:* Corporate/for profit. *Owned and managed by:* Holiday Retirement. *Average Waiting Period*: none. *Average Age*: 83. Can sometimes accommodate cognitively impaired people. Can accommodate physically challenged people (must be independent; wheelchairs, walkers, scooters are welcome). Residents have a dress code (casual, no sleepwear in common areas). Smoking allowed (in own apartment). Alcohol allowed (in own apartment). *Procedures to leave the premises on a temporary basis...* Overnight & Holidays: let Front Office know. *Languages:* English. Will accept Public Guardian and Trustee clients. Main doors of residence

secured at night only. *Close to:* Public Transit, Shopping, Churches, Seniors' Centre, Library, Major Highway and Local Hospital.
STAFFING: *External services arranged by:* family/resident. 24-hour staff. Can retain own MD. Staff members are bonded.
HEALTH SERVICES: Will accept (but not provide special assistance for) residents who require oxygen, catheters, ostomies and feeding tubes. Residents can purchase outside resources and use agency of their choice. Will help locate higher level of care if needed (information).
ACCOMMODATION: *Choice of suites available*: studios, 1-bedrooms, 2-bedrooms, 1-bedroom cottages & 2-bedroom cottages. *In all suites*: locks, kitchenette, bar fridge, storage, window coverings, light fixtures, linens, fire alarm, smoke detector, sprinkler, call bell, air conditioning (wall unit) and thermostats for heating & cooling. Most have patios/balconies. Private bathrooms with call bells, tubs and showers with non-slip surfaces. In-suite cable TV provided by residence. Can have own phone number if resident arranges with phone company. Furnished & unfurnished suites available. *Restrictions on electrical appliances*: no stoves or hot plates. Suites can be shared, roommate picked by resident. Pets allowed.
DINING SERVICE: All meals included in fee and served in dining room daily. *Sittings per meal:* Breakfast: 1, Lunch: 1, Dinner: 1. *Menu choices available:* Breakfast: 5, Lunch: 6, Dinner: 5. *Guest Meals*: Breakfast $8.00, Lunch $12.00, Dinner $8.00. *Special Diets*: Vegetarian, Low Salt and Diabetic. Tray service to room if ill. 1 snack/day. Party facilities. Private Dining Area. Large meal of day served at noon-time. Fresh fruit, coffee, tea & goodies available all day.
AMENITIES AND ACTIVITIES: Parking available (outdoor, for visitors and residents). *4 lounges with:* TV (1), piano (1), games room (1) and craft room (1). Guest suites available ($75.00/night). *Residence has a:* library, chapel, barber/beauty shop and laundry room(s) (no cost). Resident can arrange newspaper delivery to individual suite. Mail delivered to private mailbox with key. *Recreation Facilities*: pool table, billiards, shuffleboard, exercise room, craft room and card room. Posted schedule of activities. Internal newsletter for residents. *Recreational Programs*: exercise, shopping, theatre, parties, entertainment, art classes, pet visiting, day trips and resident suggestions.
OTHER SERVICES: *Housekeeping*: weekly (included in fee). *Laundry*: linen & towel (included in fee). Free laundry rooms for personal use. Transportation to medical appointments and for group social activities. 24-hour security. Cable TV & Utilities (included in fee).
RENTAL INFORMATION: Rates may vary. Rate listed above is based on single occupancy. Extra cost for 2nd person sharing suite (please call for specifics). Rent paid monthly. *Payment Options*: cheques, post-dated cheques and pre-authorized payments. Rent increases indexed to inflation as per Provincial Tenancy Legislation, annual for resident with 3 months' notice given. Will help resident move into residence. Trial stays available (see Managers).

THE VILLAGE OF TAUNTON MILLS

3800 Brock Street North, Whitby, ON L1R 3A5
Tel: (905) 666-3156
Email: **rosemary.coolen@schlegelvillages.com**
Website: **www.schlegelvillages.com**
Contact: **Rosemary Coolen**
Capacity: **220 residents** • Subsidies: **none**
Price: **$3,199.06/month and up**

The Village of Taunton Mills is Whitby's unique continuum of care community for seniors offering a full range of care support levels. Our residences are modern and attractive, set on beautifully landscaped grounds, without the institutional feeling of nursing and retirement homes of the past. Our internal Main Street offers the conveniences of a small town without having to go outside: winter, summer, rain or shine! Residents, both singles and couples, can choose from cozy studios that emphasize care to

generous 1-bedroom or 2-bedroom apartments that emphasize independence. Four levels of care are offered at Taunton Mills: Full Service Retirement Suites, Assisted Care, Independent Living and Long-Term Care.

RESIDENCE INFORMATION: 6 years in operation. *Near:* Brock Street and Taunton Road. Handrails in hallways. 8 floors, 2 elevators. Wheelchair accessible. Central PA system. *Funding Base:* Corporate/for profit. *Owned by:* Schlegel Villages. 184 units. *Average Waiting Period*: 6 - 12 months. Can sometimes accommodate cognitively impaired people (depends on assessment and risk of elopement). Can accommodate physically challenged people. Smoke-free residence. Alcohol allowed. *Procedures to leave the premises on a temporary basis*...please notify Neighbourhood Coordinator. *Languages:* English. Will accept Public Guardian and Trustee clients. Main doors of residence secured at night only. *Close to:* Public Transit, Shopping, Churches, Seniors' Centre, Library, Major Highway and Local Hospitals (Lakeridge Health - Oshawa General Hospital Site & Port Perry Site & Rouge Valley Health System – Ajax and Pickering Health Centre Site). Member of ORCA. Licensed under the Retirement Homes Act.
STAFFING: *Available Staff/Services*: Pharmacy, Social Work (CCAC), Recreation Therapy, Occupational Therapy (CCAC), Visiting Dentist, Physiotherapy, Dietitian, Companions, Podiatry, Chaplaincy, Speech Pathology (CCAC), Chiropody, Massage Therapy and Chiropractor. *External services arranged by:* residence and/or family/resident. Staff trained *re*: visually, hearing and cognitively impaired. 24-hour nursing and other staff. RNs, RPNs, HCAs, PSWs and UCPs on staff. Visiting MD. Can retain own MD. Police Check or Vulnerable Person Screening is done for all new staff.
HEALTH SERVICES: Medication administration and/or supervision. Vitals monitored if required. Will accept and provide special assistance for residents who require oxygen, catheters and ostomies. Assistance with dressing available. Weekly assistance with bathing available. *Extra baths:* $27.00/hour. Care plans done. Different levels of care available. Private Duty/Extra Care available ($27.00/hour). Assisted Living Area (1 - 2 month waiting period). Lab service (visiting). Residents can purchase outside resources and use agency of their choice. Clinic area for medical visits. Will help locate higher level of care if needed (guidance can be given by Director of Retirement Care or Neighbourhood Coordinator).
ACCOMMODATION: *Choice of suites available*: studio, 1-bedroom, 1-bedroom + den & 2-bedroom units. *In all suites*: locks, storage, window coverings, light fixtures, linens, fire alarm, smoke detector, sprinkler, call bell, emergency response system with wearable pendant/bracelet, air conditioning (central) and thermostats for heating & cooling. Independent Living Suites have full kitchens & washer/dryers; all other suites have modified kitchens. Private bathrooms with call bells, grab bars, showers with non-slip surfaces and elevated toilet seats. In-suite cable TV provided by residence (residence charges extra $37.00/month). Can have own phone number provided by residence (residence charges extra $30.00/month). Unfurnished suites, furnished suites available for short stays. Suites can be shared, roommate picked by resident. Pets allowed.
DINING SERVICE: Independent Living - meals can be purchased. Retirement Apartments - Lunch and Dinner included. All others - 3 meals/day. All meals served in dining room daily. *Guest Meals*: Available. *Special Diets*: Vegetarian, Low Salt and Diabetic. Tray service to room if ill. Unlimited snacks available at any time. Party facilities.
AMENITIES AND ACTIVITIES: Parking available (outdoor, for visitors and indoor & outdoor for residents). *Residence has a:* library, chapel, barber/beauty shop, laundry room(s) (no cost) and tuck/gift shop. Mail delivered to individual suite. *Recreation Facilities*: pool table, shuffleboard, exercise room, greenhouse, craft room and card room. Posted schedule of activities. Internal newsletter for residents. *Recreational Programs*: exercise, shopping, theatre, parties, entertainment, art classes, pet visiting and day trips.
OTHER SERVICES: *Housekeeping*: weekly (included in fee). *Laundry*: linen & towel (included in fee); personal ($30.00/month). Staff label clothing ($60.00 one-time fee). In-suite washers and dryers available in many suites. Transportation for group social activities. Telephone ($30.00/month). Cable TV ($37.00/month). Utilities (included in fee). Additional Care Levels available at $27.00/hour spread across a 24-hour period.

RENTAL INFORMATION: Rates may vary. Starting Rates: Independent Living - $3,864.00/month; Retirement Suites - $3,199.06/month; Full Service Retirement - $3,488.64/month; Assisted Care - $4,146.23/month. Extra cost for 2nd person sharing suite (couples receive rate per individual). Option to purchase unit available (Condo Life Equity Unit Agreements are available on select suites). Rent paid monthly. *Payment Options*: cheques and pre-authorized payments. Rent increases as per Provincial Tenancy Legislation, annual for resident with 3 months' notice given. Short-term respite and trial stays available.

♦ WINDSOR ♦

BAYBRIDGE - KENSINGTON COURT

1953 Cabana Road West, Windsor, ON N9G 2X6
Tel: (519) 966-8558 • Fax: (519) 966-9542
Email: **marline.forton@Kensington-Court.com**
Website: **www.Kensington-Court.com**
Contact: **Marline Forton**
Capacity: **114 units** • Subsidies: **none**
Price: **$1,992.00/month and up**

At Kensington Court we believe retirement living should be relaxing and carefree, spent doing the things you love. That's why our community provides a unique independent retirement lifestyle in a warm and welcoming environment. In one affordable, all-inclusive month-to-month rent, residents enjoy 3 delicious chef-prepared meals daily, enriching activities to share with friendly neighbours, housekeeping service, complimentary transportation, and so much more. We do not provide any health care services; however, residents are welcome to receive services from any outside home health care provider of their choice to help them continue enjoying life independently at our community. Discover the peace-of-mind, happiness and fulfillment you deserve. Contact us today to schedule your personal tour!

RESIDENCE INFORMATION: 16 years in operation. *Near:* Cabana Street and Huron Church Avenue. Handrails in hallways. 3 floors, 1 elevator. Wheelchair accessible. Central PA system. *Funding Base:* Corporate/for profit. *Owned and managed by:* BayBridge Senior Living. *Average Waiting Period*: varies. *Average Age*: 83. Can accommodate cognitively impaired people with restrictions. Can accommodate physically challenged people (must be independent; walkers, wheelchairs, scooters are welcome). Residents have a dress code (casual, no sleepwear in common areas). Smoking allowed (on balcony or patio only). Alcohol allowed (in own apartment or in the dining room). *Procedures to leave the premises on a temporary basis*...let Office know. *Languages:* English. Will accept Public Guardian and Trustee clients. Main doors of residence secured at night only. *Close to:* Public Transit, Shopping, Churches, Synagogues, Seniors' Centre, Library and Major Highway.
STAFFING: *Available Staff/Services*: Social Work (CCAC), Occupational Therapy (CCAC), Physiotherapy (CCAC) and Chaplaincy. *External services arranged by:* residence and/or family/resident. Can retain own MD. Police Check or Vulnerable Person Screening is done for all new staff.
HEALTH SERVICES: Will accept (but not provide special assistance for) residents who require oxygen, catheters, ostomies and feeding tubes. Residents can purchase outside resources and use agency of their choice. Will help locate higher level of care if needed (information available from Front Office and local government health agencies).
ACCOMMODATION: *Choice of suites available*: studio, 1-bedroom & 2-bedroom/2-bath suites. *In all suites*: locks, kitchenette, refrigerator, storage, window coverings, light fixtures, linens, fire alarm, smoke detector, sprinkler, call bell, air conditioning (wall unit) and thermostats for heating & cooling. Most have

patios/balconies. Private bathrooms with call bells, grab bars, tubs and showers with non-slip surfaces and elevated toilet seats. In-suite cable TV provided by residence. Can have own phone number if resident arranges with phone company. Unfurnished suites, furnished suites available for short stays. *Restrictions on electrical appliances*: no hot plates or stoves. Suites can be shared, roommate picked by resident. Pets allowed (cats and small dogs only).
DINING SERVICE: All meals included in fee and served in dining room daily. *Sittings per meal:* Breakfast: 1, Lunch: 1, Dinner: 1. *Menu choices available:* Breakfast: 5, Lunch: 6, Dinner: 5. *Guest Meals*: Breakfast $10.00, Lunch $12.00, Dinner $10.00. *Special Diets*: Vegetarian, Low Salt and Diabetic. Tray service to room if ill (no charge for a maximum time of 5 days). Unlimited snacks available at any time. Fresh fruit, coffee, tea and goodies available all day. Large meal at noon-time. Party facilities. Private dining room.
AMENITIES AND ACTIVITIES: Parking available (outdoor, for visitors and residents). *4 lounges with:* TV (1), piano (1), computer kiosk (1) and pool table (1). Guest suites available. *Residence has a:* library, visiting library, chapel, barber/beauty shop and laundry room(s) (no cost). Resident can arrange newspaper delivery to individual suite. Mail delivered to private mailbox with key. *Recreation Facilities*: pool table, billiards, shuffleboard, exercise room, card room and activity room with full kitchen. Posted schedule of activities. Internal newsletter for residents. *Recreational Programs*: exercise, shopping, theatre, parties, entertainment, art classes, pet visiting, day trips, religious services and Seniors for Seniors Program.
OTHER SERVICES: *Housekeeping*: weekly (included in fee). *Laundry*: linen & towel (included in fee); personal (extra cost; resident does own personal laundry). Free laundry rooms for personal use. Transportation to medical appointments and for group social activities. 24-hour security. Cable TV & Utilities (included in fee).
RENTAL INFORMATION: Rates may vary. Rate listed above is based on single occupancy. Extra cost for 2nd person sharing suite (please call for specifics). Rent paid monthly. *Payment Options*: cheques, post-dated cheques, direct deposit and pre-authorized payments. Rent increases as per Provincial Tenancy Legislation, annual for resident with 3 months' notice given. Will help resident move into residence (extra cost). Trial stays available (see Managers).

Health Related Resources:

- Health Canada: **www.hc-sc.gc.ca** or **(866) 225-0709**
- Kidney Foundation: **www.kidney.ca** or **(800) 387-4474**
- Canadian Diabetes Association: **www.diabetes.ca** or **(800) 226-8464**
- Parkinson Society of Canada: **www.parkinson.ca** or **(800) 565-3000**
- Heart and Stroke Foundation of Canada: **www.heartandstroke.com** or **(613) 569-4361**
- The Canadian National Institute for the Blind: **www.cnib.ca** or **(800) 563-2642**
- Alzheimer Society of Canada: **www.alzheimer.ca** or **(800) 616-8816**
- Canadian Cancer Society: **www.cancer.ca** or **(416) 961-7223**
- The Canadian Hearing Society: **www.chs.ca** or **(877) 347-3427**
- Canadian Lung Association: **www.lung.ca** or **(888) 344-5864**
- Canadian Fitness and Lifestyle Research Institute: **www.cflri.ca** (Fitness Tips for Seniors) or **(613) 233-5528**
- Public Health Agency of Canada: **www.phac-aspc.gc.ca/index-eng.php** or **(416) 973-0003**
- The Safe Living Guide: **www.phac-aspc.gc.ca/seniors-aines/publications/public/injury-blessure/safelive-securite/index-eng.php** (A Guide to Home Safety for Seniors) or **(416) 973-0003**

Long-Term Care Homes

Photos provided by Four Elms Retirement Residence and Stouffville Creek Retirement Residence

LONG-TERM CARE HOMES – GENERAL INFORMATION

Long-Term Care homes (formerly called Nursing Homes) offer 24-hour/day care and assistance to medically stable individuals in a secure, supervised environment. Homes are able to offer help with all activities of daily living including eating, bathing, personal care, medication administration and nursing care while also providing basic furniture, linens, medical devices, housekeeping, laundry services, recreation activities and all meals for residents. They tend to offer more care than is usually available in a seniors building, retirement residence and even most assisted living settings and are able manage special needs such as dementia. There is usually a physician attached to each home that visits regularly and sees residents who require non-acute medical attention. They are licensed, funded and inspected by Ontario's Ministry of Health and Long-Term Care who also sets the 'co-payment' rates annually for all homes. Rates vary minimally depending on when a resident was admitted and when specific homes were built or renovated[22]. The governing legislation is the *Long-Term Care Homes Act, 2007.* The Ministry covers the cost of care while the resident is responsible for their 'room and board' cost (or co-payment). While many residents are admitted from a hospital, there are others who are admitted from their own homes or another type of residence.

Long-Term Care homes offer permanent or short-term (respite or convalescent) stays. Regardless of the type of stay you want, application for admission is made through your local CCAC (Community Care Access Centre). They determine eligibility, monitor applications and notify the family and resident when a bed becomes available in one of their chosen homes. Once a bed is accepted they ensure that arrangements are made for transfer and admission. Contact information for all CCACs in Ontario can be found on **page 54.** Alternately, you can visit **www.ccac-ont.ca** or call **310-2222** to locate the CCAC that serves your area.

As you know from **Part 1** of this *Guide*, relocation of any kind can be a very difficult process and long-term care is no exception. Often, when someone requires long-term care there is a clear sense of urgency to get them necessary support, especially if the family is struggling to manage at home and, the place you want has a long waiting list. There is no 'easy' way to choose even though to a certain degree, there is a limit to the choices you have. CCAC determines the maximum number of homes you can choose (maximum is 5) and the first place that comes up must be accepted or your application will be cancelled (in the situation where a 'crisis' placement is required, there may in fact be no choice as often the person will go to a place that has a bed and can meet their current needs and then, if desired, the

---

[22] Monthly Room Rates: **As of July 1, 2013**

Basic (depending on when a home was built or renovated this can mean up to 4 residents in a room, in newer homes it is usually 2 people per room) – daily rate is $56.14/day or $1,701.59/month

Semi-private (usually 2 people per room) - $64.14/day ($1,950.93/month) in an older bed or in a newer bed if admitted prior to July 1, 2012; $65.14.day ($1,981.34/month) if resident was admitted to a newer bed on or after July 1, 2012 but before July 1, 2013; $66.14/day ($2,011.76/month) in a newer bed if admitted July 1, 2013 or after.

Private (one person per room) - $74.14/day ($2,255.09) in an older bed or if admitted before July 1, 2012; $75.89/day ($2,308.32/month) if resident was admitted to a newer bed on or after July 1, 2012 but before July 1, 2013; $77.64/day ($2,361.55/month) in a newer bed if admitted July 1, 2013 or after.

Short-stay Rate – (for Respite/Caregiver Relief: the maximum is 60 continuous days or 90 accumulated days in a calendar year; for Convalescent Care the maximum stay is 90 days in a calendar year) - $36.34/day

Note: fees are increased periodically so please check with your local CCAC for up-to-date rates.

These fees do not include optional services like cable, phone or things like, transportation and hairstylist visits. Please see section 245 of the Long-Term Care Homes Act for 'non-allowable resident charges'.

For residents who cannot afford the set co-payment rate, a rate reduction is possible. Eligibility is based on annual income not personal assets. Contact your local CCAC to find out if you are eligible.

family can move them to another place at a later date.) In addition to choice, in situations where long-term care is required, even in a non-crisis situation, time may be a limiting factor often because a caregiver or a hospital is in need of a fairly quick decision & application. Despite these issues, multiple relocations can be difficult on a frail senior, especially one that also has some cognitive issues, so if at all possible before choosing we recommend that you take the time to visit & research places you are considering. If you can, take tours of the homes that are either recommended to you or ones you believe, based on proximity or services, you are thinking of applying to. If at all possible, consider homes that are close to family and friends so your loved one can have frequent visitors. It will most certainly benefit in the adjustment to their new surroundings if familiar faces come to visit. Once you choose the homes you want to see, call them to find out when they have tours or if your time is limited, if they are willing to take you on a private tour.

Recognizing that looking for a retirement home and a long-term care home are two very different things, I have created a shortened questionnaire for those of you going through the process of choosing a long-term care home. Using a similar format to our well-used Retirement Residence Visiting Tips questionnaire, I have narrowed down questions based on what I know often separates the search for retirement residences from that of long-term care homes - time and circumstances. There are often significant differences between a person who requires one level of care instead of the other and in the actual care and options that are available between the two levels. Prior to going on your tours, it would be best to review the questionnaire below, add any additional questions you might have and take a new questionnaire to each place that you visit. While on your tours, speak with others you meet currently going through the process, families visiting the homes who have gone through the process themselves and current residents (provided they are cognitively alert) for added insight and assistance.

LONG-TERM CARE HOME VISITING TIPS

Residence Name:____________________ **Date of Visit:**____________

Residence Address:______________________________

Residence Phone Number:__________________________

Tour Guide/Contact Person:_________________________

SMELL	COMMENTS
1. Does the residence smell clean? (Notice the common areas, hallways, kitchen, dining area, different floors of the building and suites.)	
2. Is the building well ventilated so smells do not linger?	

TOUCH	COMMENTS
3. What is the air quality like? Does it seem stale or fresh inside?	
4. Is the temperature in the building and rooms comfortable?	
5. Is there air-conditioning in rooms and common areas?	

SIGHT	COMMENTS
6. Is there an alarm system on the doors?	
7. Are all doors locked 24-hours a day or only at night?	
8. Is there a 24-hour attendant at the main desk?	

9. Does the building & grounds look clean and well-maintained?	
10. Is there a patio area/shady spots/garden with seating for residents and their visitors?	
11. Is the location convenient for friends and family to visit?	
12. Do residents seem to be well cared for/dressed/clean?	
13. What is the atmosphere like? Is there a lot of activity around? Are there many residents in the common areas?	
14. Note the location of fire exits and the fire alarm and/or sprinkler system. Are they easily accessible and well-marked?	
15. What is the lighting like in the residence? Is it bright and well-distributed or dark in hallways and public areas?	
16. Ask if you can see the kitchen. Does it appear clean?	

Look for bulletin boards and read the posted items. It will give you an idea of activities currently going on in the home and any upcoming events.

ROOMS	COMMENTS
17. What kind of accommodation is available – ward, semi, private?	
18. If the room is shared, is there an opportunity for privacy for residents?	
19. Are bathrooms clean and in good condition?	
20. Does each room have its own full bathroom?	
21. Which assistive devices are present in bathrooms?	
22. Do rooms have sprinklers, smoke detectors, heat detectors, CO detectors?	
23. Can you have your own TV (is there cable) and phone in your room & what is the cost of this per month?	
24. What furniture/possessions of your own can you bring? What is provided?	
25. Is there a secure place for any valuables in the room?	

TASTE/FOOD	COMMENTS
26. Are all/some meals prepared on site from scratch?	
27. Is there a dietitian on staff?	
28. Are fresh fruits and vegetables served year-round?	
29. Are special meals available?	
30. If required, can cultural meals be accommodated?	
31. Are menu choices available at each meal?	
32. What kinds of refreshments are offered between meals and at what time of day?	

SOUND: *Speak with residents' family members if you meet any during your visit* ***(Remember – they know best what the residence and staff are like and whether it is a place that is safe and enjoyable to live in)***

	COMMENTS
33. Do they like the residence, and if not, why not?	
34. Are their loved ones needs being met?	
35. Are they satisfied with the home and would they recommend it?	

Observe the attitude of the staff & their interaction with residents	**COMMENTS**
36. Are staff members friendly, polite and available?	
37. Do they know the residents by name and greet them respectfully?	

Speak with the administrator and other staff members	**COMMENTS**
38a. Is there a waiting list to get into the residence?	
38b. If yes, how long is it for the type of room you would like? (e.g. some homes have a longer wait for private vs. ward.)	
39a. Who owns/manages the residence?	
39b. How long have they owned/managed it?	
39c. How many other residences do they own/manage?	
39d. What is their reputation? (You might also want to research this online)	
40. Are there visiting hours? What are they?	
41. Are families involved in the residents' plan of care?	
42. How often are family meetings held (to update and provide information)?	
43a. Is the residence a member of any organizations or accredited by any independent organizations (e.g. Accreditation Canada, CARF)?	
43b. If yes, is their membership prominently displayed in the lobby and is it up-to-date?	
44a. When was their last inspection by the Ministry of Health and Long-Term Care? (report should be posted in home)	
44b. What rating were they given? (You can view inspection reports online at **http://publicreporting.ltchomes.net/en-ca/default.aspx**)	
45. What is the smoking policy? Is there a smoking room?	
46. What is the policy around alcohol consumption?	
47. Are there scheduled activities in the evenings and on weekends?	
48. What kind of activities are there in the residence?	
49. Are religious/cultural holidays celebrated at the residence? Which ones?	
50a. Is there a Family &/or Resident Council?	
50b. If yes, what is the process to join it and what kinds of decisions are they able to make?	
51. Are there restrictions around certain medical conditions that cannot be managed in this home (conversely, what special needs can be managed)?	
52. Does the home have a secure Dementia Area?	
53. What kind of security is available to prevent residents with dementia from wandering off the unit and out of the residence?	
54. What is included in the basic monthly rent package?	
55. If you require a rate reduction: what is available, who provides the documents to be completed, what do they need from you and when is the paperwork started/completed?[23]	
56. How is rent paid (cheques, pre-authorized payments etc.)?	
57. Are there extra mandatory monthly costs? What are they?	

[23] For information on rate reductions through the Ministry of Health contact your local CCAC or visit **http://www.health.gov.on.ca/en/public/programs/ltc/15_facilities_rate_reduction.aspx**

58. What are the optional monthly costs?	
59. What is the ratio of staff to residents?	
60. How many residents are in this home at maximum?	
61. Does the ratio differ between the day-time and night-time and weekends?	
62. Does home offer extra services like Physiotherapy or Occupational Therapy, Podiatry etc.? How often? Is there an extra cost?	
63. How often does the doctor visit?	
64. What is the procedure if residents need to see a doctor outside of regular hours?	
65. If language is an issue, are there staff that speak your (or your loved one's) language? If not, how do they communicate with residents who speak unfamiliar languages?	
66. Is management staff on site seven days/week?	
67. Which hours do they work? (Mangement Staff)	
68. Are there regular fire drills, fire inspections and staff training sessions for emergency situations?	
69. What kind of safety procedures are in place? (i.e. with respect to emergency situations, fire, exit doors etc.)	
70. If you have not been able to speak to any residents or families of residents during your tour, will they give you family references to contact?	

Before leaving, ask for sample menus, activity calendars, newsletters and any additional documentation they are willing to share.

Did you know?

Diabetes is considered to be a "Public Health Challenge" in Ontario because of the great number of people being diagnosed with the chronic disease every day. It impacts both young and old but "Seniors are especially at high risk for developing diabetes. As they age, seniors are less likely to be physically active, either by choice or because of disabling conditions. The risks of obesity and abdominal fat accumulation are increased. The combination of high risk factors and the aging process increases the occurrence of type 2 diabetes with age. The rate of diabetes in Ontario is increasing along with the growth of its aging population." To help decrease the number of people suffering from this disease, Ontario's Chief Medical Officer of Health has created a report along with strategies to help prevent the disease. To view the report and recommendations visit **www.health.gov.on.ca**.

Quoted from: **www.health.gov.on.ca/en/common/ministry/publications/reports/diabetes/diabetes.aspx#guidelines** October 2013

Did you know?

Many long-term care homes not listed in this edition of *The Guide* are available online at **www.senioropolis.com.** Please visit our site often for extra information and additional homes.

LONG-TERM CARE HOMES RESIDENTS' BILL OF RIGHTS

Quoted directly from: **www.e-laws.gov.on.ca/html/statutes/english/elaws_statutes_07l08_e.htm#BK5**

Residents' Bill of Rights

Every licensee of a long-term care home shall ensure that the following rights of residents are fully respected and promoted:

1. Every resident has the right to be treated with courtesy and respect and in a way that fully recognizes the resident's individuality and respects the resident's dignity.
2. Every resident has the right to be protected from abuse.
3. Every resident has the right not to be neglected by the licensee or staff.
4. Every resident has the right to be properly sheltered, fed, clothed, groomed and cared for in a manner consistent with his or her needs.
5. Every resident has the right to live in a safe and clean environment.
6. Every resident has the right to exercise the rights of a citizen.
7. Every resident has the right to be told who is responsible for and who is providing the resident's direct care.
8. Every resident has the right to be afforded privacy in treatment and in caring for his or her personal needs.
9. Every resident has the right to have his or her participation in decision-making respected.
10. Every resident has the right to keep and display personal possessions, pictures and furnishings in his or her room subject to safety requirements and the rights of other residents.
11. Every resident has the right to,
    i. participate fully in the development, implementation, review and revision of his or her plan of care,
    ii. give or refuse consent to any treatment, care or services for which his or her consent is required by law and to be informed of the consequences of giving or refusing consent,
    iii. participate fully in making any decision concerning any aspect of his or her care, including any decision concerning his or her admission, discharge or transfer to or from a long-term care home or a secure unit and to obtain an independent opinion with regard to any of those matters, and
    iv. have his or her personal health information within the meaning of the *Personal Health Information Protection Act, 2004* kept confidential in accordance with that Act, and to have access to his or her records of personal health information, including his or her plan of care, in accordance with that Act.
12. Every resident has the right to receive care and assistance towards independence based on a restorative care philosophy to maximize independence to the greatest extent possible.
13. Every resident has the right not to be restrained, except in the limited circumstances provided for under this Act and subject to the requirements provided for under this Act.
14. Every resident has the right to communicate in confidence, receive visitors of his or her choice and consult in private with any person without interference.
15. Every resident who is dying or who is very ill has the right to have family and friends present 24 hours per day.
16. Every resident has the right to designate a person to receive information concerning any transfer or any hospitalization of the resident and to have that person receive that information immediately.
17. Every resident has the right to raise concerns or recommend changes in policies and services on behalf of himself or herself or others to the following persons and organizations without

interference and without fear of coercion, discrimination or reprisal, whether directed at the resident or anyone else,

i. the Residents' Council,

ii. the Family Council,

iii. the licensee, and, if the licensee is a corporation, the directors and officers of the corporation, and, in the case of a home approved under Part VIII, a member of the committee of management for the home under section 132 or of the board of management for the home under section 125 or 129,

iv. staff members,

v. government officials,

vi. any other person inside or outside the long-term care home.

18. Every resident has the right to form friendships and relationships and to participate in the life of the long-term care home.
19. Every resident has the right to have his or her lifestyle and choices respected.
20. Every resident has the right to participate in the Residents' Council.
21. Every resident has the right to meet privately with his or her spouse or another person in a room that assures privacy.
22. Every resident has the right to share a room with another resident according to their mutual wishes, if appropriate accommodation is available.
23. Every resident has the right to pursue social, cultural, religious, spiritual and other interests, to develop his or her potential and to be given reasonable assistance by the licensee to pursue these interests and to develop his or her potential.
24. Every resident has the right to be informed in writing of any law, rule or policy affecting services provided to the resident and of the procedures for initiating complaints.
25. Every resident has the right to manage his or her own financial affairs unless the resident lacks the legal capacity to do so.
26. Every resident has the right to be given access to protected outdoor areas in order to enjoy outdoor activity unless the physical setting makes this impossible.
27. Every resident has the right to have any friend, family member, or other person of importance to the resident attend any meeting with the licensee or the staff of the home. 2007, c. 8, s. 3 (1).

For Additional Information & the complete Long-Term Care Homes Act, 2007 visit http://www.e-laws.gov.on.ca/html/statutes/english/elaws_statutes_07l08_e.htm

Did you know?

The Long Term Care Planning Network is a national resource devoted to providing information and education on aging and long-term care planning. They have information for caregivers and professionals that can be accessed through their website **www.ltcplanningnetwork.com.**

LONG-TERM CARE HOME COMPLAINTS

All long-term care homes must be settings where residents feel safe and secure and have all of their needs met. If you have specific concerns about an Ontario Long-Term Care Home you may first want to discuss your concerns with the administrative staff of the home. There should be a document available and posted in the home detailing the process for filing a complaint within the home. If there is ANY concern about potential harm impacting residents of the home, it must be investigated right away. For other issues there is the allowable timeline of 10 business days to respond and investigate. If the issue is not resolved to your satisfaction or you would prefer not to go directly to the home's staff, you can call the Long-Term Care ACTION Line at **(866) 434-0144** or send a letter to the Director of Performance Improvement and Compliance at the Ministry of Health and Long-Term Care. The address to send the letter to is: 1075 Bay Street, 11th Floor, Toronto, ON M5S 2B1. Should you go directly to the Ministry you will need to provide name and address information about the home and a full description of the issue, involved parties, where and when the incident occurred. You can send a complaint anonymously however, should you wish to know the result of your complaint, you would have to then provide contact information.

Depending on the gravity and nature of the complaint to the Ministry, an inspector may visit the home in question. In any event, the inspector will ensure that the home complies with the *Long-Term Care Homes Act, 2007*. If they are not complying he will complete an inspection report with problems detailed and an expectation that they will be fixed. Privacy of all residents and those who launch a complaint is respected. The legislation does protect those who complain and any residents involved from retaliation.

Inspection reports for all Ontario Long-Term Care Homes can be viewed online at
http://publicreporting.ltchomes.net/en-ca/default.aspx

Keep in mind...

The most important factor in determining quality of care in any residence or care situation is that of the staff. You can determine this easily if you take the time to watch and listen during your visits. Watch other residents when you visit; get to know them, their families/regular visitors and talk to them. Developing relationships with both staff and residents in the home is important and will ensure that if there are issues, you are notified of them. Focus on the food quality, cleanliness and staff attitude. Join a Family Council if there is one or encourage your loved one to join a Residents' Council if they are able to participate. If you have the time, join in activities in the residence. This is a way to help your loved one adjust while creating opportunities for you to get to know other residents and staff by observing and interacting.

Did you know?

The Ontario Senior's Secretariat has created and posted online a Substitute Decision-Maker Wallet Card for emergency situations. To download a wallet card visit:
www.seniors.gov.on.ca/en/advancedcare/docs/AdvancedCare.WalletCard.pdf
It allows you to specify if you have a Power of Attorney for Personal Care and who your substitute decision maker is. It does not however, replace a Power of Attorney.

◆ ALEXANDRIA ◆

COMMUNITY NURSING HOME ALEXANDRIA

92 Centre Street, Alexandria, ON K0C 1A0
Tel: (613) 525-2022 • Fax: (613) 525-2023
Email: **tdube@clmi.ca**
Website: **www.cnhalexandria.ca**
Contact: **Terry Dube**
Capacity: **70 residents**
Subsidies: **yes**

Nestled amongst mature trees, ample green space with a running brook, Community Nursing Home Alexandria is situated in the quiet, rural town of Alexandria. An accredited community since 1992 and licensed by the Ministry of Health and Long-Term Care, Community Nursing Home Alexandria offers a warm, friendly and home-like environment. A true sense of community is established through a dedicated and caring professional team. As a team, the staff of Community Nursing Home Alexandria believe in a high standard of care, through which we consider each and every resident as an individual. We employ a sincere and personal approach, in assisting the resident in attaining the maximum possible potential in all areas of functioning. We support the resident's right to self-determination and independence, for as long as possible, stressing a supportive family input, thus preserving Quality of Life while ensuring each one's confidentiality and dignity.

GENERAL HOME INFORMATION: 38 years in operation. *Near:* Bishop Street and Centre Avenue. Decorated in 2012. Handrails in hallways. 2 floors, 1 elevator. Wheelchair accessible. Central PA system. *Funding Base:* Corporate/for profit. *Owned and managed by:* Community Lifecare Inc. 70 units. *Average Waiting Period*: varies. *Average Age*: 90. Can accommodate cognitively impaired & physically challenged people. Smoke-free residence. Alcohol allowed (as per physician's order). *Restrictions around Visitors/ Visiting Hours:* 10:00 a.m. - 8:00 p.m. *Procedures to leave the premises on a temporary basis...*Short-term: as per legislation. Holidays: up to 21 day LOA (Leave of Absence) permitted. *Languages:* English & French. Will accept Public Guardian and Trustee clients. Main doors of residence secured at all times. *Close to:* Shopping, Churches, Seniors' Centre and Local Hospital (Glengarry Memorial Hospital). *Predominant Cultural Group:* French Canadian. Member of OLTCA.

◆ CORNWALL ◆

PARISIEN MANOR NURSING HOME

439 Second Street East, Cornwall, ON K6H 1Z2
Tel: (613) 933-2592 • Fax: (613) 933-3839
Email: **tdube@clmi.ca**
Website: **www.parisienmanor.ca**
Contact: **Terry Dube**
Capacity: **65 residents**
Subsidies: **yes**

For more than 40 years, Parisien Manor has established itself as a long-term care home which focuses on reflecting the cultural history of Cornwall. Conveniently located across from Cornwall Community Hospital – Second Street Site. An accredited community since 1982 & licensed by The Ministry of Health and

Long-Term Care, Parisien Manor offers a warm, friendly, home-like environment. A true sense of community is established through the skilled and experienced staff who are a dedicated & caring professional team committed to ensuring the physical well-being of each resident, while preserving the respect & honour they have earned. The enhancement of the human spirit & the safeguarding of each individual's dignity & independence is foremost in our hearts.

GENERAL HOME INFORMATION: 42 years in operation. *Near:* Marlborough Avenue and Second Street. Decorated in 2011. Handrails in hallways. 2 floors, 2 elevators. Wheelchair accessible. Central PA system. *Funding Base:* Corporate/for profit. *Owned and managed by:* Community Lifecare Inc. 65 units. *Average Waiting Period*: 6 - 12 months. *Average Age*: 90. Can accommodate cognitively impaired & physically challenged people. Smoke-free residence. Alcohol allowed (as per physician's order). *Restrictions around Visitors/Visiting Hours:* 10:00 a.m. – 8:00 p.m. *Procedures to leave the premises on a temporary basis...* Short-term: as per legislation. Holidays: up to 21 day LOA (Leave of Absence) permitted. *Languages:* English & French. Will accept Public Guardian and Trustee clients. Main doors of residence secured at all times. *Close to:* Public Transit, Shopping, Churches, Library, Major Highway and Local Hospital (Cornwall Community Hospital). Member of OLTCA.

♦ GEORGETOWN ♦

MOUNTAINVIEW RESIDENCE CARE WING

222 Mountainview Road North, Georgetown, ON L7G 3R2
Tel: (905) 873-1800 • Fax: (905) 873-9083
Email: **info@mountainviewresidence.com**
Website: **www.mountainviewresidence.com**
Contact: **Christoph Summer**
Capacity: **24 residents**
Subsidies: **none**

*COMING SOON....CURRENTLY UNDER CONSTRUCTION *

Mountainview Care Wing is an intimate and specialized care facility for persons who can no longer live independently and require 24-hour nursing services. Included will be a Supportive Dementia Care Program for persons who have Alzheimer's Disease or other forms of dementia. Our facility will also accommodate persons that have physical impairments and are in wheelchairs. 24 rooms in total. Privately owned, not subsidized.

GENERAL HOME INFORMATION: New residence. *Near:* John Street and Mountainview Road. Decorated in 2014. Handrails in hallways. 2 floors, 2 elevators. Wheelchair accessible. *Funding Base:* Corporate/for profit. *Owned by:* Christoph & Ursula Summer. 24 units. *Average Waiting Period*: none. Can accommodate cognitively impaired people (Alzheimer's, dementia, memory loss). Can accommodate physically challenged people (wheelchair). Smoke-free residence. *Procedures to leave the premises on a temporary basis...*must leave instructions with nursing staff. *Languages:* English & German. Will accept Public Guardian and Trustee clients. Main doors of residence secured at all times. *Close to:* Shopping, Churches, Seniors' Centre, Library and Local Hospital (Halton Healthcare Services Corporation – Georgetown and District Site).

◆ HAMILTON ◆

DUNDURN PLACE CARE CENTRE

39 Mary Street, Hamilton, ON L8R 3L8
Tel: (905) 523-6427 • Fax: (905) 528-0610
Email: **debbie.boakes@dundurnplacecarecentre.ca**
Website: **www.dundurnplacecarecentre.ca**
Contact: **Debbie Boakes**
Capacity: **201 residents**
Subsidies: **Ministry of Health & Long-Term Care**

Dundurn Place Care Centre is in the heart of downtown Hamilton close to shops, restaurants and public transportation. Dundurn Place Care Centre is an accredited 201 bed residence that offers semi-private and ward accommodation as well as 6 respite stay beds and 20 convalescent beds. We also offer Care Programs that include Nursing Rehabilitation and Physiotherapy. Our residents are involved in a variety of exciting programs which focus on independence such as outings to local sports events, cooking classes and our 2 signature programs, Java Music and Montessori. We have long-term employees who take pride in providing the best care, home-cooked meals, and a safe and clean environment. Enjoy our beautiful enclosed garden with mature trees just off our main floor dining room. Our residence has indoor smoking facilities for those who choose to smoke.

GENERAL HOME INFORMATION: 3 years in operation. *Near:* Mary Street and King William Street. Decorated in 2013. Handrails in hallways. 4 floors, 3 elevators. Wheelchair accessible. Central PA system. *Funding Base:* Corporate/for profit. *Managed by:* Responsive Management Inc. *Average Waiting Period*: varies. *Average Age*: 75. Can accommodate cognitively impaired & physically challenged people. Smoking allowed (inside home designated room and outdoor courtyard). Alcohol allowed (as prescribed by physician). *Procedures to leave the premises on a temporary basis...*as per Ministry Of Health Guidelines & physician orders. *Languages:* English, Filipino, French, Italian & Polish. Will accept Public Guardian and Trustee clients. Main doors of residence secured at all times. *Close to:* Public Transit, Shopping, Churches, Synagogues, Seniors' Centre, Library, Major Highway and Local Hospital (St. Joseph's Health Care System - Hamilton).

Operated by Responsive Management Inc.

◆ LEAMINGTON ◆

FRANKLIN GARDENS

324 Franklin Road, Leamington, ON N8H 4B7
Tel: (519) 326-3289 • Fax: (519) 326-0102
Email: **franklin@meritascare.ca**
Website: **www.meritascare.ca**
Contact: **Shelley Dobson**
Capacity: **120 residents**
Subsidies: **Ontario Ministry of Health and Long-Term Care**

Franklin Gardens is a 120-bed home licensed by the Ministry of Health and Long-Term Care. We are located in Leamington, situated on 5 lovely and well groomed acres overlooking the Leamington Marina. Our home is bungalow style with all rooms and service areas situated on one floor. We offer private,

semi-private and ward accommodation in a well-maintained home. But it's all about the people. Our staff makes the difference – dedicated, caring, professionally trained individuals committed to the well-being of our residents. Residents and their families are our customers and as such we are respectful of individual resident and family needs and concerns. We offer a comprehensive range of social, spiritual, intellectual, restorative and therapeutic programs and activities specifically tailored to individual resident needs and interests. Call today and arrange a tour to learn about how Franklin Gardens enhances the quality of life of our residents.

GENERAL HOME INFORMATION: 41 years in operation. *Near:* Seacliff Drive and Erie Street. Decorated in 2012. Handrails in hallways. 1 floor, no elevator. Wheelchair accessible. Central PA system. *Funding Base:* Corporate/for profit. *Owned by:* Meritas Care Corporation. 56 units. *Average Waiting Period*: 1 - 2 months. *Average Age*: 82. Can accommodate cognitively impaired & physically challenged people. Smoke-free residence. Alcohol allowed (physician order; kept in medication room). *Restrictions around Visitors/Visiting Hours:* preferred between 9:00 a.m. and 9:00 p.m. but, exceptions made for illness. *Procedures to leave the premises on a temporary basis*...sign out. *Languages:* English & several other languages, generally European. Will accept Public Guardian and Trustee clients. Main doors of residence secured at all times. *Close to:* Shopping, Churches, Library, Major Highway and Local Hospital (Leamington District Memorial Hospital). Member of OLTCA.

◆ LONDON ◆

EARLS COURT VILLAGE

1390 Highbury Avenue, London, ON N5V 5A4
Tel: (519) 655-2420
Email: **paula.thomson@bonniebrae.ca**
Website: **www.svch.ca**
Contact: **Paula Thomson**
Capacity: **128 residents**
Subsidies: **none**

There are many reasons why our residents have chosen to live in a Sharon Village Care Home Property. For some, it's the benefit of living together in a safe and caring community. For others, it's the access to discrete Assisted Living services in a continuum of care model. Whatever the reason, Sharon Village Care Homes is committed to enriching the mental and physical welfare of our residents through the comforts of home. Earls Court Village is a 128-bed facility currently under construction in North East London. Opening is planned tentatively for July of 2014. Paula Thomson is the Administrator at Bonnie Brae Health Care Centre in Tavistock and will attempt to answer any questions you may have about Earls Court Village. Residents currently residing at Bonnie Brae Health Care Centre will be transferred to Earls Court Village when the new facility opens, if that is where they wish to reside.

GENERAL HOME INFORMATION: New residence. *Near:* Huron Street and Highbury Avenue. Decorated in 2014. 4 floors, 2 elevators. Wheelchair accessible. Central PA system. *Funding Base:* Corporate/for profit. *Managed by:* Sharon Village Care Homes. *Average Waiting Period*: none. *Average Age*: 75. Can accommodate cognitively impaired & physically challenged people. Smoke-free residence. *Procedures to leave the premises on a temporary basis*...signed out by family/POA with physician's orders. *Languages:* English. Will accept Public Guardian and Trustee clients. Member of OLTCA.

KENSINGTON VILLAGE RETIREMENT/NURSING HOME

1340 Huron Street, London, ON N5V 3R3
Tel: (519) 455-3910 • Fax: (519) 455-1570
Email: **sbrooks@kensingtonvillage.org**
Website: **www.svch.ca**
Contact: **Sharron Brooks**
Capacity: **126 residents**
Subsidies: **through Ministry of Health & Long-Term Care**

There are many reasons why our residents have chosen to live in a Sharon Village Care Home. For some, it's the benefit of living together in a safe caring environment. For others, it's access to discrete Assisted Living services in a continuum of care model. Whatever the reason, Sharon Village Care Homes is committed to enriching the mental and physical welfare of our residents through the comforts of home.

GENERAL HOME INFORMATION: 30 years in operation. *Near:* Highbury Avenue and Huron Street. Decorated in 2010. Handrails in hallways. 2 floors, 1 elevator. Wheelchair accessible. Central PA system. *Funding Base:* Corporate/for profit. *Managed by:* Sharon Village Care Homes. 126 units. *Average Waiting Period*: varies. *Average Age*: 85. Can accommodate cognitively impaired & physically challenged people. Residents have a dress code (must be dressed in street clothes for lunch and dinner). Smoking allowed (smoking gazebo provided away from entrances). Alcohol allowed (must be ordered by physician). *Procedures to leave the premises on a temporary basis...*sign out and advise staff. *Languages:* English, Dutch, German, Italian, Polish & Spanish. Will accept Public Guardian and Trustee clients. Main doors of residence secured at night only. *Close to:* Public Transit, Shopping, Churches, Synagogues, Library and Local Hospital (London Health Sciences Centre). Member of ORCA & C.A.R. F. Retirement Home is licensed under the Retirement Homes Act.

◆ MISSISSAUGA ◆

TYNDALL NURSING HOME

1060 Eglinton Avenue East, Mississauga, ON L4W 1K3
Tel: (905) 624-1511 • Fax: (905) 624-5027
Email: **pbedford@tyndallnursinghome.com**
Website: **www.svch.ca**
Contact: **Pat Bedford**
Capacity: **151 residents**
Subsidies: **none**

There are many reasons why our residents have chosen to live in a Sharon Village Care Home property. For some, it's the benefit of living together in a safe and caring community. For others, it's the access to discrete Assisted Living services in a continuum of care model. Whatever the reason, Sharon Village Care Homes is committed to enriching the mental and physical welfare of our residents through the comforts of home. Tyndall Seniors Village/Nursing Home has served the Mississauga Community since 1976.

GENERAL HOME INFORMATION: *Near:* Tomken Street and Dixie Avenue. Decorated in 2012. Handrails in hallways. 4 floors, 2 elevators. Wheelchair accessible. Central PA system. *Funding Base:* Corporate/for profit. *Managed by:* Sharon Village Care Homes. *Average Age*: 86. Can accommodate cognitively impaired & physically challenged people. Smoke-free residence. Alcohol allowed (with physician's order). *Restrictions around Visitors/Visiting Hours:* 8:00 a.m. to 9:00 p.m.; other times available according to individual needs. *Procedures to leave the premises on a temporary basis...*with

physician's order. *Languages:* English, Portuguese, Italian, Tamil, Urdu & German. Will accept Public Guardian and Trustee clients. Main doors of residence secured at all times. *Close to:* Public Transit, Shopping, Churches, Synagogues, Seniors' Centre, Library, Major Highway and Local Hospital (Credit Valley Hospital & Trillium Health Partners).

◆ MOUNT FOREST ◆

SAUGEEN VALLEY

465 Dublin Street, Mount Forest, ON N0G 2L3
Tel: (519) 323-2140 • Fax: (519) 323-3540
Email: **administrator@svnc.ca**
Website: **www.svch.ca**
Contact: **Cate MacLean**
Capacity: **87 residents**
Subsidies: **yes**

There are many reasons why our residents have chosen to live in a Sharon Village Care Home property. For some, it's the benefit of living together in a safe and caring community. For others, it's the access to discrete Assisted Living services in a continuum of care model. Whatever the reason, Sharon Village Care Homes is committed to enriching the mental and physical welfare of our residents through the comforts of home.

Here at Saugeen Valley Nursing Center, we believe *Home is where the heart is . . . and this Home has lots of heart!* We are dedicated and passionate in the care we provide. We take a strong interest in you, the person – it's about the relationship we develop with you that makes the difference. We hope that you will invite us to participate in your life experiences as you make our home your home. We look forward to getting to know you & your family.

GENERAL HOME INFORMATION: 21 years in operation. Handrails in hallways. 3 floors, 2 elevators. Wheelchair accessible. Central PA system. *Funding Base:* Corporate/for profit. *Managed by:* Sharon Village Care Homes. 87 units. *Average Waiting Period*: less than 2 weeks. *Average Age*: 87. Can accommodate cognitively impaired & physically challenged people. Smoke-free residence. Alcohol allowed (as ordered by physician). *Procedures to leave the premises on a temporary basis*...signed Release of Responsibility while on LOA (Leave of Absence). *Languages:* English. Will accept Public Guardian and Trustee clients. *Close to:* Local Hospital (Louise Marshall Hospital). Member of OLTCA & CARF.

Did you know?

"The Canadian Caregiver Coalition is the national voice for the needs and interests of family caregivers. [They] are a bilingual, not-for-profit organization made up of caregivers, caregiver support groups, national stakeholder organizations and researchers. [They] provide leadership in identifying and responding to the needs of caregivers in Canada." For further information visit **www.ccc-ccan.ca.**

Quoted from: **www.ccc-ccan.ca** October 2013

♦ PICKERING ♦

COMMUNITY NURSING HOME PICKERING

1955 Valley Farm Road, Pickering, ON L1V 3R6
Tel: (905) 831-2522 • Fax: (905) 831-5033
Toll Free: (866) 471-9037
Email: **ghopkins@clmi.ca**
Website: **www.cnhpickering.ca**
Contact: **Garry Hopkins**
Capacity: **233 residents**
Subsidies: **yes**

Community Nursing Home Pickering is part of a unique senior's care community known as Village Retirement Centre, which consists of a private retirement residence (Orchard Villa) as well as a long-term care home (Community Nursing Home). Licensed & regulated by the Ontario Ministry of Health and Long-Term Care, Community Nursing Home, Pickering is an established long-term care home that has been serving the Durham region for over 30 years. We are conveniently located at 1955 Valley Farm Road in Pickering, nestled in a quiet, residential neighbourhood that is easily accessible to the 401, Highway 2 & public transit. Community Nursing Home Pickering is home to 233 residents offering a warm, friendly & home like environment. A true sense of community is established through a dedicated & caring professional team. Community Nursing Home Pickering features a koi pond & beautifully landscaped gardens. Our courtyard features a walking path & gazebo.

GENERAL HOME INFORMATION: 34 years in operation. *Near:* Kingston Road and Brock Road. Decorated in 2010. Handrails in hallways. 2 floors, 2 elevators. Wheelchair accessible. Central PA system. *Funding Base:* Corporate/for profit. *Owned and managed by:* Community Lifecare Inc. 233 units. *Average Waiting Period*: varies. *Average Age*: 85. Can accommodate cognitively impaired & physically challenged people. Smoke-free residence. Alcohol allowed (as per physician's orders). *Procedures to leave the premises on a temporary basis...*Short-term: as per legislation. Holidays: up to 21 day LOA (Leave of Absence) is permitted. *Languages:* English. Will accept Public Guardian and Trustee clients. Main doors of residence secured at night only. *Close to:* Public Transit, Shopping, Churches, Seniors' Centre, Library, Major Highway and Local Hospital (Rouge Valley Health System - Ajax and Pickering Health Centre Site). Member of OLTCA.

♦ PORT HOPE ♦

COMMUNITY NURSING HOME PORT HOPE

20 Hope Street South, Port Hope, ON L1A 2M8
Tel: (905) 885-6367 • Fax: (905) 885-6368
Email: **njordan@clmi.ca**
Website: **www.cnhporthope.ca**
Contact: **Nancy Jordan**
Capacity: **97 residents**
Subsidies: **yes**

Community Nursing Home Port Hope is a well-established long-term care home providing care for over 30 years. Located in a beautiful, residential community in the Town of Port Hope, we are an accredited community & licensed by The Ministry of Health and Long-Term Care. Community Nursing Home Port

Hope offers a warm, friendly, home-like environment. A true sense of community is established through a dedicated & caring professional team. Our multi-level home is designed for residents' comfort & provides easy access to all areas. Bedrooms - private & shared - are spacious & attractively decorated & feature en-suite bathrooms. Corridors are wide & accommodating. Residents can socialize and enjoy visits with family & friends in our comfortable lounges, private family room, outside garden area, which features raised flowerbeds & a specially designed walking path.

GENERAL HOME INFORMATION: 37 years in operation. *Near:* Hope Street South and Ward Street. Decorated in 2002. Handrails in hallways. 3 floors, 1 elevator. Wheelchair accessible. Central PA system. *Funding Base:* Corporate/for profit. *Owned and managed by:* Community Lifecare Inc. 97 units. *Average Waiting Period*: varies. *Average Age*: 82. Can accommodate cognitively impaired & physically challenged people. Smoke-free residence. Alcohol allowed (as per physician's order). *Procedures to leave the premises on a temporary basis...*Short-term: as per legislation. Holidays: up to 21 day LOA (Leave of Absence) is permitted. *Languages:* English. Will accept Public Guardian and Trustee clients. Main doors of residence secured at all times. *Close to:* Public Transit, Shopping, Churches, Seniors' Centre, Library, Major Highway and Local Hospital (Northumberland Hills Hospital). Member of OLTCA.

◆ PORT PERRY ◆

COMMUNITY NURSING HOME PORT PERRY

15941 Simcoe Street, Port Perry, ON L9L 1N5
Tel: (905) 985-3205 • Fax: (905) 985-3721
Email: **czacharuk@clmi.ca**
Website: **www.cnhportperry.ca**
Contact: **Carolyn Zacharuk**
Subsidies: **none**

Community Nursing Home Port Perry is located at 15941 Simcoe Street, with the nearest intersection being Reach & Simcoe Street. We have strong ties to the community with an army of volunteers, connections with area churches, schools and community clubs. Our activity department has a wide variety of dynamic programs to keep you busy. We are known for our regular outings, which take place weekly in the warm months and regularly throughout the year. Our activities personnel arrange fun trips like shopping, lunch, movies, bowling, plays, picnics; the list goes on and on. We even go on overnight trips! Our staff members focus on individualizing care for each resident to ensure they feel at home. We strive to provide the most comfortable and personalized care possible and we are always open to suggestions. You never feel like a stranger at Community Nursing Home because there is always a smiling face to greet you!

GENERAL HOME INFORMATION: *On:* Simcoe Street and Reach Street. Decorated in 2007. Handrails in hallways. Wheelchair accessible. Central PA system. *Funding Base:* Corporate/for profit. *Owned and managed by:* Community Lifecare Inc. Can accommodate cognitively impaired & physically challenged people. Smoke-free residence. Alcohol allowed (as per doctor's orders). *Procedures to leave the premises on a temporary basis...*Short-term: as per legislation. Holidays: up to 21 day LOA (Leave of Absence) permitted. *Languages:* English. Will accept Public Guardian and Trustee clients. Main doors of residence secured at all times. *Close to:* Public Transit, Churches and Local Hospital (Lakeridge Health - Port Perry Site). Member of OLTCA.

◆ TORONTO (ETOBICOKE) ◆

EATONVILLE CARE CENTRE

420 The East Mall, Toronto, ON M9B 3Z9
Tel: (416) 621-8000 • Fax: (416) 621-8003
Email: **marsha.deboer@eatonvillecarecentre.ca**
Website: **www.eatonvillecarecentre.ca**
Contact: **Marsha DeBoer**
Capacity: **247 residents**
Subsidies: **none**

Eatonville Care Centre is situated in a friendly residential neighbourhood in the heart of Etobicoke. Our long-term care home is accredited and has served our 247 multicultural residents since 1971. Centrally located, we are just minutes from shops, City Hall and Highway 427. Residents and families praise our caregivers for their skill, warmth and compassion. Staff promote inclusion, independence and autonomy for all our residents. Our team of families, physiotherapists, social workers, recreation therapists, dietician, doctors and nurses work closely to serve each individual. Our well-established programs include restorative care, sensory stimulation, music, art therapy, Java Music and Montessori. These programs enhance residents physically, mentally, emotionally and spiritually. Join us for a tour, take a stroll through our courtyard and make our home yours.

GENERAL HOME INFORMATION: 43 years in operation. *Near:* Burnhamthorpe Road and The East Mall Avenue. Redecorating scheduled for 2014. Handrails in hallways. 4 floors, 2 elevators. Wheelchair accessible. Central PA system. *Funding Base:* Corporate/for profit. *Managed by:* Responsive Management Inc. *Average Age*: 76. Can accommodate cognitively impaired people (Alzheimer's, dementia). Can accommodate physically challenged people (impaired mobility). Smoke-free residence. Alcohol allowed (as per doctor's orders). *Restrictions around Visitors/Visiting Hours:* 10:00 a.m. - 9:00 p.m. depending on situation. *Procedures to leave the premises on a temporary basis...*leave of absence procedure in place; must be approved by physician. *Languages:* English, Polish, Ukrainian, Serbian & Italian. Will accept Public Guardian and Trustee clients. Main doors of residence secured at night only. *Close to:* Public Transit, Shopping, Churches, Library, Major Highway and Local Hospital (St. Joseph's Health Centre).

Operated by Responsive Management Inc.

◆ TORONTO (NORTH YORK) ◆

HAWTHORNE PLACE CARE CENTRE

2045 Finch Avenue West, Toronto, ON M3N 1M9
Tel: (416) 745-0811 • Fax: (416) 745-0568
Email: **christine.murad@hawthorneplacecarecentre.ca**
Website: **www.hawthorneplacecarecentre.ca**
Contact: **Christine Murad**
Capacity: **225 residents**
Subsidies: **none**

Hawthorne Place Care Centre is located near Finch Avenue and Highway 400. This long-term care home opened in 1973 and has established many relationships within the community over the years. Hawthorne

Place is just steps away from local restaurants and shopping centres. We are proud to say we partner together with Humber River Regional Hospital on Finch Avenue. This 225 multicultural bed home prides itself on providing excellent care and specialty programs such as Convalescent, Java Music and Montessori. Our Convalescent Program has 24 beds and its multi-disciplinary team specializes in restorative care with a separate dedicated physiotherapy team. A variety of recreation programs keep our residents independent, active and entertained. Residents can enjoy music therapy, monthly outings and weekly Italian cooking. Join us for a tour, enjoy a home-cooked meal in a clean friendly environment and make our home yours.

GENERAL HOME INFORMATION: 41 years in operation. Decorated in 2011. Handrails in hallways. 3 floors, no elevator. Wheelchair accessible. *Managed by:* Responsive Management Inc. Can accommodate cognitively impaired people (dementia/secure unit). Smoking allowed (smoking room on first floor). *Languages:* English. Will accept Public Guardian and Trustee clients. Main doors of residence secured at all times. *Close to:* Public Transit, Shopping, Churches, Library, Major Highway and Local Hospital (Humber River Regional Hospital – Finch Street Site).

Operated by Responsive Management Inc.

♦ WARKWORTH ♦

COMMUNITY NURSING HOME WARKWORTH

97 Mill Street P.O. Box 68, Warkworth, ON K0K 3K0
Tel: (705) 924-2311 • Fax: (705) 924-1711
Email: **lallanson@clmi.ca**
Website: **www.cnhwarkworth.ca**
Contact: **Lisa Allanson**
Capacity: **60 residents**
Subsidies: **yes**

The warm, caring, clean environment created in our home is the result of the efforts of caregivers who have devoted decades of experience to the seniors of our local area. Our home is a 60-bed residence which features a tradition of quality care and services, enhanced by a unique blend of décor and large, clean, spacious dining and social rooms. Caregiving has evolved over the years and we have continued to prosper through careful planning, innovative thinking, along with our strong desire to meet the emerging needs and desires of our clients and their families. We are fully accredited by the Canadian Council on Health Services Accreditation and licensed and regulated by the Ontario Ministry of Health and Long-Term Care. Nestled in a quiet, residential area within the village, enhanced by our many compassionate, dedicated staff and volunteers, we continue to remain *"People you Trust, Caring for People you Love!"*

GENERAL HOME INFORMATION: 44 years in operation. *Near:* Banta Road and Mill Street. Decorated in 2010. Handrails in hallways. 1 floor, no elevators. Wheelchair accessible. Central PA system. *Funding Base:* Corporate/for profit. *Owned and managed by:* Community Lifecare Inc. 60 units. *Average Waiting Period*: varies. *Average Age*: 88. Can accommodate cognitively impaired & physically challenged people. Smoke-free residence. Alcohol allowed (as per doctor's orders). *Procedures to leave the premises on a temporary basis*...Short-term: as per legislation. Holidays: up to 21 days LOA (Leave of Absence) is permitted. *Languages:* English. Will accept Public Guardian and Trustee clients. Main doors of residence secured at all times. *Close to:* Churches, Library, Major Highway and Local Hospital (Campbellford Memorial Hospital). Member of OLTCA.

Have you found our Guide helpful?

Please let the homes you contact know that you found them here!!!

NOTES

Thank you for using our Guide!

Please feel free to contact us with feedback and suggestions for future editions at **info@senioropolis.com**

How to Obtain More Copies of this *Guide*

Please send a cheque for **$28.94** ($18.95 plus $1.99 taxes, and $8.00 Shipping & Handling)

Payable to:

Senioropolis Inc.
8000 Bathurst Street, Unit 1,
P.O. Box # 30033 RPO New Westminster
Vaughan, Ontario L4J 0C6

With your cheque, please include an order form (which can be printed from **www.senioropolis.com**), or on a separate piece of paper, indicate the name and address of the person you would like us to ship the book to and whether you would prefer it on CD ROM or in soft-cover printed format.

Allow two to four weeks for delivery.

If you prefer to pay by credit card, please visit our website, **www.senioropolis.com**, select the *Online Store* link and order through our shopping cart. Payment can be made through PayPal and orders will be filled as soon as they are received.

For large orders or further information, please contact us at:
PHONE: **(416) 457-6554**
FAX: **(905) 482-9142**
Email: **info@senioropolis.com**

Visit our dynamic, detailed website, **www.senioropolis.com**, for the most up-to-date information on retirement residences, long-term care homes and an array of resources for seniors

Esther Karen Hemi Goldstein obtained a Bachelor degree in Science from the University of Toronto in 1986 and in Social Work from Ryerson University in 1990. She is a registered member of the Ontario College of Social Workers and Social Service Workers.

Esther worked as a hospital social worker in the Greater Toronto Area for 12 years, primarily with the geriatric population. A significant portion of her work involved counselling senior clients and their families about the difficult task of relocating to care homes and assisting them with the process. As Ontario's health care system evolved, people began turning to the private sector to care for their elderly relatives who could not be managed at home. Information about retirement residences and many other private services was limited and hard to find, so Esther created this *Guide* out of a need she had for this information. Over time, the *Guide* has evolved and expanded to become what you hold in your hand today. Currently Esther works full-time on this publication and its affiliated website, **www.senioropolis.com.**

As of 2009, Senioropolis.com® expanded to cover all of Canada. It continues to build its database of information on housing options (retirement residences, long-term care homes, etc.) and services for seniors across the country as it strives to become a portal for "all things senior".

In September 2013, Esther was appointed to the Stakeholders Advisory Council of Ontario's new Retirement Homes Regulatory Authority for a 1 year term.

Esther also shares her knowledge through lectures and workshops on 'Senior Living Options' and related topics at venues including retirement homes, community agencies and private companies and organizations.

45 life lessons and 5 to grow on

by Regina Brett, The Plain Dealer (first published May 28, 2006)

1. Life isn't fair, but it's still good.
2. When in doubt, just take the next small step.
3. Life is too short to waste time hating anyone.
4. Don't take yourself so seriously. No one else does.
5. Pay off your credit cards every month.
6. You don't have to win every argument. Agree to disagree.
7. Cry with someone. It's more healing than crying alone.
8. It's OK to get angry with God. He can take it.
9. Save for retirement starting with your first paycheck.
10. When it comes to chocolate, resistance is futile.
11. Make peace with your past so it won't screw up the present.
12. It's OK to let your children see you cry.
13. Don't compare your life to others'. You have no idea what their journey is all about.
14. If a relationship has to be a secret, you shouldn't be in it.
15. Everything can change in the blink of an eye. But don't worry; God never blinks.
16. Life is too short for long pity parties. Get busy living, or get busy dying.
17. You can get through anything if you stay put in today.
18. A writer writes. If you want to be a writer, write.
19. It's never too late to have a happy childhood. But the second one is up to you and no one else.
20. When it comes to going after what you love in life, don't take no for an answer.
21. Burn the candles, use the nice sheets, wear the fancy lingerie. Don't save it for a special occasion. Today is special.
22. Overprepare, then go with the flow.
23. Be eccentric now. Don't wait for old age to wear purple.
24. The most important sex organ is the brain.
25. No one is in charge of your happiness except you.
26. Frame every so-called disaster with these words: "In five years, will this matter?"
27. Always choose life.
28. Forgive everyone everything.
29. What other people think of you is none of your business.
30. Time heals almost everything. Give time time.
31. However good or bad a situation is, it will change.
32. Your job won't take care of you when you are sick. Your friends will. Stay in touch.
33. Believe in miracles.
34. God loves you because of who God is, not because of anything you did or didn't do.
35. Whatever doesn't kill you really does make you stronger.
36. Growing old beats the alternative - dying young.
37. Your children get only one childhood. Make it memorable.
38. Read the Psalms. They cover every human emotion.
39. Get outside every day. Miracles are waiting everywhere.
40. If we all threw our problems in a pile and saw everyone else's, we'd grab ours back.
41. Don't audit life. Show up and make the most of it now.
42. Get rid of anything that isn't useful, beautiful or joyful.
43. All that truly matters in the end is that you loved.
44. Envy is a waste of time. You already have all you need.
45. The best is yet to come.
46. No matter how you feel, get up, dress up and show up.
47. Take a deep breath. It calms the mind.
48. If you don't ask, you don't get.
49. Yield.
50. Life isn't tied with a bow, but it's still a gift.